FRESHWATER

FISHES

OF THE WORLD

by

Günther Sterba

Director of the Zoological Institute,
University of Leipzig

TRANSLATED AND REVISED BY

DENYS W. TUCKER

Doctor of Science

A STUDIO BOOK · THE VIKING PRESS
NEW YORK

Author's Preface

In the course of time the aquarium-keeping hobby has amassed a multitude
of valuable observations on the biology of fishes which, once they have been
classified and sorted, not only form an essential constituent of our knowledge
of this group of animals but can also become the foundation and incentive
to further developments.

The last (German) encyclopaedic survey, published nearly 25 years ago,
Fremdländische Süßwasserfische (Exotic Freshwater Fishes) by Paul Arnold
and Ernst Ahl, succeeded in stimulating and systematising the whole subject
and in directing the attention of scientists to the abundance of unsolved problems in this field. It can fairly be said today that many discoveries of modern
biological research have arisen through the following up of aquarists' observations and that this field of study has therefore received the highest recognition that it could possibly desire. On the other hand the techniques and
attitudes of aquarists have, through the impact of scientific advances in water-
chemistry, behaviour studies and the general biology of reproduction, under-
gone a fundamental revolution which has undoubtedly led them towards an
approximation to scientific research.

This situation, together with the accumulation of new observations in
recent years, has prompted this effort to set forth a new general synthesis of
biological and ecological observations. The author hopes that it will serve,
not only as a new reference book for aquarists, but also as a stimulus to still
further progress. The work should, furthermore, be the means of imparting
an insight into the underlying principles of the specialty and of showing that
the hobby has more possibilities than mere haphazard amateurism can realise.

5

At this point it is a very great pleasure to me to thank all those who have so unselfishly sent me freshwater fishes from all over the world. My very warmest thanks are due to Dr. Walter Foersch for providing me with many photographs which have greatly enriched this book. Further, for their understanding cooperation and for making many specimens available, I thank the Director of the Hellabrunn Aquarium, Munich, Dr. L. Heck Jr. and his colleagues; the Director of the Tropicarium at Frankfurt a. M., Mr. Hans Schmidt, and his brother, Dr. Eduard Schmidt: the Director of the Erfurt Aquarium, Mr. W. Hildebrandt and his colleagues; also the firm of Andreas Werner, Zoo-Import und -Export, Munich.

Individual photographs were kindly placed at my disposal by Dr. W. Villwock, Zoologisches Staatsinstitut, Hamburg; Prof. M. Poll, Musée Royal d'Afrique Centrale, Tervuren; Dr. W. Schapitz, Zoophysiologisches Institut, Tübingen; Dr. K. H. Lüling, Zoologisches Forschungsinstitut und Museum Alexander Koenig, Bonn; Mr. F. Unger, Esslingen; Mr. H. Stettler, Berne and Mr. P. Chlupaty, Munich, to all of whom I give grateful thanks, as well as to Messrs. W. Mönnig and H. J. Franke for technical assistance. Dr. K. Deckert, Mr. H. Meinken and the late Dr. O. Schindler were helpful in procuring literature.

I am furthermore most grateful to Dr. C. Schönfeld for the preparation of the drawings of fishes, to Dr. H. Feustel for the distribution-maps and to my colleagues of the Urania-Verlag and of Edition Leipzig for their conspicuous care over the production of this book.

In my opinion the English translation of the German edition is a most successful one. Dr. Tucker has harmoniously added to the text short references of a special interest for English and American readers. Further, he has considered into several passages of the book newer systematical findings. I am glad that my book is now also available to English-speaking readers and trust that it will find a wide distribution all over the world.

Leipzig, July 1962 . *Günther Sterba*

Foreword

In our incessant straining after new knowledge it is a good thing that we should pause occasionally and consider the builders of the pyramid upon which we stand. The origins of scientific ichthyology must always remain obscure, if only for the reason that it is impossible to draw a dividing line between unscientific and scientific observations. The first sub-humans to recognise that this fish was good to eat, that that one invariably produced a stomach-ache and that yet another too often led to a poisoned hand, were already scientific ichthyologists of a sort, able to identify and classify with some sort of logical system. The first fisherman to predict the arrival of the Grey Mullet shoals, the first Bantu to predict the season and place in which the fat aestivating Lung-fishes would be found, were applying impeccably scientific methods. Many thousands of years ago a Perigordian sculptor carved a Salmon on the roof of the Gorge d'Enfer in the French Dordogne; Ancient Egyptians, considerably closer to our own time, left exquisite bas-reliefs of Nile Cichlids and Mormyrids inside a Pharaoh's tomb now in the Louvre. These, too, were craftsmen whose mystical purposes had been served by intensive study of the forms of fishes; systematic ichthyologists, already, of a sort.

It is in the Natural Histories of Aristotle in the third century B.C. and of Pliny in the first century A.D. that we find the beginnings of a purely philosophical interest in ichthyology, of fundamental as opposed to applied science. Then, after fourteen centuries of darkness, three great treatises were published by Belon, Rondelet and Salviani, all between 1553–57, soon followed by further vast tomes by Gesner and by Aldrovandus. The end of this epoch came with the great advances in the *Historia Piscium* of Willughby and Ray (1686) and in Ray's *Synopsis Methodica Piscium* (1713). But the true father of modern systematic ichthyology was a Swede, Peter Artedi (1705–35), whose classification of fishes was taken over by Linnaeus in his *Systema Naturae*, the great work whose tenth edition (1758) is now taken as the internationally-agreed starting-point in the naming of fishes and of all other animals.

The origins of aquarium-keeping, however, are more easily defined. The first man to transfer a living fish to a garden pond or domestic vessel, not because he hoped to eat it a few days later but because it afforded him some intellectual or aesthetic pleasure, *was* an aquarist, and the indications are that he was probably an eleventh century Chinese. From that country, too, comes the first known treatise on the subject: *Chu sha yu p'u* (The Book of the Vermilion Fish), written by Chang Chi'en-tê in 1596, gives a full account of the management of the Goldfish. By 1665 something was afoot in Europe, for we find Samuel Pepys noting in his diary: – 'Thence home and to see my lady Pen, where my wife and I were shown a fine rarity: of fishes kept in a glass of water, that will live so for ever; and finely marked they are, being foreign.' If C.W.Coates is correct in his belief that these were probably not Goldfish but Paradise-fish (*Macropodus opercularis*), then Europe may have been well on the way towards the modern cult.

Truly scientific aquarium-keeping may be claimed as a British invention, with the publication of the first paper on the theory and practice of the 'balanced' aquarium by Robert Warrington in 1850, and within the next decade both freshwater and marine aquaria became fashionable furnishings of the Victorian drawing-room, thanks to the enthusiastic propaganda of Philip Henry Gosse, Thomas Rymer Jones, Shirley Hibberd, Charles Kingsley and others. During the same period the first public aquarium was established in London and other European countries were quick to follow this lead.

The new art was taken up with characteristic thoroughness in Germany; very soon aquarium-keeping societies and periodicals were founded and by the end of the nineteenth century Germany had established an ascendency in the importation, culture and re-exportation of tropical fishes, an ascendency which she has retained ever since. It was Germany that exported tropical fishes to the United States at the turn of this century, and Germany that nourished the belated beginnings of the tropical fish fancy in Great Britain in the early 1920's. Even today, when plastic bags of live fishes have become standard freight on the airliners of the world, and when Florida farms exotic fishes on a vast scale in outdoor ponds in her hospitable climate (and fills her hospitable ditches with escapes!), Germany still leads the world in 'know-how' and in pioneering effort.

This is well-represented in the German literature. Her aquarium magazines may be less lurid in appearance and language than those of some other countries, but they are cram-full with the results of long hours of meticulous observation and experiment by men who, if they are not often trained zoologists, often have the benefit of having followed the discipline of another learned profession. (Dr. Foersch, who has contributed many illustrations to this book, is himself a medical man!) Periodically this knowledge and skill has been gathered together in a typically Teutonic encyclopaedic *Lehrbuch* of surpassing scholarship, comprehensiveness and bulk, as in the works of Arnold & Ahl, of Holly, Meinken & Rachow, and in the present work by Professor Günther Sterba.

This is the first time that a major German text on aquarium fishes has been translated into English and, consequently, the first time that the barrier between German knowledge and expertise and the non-German reader has been really broken down. The result is a work of reference which, at one bound, must establish itself in the forefront of the best works on this subject available in the English language. This book deals with the identification, biology and care of something like thirteen hundred species, the vast majority of which are illustrated; it therefore comfortably exceeds in comprehensiveness the scope of any English-language competitor, not only dealing with species and genera – even whole families and orders – which other books do not mention, but also getting to grips with the groups from temperate climates, the supposedly-uninteresting 'uglies' and the larger species to which the public aquarium director has no other handy guide.

Professor Sterba's scholarship and industry are ably matched by his photographic skill and that of his collaborators. Here is a gallery of fish-portraits more extensive than that available in any comparable book, with a galaxy of colour-photographs reproduced with a faithfulness which can challenge comparison with the best. And even if this, like any other book, must acknowledge some debt for its illustrations to that well-loved authority Dr. William T. ('Ole Bill') Innes, it is at most a respectably modest debt that must be admitted and not a wholesale piracy; the vast majority of these photographs are new. The translator, as a professional systematic ichthyologist, must also admit the high quality of the drawings, distribution-maps and anatomical figures produced by Professor Sterba's excellent illustrators.

In essentials the English edition is substantially the same as the German, but it has nevertheless been revised as thoroughly as knowledge and time allowed. The changes incorporated have varied from minor corrections of dates and spelling, through interpolations of additional crumbs of biological information and taxonomic changes to bring the book into line with the latest revisions, to drastic re-writing of *Anguilla* and other genera, additions of new species, full revision of the African Cichlids and the addition of an entirely new section on the *Gymnarchidae*. Acknowledgement must be made here for the advice given by Dr. Ethelwynn Trewavas, *doyenne* of the students of African freshwater fishes, and to Dr. P. H. Greenwood, a young man with already several years' experience of those same fishes in the field and in the museum. Errors must undoubtedly remain, but it is to be hoped that those competent to discover them will realise that perfection is unattainable in a work of this scope on such a rapidly-evolving subject, and will accordingly be charitable.

A few special matters remain to be dealt with. The English edition carries a little more judiciously-inserted material on the diagnoses of the higher groups which should, without overburdening the lay reader, make the book of greater use to those, unfortunately few, enlightened institutions which give courses in ichthyology. A great many cases remain where the diagnosis of a family or genus is not adequate or complete, but it has seemed of little use to this translator to expect a lay aquarist to discover whether a live tiddler has united parietal bones, or teeth on its microscopic vomer.

The telegraphic style of much of Professor Sterba's writing has been deliberately retained; while, as Aldous Huxley has said, 'all communications are literature', he has also admitted the inferior potentialities of a description of a fish! We may as well, therefore, accept his authority and confine ourselves to presenting the maximum amount of information for reference in the minimum of space.

Nomenclature follows current practice as far as possible. Species attributed to Cuvier AND Valenciennes continue to be so credited, notwithstanding the idiotic decision to the contrary recently taken by the International Commission on Zoological Nomenclature. That reference, or even the abbreviated 'C.V.', has told many generations of ichthyologists that a first description of a species is to be found in *L'Histoire Naturelle des Poissons* and has thereby discharged the only *raison d'être* of an author-reference. It is further certain that Valenciennes' work was fully overseen by Cuvier and that the latter left his stamp even on the sections of the treatise published after his death. To solemnly apportion responsibility between the two authors after all these years, with the result that future workers will have to give full references or search the bibliographies of these authors, is absurdly unnecessary; as to the labours of those who are currently publishing solemn discriminatory lists, the less said the better!

Popular names cited are either those established in current use, translations of suitable German names, or, in a very few cases, new ones coined to fill a gap. Pending some agreed standardisation of popular names, the recommendations of the Committee of the American Fisheries Society (see R. M. Bailey, *Trans. Amer. Fish. Soc.* **84**, 368: 1954) are well worth consideration. The major lead must be given by the authors of such textbooks as the present, and to the translator it seems singularly useless to coin a name like 'Meinken's Rasbora' which means no more to the man-in-the-fish-house than *Rasbora meinkeni*; to talk of 'The Many-spined Ctenopoma' when there are several species with as many or more spines than *C. multispinis;* or to continue presenting laymen with the name 'Dwarf Panchax' long after *Panchax* has been replaced by the earlier name *Aplocheilus.*

In conclusion, it must be emphasized that there remains a considerable contribution to be made to scientific knowledge by the aquarist. Many problems are obviously indicated in Professor Sterba's book; species in which no secondary sexual characters have been described, or in which it has not been possible to induce breeding; species for which no suitable food has been discovered, or whose young invariably die within a few days for the same reason. Very many species have patterns of markings which conceal the true shape, camouflage the eyes or substitute counterfeit eyes on the body or fins; a study of Dr. Hugh B. Cott's *Adaptive Coloration in Animals* will suggest a large field of research here. Some groups insist on hard water, others on soft; is there any correlation between these conditions and the calcification of the scales and skeleton? Some species are here stigmatised as 'hardy', others as 'delicate'; is it that we have failed to find the exact conditions which they need, or are we dealing with generalised and specialised forms, the latter being intensively adapted to very narrow ecological niches through intense competition with other closely-related species? What are the differences in territorial behaviour and needs which lie behind the labels 'quarrelsome' and 'peaceful'? Is it not remarkable that Pike-like forms and Darter-like forms occur among the Characins, and how close is the correspondence? Do any bright colour-patterns have any relation with Batesian or Müllerian mimicry? (What's that, pray? We are suggesting that *you* find out!)

One of the most important fields of research, limited almost to the aquarist, is the study of fish-behaviour. In the early days it was sufficient to observe, describe and admire the courtship of the Stickleback, the devoted parental brood-care the Cichlids give their young, the bubble-nests of the Paradise-fishes. The behaviour-patterns involved seemed so excellently contrived by 'Nature', the actions so complicated and intelligent. Then we noticed courtships that were broken off for no apparent reason, fishes that ate their first clutch of eggs instead of brooding them, mad deprived mothers which herded waterfleas into a 'school' and guarded them for a few days before absent-mindedly eating the lot! We now know that courtship is often a case of 'chain behaviour' in which each partner alternately supplies the linking-stimulus necessary to provoke the next linking-response; that fishes will react amorously or belligerently to fish-shaped objects of inappropriate colour, or un-fishlike objects of the right colour; that brood-care is often a form of temporarily inhibited feeding-behaviour. In this fascinating field of study the published books and papers of Tinbergen, Lorenz, Baerends and others of their school provide adequate blue-prints, as it were, which any keen amateur should be able to follow.

It is to be hoped that the aquarium-world at large will find Professor Sterba's book as stimulating as this translator has during the last five months.

London, May 1961   *Denys W. Tucker*

Contents

In the systematic description of each family of fishes this book gives the general ground-plan of the family and particularly emphasises any departure from this.

In the definition of a species, on the other hand, as well as a short description of the body-form, a range of measurements may be given which pro-

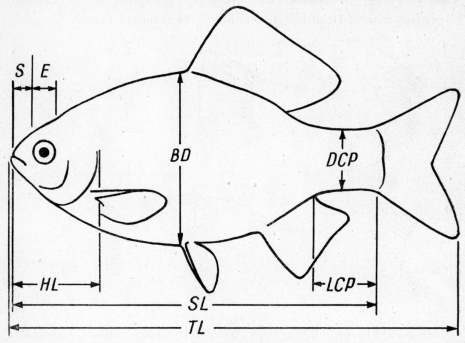

Fig. 2

Diagram of the most important measurements used in describing fish species. BD Body Depth; DCP Depth of Caudal Peduncle; E Eye Diameter; HL Head Length; LCP Length of Caudal Peduncle; S Snout Length; SL Standard Length (= Body Length); TL Total Length.

vides a good idea of the body-proportions. It is, of course, understood that these measurements, unless there is any indication to the contrary, hold good for normal well-nourished adult animals. The important body-measurements are diagrammatically explained in Fig. 2. The single measurements themselves are not given in any absolute units of length but as proportions; that is to say, we state how many times the shorter measurements are contained in the longer. For example, how many times the length of the head, the greatest body-depth or the depth of the caudal peduncle, is contained in the Standard Length (= Body Length) or Total Length. In the case of small measurements reference is usually made to a longer one drawn from the next higher class. It is usual, for instance, and more helpful, to express the Eye Diameter as a proportion of Head Length and not of the Standard Length.

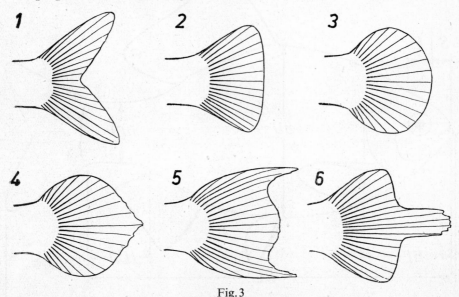

Fig. 3
Common caudal fin shapes in bony fishes. (1) forked; (2) squarely truncated; (3) rounded; (4) pointed; (5) three-lobed; (6) with elongated middle rays.

Many modern authors employ a new system for describing the body form. They take the Standard Length as 100 and give the shorter measurements as percentages of this. Thus the form : – 'Head Length 32:100' means: – 'If the Standard Length is taken as 100 units, the Head Length is equal to 32 of these.' This, like the previous method, permits comparison of the body forms of specimens of different sizes.

Use of the Standard Length is to be preferred to that of the Total Length for scientific work, since this avoids uncertainty due to damaged caudal fin-rays. In fishery biology, however, Total Length is often used, simply because this measurement is more easily and speedily taken when working under difficult conditions at sea.

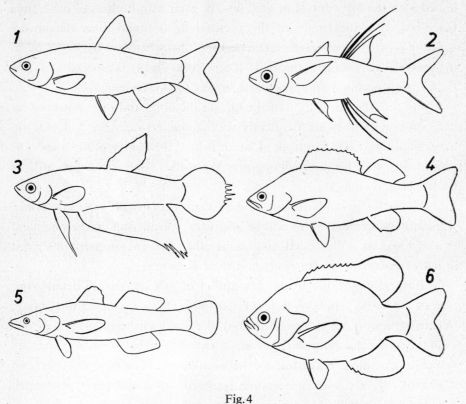

Fig. 4
Disposition of fins on the fish body.
(1) Cyprinid; (2) Atherinid; (3) Fighting Fish; (4) Perch; (5) Sleeper Goby; (6) Sun-fish.
The ventral fins are abdominal in 1 and 2; thoracic in 3, 4, 5 and 6.
1 and 3 have a single dorsal fin; 2, 4 and 5 have an anterior spinous dorsal and a posterior soft dorsal; in 6 the two dorsal fins are united.

Next in importance to the body dimensions come the fin shapes and the separate fin-measurements. Unless we are dealing with very striking fin changes, such as considerable lengthening of individual fins or fin-rays, or with very considerably reduced or wholly absent fins, it will be sufficient to confine ourselves to the description of the caudal fin. This can be rounded, squarely truncated, moderately or deeply forked, drawn out into a point or even thread-like. (Fig. 3). By no means rarely the caudal fin is continuously united with the long dorsal or anal fins, or even with both as in our native Eel. Frequently the length of the pectoral fin is found to be diagnostic, hence it is often mentioned: – 'The pectoral fins, when laid back, extend to the ventrals', or, 'as far as the anal'. If a pectoral fin-ray is especially long or thick then it becomes an appropriate subject for measurement.

Again, too, the disposition of the fins on the body and their positions relative to one another are frequently very characteristic. Thus a dorsal fin, for example, may begin in front of, at, or behind the middle of the body. The ventral fins may be inserted opposite the dorsal, or further forward, or further behind (Fig. 4).

In this book the standard body- and fin-shapes are usually briefly described without measurements. This will be adequate, considering on the one hand that each species is illustrated, and on the other, that the specialist interested in body-measurements can easily find these elsewhere.

Of further importance in the description of fish species are details concerning the fin-rays. In bony fishes (Teleostomes) these rays are always bony; in cartilaginous fishes (Elasmobranchii) like the dogfishes and rays, as well as in the lung-fishes (Dipnoi), they are horny. The fin-rays of bony fishes can be further classified. We distinguish between *hard rays* (spines) and *soft rays*. The hard rays are as a rule smooth, pointed, solid and never articulated (divided into segments). Spinous fins are composed entirely of hard rays. Soft rays come in three forms (Fig. 5):–

a) unbranched and non-articulated soft rays.

b) unbranched and more or less completely articulated soft rays.

c) soft rays which are branched fan-wise and entirely articulated.

The terms hard- and soft-rays themselves are somewhat misleading and not to be taken too literally. Many unbranched soft rays are so heavily calcified that they attain spine-like rigidity. Conversely, hard rays are often remarkably soft and flexible. There is, however, one sure means of discrimination, though it usually calls for the use of a dissecting microscope and a little manual skill. Soft rays are so constructed that they can be fairly readily split into right and left halves in the median (dorsal, anal and caudal) fins; hard rays, being solid, do not have this natural cleavage-plane.

The form and number of the fin-rays are often characteristic of the species

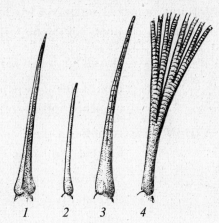

Fig. 5
Fin-rays: (1) hard ray (spine);
(2) unbranched, non-articulated soft ray;
(3) unbranched, articulated soft ray;
(4) branched, articulated soft ray.
(after Günther, altered).

and are expressed for the several fins by the so-called Fin-Formula. This is so constructed that the initial letter of the name of the fin in question comes first.

These initial letters are as follows:—

Dorsal	D
if two dorsals, then	D_1, D_2
Anal	A
Pectoral	P
Ventral or Pelvic	V
Caudal	C

The number of fin-rays in a fin-formula is so given that without difficulty their type can be recognised too. Roman figures indicate true hard rays, Arabic figures soft rays of whatsoever form. As a rule the rays of a fin are not all uniform. For example, hard rays and branched soft rays, or unbranched and branched soft rays, may be grouped. Further, one must bear in mind that, almost without exception, the branched soft rays are in the hinder part; the hard rays and unbranched soft rays are always at the beginning of the fin. (Exceptionally the last ray of a fin may be an unbranched simple soft ray too.) In the fin-formula the number of hard rays or unbranched soft rays may therefore be separated by an oblique stroke from the number denoting branched soft rays. The following examples indicate the use, and incidentally economy, of the fin-formula:—

D II/8 = Dorsal fin of two hard rays followed by eight soft rays.

D 2/8 = Dorsal fin of two unbranched soft rays followed by eight branched soft rays.

A III-IV/6-8 = Anal fin of three or four hard rays, followed by six to eight branched soft rays.

C 2/10/2 = Caudal fin having two unbranched soft rays on the upper edge and two on the lower, and between these ten branched soft rays.

In the present work this form of fin definition will be employed exclusively. Readers may occasionally meet with bracketed numbers in the fin-formula, as for example D III/8(−9). The figure in brackets signifies 'exceptionally'. A number not further differentiated, like D 10, does not mean that all the soft rays are branched, but is rather to be understood as saying that no differentiated data exist. We must, however, warn readers that not everywhere in the literature is this modern type of fin-formula found, and unbranched soft rays, in particular, are often wrongly represented by Roman figures elsewhere.

As well as the body, fin forms and positions of fins, and fin-formula, the hard inclusions in the skin interest the systematist. In general in the bony fishes these are scales, but bony scutes and bony plates may also occur. The skin of many fishes is naked. Scales may be divided into two basic forms (Fig. 6): –

      a) Comb-edged or *Ctenoid* Scales.

      b) Round or *Cycloid* Scales.

The form of the scales is often characteristic of the family.

Important diagnostic characters may be the arrangement and number of the scales, and of the bony plates or scutes when present. In general the scales are regularly arranged in longitudinal and transverse series, overlapping like tiles on a roof. Often the individual scales of one longitudinal

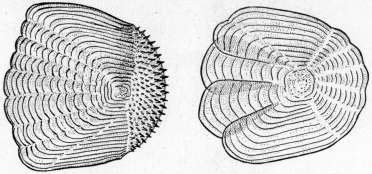

Fig. 6
Left, Ctenoid; right, Cycloid scale.

series each have two little longitudinal stripes which may be more darkly coloured. Microscopical examination reveals these little streaks as the visible borders of a fine canal which bores obliquely through the scale; occasionally instead of a canal there is only a groove or incision. Through these scale-canals the sense-organs of the underlying lateral line system are placed in communication with the outside world and thus carry to the body information about the adjacent water-movements. The lateral line begins, as a rule, in the upper region of the hind edge of the operculum (= gill-cover) (visibly or invisibly the system is continued forwards over the head by further branched canals in the dermal bones of the skull) and extends straight or curved to the root of the tail (lateral line complete), or only a little way along the body (lateral line incomplete). But lateral lines in two parts are also not rare (Fig. 8, 5).

All these peculiarities of the squamation and the associated lateral line are systematically of great value and, with the exception of the form of the lateral line which will be separately described, are included in the Scale-Formula. This gives first the number of scales in the lateral line series or,

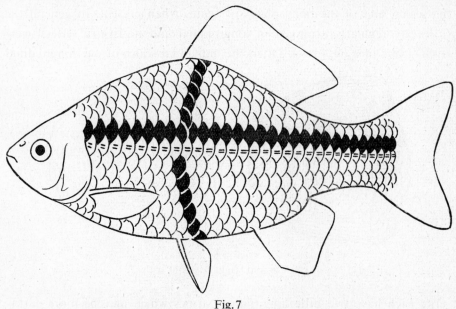

Fig. 7

Arrangement of scales on fish body (Crucian Carp). The scales filled in in black indicate how the longitudinal and transverse series are to be counted.

if the lateral line is absent, how many scales occur in a middle longitudinal series. The number of these is, as a rule, the number of transverse rows of scales. Further, the scale-formula includes the number of scales in a transverse series. If no special information, as for example, 'Transverse series in front of the dorsal fin', is given, the statement goes for a transverse series in the region of the deepest part of the body. The transverse series are counted from the ridge of the back to the lateral line, and from here to the mid-line of the belly; if there is no lateral line one counts right through.

In addition it may sometimes be important to give the number of scales between the lateral line and the ventral fin, or the number of scales around the caudal peduncle.

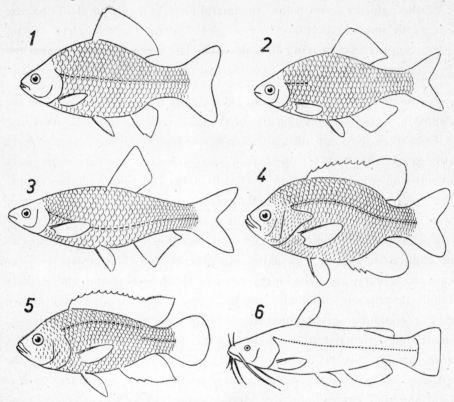

Fig. 8

Shape and course of the lateral line: (1) complete, straight lateral line in the Crucian Carp; (2) incomplete, short lateral line in the Bitterling; (3) complete, downward-curving (down-bowed or ventrally convex) lateral line of the Striped Bleak; (4) complete, arched (dorsally convex) lateral line of a Sunfish; (5) divided lateral line of a Cichlid; (6) complete, straight lateral line of a scaleless Catfish.

The scale-formula in the present work is intentionally simplified, giving the number of scales in a middle longitudinal series (LL) and often in a transverse series (TR). So 'LL 36–38; TR 10' means: – 'In a longitudinal series there are 36–38, in a transverse series 10, scales.' In forms possessing a lateral line it is more usual to use the expression 'TR 5/6' (or whatever values may be appropriate). The figure on the left side of the stroke gives the scale-count above, that on the right the count below, the lateral line. As a rule we shall dispense with this notation and merely say:–'lateral line complete' or 'incomplete', or 'piercing 10 scales'. The last statement signifies that the lateral line extends only over the first ten scales (Fig. 8).

A complete species-diagnosis should properly include information on the dentition, anatomical peculiarities of the gills, viscera and other structures. All too often these are difficult matters which can only be evaluated by a trained specialist and, for this reason, such statements are here deliberately avoided or, where alluded to, included in the description of the family. Without loss in exactitude we shall therefore give the simplest description of a species which is commensurate with a reliable identification.

The sections on colouring, care and breeding in the separate species descriptions require no elucidation. In general only short instructions for care and breeding are given for each species. On the other hand, almost every family description, often also the descriptions of individual well-known genera, contain a very detailed treatment of these matters. The symbols ♂ (male) and ♀ (female) are used throughout; for those not already familiar with them it may be useful to remember that they were originally the astrological signs for Mars and Venus respectively, and that Mars, the War God, the Male, carries an arrow. Metric-system units of length, temperature and occasionally volume have been retained in the English edition since these are universally employed in modern scientific literature. However, conversion–tables are given at the end of the book for those who need them.

Every description of a species ends with a note of the import date for Central Europe*. For years prior to 1945 a following + or – sign indicates whether or not the species was again imported after 1945.

* The reason for retaining this date in the English-language edition is that, except for a handful of species endemic to North America, the German import date is effectively the date of introduction to the aquarium world at large.

The personal names following the scientific (Latin or Latinised, binominal) names of the species indicate the name of the first describer of the species and the date of the first description. If both are placed in brackets, this means that the first describer originally classified the species under another genus. For subspecies a third name stands after the usual binomen. It should be said in this connection that often and deliberately the original account of a species is used, sometimes at the expense of literal accuracy.

The system of classification used in the *Zoological Record* for 1957 is adopted almost unchanged. It is essentially that expounded by the late Dr. Charles Tate Regan in the article 'Fishes' in the 14th edition of the *Encyclopaedia Britannica* (1929), and in the *Natural History* edited by him (Ward Lock, London, 1936). This classification is set out in the following table which, as a rule, embraces only those families which appear in the present work. On the other hand, the orders and sub-orders of the Osteichthyes are almost all listed.

Typical Genera (Freshwater examples only)

Class: **Marsipobranchii**

    Order: Cyclostomata

        Fam. Petromyzonidae   Petromyzon, Lampetra
        Fam. Myxinidae

Class: **Placodermi**

Class: **Selachii**

Class: **Osteichthyes**

  Sub-class: Palaeopterygii

    Order: Cladistia

        Fam. Polypteridae   Polypterus, Calamoichthys

    Order: Chondrostei
        Fam. Acipenseridae   Acipenser, Scaphirhynchus, Polyodon

29

Sub-class: Neopterygii

Order: Protospondyli
    Fam. Amiidae   Amia

Order: Ginglymodi
    Fam. Lepisosteidae   Lepisosteus

Order: Isospondyli
    Fam. Phractolaemidae   Phractolaemus
    Fam. Clupeidae
    Fam. Salmonidae   Salmo, Salvelinus, Coregonus
    Fam. Thymallidae   Thymallus
    Fam. Osmeridae   Osmerus
    Fam. Osteoglossidae   Osteoglossum, Arapaima
    Fam. Pantodontidae   Pantodon
    Fam. Notopteridae   Notopterus, Xenomystus
    Fam. Mormyridae   Mormyrus, Gnathonemus
    Fam. Gymnarchidae   Gymnarchus

Order: Haplomi
    Fam. Esocidae   Esox
    Fam. Umbridae   Umbra

Order: Apodes
    Fam. Anguillidae   Anguilla

Order: Iniomi

Order: Mirapinnati

Order: Giganturoidea

Order: Congrobranchii

Order: Lyomeri

Order: Ostariophysi
    Sub-order: Cyprinoidea
        Fam. Characidae   Hemigrammus, Hyphessobrycon,
                                Serrasalmus, Metynnis,
                                Moenkhausia, Copeina
        Fam. Anostomidae   Anostomus, Leporinus
        Fam. Hemiodontidea Nannostomus

30

Fam. Citharinidae	Neolebias, Nannaethiops, Citharinus
Fam. Gasteropelecidae	Carnegiella, Gasteropelecus
Fam. Cyprinidae	Cyprinus, Barbus, Rasbora, Danio
Fam. Gyrinocheilidae	Gyrinocheilus
Fam. Cobitidae	Noemacheilus, Cobitis, Botia, Acanthophthalmus
Fam. Electrophoridae	Electrophorus
Fam. Gymnotidae	Gymnotus
Fam. Rhamphichthyidae	Eigenmannia, Hypopomus
Fam. Sternarchidae	Sternarchus, Sternarchella

Sub-order: Siluroidea

Fam. Doradidae	Doras
Fam. Auchenipteridae	Centromochlus
Fam. Plotosidae	Plotosus
Fam. Siluridae	Silurus
Fam. Bagridae	Bagrus
Fam. Ameiuridae	Ameiurus
Fam. Chacidae	Chaca
Fam. Schilbeidae	Schilbe
Fam. Clariidae	Clarias
Fam. Mochokidae	Synodontis
Fam. Pimelodidae	Pimelodus, Microglanis
Fam. Pygidiidae	Pygidium, Vandellia
Fam. Helogenidae	Helogenes
Fam. Bunocephalidae	Bunocephalus
Fam. Malapteruridae	Malapterurus
Fam. Callichthyidae	Corydoras, Callichthys
Fam. Loricariidae	Loricaria, Plecostomus, Hoplosternum

Order: Heteromi

Order: Microcyprini

Fam. Cyprinodontidae	Aphyosemion, Epiplatys, Fundulus, Rivulus, Cynolebias, Gambusia, Limia, Xiphophorus
Fam. Goodeidae	Goodea
Fam. Amblyopsidae	Chologaster, Amblyopsis

31

Order: Synentognathi
    Fam. Belonidae   Belone
    Fam. Hemiramphidae   Dermogenys, Hemiramphus
Order: Solenichthyes
    Fam. Syngnathidae   Nerophis, Syngnathus
Order: Salmopercae
    Fam. Percopsidae
    Fam. Aphredoderidae   Aphredoderus
Order: Anacanthini
Order: Allotriognathi
Order: Berycomorphi
Order: Zeomorphi
Order: Percomorphi
   Sub-order: Phallostethidioidea
   Sub-order: Percoidea
    Fam. Theraponidae   Therapon
    Fam. Serranidae
    Fam. Lobotidae
    Fam. Centrarchidae   Mesogonistius, Elassoma, Lepomis
    Fam. Percidae   Perca, Boleosoma
    Fam. Centropomidae   Centropoma, Chanda
    Fam. Toxotidae   Toxotes
    Fam. Monodactylidae   Monodactylus
    Fam. Scatophagidae   Scatophagus
    Fam. Nandidae   Nandus, Polycentrus
    Fam. Cichlidae   Astronotus, Cichlasoma, Nannacara,
                            Apistogramma, Tilapia,
                            Pterophyllum, Symphysodon

    Fam. Embiotocidae
   Sub-order: Acanthuroidea
   Sub-order: Siganoidea
   Sub-order: Trichiuroidea
   Sub-order: Scombroidea
   Sub-order: Gobioidea
    Fam. Eleotridae   Eleotris, Mogurnda
    Fam. Gobiidae   Periophthalmus, Brachygobius

32

Sub-order: Blennioidea
Sub-order: Ophidioidea
Sub-order: Stromateoidea
Sub-order: Anabantoidea
 Fam. Anabantidae   Anabas, Macropodus, Betta, Colisa,
            Ctenopoma
 Fam. Luciocephalidae   Luciocephalus
Sub-order: Ophicephaloidea
 Fam. Ophicephalidae   Ophicephalus, Channa
Sub-order: Mugiloidea
 Fam. Mugilidae   Mugil, Chelon
 Fam. Atherinidae   Telmatherina
Sub-order: Polynemoidea

Order: Scleroparei
Sub-order: Scorpaenoidea
 Fam. Cottidae   Cottus

Order: Thoracostei
 Fam. Gasterosteidae   Gasterosteus, Pygosteus

Order: Hypostomides

Order: Heterosomata
 Fam. Soleidae   Achirus
 Fam. Pleuronectidae   Platichthys

Order: Discocephali

Order: Plectognathi
 Fam. Tetraodontidae   Tetraodon

Order: Malacichthyes

Order: Xenopterygii

Order: Haplodoci

Order: Pediculati
Sub-order: Lophioidea
Sub-order: Antennarioidea
Sub-order: Ceratioidea

Order: Opisthomi
 Fam. Mastacembelidae   Mastacembelus

Order: Synbranchia
      Fam. Synbranchidae   Monopterus, Synbranchus
      Fam. Amphipnoidae   Amphipnous

Sub-Class: Crossopterygii

Order: Actinistia
      Fam. Coelacanthidae
      Fam. Latimeriidae

Order: Dipnoi
      Fam. Lepidosirenidae   Lepidosiren, Protopterus
      Fam. Ceratodontidae   Epiceratodus

With few exceptions all the species which have been kept in Central Europe (dateline 30. 6. 1958) are taken into consideration.

Descriptions of Families and Species

Family Petromyzonidae (Lampreys)*

To the biologist the most interesting fishes, or more correctly fish-like animals, in our waters are the Lampreys *(Petromyzonidae)*.

The life-cycle of the lamprey passes through the following distinctly-separated phases: the embryonic stage, larval stage, metamorphosis, feeding stage and reproductive stage. These several phases in the life of the River Lamprey had better be sharply defined. From a yellowish fertilised egg the size of a millet-seed there develops a retort-shaped embryo which, after 18 to 21 days, quits the egg-membrane and in a short time becomes transformed into a typical larva, the Pride or *Ammocoete* (Fig. 41). The pride is eel-shaped, muddy-yellow in colour and often marbled with brown on the upperside. The ventral mouth, surrounded by a hood-like lip, opens through the buccal cavity into the gill-apparatus, which has seven pore-like gill-slits on either side through which the water taken in is discharged. Coarse particles are prevented from entering by a branched filtering-apparatus just inside the mouth, and small organisms which form the food of the larva are trapped in a stream of mucus driven along by the beating of fine hair-like cilia and carried back into the gut. The lamprey larva is therefore a filter-feeder, that is to say, an animal which filters its food from the water. The larval stage lasts a little less than four years; during this period the animals live concealed in burrows which they build in the mud and which they only very seldom leave. By the fourth year of development the blind larvae are about 15 cm. long and now, in the months of August and September, assume their final form.

* The vernacular names are given in brackets.

First the large silver eyes appear on the surface of the head; then, along the back, two distinct dorsal fins and a tail fin are formed out of the continuous fin-fold which previously extended from head to tail and around to the ventral surface to form the anal fin; the filter-system is lost; the mouth becomes transformed into a suctorial mouth equipped with pointed teeth and the skin of the belly becomes a shining silvery-white. The animals now leave the mud and migrate to the sea where they go in pursuit of fishes in coastal waters; the perfect animal, therefore, in contrast to the larva, is a predatory animal. The lampreys principally attack Shad, but also Herring and Salmon, attaching themselves by the oral sucker to the body of their prey, through which they rasp an opening with their teeth and suck out a portion of the viscera. On such nourishing food they grow quickly and after another year are already 30 to 50 cm. in length. Slowly their appetite wanes and in autumn the animals commence their spawning migration which leads them back to the mill-streams and lowland brooks. Here they remain without feeding until, during a breeding period of seven days in April or May of the following year, they mate. The numerous eggs sink into the mud; shortly after breeding the utterly exhausted animals perish.

As well as the River Lamprey or Lampern our waters harbour the Brook Lamprey, whose larval stage is indistinguishable from that of the former. By contrast, however, in the Brook Lamprey the adult feeding-stage is omitted; after metamorphosis the reproductive stage is reached in the following spring. From the beginning of metamorphosis until death these animals take no further nourishment but live on the food-resources stored up during their larval phase.

Further peculiarities of the lampreys are the unpaired nostril and the cartilaginous skull, which encloses the brain and sense organs but includes no supporting elements such as true jaws for the round suctorial mouth. On this account the systematist classifies the lampreys with the *Agnatha* (= 'jawless ones'). The German vernacular name 'Neunaugen' (= 'nine-eyes') arises from a misunderstanding on the part of earlier observers who interpreted the nostril as well as the seven round gill-slits as eyes.

Comparative anatomy and physiology derive special interest from this group of animals. The very primitive organisation of the lampreys makes deductions possible concerning the origins, structure and function of many organ-systems of higher vertebrates.

In a well-aerated coldwater aquarium the larvae of the Brook Lamprey at least are well cared-for, provided a sufficiently thick layer of fine-grained sand gives them the opportunity to dig themselves in. They should be fed with the finest powdered food, soaked stinging-nettle meal, or dried food which has been finely grated and shaken up with water. Animals near metamorphosis have a heavy oxygen-requirement and on this account are difficult to maintain. For experimental work the installation of a centrifugal pump is recommended which guarantees a vigorous circulation. Under specially favourable conditions the animals will spawn in the aquarium.

River Lampreys, soaked in oil or smoked, were formerly regarded as a great delicacy and one English monarch (Henry I) is said to have died of a surfeit of them.

Lampetra fluviatilis (*Linnaeus* 1758)   River Lamprey, Lampern
Coastal waters of Europe, northern and eastern Asia and southern Greenland; the larvae (Prides) live, like the Brook Lamprey, in gravelly, moderately muddy streams; to 50 cm.

The larvae (to 17 cm.) cannot be distinguished from those of the Brook Lamprey. Full-grown animals (to 50 cm.) are bluish-grey on the upperside, pale yellowish-silver or silver on the underside.

Only distinguishable from the following species by the size and by biological differences. The River Lamprey migrates to the sea after metamorphosis and lives as a predator on fishes. The pointed dentition developed for that purpose is shed during the breeding migration upstream and replaced by a second, blunt dentition.

For biology and care, see family description.

Lampetra planeri (*Bloch* 1784) (Figs. 28, 39)   Brook Lamprey
Europe, northern, central and eastern Asia, western North America; to 17 cm. Larvae (to 17 cm.) eel-like, without a sucking mouth and without eyes; fin-margin undivided. Upperside brownish, often mottled with darker; underside yellowish, usually muddy yellow.

37

Full-grown animals (to 17 cm.) eel-like, with a large sucking mouth and large silvery eyes; fin-margin elevated and divided into two distinct dorsal fins, one behind the other. Upperside olive-brown to blue-grey; underside brilliant silver. In the larval stage the species is indistinguishable from the foregoing, except that microscopic examination reveals fewer oocytes (parent cells of the future eggs) in the ovaries.

Differences formerly supposed to characterise mature animals of the two species for the most part do not really exist or are valid only at certain stages of the life-history. The only peculiarities of *L. planeri* are the small size of the mature animals (usually 15 cm.), the lack of a first generation of pointed teeth and, above all, the absence of a parasitic phase. After metamorphosis the gut is partly blocked by tissues.

For biology and care, see family description.

A third species, the Sea Lamprey, *Petromyzon marinus* Linnaeus 1758, inhabits the seas of northern Europe. Its larvae live in the lower reaches of rivers. In North America this species has in recent years invaded the Great Lakes, which take the place of the sea for it. Its depredations ruined the lake fisheries but electrical and chemical control-methods in the tributary streams are now achieving a great deal of success, destroying the lampreys during their migrations.

Family Polypteridae (Bichirs and Reed-fish)

Fishes confined to tropical Africa; of elongate, in one case serpentine, form. Dorsal fin composed of a series of several finlets, which may be erected or laid back. Also strikingly peculiar are the fan-like, as it were stalked, pectoral fins, which are used as paddles in swimming and as supports for the front of the body which is often raised when the fish is at rest. Head broad; mouth large; nostrils tubular; skin covered with hard, rhombic, shiny ('ganoid') scales. Of the anatomical peculiarities of these fishes, which often present archaic features, only the swim-bladder will be mentioned. This consists of a small, left, and a large, right, sac; both parts lie, like the lungs of higher animals, ventrad to the oesophagus to which they are united by a common trunk. This apparatus, reminiscent in its entire organisation of a primitive lung, serves the Bichir as an accessory breathing-organ. There is in fact evidence to suggest that the swim-bladder originated as a lung and only later evolved as a hydrostatic organ. Bichirs that are denied access to the air die after a short while, although their gills, too, are fully functional. Bichirs are among the most interesting fishes for anatomical and evolutionary studies.

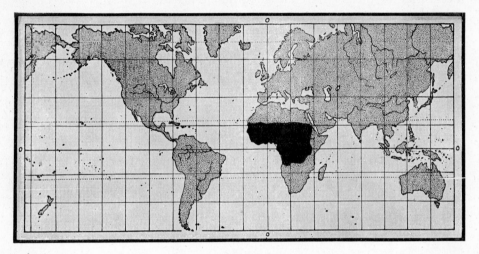

Fig. 9
Distribution of the *Polypteridae*

In their natural habitats these fishes mainly inhabit the overgrown margins and flood-zones of rivers. During the day they rest concealed on the bottom and by night they go in search of food. They capture their prey – worms, insect-larvae, various crustaceans and small fishes, among others – in much the same fashion as newts; that is to say, the prey is stalked, suddenly seized and swallowed whole. Courtship is initiated by springing out of the water. Later both partners pursue one another, pressing close together through the water, or else the ♂ swims alongside the resting ♀ and gently nudges her with his mouth or brushes her with his anal fin which, according to Budgett, is swollen and folded at this time. About the spawning itself scarcely anything

39

is known; the young animals which emerge from the eggs are larvae, which have arborescent (= tree-like) external gills and are very like newt-larvae in appearance (Fig.11).

In recent years various Bichirs have been kept successfully, both in large public aquaria and in the tanks of amateurs. In general these fishes prove very hardy and resistant against variations in temperature. The paramount necessities for their welfare are good hiding-places, such as cavities among stones and tangled roots; these are particularly valuable when the fishes are kept in a community tank. Under suitable conditions the Bichirs, though at first shy, will become very tame; they then generally leave their hiding-places in the evening and go to the place where they are accustomed to be fed. In this way they exhibit a behaviour quite uncommon among fishes. Like Salamanders, on their nocturnal feeding-prowl they inch themselves forward a little, halt, and then, slightly raising the head, orientate themselves and 'sniff around'. It may be a considerable time before the next advance is made. Apparently the Bichirs are pretty tolerant of the quality of the water, but water which is not too hard suits them best. Temperature, according to origin, about 22–28 °C. Large live food is generally willingly taken, e.g. earthworms, *Tubifex*, maggots, bloodworms (*Chironomus* larvae), and occasionally even meat and small frogs, but mealworms are most popular. Growth is fairly slow. Bichirs are generally peaceful with other fishes, provided the latter are not too small. They do occasionally snap at one another, however, when there are not enough hiding-places. Highly interesting fishes, much to be recommended to keen amateurs, and beautiful showpieces for large public aquaria.

Figs. 10–14

Fig. 10. *Polypterus bichir* (Nile Bichir); adult, greatly reduced.
Fig. 11. Larva of *Polypterus lapradei*, showing external gills. (Re-drawn, after Kerr).
Fig. 12. *Lepisosteus platostomus* (Shortnose Gar); adult, greatly reduced.
Fig. 13. *Osteoglossum bicirrhosum*; young, about natural size.
Fig. 14. *Scleropages formosus*; adult, greatly reduced.

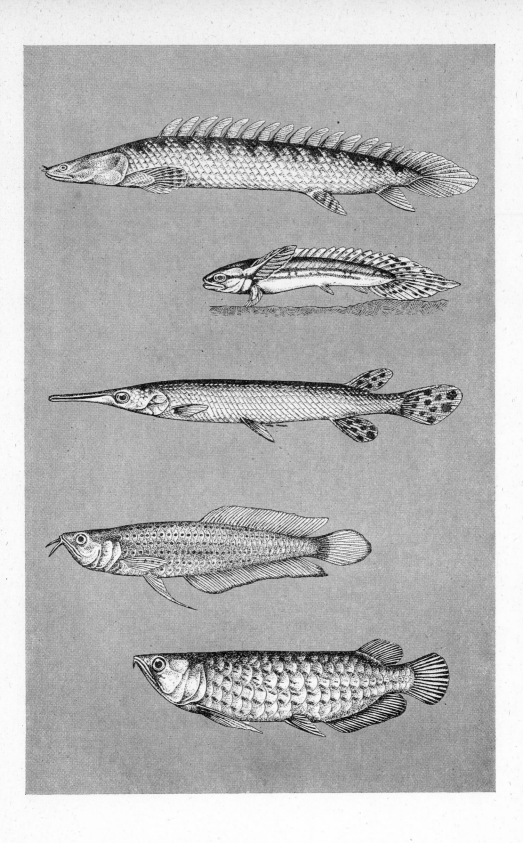

Polypterus bichir *Geoffroy* 1802 (Fig. 10)   Nile Bichir
Nile, Lake Rudolf and Lake Chad and tributary streams; to 70 cm.

D 14–18 spines (finlets); A 11–15; LL 63–70. Body elongate, almost cylindrical, sides slightly compressed. The high number of dorsal finlets and the slightly projecting lower jaw are characteristic of this species; the tip of the pectoral fin reaches to the level of the second dorsal finlet. Upperside olive-green, flanks grey, belly yellowish. Young fishes have 10–13 wedge-shaped transverse bars and 2–3 longitudinal stripes; several dark spots are retained in older fishes. Fins colourless to grey; pectoral and ventral fins with dark transverse markings.

For care, see family description; a snappy and quarrelsome species, according to Arnold. 1903/−.

Polypterus delhezi *Boulenger* 1899 (Fig. 16)
Upper and Middle Congo; to 35 cm.

D 10–11 spines (finlets); A 11; LL 56. Similar to *P. bichir*, but with fewer finlets; either the upper and lower jaws reach to the same level, or the lower jaw is a trifle shorter; also the pectoral fin does not extend as far as the first dorsal finlet. Yellowish-brown, with 6–7 very irregular but strikingly prominent transverse bars which extend from the back to the middle of the side and have pale borders in fine specimens; between the bars and under their lower ends are separate spots and blotches. Belly white. Fins yellowish, to some extent with dark transverse marks. A very attractive species.

For care, see family description. The young fishes, like the adults, are very quarrelsome among themselves. 1953.

Polypterus ornatipinnis *Boulenger* 1902 (Fig. 20)
Upper and Middle Congo; to 37 cm.

D 10–11 spines (finlets); A 15; LL 62–63. Similar to *P. bichir*, but still more elongate and somewhat more compressed. The snout only slightly overhangs the lower jaw; the pectoral fin ends well before the first dorsal finlet. Back and flanks with irregular dark reticulations on a white or grey ground, posteriorly on a yellow ground. Head finely reticulated. Underside yellowish. Dorsal fins white with black spots; paired fins with beautiful transverse black marks on a pale to bright yellow ground. A very beautiful species.

For care, see family description. 1953.

Polypterus palmas *Ayres* 1850 (Figs. 18, 19)
Sierra Leone, Liberia, Congo; to 30 cm.

D 5–9 spines (finlets); A 12–15; LL 52–56. This species is markedly distingu-

42

ished by the low number of dorsal finlets and the ventral mouth; the pectoral fin ends well before the first dorsal finlet. Upperside grey to grey-green; flanks some-what paler, in young fishes with numerous irregular dark bars or blotches arranged in a chessboard pattern which, on the tail, may alternate with yellowish areas; this pattern may totally disappear with increasing age. Underside yellowish. Fins more or less marked with dark; a more or less distinct black blotch on the fleshy base of the pectoral.

For care, see family description. 1953.

Polypterus weeksi *Boulenger* 1898 (Fig. 17)
Katanga, Upper Congo; to 40 cm.

D 9–10 spines (finlets); A 10–11; LL 60–65. Body, by contrast with other *Polypterus* spp., rather strongly compressed. The snout slightly overhangs the lower jaw. The pectoral fin, being laid back, ends well before the first dorsal finlet. Upperside olive-green to grey; belly yellowish. Numerous irregular dark transverse bars, characteristically forked, on the flanks. Fins spotted with black, or even with transverse dark bars; a deep black blotch on each finlet is especially striking in the young.

For care, see family description; snappy. 1953.

Calamoichthys calabaricus *Smith* 1865 (Fig. 15)   Reed-fish
Niger Delta, Cameroons, Chiloanga; to 90 cm.

D 7–13 spines (finlets); A 9–14; LL 106–114. Body eel-like, not compressed. The finlets, which are usually depressed, are well separated. No ventral fins. Upper-side a beautiful olive-green; flanks paler green; underside yellow. Pectoral fins with a large black blotch. The sexes are said to be distinguished by the number of anal fin-rays: ♀ 9–12, ♂ 12–14.

For care, see family description; very hardy and peaceful. This species moves snake-wise over the bottom, but can also side-wind quite rapidly through the water. 1905/+.

Family Acipenseridae (Sturgeons)

The Sturgeons, a group exclusively inhabiting the North Temperate regions, have existed as a well-defined group for about 200 million years and have to this day retained several quite primitive features, such as a persistent

43

notochord and a failure to develop vertebral centra. The incomplete ossification of the skeleton, formerly thought to be a primitive character also, is now regarded by modern authorities as a secondary modification. The characteristic physiognomy of the Sturgeon is accounted for by the rostrum, a median forwardly-directed process of the head, and by five series of large bony plates or scutes which overlap like tiles on a roof in the otherwise naked skin of the body. The ventral mouth is protrusible and in front of it are four barbels. However, numerous further peculiarities of the internal organs indicate that the Sturgeon is at a relatively primitive level of organisation. The Sturgeons are voracious bottom-living fishes which live in the open sea, the brackish-water zone or in large inland lakes, from whence they ascend the rivers; some species, like the Sterlet, have become almost purely river fishes. When young they feed largely upon snails, mussels, worms and crustacea; older fishes become fish-predators. All Sturgeons are extraordinarily fertile. The roe of almost every species is made into caviare; isinglass is obtained from the large swim-bladder and the flesh is valued as food.

Young Sterlets are often exhibited in the public aquaria of Europe; less frequently Sturgeons and even Huso.

Acipenser ruthenus *Linnaeus* 1758 (Fig. 22)   Sterlet
In the Black Sea and Sea of Azov, and in rivers entering these, also in northern Russia and northern Siberia; to 1 m.

Body spindle-shaped; head with a very long, somewhat upcurved snout; upper side of head covered with bony scutes; scutes in mid-line of back with sharp, backwardly-directed spines; lateral scutes (60–70) very close together; 4 barbels with short fringes; upper lobe of caudal longer and more pointed than lower (tip of vertebral column turns up, as in sharks, and tail is described as heterocercal); pectoral fin with a very strong first spine; mouth protrusible.

Plate 1

Fig. 15. *Calamoichthys calabaricus* (Reed-fish); adult, about 60 cm. in length. (Original)
Fig. 16. *Polypterus delhezi*; adult of nearly 30 cm. length. (Original)
Fig. 17. *Polypterus weeksi*; half-grown, somewhat reduced. (Original)

Plate 1

Plate 2

Plate 2

Fig. 18. *Polypterus palmas*; young, natural size. (Photo Dr. Foersch)
Fig. 19. *Polypterus palmas*; adult, 25 cm. long. (Original)
Fig. 20. *Polypterus ornatipinnis*; young, about natural size. (Original)

Back and sides reddish-brown to blue-grey; underside pale, sometimes yellowish or delicate red. Fins dark with a light margin; anal fin often completely white. Series of scutes, particularly in young fishes, yellowish.

The Sterlet, which sometimes ascends the Danube as far as Ulm, is a typical bottom-dweller, feeding principally on snails, insects, worms and other small animals. Spawning-season May-June. The eggs, grey and 1·5 mm. in diameter, are laid in deep gravelly stretches of the river and immediately adhere to the bottom. The young are tadpole-like and almost completely black.

The care of the Sterlet generally presents no special difficulty. Basically all that is required is a tank with a very large bottom-area so as to give the fish enough room to move about. Hardly any other fish is so fond of keeping on the move, and the striking thing about this unrest is the smoothness and uniformity of the motion. The fish glides unceasingly in an elegant, restful progress; there is no hunting about and almost no fear-reaction. Food is almost entirely taken off the bottom, preferably stirred up from the bottom. Like all bottom-fishes the Sterlet should have soft sand or not too coarse river gravel; avoid sharp gravel and above all sharp-edged aquarium furnishings because the fishes very easily damage their projecting snouts. Water-temperature not above 18°C. Many Sterlets are rather choosy over their food but take certain foods (which must first be tested) very willingly. Earthworms, mealworms, snails, bloodworms and *Tubifex* (only for small individuals); fish, beef or horseflesh and, finally, small fishes. Only small specimens are possible in a domestic aquarium and are, moreover, very difficult to keep. Watching young Sterlets of 10–15 cm. in length, exquisite little fishes, like ivory figurines from a long-vanished epoch, swimming so tirelessly on their endless tracks, is one of the most beautiful experiences that any ichthyologist can have.

The common name 'Sterlet' is given in allusion to the small bony starlets which are strewn over the skin of the fish.

Lepisosteus (Litholepis) tristoechus (*Bloch* and *Schneider* 1801) (Figs. 24, 66)

Southern U.S.A., Mexico, Central America, Cuba; to 3·5 m.   Alligator Gar

D 7–8; A 7–8; LL 53–63. Beak, at most, as long as the rest of the head; caudal fin rounded. Upperside olive-green; flanks green-silver; underside white to delicate yellow. Young fishes, especially, show dark rhombic (more rarely round) blotches on the upper half of the body, as well as fins irregularly blotched or marbled with dark. Adult fishes are almost uniformly green-silver. The species is divided into three subspecies.

Care, as given for *L. osseus*. The present species requires warm conditions; specimens from Central America, especially, should not be kept at temperatures less than 22 °C. 1915/+.

Family Amiidae (Bowfins)

The single species of this family is at the same time the sole surviving representative of a group which flourished and was widespread during the Mesozoic, particularly during the Jurassic and Cretaceous. The Bowfin is especially interesting to comparative anatomists since, in spite of its looking like a typical bony fish, it retains some peculiarities of organisation characteristic of primitive groups of fishes, such as the large bony gular plate between the rami of the lower jaw.

Amia calva *Linnaeus* 1766 (Fig. 25)   Bowfin
Mississippi Basin, Lakes Huron and Erie; to 60 cm.

D 42–53; A 10–12; LL 65–70. Body elongate, pike-like, compressed. Dorsal fin very long-based; caudal fin rounded; cycloid scales with a thin, enamel-like covering (ganoid scales). The swim-bladder serves as an accessory breathing-organ, especially in summer, and to that end its inner surface has numerous reticulate infoldings. Upperside olive-green; underside yellowish to orange; flanks coarsely marbled with light and dark green. Fins more or less brownish to light green. Dor-

Plate 3

Fig. 22. *Acipenser ruthenus* (Sterlet); young, 35 cm. in length, in the Hellabrunn Aquarium, Munich. (Original)

Fig. 23. *Lepisosteus osseus* (Common Garpike); large adult, about 1 m. in length, in the Hellabrunn Aquarium, Munich. (Original)

Fig. 24. *Lepisosteus tristoechus* (Alligator Gar); young, about 80 cm. in length, in the Hellabrunn Aquarium, Munich. (Photo Dr. Foersch)

Plate 3

Plate 4

Plate 4

Fig. 25. *Amia calva* (Bowfin); young, 30 cm. in length, in the London Zoo. (Original)
Fig. 26. *Pantodon buchholzi* (Butterfly-fish); adult, somewhat reduced. (Original)
Fig. 27. *Phractolaemus ansorgei*; young, about twice natural size. (Photo Dr. Foersch)
Fig. 28. *Lampetra planeri* (Brook Lamprey); ripe fish attached by its oral sucker to the front of the aquarium. (Original)

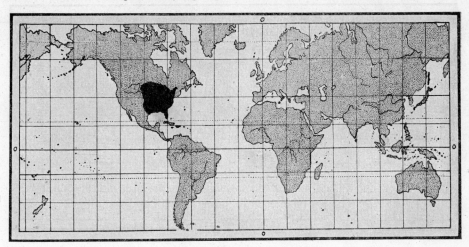

Fig. 29
Distribution of the *Amiidae*

sal fin with two dark longitudinal stripes. A round dark blotch, ringed with yellow to yellowish red, on the upper part of the caudal base of the ♂.

The predatory Bowfin is occasionally kept in public aquaria but is a rare exhibit in Europe. In general it should be treated like our native fishes, that is, kept in cool fresh water (not below 3°C.) with a constant slight through-current. Voracious; as well as fishes, crustacea, frogs and earthworms also takes horseflesh and fish. Very hardy if regularly fed. This fish best displays its striking coloration in warm water (up to about 15°C.) and under such conditions may often be seen to take atmospheric air. The dorsal fin, which serves as the propulsive organ, shows a rapid wave-like motion as the fish rises to the surface. In its natural habitat the Bowfin spawns in the months of May and June, when the males build nests in thick clumps of aquatic plants. The eggs are laid at night and are guarded by the ♂, who also takes care of the young fish which hatch 8–10 days later; not until the young are about 10 cm. long is the parental instinct lost. Not yet bred in aquaria. The Bowfin is to some extent used as a food-fish in America. 1891/+.

49

Family Phractolaemidae

This family contains only the single species described below.

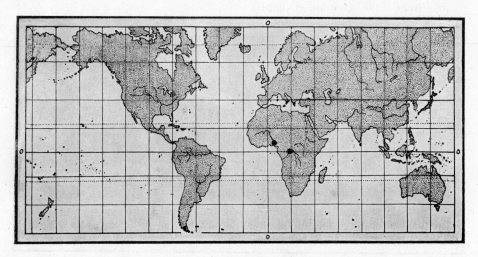

Fig. 30
Distribution of the *Phractolaemidae*; note Africa

Phractolaemus ansorgei *Boulenger* 1901 (Fig. 27)
Niger Delta, Upper Congo; to 15 cm.

D 6; A 6; LL 35–40. Body elongate, anteriorly almost cylindrical, posteriorly rather compressed, and covered with large scales. Head small and broad. Mouth very small, protrusible as a tube and almost toothless. Lateral line complete. The large swim-bladder serves as an accessory breathing-organ.

Upperside almost uniformly grey; flanks paler, often brownish; underside pale. Fins dark. Mature ♂♂ may be recognised by the whitish tubercles on the head and by two rows of pointed outgrowths from the caudal peduncle.

Figs. 31–34

Fig. 31. *Salvelinus alpinus* (Char); adult, reduced.
Fig. 32. *Salmo salar* (Salmon); adult, greatly reduced.
Fig. 33. *Salmo trutta* morpha *lacustris* (Lake Trout); adult, greatly reduced.
Fig. 34. *Coregonus albula*; adult, reduced.

In its natural habitat *Phractolaemus* inhabits muddy, weedy waters and feeds on small animals which it grubs out of the mud with its protrusible mouth. In captivity this fish should be kept in the dark and provided with a soft bottom-soil. It requires a high temperature (25–28 °C.). As food it takes small worms of all kinds (*Tubifex*, various Enchytraeids), red midge-larvae, dead waterfleas and also artificial food; according to Holly it also eats plant detritus. Unfortunately only single specimens have been imported so far, so that no attempts at breeding have yet been possible. A very interesting and rare species, concerning which very little is known. 1906/+.

Family Salmonidae (Salmon, Trout, Char, etc.)

Slim, predatory, bony fishes which inhabit the inland waters and seas of the Northern Hemisphere. (The genus *Retropinna* of New Zealand, formerly classified with the *Salmonidae*, is nowadays placed by itself in a separate family, the *Retropinnidae*). Some species are migratory fishes which, in relation to their breeding cycle, alternately live in fresh water and in the sea. The upper margin of the mouth is formed from the premaxillary and maxillary bones; a small adipose fin stands behind the dorsal fin.

This family includes many highly esteemed food-fishes, such as Trout, Salmon, Smelt, Blaufelchen, etc.

Only a few tropical fishes can charm and delight the naturalist more than our native *Salmonidae*. The word 'native', which all too often carries the false implication 'uninteresting', here conceals a splendour of colour and elegance of movement which are only matched among the Characins and Cyprinodonts. It is therefore most unfortunate that the demands made by the *Salmonidae* are usually too exacting to be met under the conditions of the domestic aquarium. All large public aquaria should, however, be able to keep our native Salmonid fishes successfully provided some reasonable attention is given to their care. The fundamental requirement is the largest possible tank. For species from running waters (Brown Trout, Rainbow Trout, Brook Trout, Grayling) one should endeavour to furnish the aquarium so as to imitate the conditions of a mountain, or better lowland, stream, providing a pebbly bottom with moss-grown stones, branches and ample suspended root-systems. At the outset one abandons the idea of introducing any higher plants. The temperature and renewal of the water are of fundamental importance, however. Lasting success can only be achieved in establishments which possess their own natural spring-water supply; tapwater today, on account of its chlorination, is only suitable when it has been allowed to stand for some time in a well-aerated reservoir tank until the chlorine has

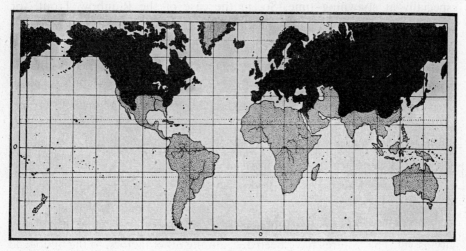

Fig. 35

Distribution of the *Salmonidae*. In many regions the fishes descend from inland waters to brackish waters and to the sea.

been completely eliminated. The temperature should not rise much above 15°C. Additional aeration is often necessary despite the constant supply of fresh water. The water level can be quite low for young fishes.

Species from large lakes or rivers (Lake Trout, Huchen, Lake Char, Blaufelchen, Whitefish, Houting, Smelt) generally need very large, dim tanks (8–10 cubic metres) with sandy bottoms. It is advantageous to screen at least a part of the tank from view with hanging root-systems or a stone wall; the same result can be achieved more naturally by planting reeds. As regards renewal of water and temperature the same conditions apply as are given above.

In stocking the aquarium hatchery fry, or the smallest fishes possible from natural waters, should be procured, since these are more easily acclimatised than large specimens and grow quite rapidly with good feeding. Grayling and Smelt are (according to Ladiges) highly susceptible to damage during capture; even the loss of scales can give rise to a fatal infection. On this account fishes required for exhibition should be dipped out of the nets and carefully transported in large containers. *Salmonidae* are very unsociable and snappy, especially at spawning-time. So, in the case of the Rainbow Trout, for example, only large specimens of the same sex can be kept together. Other species, like the Brown Trout, are territorial fishes, that is to say, fishes which monopolise one area and defend it against all comers. As far as food is concerned, most of the species have the same requirements. Small to medium-sized *Salmonidae* devour insects (cockroaches, crickets), large insect-larvae, earthworms, snails and often meat and fish-flesh; large individuals relish smaller live fishes, even of the same species. A regular and rich diet is necessary if the fishes are to flourish in captivity.

It is necessary to cover the tanks; all the species are accomplished and enthusiastic leapers!

The Salmon, *Salmo salar* Linnaeus (Fig. 32) has rarely been kept in captivity as yet. The failures have been due, among other factors, to the biological peculiarities of this species. The mature Salmon hunts mainly in the coastal regions, where food is abundant, and ascends the rivers as the breeding season approaches in order to spawn in the upper reaches. The young fishes remain for 2–4 years in freshwater and then migrate to the sea, returning to the old spawning-places year by year at the breeding season.

Of the trout which inhabit Central Europe the Rainbow and the Brown Trout may be successfully kept in captivity. In contrast to these Lake Trout

Figs. 36–38

Fig. 36. *Coregonus wartmanni* (Blaufelchen); adult, reduced.
Fig. 37. *Thymallus thymallus* (Grayling); adult, reduced.
Fig. 38. *Osmerus eperlanus* (Smelt); adult, reduced.

(*Salmo trutta* morpha *lacustris*, Fig. 33) and Sea-trout *(Salmo trutta* morpha *trutta)* can at most be kept for a short time as young fishes.

As well as the Salmonid fishes already described, the following may be kept successfully for a long time, at least in large aquaria: – the Kleine Marane (*Coregonus albula* L., Fig. 34) of the German clear-water lakes; the Blau-felchen or Grosse Schweberenke (*Coregonus wartmanni* Bloch, Figs. 36, 40) from the lakes of the Voralpen, and even the very rare Kleine Schweberenke or Kilch (*Coregonus acronius* Rapp). According to Ladiges the rearing of these fishes from the egg is quite easy in the aquarium.

Hucho hucho (*Linnaeus* 1758) (Fig. 42)   Huchen
Danube and tributaries on the right side; to 150 cm.

D 4/9–10; A 4–5/7–9; P 1/14–16; V 1/8–9; LL 180–220. Body torpedo-shaped, hardly compressed. Mouth deeply cleft; old ♂♂ with a hooked tip to the lower jaw ('kype').

Rather uniform grey-silver, older fishes also reddish-silver; upperside occasionally considerably darker; belly very pale. Numerous very small, black spots on the flanks. Young fishes black, banded with grey.

Huchen are station-holding fishes which, like the Trout, fall upon their prey, mainly fishes, from a position of concealment. The young feed upon insect-larvae, worms and other small creatures. At spawning-time the Huchen migrate upstream to spawning grounds which are usually in smaller tributaries where they make shallow redds and cover the eggs with gravel. Huchen do very well in captivity, though it is best to start with small specimens. See also family description.

Salmo gairdneri irideus *Gibbons* 1855 (Fig. 44)   Rainbow Trout
Native to western North America; introduced into Europe in 1880 and also into other regions, including New Zealand; average length 35 cm.

D 4/10; A 3/10; P 1/12; V 1/8; LL 135–150. Shape similar to that of the Brown Trout. Mouth rather larger. The species is divided into numerous subspecies which have often been crossed in fish-hatcheries. Coloration very variable.

Plate 5

Fig. 39. *Lampetra planeri* (Brook Lamprey); above, a 4-year old Ammocoete larva, below, a full-grown adult; natural size. (Original)
Fig. 40. *Coregonus wartmanni* (Blaufelchen); young, natural size. (Photo P. Unger)
Fig. 41. *Thymallus thymallus* (Grayling); length 30 cm. (Original)

Plate 5

Plate 6

Plate 6

Fig. 42. *Hucho hucho* (Huchen); full-grown, 90 cm. length, in the Hellabrunn Aquarium, Munich. (Original)
Fig. 43. *Salmo trutta* morpha *fario* (Brown Trout); young, 18 cm. length. (Original)
Fig. 44. *Salmo gairdnerii irideus* (Rainbow Trout); old ♂, 60 cm. length, in the Hellabrunn Aquarium, Munich. (Original)

Upperside usually bright green to brown; flanks paler; underside silvery to yellowish. A broad, mainly violet, band along the flanks, iridescent with all the colours of the rainbow, is characteristic of this species. Head, body and vertical fins thickly covered with black spots which to some extent are distinctly star-shaped.

The Rainbow Trout is very resistant to higher temperatures and on this account to be found in warmer waters. Some subspecies are territorial, others migratory, fishes. The rapid growth and greater hardiness of the Rainbow Trout makes it a very worthwhile subject for pond-culture in some regions. Spawning-season, according to subspecies, November to May; ♀ and ♂ make the redd. The eggs are rather smaller than in the Brown Trout.

For care in captivity, see family description.

Salmo trutta morpha **fario** (*Linnaeus* 1758) (Fig. 43)   Brown Trout
Throughout Europe, Iceland, Asia Minor; thence acclimatised as a good food-fish almost everywhere wherever environmental conditions similar to those of our trout streams are available; average length 25 cm.

D 3–4/9–11; A 3/7–8; P 1/12; V 1/8; LL 110–120. Body torpedo-shaped, moderately compressed. Older fishes especially are often thick-set. Caudal fin only slightly emarginate or squarely truncate (old Brown Trout). Coloration very variable. Upperside usually olive-green to brown-green; flanks paler green-silver or yellow-green; underside very pale yellowish. Round black and red spots on the flanks are characteristic of the Brown Trout, the red spots almost always with a broad, more or less blue, rim. Adipose fin usually with red spots. As well as very dark trout there are also very pale, yellowish ones. Young with 13 dark blotches like transverse bars.

The Brown Trout is a characteristic inhabitant of our mountain and meadow streams. Its special habitats are the reaches with a gravelly bottom (Trout Region). Under favourable conditions, such as particularly high oxygen-content, the Brown Trout may also be found elsewhere, as for example in larger rivers and in ponds with a good through-current. Brown Trout are territorial fishes which dominate a

57

move about and must be very plentifully fed. It is important for both species that they be captured without damage; damaged individuals soon perish, according to Ladiges. (See also the account of the family *Salmonidae*.)

Family Osteoglossidae

Large freshwater fishes with numerous primitive features.

The species are distributed as follows: – Tropical South America *(Arapaima gigas, Osteoglossum bicirrhosum)*; tropical Africa *(Heterotis niloticus)*; Malay Archipelago and Australia *(Scleropages formosus* and *S. scheich-hardti)*. This distribution shows a general correspondence, among others, with that of the Lungfishes and provides zoogeographical evidence of archaic land-bridges between the continents.

All the Osteoglossids possess a very remarkable squamation. The individual scales are very stout and bony, with canals which form a mosaic-like pattern. A further characteristic of the family is a curious helical organ on the fourth gill-arch which was formerly supposed to be an accessory respiratory-organ until d'Aubenton (1955) showed that in *Heterotis* it serves for filter-feeding. Water which has already been filtered through the gill-rakers passes into the helical organ and fine particles, including phytoplankton, are there trapped in mucus and carried back to the stomach. During the dry season, when the water is low, this fine food forms an important part of the diet. Aerial respiration is probably effected by the swim-bladder, which opens by a duct at the back of the pharynx.

Arapaima gigas, growing to 4·5 m. in length and 200 kg. in weight, is one of the world's largest freshwater fishes.

Plate 7

Fig.45. *Osteoglossum bicirrhosum;* adult, 35 cm. long, in the Hellabrunn Aquarium, Munich. (Original)
Fig.46. *Notopterus chitala;* young, 12 cm. long. (Original)
Fig.47. *Xenomystus nigri;* half-grown, natural size. (Original)

Plate 7

Plate 8

Plate 8

Fig.48. *Gnathonemus petersi;* adult of 17 cm. length. (Original)
Fig.49. *Gnathonemus elephas* (?); young fish, imported in 1956, natural size. (Original)
Fig.50. *Gnathonemus moori;* half-grown, approximately natural size. (Original)

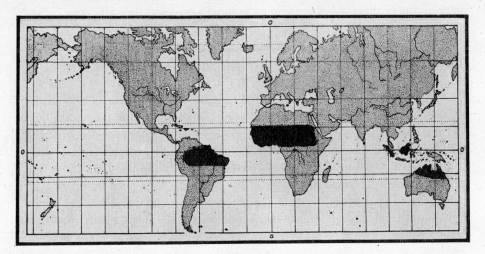

Fig.51
Distribution of the *Osteoglossidae*. Note the discontinuous distribution through South America, Africa, the Malay Archipelago and Australia.

Osteoglossum bicirrhosum *Vandelli* 1829 (Figs.13, 45)
Guiana and the Amazon basin; to 1 m.

D 42–46; A 50–55; LL 31–35. Body almost band-like, strongly compressed; belly keeled. Gape of mouth very large, upwardly directed; two forked barbels (whisker-like feelers) standing forward from the chin. Dorsal and anal fins long-based, opposite. Greyish silver to pale greenish yellow, with a gorgeous rainbow iridescence. Barbels bluish to sea-green. Throat orange to bright red. Each scale on the side of the body bears a bright red spot. Fins yellowish or pale greenish, to some extent pencilled with brownish or reddish markings.

O.bicirrhosum is not uncommon within its area of distribution; in very weedy, stagnant backwaters and shallow lakes, especially, it may occur in considerable numbers.

In captivity provide young specimens with a large, thinly-planted aquarium, soft, moderately peaty water and temperatures around 25°C. Suitable food-animals include, as well as small fishes, *Daphnia*, white and black midge-larvae and, above all, dragonfly-larvae; in exceptional cases the young fishes will take lettuce and some of the better dried foods. The young are very lively and rapid-growing and adapt themselves very well to domestic aquaria; large specimens make beautiful exhibits for public aquaria. Scarcely anything is known about the breeding, but in older accounts these fishes are said to be mouth-brooders. It is advisable to keep the tank well covered as this species is a good leaper. 1912/+.

Scleropages formosus (*Schlegel* and *Müller* 1829) (Fig. 14)
Borneo, Banka, Sumatra, Thailand; to 90 cm.
   D 20; A 26–27; LL 21–24. Body long, very strongly compressed; belly keeled. Gape of mouth very large, steeply inclined; 2 small barbels on the chin. Dorsal and anal fins relatively short, especially the former. Coloration (according to Rachow): – 'Back dark olive to brownish, sides and belly greenish with silver and gold sheen and bearing longitudinal rows of obliquely-inclined dark spots. Fins pale sea-green to sky-blue with more or less brown to red-brown fin-rays.'
   S. formosus is a predatory fish like the preceding species, inhabiting weedy, slow-flowing waters and feeding chiefly on insects; large specimens prey upon other fishes. Care and treatment essentially as for *Osteoglossum;* young *Scleropages*, however, are a great deal more lively. In this species mouth-brooding has been reliably established; according to Fährmann the large eggs are taken up by the ♀. 1932/ –.

Family Pantodontidae (Butterfly-fish)

This very isolated and distinctive family contains only the single species from West Africa described below. Greenwood and Thomson (1960) now place it among the *Osteoglossidae* and suggest a close relationship with *Osteoglossum* and *Scleropages*.

Pantodon buchholzi *Peters* 1876 (Fig. 26)   Butterfly-fish
Tropical West Africa, Niger, Cameroons, Congo Basin; to 10 cm.
   D 6; A 9–14; LL 23–30. Head and body flattened above, bluntly rounded below; general form boat-shaped. Mouth large, upwardly directed. Nostrils tubular, externally produced. Pectoral fins enlarged, wing-like; ventral fins small with 4 very long drawn-out fin-rays: anal and caudal fins enlarged, banner-like. Scales

large. Back and sides of body grey-green to brownish silver marked with very variable streaks and spots. There is nearly always a distinct sharp-edged dark streak passing forward from the occiput (hinder part of the head) onto the lower jaw. Pectoral fins distally blackish with clear or white margins. The fin-rays of all the fins are ringed alternately clear and dark.

♂ hinder end of anal fin deeply incised, the middle rays forming a tube.
♀ hinder end of anal fin rectilinear.

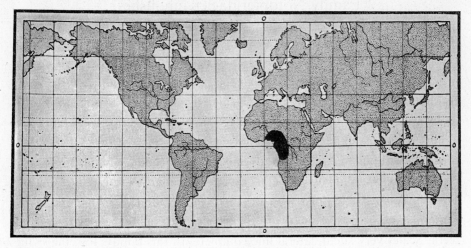

Fig. 52
Distribution of the *Pantodontidae*

Within its range this species occurs chiefly in large, standing, weedy waters and stagnant backwaters of rivers, also occasionally in small forest ponds and ditches. The principal food consists of insects which have fallen onto the surface of the water or which, more rarely, are caught on the wing. For the latter purpose the fishes leap very adroitly out of the water, meantime spreading wide their wing-like pectoral fins which enable them to glide for a short distance over the surface. On the other hand these fishes do not have the power to undertake true, flapping flight as was formerly supposed. Butterfly-fish should be kept in large, shallow tanks with sparse planting. Temperature 25 to 30°C. Live foods, principally insects such as cockroaches, crickets and soft beetles, also smaller fishes and insect-larvae.

Breeding not easy; arrange a temperature around 30°C. and provide soft, peaty water. During numerous false matings the male often rides on the back of the fe-

63

male for hours at a time, holding firmly onto her with the elongated fin-rays of his ventral fins. At the real mating the fishes twist themselves around each other. The eggs float at the surface of the water. The young hatch after 3 days. Rearing very difficult, since only springtails, plant aphides and the tiniest flies floating on the surface of the water are accepted. A very interesting species. 1905/+.

Family Notopteridae (Knife-fishes)

Rather large, elongate, strongly compressed freshwater fishes. Anus situated very far forward; anal fin long-based and narrow, united with the small caudal into a single long fringing fin which is the chief propulsive organ of the body. By rhythmic wave-like movements of this fin the body is directed forwards, or, by waves passing in the opposite direction, backwards; the fishes can swim almost equally well in either direction and so can instantly retreat before a predator without making any movements of the body. Similar locomotor mechanisms occur in other fishes, as for example in the *Gymnotidae* and *Sternarchidae*. By contrast with the anal fin, all the other fins, except the pectorals, are greatly reduced or absent. Mouth large with numerous small teeth. Scales very small, lateral line complete. In this family, too, the swim-bladder is transformed into an accessory breathing-organ and the fishes frequently rise to the surface to obtain air. Nasal tentacle conspicuous. 2 genera with a total of 5 species in tropical Africa and in S. E. Asia (including Indonesia); sometimes present in brackish water.

Throughout their range the *Notopteridae* are found in the quiet, weedy reaches of great rivers, in flood plains and in stagnant backwaters. With their heads slightly inclined downwards the fishes rest during the day, singly or in shoals, in the shelter of old stems or thick floating plants. By night, on the other hand, they move about incessantly, close over the bottom, seeking

Figs. 53–55

Fig. 53. *Notopterus afer;* young.
Fig. 54. *Notopterus notopterus;* young.
Fig. 55. *Notopterus chitala*, with characteristic juvenile markings.

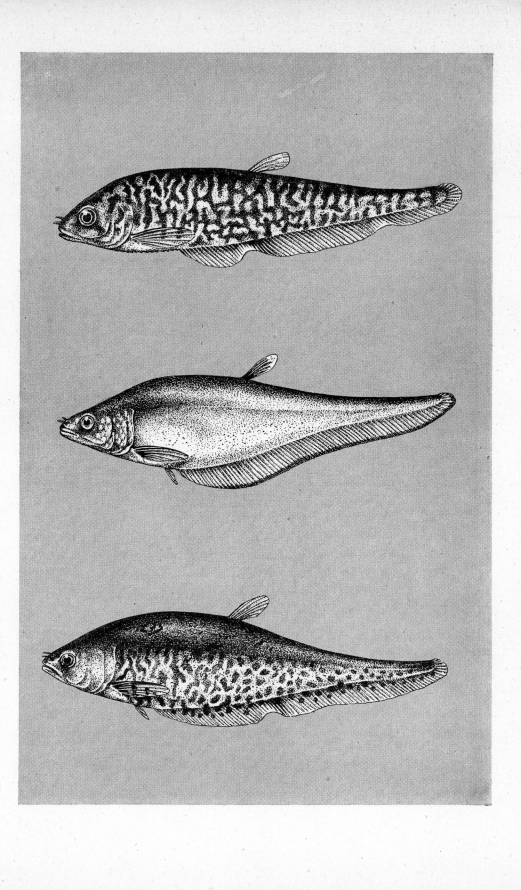

small prey such as insect-larvae, worms, small fishes and so on. Large individuals are often very predaceous and are emphatically 'lone wolves'. Unfortunately hardly anything is known about their reproductive behaviour. The *Notopteridae* of southern Asia are in some districts much esteemed as food-fishes.

Generally only young fishes are suitable for the domestic aquarium; adult specimens, on the other hand, are among the most interesting exhibits in

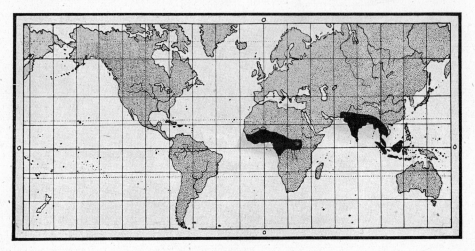

Fig. 56
Distribution of the *Notopteridae*

zoological gardens. The most important consideration, of decisive importance to the welfare of these shy fishes, is the furnishing of the tank which should be kept as dark as possible and provided with hiding-places. They do not require individual caves in which they can find shelter on all sides but rather overhanging flat rocks or oblique root-stumps under which they can move about freely. Among the African species, at least, soft peaty water is obviously preferred. As may be expected from their distribution all the *Notopteridae* require rather high temperatures of 24–28 °C., although they are not especially susceptible to temporary falls in temperature. Live food of all kinds is taken in great quantities; occasionally the fishes will accept artificial food as well. They behave quite peaceably towards other fishes provided the latter are not considerably smaller. On the other hand, members of the same species are almost invariably quarrelsome in domestic aquaria. Shoals are formed only in large spacious tanks.

Notopterus afer *Günther* 1868 (Fig. 53)
From Gambia to the Congo; to 60 cm.

D 6–7; A+C 113–130; LL 130–165. Body elongate, very strongly compressed; upper profile strongly convex; dorsal fin like a small flag, ventrals absent; ventral keel serrate. While young fishes often display a dark network, or even dark spots, on a delicate reddish or yellowish ground, older specimens are usually uniformly violet brown, rarely with pale blotches on this ground. For care, see family description; large specimens like horseflesh and fish. 1912/+.

Notopterus chitala (*Hamilton-Buchanan* 1822) (Figs. 46, 55)
Thailand, Burma, larger islands of the Malay Archipelago; to 80 cm.

D 9–10; A+C 110–135; LL over 200. Young individuals similar to the fore-going species but somewhat deeper and possessing small ventral fins; older fishes are very high-backed and plump. According to Arnold the young are handsomely marked; on a chocolate brown ground there are, on the lower half of the body and on the anal fin, numerous conspicuous vermiculations, blotches and irregular spots. According to Weber, on the other hand, young fishes bear on the back about 20 silvery, somewhat oblique, transverse bands, some of which are forked. Half-grown specimens are velvety blackish-brown. Old individuals are silver-coloured with dark blotches on the vertical fins. For care, see family description. Said to be very snappy (according to Arnold)? 1934/+.

Notopterus notopterus (*Pallas* 1780) (Fig. 54)
India, Burma, Thailand, Java and Sumatra; to 35 cm.

D 8–9; A+C 100–110; LL over 200. *N. notopterus* is distinguished from the foregoing species mainly by the scales on the gill-cover which are here considerably larger than those of the body; by contrast, in *N. chitala* the scales of the gill-cover and of the body are of equal size. Silvery-grey, considerably darker above, with numerous fine dark blotches over the whole body. Dorsal fin with a white tip, anal usually with a black margin. Iris shining gold. For care, see family description. 1933/–.

Xenomystus nigri (*Günther* 1868) (Fig. 47)

Widely distributed, from the upper tributaries of the Nile to Liberia; to 20 cm.

D –; A + C 108–130; LL 120–142. This species is easily recognised because it completely lacks a dorsal fin. Ventral fins greatly reduced, minute. Uniformly mouse-grey to dark brown, sometimes with black longitudinal stripes; belly often somewhat paler. According to Meinken, at the breeding season it is reddish-brown or purplish-red with an olive-green anal fin. For care, see family description; not yet bred in captivity; very hardy. 1909/+.

Family Mormyridae

Freshwater fishes confined to Africa, of very atypical form and often quite peculiar in appearance. As well as species with a tuberous or finger-shaped process on the jaw serving as a feeler, there are others with a greatly elongate proboscis-like snout. Eyes and mouth usually small, the latter often tubular. Skin thick, smooth and slimy; colour drab or silvery throughout the group. Many species have weak electric organs.

Almost all the *Mormyridae* are crepuscular and inhabit muddy, slow-flowing waters. Species with a mental (= chin) barbel or elongate snout are typical bottom-fishes, constantly feeling around for small prey; other *Mormyridae* prefer to live in midwater or are true midwater fishes. Only a few of the smaller species live socially; the majority are quite solitary, station-holders. On the other hand, almost all the *Mormyridae* behave peaceably towards other fishes, even when these are considerably smaller. While little is known about the breeding-habits, ♂ fishes may usually be recognised by the curved line of attachment of the anal fin.

Of particular interest on the scientific side is the brain of the *Mormyridae*, whose weight, relative to the body-weight (relative brain-weight), compares favourably with that of the human brain. In the light of this knowledge it is not surprising that the *Mormyridae* display behaviour quite unusual among fishes. Thus a remarkable play-instinct is peculiar to many species; they will busy themselves for hours on end with a leaf or with a ball of tinfoil. Also rubbing movements in the inverted position whereby these fishes, in contrast

68

to scouring fishes, glide alternately forwards and backwards, are almost peculiar to this group. Furthermore, their ability to learn is really quite impressive. Even to the ancient Egyptians about 2500 B.C. these peculiar fishes were well known, as is evidenced by the easily recognisable bas-reliefs and mural paintings discovered in tombs; especially grotesque forms were regarded as sacred. To all real fish-lovers these peculiarities provide incentive enough to give the *Mormyridae* their most devoted attention.

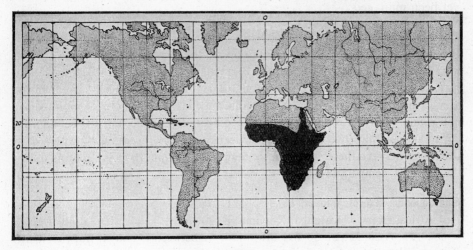

Fig. 57
Distribution of the *Mormyridae*

Care is generally not difficult. These fishes, which are rather shy by daytime, need well-planted tanks with a soft bottom and the darkest possible hiding-places such as caves in rockwork or hollow tree-stumps. The *Mormyridae* are quite accommodating in the matter of water-quality; to be sure a fresh change of water is sometimes necessary, but avoid transferring them to newly-furnished tanks. Temperature, depending on origin, 20 to 28 °C.; the majority of the species are extremely sensitive to rapid cooling. Feed small live-food of all kinds, especially the usual variety of worm-foods; many *Mormyridae* have a penchant for searching for dead waterfleas on the bottom, others look for worms in the mud and, finally, a few pick up algae and dead plant detritus. In the community tank they will settle down very well with almost any other fishes and oddly enough even the large predatory fishes hardly ever molest a Mormyrid; species with electric organs should obviously be avoided in such associations. When buying Mormyrids make sure that they are accepting food; when they are refusing food they become run down and it is difficult to get them to feed again afterwards. Many species make splendid exhibits for zoological gardens. Breeding in captivity has not yet been managed.

Gnathonemus petersi (*Günther* 1862) (Fig. 48)
From the Congo Republic and Cameroons to the Niger; to 23 cm.
  D 27–29; A 34–36; LL 63–70; TR 10–11/10–11 between D and A. Body elongate, strongly compressed; origin of the dorsal fin over the 10th–12th anal ray; a finger-like projection from the chin (this appendage very mobile); mouth small and round. Uniform dark brown, in some lights light violet-brown; between the dorsal and anal fins two clear, irregular transverse bars, occasionally with a quite black area between these. For care, see family description. Peaceful, retiring during the daytime. Temperature 24–28°C. 1950.

Gnathonemus macrolepidotus (*Peters* 1852) (Fig. 58)
East Africa, rivers of Katanga, Rovuma; to 30 cm.
  D 23–25; A 28–32; LL 50–69; TR 8–12/8–12 between D and A. Body elongate, compressed; origin of the dorsal fin over the 5th–8th anal ray; chin with a tuberous profection. Back brown or grey-brown, lower half of body pale, often silvery; belly very pale. Body and fins are sometimes more or less thickly sprinkled with small black spots. For care, see family description. 1937/–.

Gnathonemus moori (*Günther* 1867) (Fig. 50)
Cameroons, Gaboon, Congo; to 20 cm.
  D 20–25; A 25–33; LL 43–49; TR 10–11/13–15 on the body. Body elongate,

Figs. 58–61

Fig. 58. *Gnathonemus macrolepidotus;* large specimen, much reduced. (Redrawn, after Boulenger)
Fig. 59. *Marcusenius isidori;* about natural size.
Fig. 60. *Marcusenius longianalis;* adult, somewhat reduced.
Fig. 61. *Mormyrops boulengeri;* young, natural size.

very strongly compressed (body-depth 3–3¾ in body-length); chin with a tuberous projection. Brown, underside rather pale. A broad dark band between the anterior parts of the dorsal and anal fins, occasionally a second posterior to this. For care, see family description. 1953.

Gnathonemus schilthuisi (*Boulenger* 1899) (Fig. 63)
Middle Congo; to 10 cm.
D 27- 28; A 32–34; LL 49–54; TR 8/8 between D and A. Similar to the foregoing species but the body is slimmer, especially in the young (body-depth 4 in body-length). Chin with a tuberous projection. Brown with a bluish to violet lustre; head and caudal peduncle moderately dark; a black transverse bar across the body from the origin of the dorsal fin to the anal. For care, see family description. Similar-sized fishes of this species are often quite sociable; not infrequently displays a striking play-instinct. 1952.

Gnathonemus stanleyanus (*Boulenger* 1897) (Fig. 86)
Congo, Gambia rivers; to 40 cm.
D 28–32; A 35–40; LL 70–85; TR 13–16/22–15 between D and A. Similar to the foregoing species but very slim-bodied, especially in the young. Grey-brown, belly greyish-silver; numerous irregular dark blotches over the whole body and on the dorsal and anal fins. For care, see family description. 1954.

Marcusenius isidori (*Cuvier* and *Valenciennes* 1846) (Fig. 59)
Nile delta to Bahr-el-Gebel; Upper Zambesi; to 10 cm.
D 18–22; A 22–26; LL 53–60; TR 9–11/15–17 on the body. This fish has a stocky appearance and is quite short in comparison with related species; the profile of the forehead and snout is evenly rounded. The dorsal fin originates over the 3rd–4th anal rays. Back brown or grey-brown, sides of body pale, belly grey-silver to whitish. The fish has a violet lustre by reflected light. Very occasionally a dark lateral streak or black blotches may be present. For care, see family description; a sociable species. 1935/ – .

Plate 9

Fig. 62. *Rooseveltiella nattereri* (Natterer's Piranha); young, about 6 cm. long. (Original)
Fig. 63. *Gnathonemus schilthuisi;* half-grown specimens from Leopoldville, natural size. (Original)

Plate 9

Plate 10

Plate 10

Fig. 64. *Esox lucius* (Common Pike); young, 20 cm. length. (Original)
Fig. 65. *Salvelinus fontinalis* (American 'Brook Trout'); large, 30 cm. long specimen in
the Erfurt Aquarium. (Original)
Fig. 66. *Lepisosteus tristoechus* (Alligator Gar); head of a specimen in the Hellabrunn
Aquarium, Munich. (Original)

Marcusenius longianalis (*Boulenger* 1904) (Fig. 60)
Lower Niger and sporadically in the Cameroons; to 15 cm.

D 14–16; A 31–33; LL 60–66; TR 9/10–11 on the body. This species is very
elongate and slim. Anal fin very long; the substantially shorter dorsal originates
over the 16th to 17th anal rays. Brown to light fawn, back often quite black,
underside considerably paler. Commonly more or less spotted with black. Fins
dark. For care, see family description. *M. longianalis*, according to Holly, feeds on
algae. According to Arnold: –'Quarrelsome with its own kind, inoffensive with
other fishes which, apparently on account of its electrical properties, keep out of
its way.'

Mormyrops nigricans *Boulenger* 1899 (Fig. 87)
Lower Congo: to 35 cm.

D 24–25; A 38–41; LL 54–58; TR 11/13–15 on the body. All species of this
genus are very elongate and only slightly compressed; the mouth may, depending on
the species, be more or less conically produced. Anal and dorsal fins long, set far
back. At least when young *M. nigricans* is very dark coloured, even the belly being
hardly any paler. On the side of the body, especially in older fishes, there is occasionally a broad, very irregular, transverse bar; rarely pronounced black blotches
or reticulations. For care, see family description. *Mormyrops* species, during the
daytime at least, are very sluggish and lie concealed in their hiding-places under
stones. Feeding is mostly by night (midge-larvae, large waterfleas, worms, molluscs).
Not to be associated with substantially smaller fishes. Temperature 24–28 °C.

A related species *Mormyrops boulengeri* Pellegrin 1900 (Fig. 61) has been kept in
the Congo Aquarium. In contrast to *M. nigricans* this Mormyrid has the ability as
a young fish to take only very small worms, dead *Cyclops* and other small food.
Old *Mormyrops* species are splendid exhibits for public aquaria; the amateur should
confine himself to young specimens.

Mormyrus kannume *Forskål* 1776 (Fig. 68)
Nile Basin; to 50 cm.

D 57–75; A 18–21; LL 80–115; TR 23–30/28–38 on the body. Body elongate and compressed. Mouth pointed, very small. Dorsal fin long, anal short. Grey-brown to blackish-brown; sides of body often light red-brown; belly pale.

For care of this very interesting species, see family description; young specimens only for the domestic aquarium. 1934/−.

Petrocephalus bovei (*Cuvier* and *Valenciennes* 1846) (Figs. 69, 85)
Lower Nile, Senegal, Gambia River; to 50 cm.

D 22–26; A 30–35; LL 38–43; TR 9–10/11–15 on the body. *Petrocephalus* species are often very similar to *Marcusenius*. *P. bovei* is only slightly compressed but very elongate. Snout-forehead line evenly curved; upper and lower profiles well-nigh similar. Uniform grey-silver, darker on the back. Young with a short black transverse band under the dorsal origin; dorsal fin itself black. For care, see family description. 1937/+.

Stomatorhinus puncticulatus *Boulenger* 1899 (Fig. 70)
Lower Congo; to 9 cm.

D 17–18; A 21–22; LL 52–55; TR 8–9/13–14 on the body. Body elongate, strongly compressed. Profile of snout and forehead evenly convex; mouth ventral. Dorsal and anal fins lying well back. Reddish-brown with numerous black dots; dorsal and anal fins anteriorly dark. For care, see family description. 1912/−.

Family Gymnarchidae

Closely related to the *Mormyridae*, but lacking ventral, anal and caudal fins and with no teeth on the tongue or palate.

A single genus and species in the Nile and tropical Africa.

Gymnarchus niloticus *Cuvier* 1829
Upper Nile, Chad basin, Senegal to Niger; to 90 cm.

D 183–230. Scales very small, the largest ones along the middle of the side. Body elongate; head almost cylindrical with blunt snout; mouth wide with short strong teeth in a single series in both jaws; eyes very small. Body compressed, tapering to a finger-like tail beyond the end of the dorsal fin, which extends along the back

74

from just behind the head as a ribbon-like fringe. Pectoral fins short, rounded. Colour blackish steel-grey.

Like the *Mormyridae* this fish possesses weak electric organs extending along either side of the vertebrae of the posterior half of the body. From these it produces a series of impulses, surrounding itself with a weak electric field to disturbances in which it is highly sensitive. This apparatus is used as a means of navigation, far more efficient than the small eyes, and especially useful at night or in the dark, muddy waters of swamps and flood-plains. *Gymnarchus* can move equally well forwards or backwards by reversible wave-like movements travelling along the dorsal fin, just as the *Notopteridae* use the anal fin, while keeping the body rigid. Carnivorous, feeding when adult upon smaller fishes.

Has been kept in public aquaria and used for experiments on its electrical faculty. It has not yet been bred in captivity, but in the Gambia Budgett found that *Gymnarchus* constructs floating nests of grass and other plant-fragments in which about 1000 large (1 cm. diameter) amber-coloured eggs are laid, fertilised and guarded. The young hatch with long gill-filaments and a trailing yolk-sac, and regularly come to the surface for air. After about 5 days they are 7·5 cm. long, have absorbed the yolk-sac and leave the nest.

Family Esocidae (Pikes)

Long, slim predatory fishes (Order *Haplomi*) whose body, albeit compressed, is still relatively broad. Head large; mouth deeply cleft, with a formidable dentition (the maxillary, however, is toothless); snout compressed. Dorsal and anal fins short, opposite and lying well back. The distribution of the *Esocidae* is throughout the fresh and brackish waters of the Northern Hemisphere.

Esox lucius *Linnaeus* 1758 (Fig. 64)   Common Pike
Europe (excepting Spain), Asia, North America, in fresh and brackish waters; to 2 m., average length about 50–70 cm.

D 7–8/13–15; A 4–5/12–14; P 1/13; V 1/18; LL 105–130. Typical body-form of the family. Coloration very variable, according to locality. Young one-year-old fishes are mostly grass-green with grey-green shadowing (Grasspike). Older pike display a brown, moss- or dark green upper side with shining golden spots on the head. The tint of the back itself is extended in forwardly-directed stripes on the flanks; between these darker parts the pale green to yellow green tint of the belly-region insinuates itself in the form of spots and stripes. The belly itself is pale, mostly yellowish. Unpaired fins yellow-brown or reddish-brown with dark markings; paired fins more or less reddish. Eye golden.

The care of pike in captivity presents little difficulty in so far as young fishes settle down quite easily. Pike are very adaptable to higher temperatures and quite able to withstand a temporary warming to 20–22 °C. Young fishes from standing waters

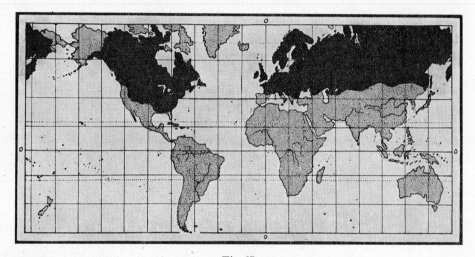

Fig. 67

Distribution of the *Esocidae*. As well as inland waters the *Esocidae* also penetrate into brackish coastal waters.

flourish with good aeration even in aquaria without a water-circulation; very large specimens, such as are shown in zoological gardens, need a continual flow of fresh water. In the usually large-scale conditions of public aquaria several specimens may be kept together, but in small domestic aquaria they must be kept singly. As in

Figs. 68–72

Fig. 68. *Mormyrus kannume*; adult, much reduced.
Fig. 69. *Petrocephalus bovei;* about natural size.
Fig. 70. *Stomatorhinus puncticulatus;* young, natural size.
Fig. 71. *Umbra limi* (Mudminnow); about natural size.
Fig. 72. *Umbra pygmaea* (Striped or Eastern American Mudminnow); adult, somewhat reduced.

their natural environment, so in aquaria Pike lie close under the surface of the water, preferably in loose plant-stands, waiting for prey, which is seized with a lightning rush. If the rush fails the predator does not follow the fleeing animal but lurks anew. Fishes, which are the main food of Pike, are swallowed head-first; if the prey is not in the right position when grasped, the Pike rotates, whirling around its long axis and snapping several times until the prey lies correctly. With good feeding, that is, a copious supply of young fishes, the Pike can literally out-grow the aquarium. Only rarely are worms or frogs accepted. Spawning time: February to May; spawning place: shallows over banks. The small ochre-coloured eggs are carefully stuck to water plants or even the grasses of flooded meadows. The Pike is a very interesting and rewarding subject for the coldwater aquarium.

Three further *Esox* ssp. occur in North America.

Family Umbridae

The *Umbridae* and Pikes (Order *Haplomi*) were apparently developed from a common stem-form during the course of the Mesozoic. Body somewhat stocky, only slightly compressed; head and body covered with large cycloid scales; mouth with velvet-like (villiform) teeth, arranged in series (jaws, vomer and palatine bones all toothed). The longish dorsal fin arises about the middle of the body and ends opposite the end of the anal; caudal fin rounded. 2 species in North America, 1 species in South-east Europe.

Umbra krameri *Walbaum* 1792 (Fig. 99)   Ribahal (Hungary)
                                                              Hundsfisch (Austria)
Middle and Lower Danube system, Lower Dniester; ♂ to 8·5 cm., ♀ to 13 cm.

D 15–16; A 7–8; LL 33–35. For body-shape, see family description. Back brownish to red-brown, flanks paler, fawn, sometimes even orange-coloured, with numerous dark blotches and a striking yellowish to copper-coloured longitudinal stripe. Dorsal fin brownish, often with a series of darker blotches.

This fish, which is nowhere abundant, is a dweller in peat-bogs and marshes where it haunts the muddy bottoms of deep pools and feeds mainly on insect-larvae. In normal forward swimming the pectoral and ventral fins move alternately, like the limbs of a running dog, while at the same time the dorsal fin displays wave-like movements similar to those which occur in sea-horses. The fish may hang in the water for hours at a time with the head obliquely up or down. A further peculiarity is the accessory air-breathing; the fishes dart to the surface, fill the mouth with air and exude bubbles through the gill-openings as they submerge. At spawning time the Hungarian *Umbra* seeks thick plant-stands or masses of roots. Here the ♀ makes a simple hollow or cave which she closes over and guards after spawning. The young emerge after 6–10 days, according to the temperature. The young fishes are very cannibalistic and in the smaller pools only 4 or 5 of them survive the struggle for existence.

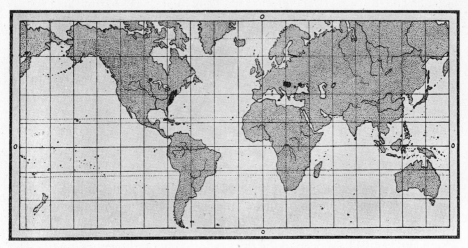

Fig. 73
Distribution of the *Umbridae;* note S.E. Europe and eastern N. America.

In captivity provide large, thickly-planted coldwater aquaria, whose temperature in summer may be allowed to rise to 23 °C. All authors agree that these fishes become very tame and learn to recognise their owners. Live food of all kinds. Slightly peaty, soft water furthers their well-being and inclination to spawn. A hardy species. 1896/ +.

Umbra limi (*Kirtland* 1840) (Fig. 71)   Mudminnow
Eastern States of U.S.A., Great Lakes region; ♂ to 10 cm., ♀ to 12 cm.
    D 14–15; A 8–10; V 6; LL 35; TR 15. For body-shape, see family description. Shaped very much like the foregoing species. Colour, according to Arnold:– 'Yellow-brown with darker stripes'; according to Jordan:–'Dull olive-green, sprinkled with darker'; 14 or more dun-coloured stripes which may regress,

79

particularly in young fishes. At the root of the tail is a strong transverse band which, however, is often inconspicuous. Lower jaw pale; fins transparent. For care and breeding, see previous species. 1901/—.

Umbra pygmaea (*De Kay* 1842) (Fig. 72) Striped or Eastern American Mudminnow Eastern States of U.S.A., Georgia, New England; ♂ to 11·5 cm., ♀ to 15 cm.

D 13; A 7–8; LL 35–37. In general somewhat plumper than the foregoing species, very slightly compressed; snout shorter, more definitely rounded. Colour, according to Jordan:–'Dark green with 12 or more pale, narrow longitudinal stripes, of which the one beginning at the upper corner of the gill-cover is twice as broad as the others. At the root of the caudal fin a strong, dark transverse band.' Lower jaw generally black. Care and breeding, as for *Umbra krameri*; breeding is very easy in large tanks well supplied with algae. 1898/—.

Family Anguillidae (Eels)

Snake-like bottom-fishes belonging to the order *Apodes*. All the species lack ventral fins. The unpaired fins are united into one fin of uniform height which commences far forward on the back and is continued around the tip of the tail and along the ventral surface as far as the anus. The scales are either minute and embedded deep in the thick, slimy skin or altogether absent. The species are distributed through the warm and temperate zones of the world. Eels as a group are predominantly marine fishes, but some migrate up rivers.

Anguilla anguilla (*Linnaeus* 1758) (Figs. 89, 90, 98)   Common or European Eel Throughout Europe, North Africa; to 150 cm.

Skin with small rudimentary scales. Head, according to the type of food taken, broad with a deep gape (broad-nosed eel; a fish-eater), or pointed with a small gape (sharp-nosed eel; a small prey-eater); at the beginning of the seaward migration the heads of all eels become pointed. Eels inhabit standing and flowing waters all over

Plate 11

Fig. 74. *Metynnis schreitmuelleri;* half-grown, natural size. (Original)
Fig. 75. *Metynnis roosevelti;* ripe adults, natural size. (Original)

Plate 11

Plate 12

Plate 12

Fig. 76. Left: *Hyphessobrycon callistus* var. *serpae* (Jewel Tetra, Serpa Characin); above
♀, below ♂.
Right: *Hyphessobrycon ornatus;* above ♀, below ♂. (Original)
Fig. 77. *Hyphessobrycon flammeus* (Red Tetra from Rio, Flame Fish); half-grown,
natural size. (Original)

Europe and remain here for about 7–12 years according to feeding-conditions and sex
(well-nourished fishes and ♂♂ leave sooner) before migrating down the rivers to the
sea. Prior to migration the eel stops feeding. Its yellow-grey colour ('Yellow Eel')
changes on the back to an olive-green or dark brown, and on the belly to a shining
silvery-white ('Silver Eel'); the eyes become enlarged and eventually the pectoral
fins too become enlarged, pointed and black. With short interruptions the eel migrates about 10–15 km. daily until it reaches the sea, where it heads westward into
the Atlantic. Whatever their eventual fate, no silver eels have ever been captured in
the open Atlantic and none ever return to the rivers after this seaward migration.

The young are very unlike the adult and are called *Leptocephalus* larvae; it was
earlier believed that they represented a distinct genus. Their bodies are willow-
leaf-shaped and quite transparent. Their origin and distribution were worked out by
Danish scientists under the leadership of Dr. Johannes Schmidt. The smallest
larvae, only 6 mm. long, occur in the region of the Sargasso Sea N. E. of the West
Indies and obviously the spawning-area must be close to this neighbourhood. The
leptocephali are carried eastward and north-eastward in the surface layers of the
Gulf Stream system until eventually, 3 years old and 6–8 cm. long, they gather in
millions off the Continental Shelf of Europe. Here metamorphosis from a transparent leaf-shaped larva to a still transparent cylindrical 'glass-eel' takes place.
The glass-eels begin to move inshore, becoming pigmented as they go, until as
'elvers', miniature eels, they ascend our estuaries in springtime in the so-called
'elver run', just three years after they were hatched in the Sargasso Sea.

Despite a great deal of study by D'Ancona and others the machinery of sex-
determination is not clearly understood; however, the males, attaining to a smaller
eventual size, tend to remain in the lower reaches of the rivers while the females
penetrate far inland, and overland in wet weather, to almost every stream and pond.
During the long growing-period the eel develops an immense feeding-capacity,
taking every kind of living food and carrion, and even small water-birds and other
eels very little smaller than itself.

From the beginning of the 20th century it was naturally assumed that the migrating silver eels were the parents of the larvae which appeared from out of the

81

Sargasso Sea. In 1959, however, Tucker suggested an alternative explanation of the known facts; according to his view the European Eel does not complete its breeding-migration. He suggests that the European Eel *A. anguilla* and the American Eel *A. rostrata* (Le Sueur) are in reality the same species; that all the *Anguilla* leptocephali in the Atlantic are descended from American parents and that the differences between the two 'species' are due to the effects of temperature upon larvae rising to the surface from different parts of a common spawning-ground. Subsequent differences in the temperature and transportation of the surface water-masses would account for the differing fates of the two types of larvae.

Eels are the hardiest fishes of our waters. In aquaria the glass-eels and elvers – the latter are caught off the coast and transported to eastern rivers in the interests of fisheries – do very well. It is quite interesting to follow the change in colour of the glass-eel. Any vessel is suitable, even a quite small tank; fine sand is suitable for the bottom as the eel likes to dig in. The temperature should not rise above 16°C. Eats anything, especially fly-larvae, Enchytraeids and earthworms. Cover the tank well! Eels have lived up to 90 years in captivity.

Anguilla rostrata (*Le Sueur* 1817) American Eel
Eastern and Central North America, Mississippi Basin; to 150 cm.

Outwardly indistinguishable from the European species; apart from small differences only discoverable as population parameters, the only real difference is in the numbers of vertebrae: – 103–111 in *A. rostrata*, 110–119 in *A. anguilla*.

The American Eel, probably in relation to better feeding-conditions, attains a greater average weight than the European and migrates to the sea in an earlier phase as the 'bronze eel'; the assumption of the silver ventral coloration, etc., if it occurs, must take place in the sea, where it has not yet been observed. For whatsoever reason the *leptocephalus* larvae of the American Eel appear to originate in an area of the Sargasso Sea S. W. of the supposed spawning-ground of the European ones, and the larvae take only one year for the journey back to freshwater. In the St. Lawrence especially, as in Europe, commercial fisheries for migrating eels have great economic importance. Otherwise general biology and care are much the same as for the previous species.

Family Characidae (Characins)

Fishes of very *Barbus*-like appearance, but always lacking barbels. Body scaled; mouth not protrusible, toothed, some parts of the dentition very strongly developed. The majority of the species possess a small adipose fin which distinguishes them from the often very similar *Cyprinidae*. Modern systematists have removed several groups from the Family *Characidae* as it was formerly understood and accordingly these newer families *(Anostomidae, Hemiodontidae, Citharinidae,* and *Gasteropelecidae)* will likewise be separately dealt with in the present work. The *Characidae* now include about 1350 known species which are distributed through South America (exclusive of

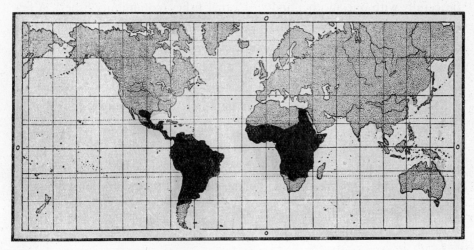

Fig. 78
Distribution of the *Characidae*

the southernmost part and the Pacific slope of Chile) northwards through Central America as far as Texas; a few isolated genera, such as *Micralestes, Alestes* and *Petersius,* live in Central Africa.

The great majority of Characins are carnivores; a few are herbivores or omnivores. Generally the eggs are expelled during the spawning act and fertilised in the water. In one group however, including *Mimagoniates* and *Corynopoma,* the male, during a quite complicated mating process, transfers his milt to the female in a sort of capsule (spermatophore) which is stored in the oviduct. Fertilisation subsequently takes place internally in the mother shortly before egg-laying. Live-bearing species are unknown in this family;

83

on the other hand certain species, such as *Copeina arnoldi*, practise intensive brood-care.

Like the Carps *(Cyprinidae)* and the various families of Catfishes, the *Characidae* have a chain of small bones linking the air-bladder and the inner ear. These are known as the Weberian ossicles and enhance the sense of hearing in the fishes possessing them.

Many Characins are brilliantly coloured, always on the move and live peacefully with one another and with other fishes (community fishes). A few exceptions, like the dreaded Piranhas of South America, must be numbered among the most dangerous inhabitants of fresh water and, attacking in packs with their sharp teeth, are known to be able to overwhelm quite large animals in a very short time.

The majority of the species prefer lime-free, mildly peaty water like the dark-coloured water of our moorland streams.

Their small size, diversity of colour, grace, liveliness and above all, undemanding nature, make the Characins ideal and favourite aquarium fishes. For care and breeding, see under the separate descriptions.

South American Characidae

Acestrorhamphus hepsetus *(Cuvier* 1842) (Fig. 79)
South-east Brazil, widely distributed; to 20 cm.

D 11; A 30; LL 72. Body elliptical to elongate, compressed. Dorsal fin origin about the middle of the body; anal base long; adipose fin present. Scales small; lateral line complete, slightly downcurved. Gape large, dentition powerful. Upperside olive brown; flanks silvery with a slight bluish sheen; a dark longitudinal stripe arises in the dark shoulder-spot and is continued posteriorly into a lozenge-shaped blotch which is usually margined with light yellow. Fins colourless.

Sex-distinctions unknown.

The very voracious predatory fishes of the genus *Acestrorhamphus* are scarcely suitable for domestic aquaria but make interesting and hardy exhibits for zoological gardens. Unfortunately these species are seldom imported. Preferred temperature 24–25°C. Live food such as fishes and large insect-larvae, veal and horseflesh. sometimes oatmeal also. 1914/−.

84

Acestrorhynchus microlepis (*Schomburgk* 1841) (Fig. 80)
Amazon Basin, Guiana; to 30 cm.

D 11; A 28–33; LL 93–114. Body elongate, spindle-shaped. Head pike-like. The strongly toothed mouth has a deep gape. Dorsal fin insertion very far back. Scales very small. Coloration, according to Rachow:–larger fishes very gaily coloured; back and crown of head greenish; hinder part of head, breast and belly reddish; flanks bluish-green with a conspicuous longitudinal series of dark spots which ends in a large dark spot at the root of the caudal. The dark shoulder-spot is especially characteristic of this species. Dorsal and adipose fins and upper part of caudal brick-red; middle of caudal fin dark, its lower lobe yellowish to orange; the other fins are bluish, the anal with dark blue spots. Young fishes light brown with a more conspicuous longitudinal series of spots.

Sex-distinctions so far not described.

This beautiful species, recognisable by its shape as a pike-like predator, does not easily adapt itself to captivity. Above all, the problem is how to satisfy its rapacious appetite; it lives almost exclusively on small fishes. Large aquaria with the corners thickly planted are best suited to its needs. Temperature 24–28°C. Only young specimens are suitable for domestic aquaria. Not yet bred in captivity. 1913/ –.

Luciocharax insculptus *Steindachner* 1878 (Fig. 81)
R. Magdalena basin; to 70 cm.

D 10; A 12; P 20; V 8; LL 43–44. Body very elongate, only moderately compressed, pike-like. Head acute; jaws long, beak-like; premaxillary somewhat angular below, front end expanded, somewhat spoon-like. Dorsal fin-insertion far back; lower caudal lobe somewhat the larger. Lateral line incomplete. Very attractively coloured: upperside olive-green to brown; flanks muddy yellow; belly silvery; lower part of caudal peduncle delicate violet or reddish; deep-black tail-spot margined with yellow. Dorsal and anal fins yellowish with a faint blackish edge. Caudal fin brick-red at the base, distally pale violet.

Sex-distinctions not so far described.

This very interesting predator, reminiscent in the shape of its body of the North American Garpikes, is, like the related *Hydrocinus* spp., unfortunately but seldom imported. Even the few attempts to import it have usually not been very successful; it easily sustains damage to its pointed snout during transport, damage which can seldom be healed and which usually soon leads to death. In captivity *Luciocharax*, and also *Hydrocinus* spp., remain very shy and timid. On this account these rarities should only be kept in very large, well-planted aquaria; only quite young specimens are suitable for domestic aquaria but large ones make splendid exhibits for zoological gardens. Temperature, according to origin, 22–24 °C. Feeds almost exclusively on fishes, even seizing and swallowing prey half as large as itself. 1905/ –.

Hydrocinus cuvieri (*Agassiz* 1829) (Fig. 82)
Amazon (?); to 60 cm.

D 10; A 10; LL about 105. Body similar in shape to that of *Luciocharax*, to which this genus is closely related. Important distinguishing characters are the complete lateral line, the somewhat more anterior dorsal fin and the knob-like tip of the snout. Coloration, according to Meinken: – upperside dusky yellow-olive; flanks somewhat paler, greenish-white; a broad, vaguely-defined and sometimes even inconspicuous dark longitudinal band below the lateral line, extending from the eye to the root of the tail and forming a conspicuous, almost triangular, blotch on the gill-cover; upper jaw completely black, lower jaw black only in front and along the edge of the gape; a deep-black round blotch at the root of the tail. Caudal fin, especially in the outer parts, brown-black to black with a beautiful pale brown margin to the upper and lower edges; dorsal, anal and ventral fins colourless with dark bands.

Sex-distinctions not so far described. Care of this very interesting species as for *Luciocharax insculptus* above. 1935/ –.

Hydrocinus maculatus (*Cuvier* and *Valenciennes* 1848) (Fig. 83)
Amazon basin; to 35 cm.

D 10; A 10; LL about 75. Very similar to the foregoing species. Upperside dark brown to blackish; flanks pale greenish-brown with a broad, very dark longitudinal band, with a near-white lower margin, which begins on the edge of the upper jaw and extends to the root of the tail; underside yellowish to white. The flanks and caudal fin further display numerous more or less prominent irregular dark blotches of varying size. Caudal peduncle often with a reddish lustre. Dorsal and anal fins yellowish with blackish bases.

Sex-distinctions unknown. Care as for *Luciocharax insculptus* above. 1913/ –.

Erythrinus erythrinus (*Schneider* 1801) (Fig. 91)
Northern and central South America; to 20 cm.

D 10–12; A 9–12; LL 31–34. Body very elongate, anteriorly cylindrical, caudal peduncle strongly compressed; lateral line straight; no adipose fin; caudal rounded. Very variable, in relation to the wide area of distribution. Sexually mature fishes

86

are intense clay-yellow to light brown, darker above with a greenish lustre, whitish below. From the hind edge of the eye to the root of the tail there extends a blue-black longitudinal band which narrows posteriorly and ends in a large round black spot which is generally pale-margined; on the gill-cover this longitudinal bar includes a light green iridescent spot. A few ill-defined transverse bars on the hinder region of the body; on the head, dark bars radiating from the eye. Vertical fins yellowish with delicate dark series of spots. Anal and paired fins often delicate reddish.

♀ dorsal fin rounded, short.

♂ dorsal usually drawn out to a point, much elongated.

Erythrinus is a predatory fish with a pike-like habit of lurking motionless among weeds. It requires large aquaria with a dim toplight, dense groups of plants, dark background and soft to medium hard water. Throughout the day the fishes rest, usually on the bottom, and lie in wait for prey to swim past; this species only becomes active at dusk. Temperature 24–26°C. Give live food, especially small fishes, large insect-larvae and worms; waterfleas alone are not sufficient. Only larger species are suitable as tank companions. Not yet bred in captivity. Scientific interest attaches mainly to the swim-bladder, which is modified as an accessory breathing-organ. 1910/–.

Hoplias malabaricus (*Bloch* 1794) (Fig. 92)   Tiger-fish

Northern and central South America, widely distributed and abundant; to 50 cm., but in captivity remains much smaller.

D 13–14 (15); A 10–11; LL 39–41 (–43). Shape similar to the foregoing species; dentition outstandingly powerful. In correspondence with the wide area of distribution, very variable. Young immature fishes: olive to reddish-brown above, laterally paling to a pleasing light fawn to yellow-brown tone which gradually merges into the delicate yellowish or reddish colour of the belly. On the sides of the head there are bizarre dark bands which become blackish-red towards the throat. A broad dark longitudinal band, often with a greenish lustre, extends from the gill-cover to the root of the tail. A black spot on top of the caudal peduncle. Fins delicate brownish with dark blotches or series of spots. At the beginning of sexual maturation the longitudinal band becomes divided into a darker series of spots which may completely vanish with increasing age. Old individuals are a dull green to brownish-olive.

♀ more robust, ventral profile more strongly convex.

♂ noticeably slimmer, ventral profile almost straight.

87

Care as given for *Erythrinus*; very fast-growing and not suitable for breeding in domestic aquaria. 1895/+.

Exodon paradoxus *Müller* and *Troschel* 1845 (Fig. 234)
Rio Branco and R. Rupunini (north-eastern South America); to 15 cm.

D 10–11; A 19–22; LL 39; TR 9/6. Body elongate, strongly compressed. Adipose fin present, anal fin short. Younger fishes are very beautifully coloured; old specimens often uniformly yellow-grey with inconspicuous blotches. Ground colour delicate yellowish with brilliant iridescent areas on the lower parts of the flanks which display intense silver or rainbow reflexions according to the light; underside silvery. Two large, round deep black blotches, often with pale margins, are particularly characteristic of this species (see Fig. 234). Fins yellowish, at least at the bases; middle and tip of dorsal fin, tip of caudal, anterior margin of the anal and almost the whole of the ventral fins brilliant blood-red.

♀ more robust, at least during the breeding period.

This very lively, actively-leaping species displays its splendour to best advantage in a large aquarium which gives sufficient room for free swimming. Dim sunlight and soft, slightly peaty water noticeably further its well-being. Temperature 23–28 °C. Live food of all kinds; not compatible with smaller species. Spawns with very violent driving among water plants. Rearing of the young fish, which hatch after 25–30 hours, is not easy. *E. paradoxus* is one of the most beautiful Characins. 1935/+.

Roeboides guatemalensis (*Günther* 1864) (Fig. 118) Guatemala Glass-characin
Central America; in the eastern parts very abundant; to 10 cm.

D 11; A 47–52; LL 82–89. Body elongate, strongly compressed, back very high. Anal fin with long base, adipose fin present. Lateral line complete and straight. The whole body is translucent, delicate yellowish in colour, with numerous minute shining spots which are silvery by reflected light. From the hind end of the gill-

Figs. 79–83
Fig. 79. *Acestrorhamphus hepsetus;* adult, reduced.
Fig. 80. *Acestrorhynchus microlepis;* adult, greatly reduced.
Fig. 81. *Luciocharax insculptus;* adult, greatly reduced.
Fig. 82. *Hydrocinus cuvieri;* adult, greatly reduced.
Fig. 83. *Hydrocinus maculatus;* adult, greatly reduced.

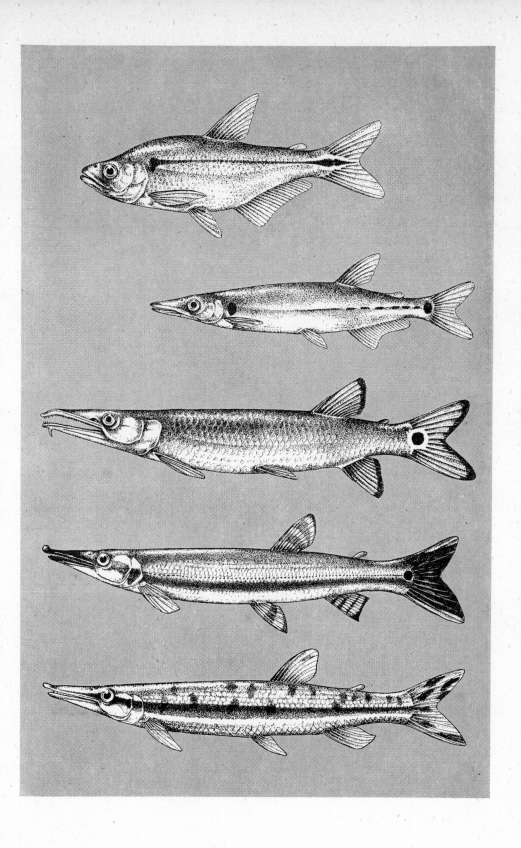

cover to the root of the tail there extends a dull silver longitudinal band, reflecting turquoise blue in some lights, sometimes accompanied by a dark line, especially on the caudal peduncle. A conspicuous dark blotch at the root of the tail. Fins delicate yellowish or colourless, tips sometimes touched with rust-red.

♀ very robust at breeding time; dorsal fin generally rounded.
♂ dorsal almost always pointed.

The Guatemala Glass-characin swims like its relatives *R. microlepis* and *Charax gibbosus*, not with the body in the normal horizontal position but slightly inclined forwards. Possibly in correlation with this mode of locomotion the lower lobe of the caudal fin in older individuals may be considerably stronger than the upper. These very lively fishes require large aquaria, not too thickly planted, and sunlight which may be dimmed in places by screens of floating plants. Clear water of medium hardness is also sufficient inducement to spawning. In spite of their liveliness they are reasonably peaceful with other fishes, provided the latter are not smaller; only when in competition for food do they become snappy. Temperature 23–25 °C.; temporary cooling usually well tolerated. Live food of all kinds. Breeding not difficult; they spawn among water plants after quite a lively courtship; very prolific. Rearing the young, which hatch after 25–30 hours, is easy; quick-growing. 1933/+.

Roeboides microlepis (*Reinhardt* 1849) (Fig. 100)   Small-scaled Glass-characin
Western Amazon basin, Bolivia, Rio Paraguay; to 10 cm.
    D 12; A 55–60; LL over 100. In shape and translucency *R. microlepis* is similar to the foregoing species, at least in the young. Delicate clay-yellow, back darker and more olive-yellow with numerous rather irregular, narrow, dark, transverse bars. From the shoulder-blotch, which is usually not very conspicuous, a greenish dull silvery longitudinal stripe runs along the side of the body to a dark blotch at the root of the tail. Fins colourless to delicate yellowish.

♀ at maturity considerably more robust.
♂ usually of a stronger yellow, often with an orange-coloured throat at breeding time. Anal fin broader than in the ♀.

Care and breeding, as for the foregoing species. *R. microlepis* likewise stands in the water with the head obliquely downwards. Importation before 1945 very questionable; the species so named by Arnold, among others, was probably *Charax gibbosus*, which is of similar form and coloration, at least in the young.

Charax gibbosus (*Linnaeus* 1758) (Fig. 94)   Humpbacked Headstander
Guiana, middle and lower Amazon, Rio Paraguay; to 15 cm.

D 11; A 38–45; LL 53–60; TR 16/9. Reminiscent, as regards body-form, of the well-known Guatemala Glass-characin, to which this species is closely related. Delicate yellowish-brown with a silvery sheen, translucent, especially in the young; upperside often only a very little darker with greenish lustre; belly pale. The upper part of the body particularly is thickly sprinkled with metallic spots which, according to lighting, reflect silvery to brassy colours or green; a darker, elongate houlder-blotch behind the gill-cover. Fins colourless, translucent, or at most with dselicate brownish or greenish bases.

♀ generally somewhat larger and fuller.
♂ slimmer; at breeding time the yellow tints are more marked.

Care, as for *Roeboides guatemalensis;* quite peaceful. Breeding has already been achieved in large domestic aquaria. 1910/ –.

Chalcinus (Triportheus) elongatus *Günther* 1864 (Fig. 93)
Amazon, Rio Negro, Orinoco, Guiana; to 20 cm.

The genus *Chalcinus* comprises river fishes of South America whose elongate, compressed body-form with its deeply-convex keeled breast is remotely reminiscent of the Hatchet-fish. Dorsal fin placed far back, adipose fin present. The middle rays of the emarginate caudal fin are produced to form a nipple-like lobe; the pectoral fins are very large.

D 11; A 27–31; LL 40–50; TR 6–7/3–4. Body very elongate, as above. Upperside brownish to olive-colour, flanks silvery with a greenish lustre and a narrow dusky to black longitudinal band which is strongly broadened on the root of the tail and continued onto the middle fin-rays. Sometimes a fine brownish spotting is evident on the flanks. Fins colourless with delicate brownish spots; tips of caudal lobes and anal fin edged with black.

Sex-distinctions unknown.

This very contented, lively species is easily kept in large sunny aquaria. Temperature 24–27°C. Larger live food of all kinds, also dried foods. Has not yet been bred in captivity. 1909/ –.

In addition, in 1934 a *Chalcinus* sp. was imported which was known as *Chalcinus angulatus* (Spix 1824) but it was not distributed. We only mention here that these fishes should probably have been identified as *Chalcinus nematurus* (Kner 1860).

91

Saw-bellied Characins of the genera Serrasalmus, Rooseveltiella and Pygocentrus: Care

The Characins which are included in the genera above are commonly known under the name Piranha or Piraya. Their extraordinarily powerful and sharp dentition (Fig. 84) enables these very voracious and almost always shoaling fishes

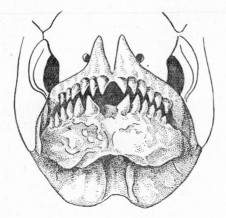

Fig. 84
Dentition of a Piranha

to overwhelm, and in a very short time to skeletonise, the largest prey, even Man himself. Their dangerousness is a great deal exaggerated in travellers' tales, however, and may be greatly reduced in practice. Thus, in specially dangerous districts, warning-stations are set up which can give timely warning of the arrival of large Piranha shoals in their neighbourhoods. There seems to be real danger only if persons with freely-bleeding wounds enter the water.

Serrasalmus rhombeus (*Linnaeus* 1766) (Fig. 95)   White Piranha, Spotted Piranha Amazon system and north-eastern South America; to 35 cm.
D 16–17 (19); A 31–36; LL 87–91; 37–39 scutes along ventral keel. Body deep, strongly compressed, stocky. Ventral keel strongly toothed from the level of the pectoral fins. Anal fin long. Eye large. Palatines toothed. Back of head and upper

Plate 13
Fig. 85. *Petrocephalus bovei;* young, somewhat reduced. (Photo Dr. Foersch)
Fig. 86. *Gnathonemus stanleyanus;* young, natural size. (Original)
Fig. 87. *Mormyrops nigricans;* young, natural size. (Original)

Plate 13

Plate 14

Plate 14

Fig. 88. Head of *Synbranchus marmoratus;* about twice natural size, in the Museum Alexander Koenig, Bonn. (Photo van Hengel)

Fig. 89. *Anguilla anguilla* (Common or European Eel); length 30 cm. (Original)

Fig. 90. Head of European Eel; about twice natural size. (Original)

parts of body dark grey to olive-green; lower half of body dirty white to silvery. Large dark spots of irregular form occur, especially on the upper parts. A shoulder-blotch of similar colour may generally be recognised. Fins grey. Base and hinder edge of caudal fin blackish, middle part reddish. Fins of young glass-clear. Old specimens often completely black ('Black Piranhas').

Sex-distinctions unknown. Care as given above. 1913/+.

Only young fishes are suitable for large domestic aquaria; older specimens are interesting subjects for public aquaria. Care is by no means as simple as might perhaps be assumed from the robust appearance. The greatest difficulty arises from their obstinate unsociability which even presents a problem in transport. Any companion of the same species which is only a little weaker is badly treated. Nevertheless, acclimatised fishes are quite hardy and can be kept well for a long time on raw meat and fish. A community tank with strong, healthy fishes of other species is possible. Temperature 24–27°C. Not yet bred in captivity.

Serrasalmus spilopleura *Kner* 1860 (Fig. 103)

Orinoco (?), Amazon to La Plata basin; to 24 cm.

D 14–16; A 33–36; P 14–15; 29–36 scutes along ventral keel. Body deeper and more robust than in *S. rhombeus* but very similar to that of *Rooseveltiella nattereri.*

Innes (1954) gives a coloured figure of *S. spilopleura* on p. 176. Although the body form agrees in all details with the photograph published by Arnold and Ahl (1936, p. 120), the colour differs very much from the description by Arnold. According to Innes' colourplate, *S. spilopleura* agrees in colour completely with the species *Rooseveltiella nattereri* and *Pygocentrus piraya* (q. v.). In Arnold and Ahl (1936) the following description is given:–

'Colour in young grey-green with strong silvery sheen, dark round spots on the sides of the body and an inconspicuous vaguely-delimited shoulder-blotch. These spots vanish completely in the older fish. Anal fin quite black, or with a broad blackish outer edge. In the young there is a black band in front of the outer edge of the caudal fin which, however, usually passes into a broad blackish marginal zone.'

This description resembles pretty well that given by Norman (1928) for spirit specimens. Ahl (1922) says, concerning the caudal fin:–

'...with a broad, dark blue band which includes the middle of the base, the broad margin yellowish-white.'

To sum up, all that can be established concerning life-colours at all stages is that nothing accurate is known.

Sex-distinctions unknown.

Care, as given in the genus description. Bred in America (*The Aquarium*, Jan. 1960). Spawns Cichlid-fashion on plants; ♂ guards young. Allegedly 1899/ – .

Rooseveltiella nattereri (*Kner* 1859) (Figs. 62, 96) Red Piranha, Natterer's Piranha
The genus *Rooseveltiella* is mainly distinguished from *Serrasalmus* by the toothed palatine bones.

Widely distributed and abundant, Amazon basin, Orinoco, Paraná basin; to 30 cm.

D 16–18; A 28–32; LL 85–100; 24–31 scutes in ventral keel. Body very deep and strongly compressed; edge of belly serrate. Caudal fin slightly emarginate; anal fin-base long, in old individuals fin produced to a point anteriorly. Coloration very variable, depending on age and environmental conditions; the body-depth and form of the head likewise change with age. Healthy, 10–15 cm. long fishes are blue-grey to brown-grey on the back; flanks pale brown above to delicate olive, silvered with numerous tiny metallic spots; underside, including the keel and belly, pectoral and ventral fins and anterior part of the anal, gleaming cinnabar to blood-red; dorsal and caudal fins dark, the latter with a pale inner field; anal fin red with a broad black margin.

Sex-distinctions unknown.

Peculiarities and care as in description of genus. About 1912/ + .

Pygocentrus piraya (*Cuvier* 1819) (Fig. 97)   Piraya, Piranha
Lower course of the Amazon and southern tributaries thereof, Rio San Francisco, basin of the upper Paraguay R.; to 35 cm.

Figs. 91–94

Fig. 91. *Erythrinus erythrinus;* half-grown, natural size.
Fig. 92. *Hoplias malabaricus* (Tiger-fish); young.
Fig. 93. *Chalcinus elongatus;* ripe fish, natural size
Fig. 94. *Charax gibbosus* (Humpbacked Headstander); somewhat reduced.

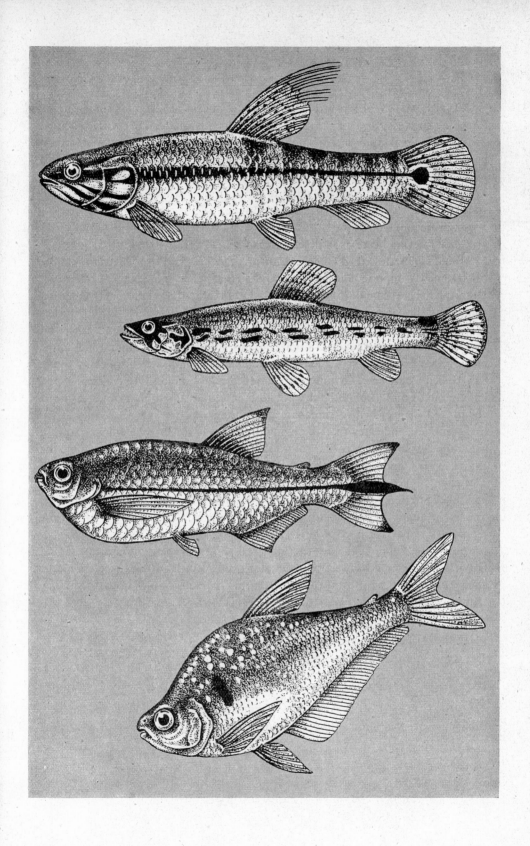

D 17–18; A 31–32; LL over 100; 22–24 scutes in ventral keel. Very similar to the foregoing species; fishes of the same age are distinguishable only with difficulty, the young scarcely differing in colour. (*P. piraya*, according to Rachow, shows a ground-colour tending more towards blue-green.) The diagnostic character of this species (the only member of the genus) first appears in older fishes from about 12 cm. length and is, that the adipose fin is fringed while in *Serrasalmus* and *Rooseveltiella* it always remains a rounded lobe.

Sex-distinctions unknown.

Peculiarities and care as in description of genus. 1912/–.

Arnold (1939) described (*Wochenschrift f. Aquarien- u. Terrarienkunde*, Vol. 36, p. 611) a newly-imported Piranha and believed that he recognised in it *S. serrulatus*. Unfortunately I cannot find any information about an exact determination confirming this opinion in later literature. The colour given for the young fishes in question scarcely allows any conclusion as to species-identification, since, on the one hand, the original description contains nothing on life colours, and on the other, a vague shoulder-spot and brown blotching are characteristic of many young Saw-bellied Characins. To this may be added that Arnold's observation, 'Upon killing it in formol-alcohol the throat and breast gradually took on an orange-red colour and then passed to cinnabar, a colouring which I had never seen in the living animal', indicates that the living animal was not in very good health, a condition which influences the coloration in various ways. On this account the record of the importation of the species *S. serrulatus* must remain very doubtful. The same applies to *Serrasalmus hollandi* Eigenmann 1915 (Fig. 101), which was described and figured as a new import by Arnold in *Taschenkalender*, 1940, p. 71. The same applies yet again to *Serrasalmus niger* Schomburgk 1841 (Fig. 102), reported for the year 1939. The two last-named species are distinguished by a tuberous chin. On principle the determination of the Saw-bellied Characins should not be attempted on the basis of colour alone, since our knowledge concerning the changes of colour and form with age, and of local colour-variations, is still too slight to enable us to recognise fine distinctions.

Piaractus nigripinnis (*Cope* 1878) (Fig. 108)
The genus *Piaractus* is characterised by the fact that the adipose fin, at least in its anterior part, possesses jointed fin-rays.

Amazon basin; to 25 cm.

D 16–17; A 25–27; LL 75–82; 45–50 scutes in ventral keel. Body disc-shaped, elongate-oval. Anal fin flag-like, its hinder edge almost vertical. Serrations of the ventral keel moderate. Coloration, according to Rachow: – metallic silver with green glints; upperside more brownish to copper-coloured; the whole flanks are beset with large grey-blue to deep black spots and sprinkled over with tiny metallic spangles; dorsal and caudal fins reddish at the base, outside this yellowish; caudal sometimes with dark spots; anal fin bright brick-red.

Sex-distinctions in coloration not described.

♂ dorsal fin produced to a point.

Care, as for *Metynnis roosevelti*. Not yet bred in captivity. 1912/–.

Mylossoma argenteum *E. Ahl* 1929 (Figs. 110, 116)
The representatives of the genus *Mylossoma* are distinguished from members of the genera *Metynnis* and *Piaractus* by, among other characters, the more or less semicircular form of the anal fin, which is furthermore scaly on the base.

Southern Amazon basin, Upper Paraguay; to 20 cm.

D 18; A 38; 44–46 scutes in ventral keel (+ 5–7 on the hinder parts). Body-form and finnage as in *M. duriventris*. Coloration, according to E. Ahl: –uniform dark grey to brown-yellow or greenish; flanks and underside paler with a strong silvery sheen; throat and surroundings of pectoral fins dark-pigmented; a dark spot, striking for its almost rectilinear form, on the gill-cover. Dorsal, adipose and caudal fins delicate reddish; anal fin bright red, its edge dark black-red; pectorals and ventrals colourless.

Sex-distinctions unknown.

Care, as for *Metynnis roosevelti*. 1927/+.

Mylossoma duriventris (*Cuvier* 1817) (Fig. 109)
Southern Amazon basin, Paraguay, Paraná, La Plata; to 23 cm.

D 16–18; A 37–42; LL about 100; 42–53 scutes in ventral keel. Body disc-shaped; anal fin large, semicircular; ventral keel toothed.

Adult: light brown, rather like a walnut-shell or rather darker, with a dull silver sheen, particularly on the flanks and on the considerably paler underside. Upperside markedly darker brown. Gill-cover with an inconspicuous dark spot. Transverse bands completely absent. Fins glass-clear or delicate brownish; caudal and anal quite dark, the latter, in fine specimens, with a reddish-yellow margin. Eye velvet black, its upper edge gleaming red.

Fishes of 8–10 cm.: sides of body with 6–8 wedge-shaped dark transverse bands which gradually disappear below the lateral line.

Fishes of 4–6 cm.: transverse bands present, also a black, light-edged spot below the dorsal fin.

Sex-distinctions not described.

Care, as for *Metynnis roosevelti*. 1908/+.

Arnold and Ahl (1936) also list *Mylossoma aureum* Agassiz 1829 among the species imported. Their figure, however, shows a young specimen of *M. duriventris* which the corresponding description also fits very well. Since, moreover, the locality-data fall within the distribution of *M. duriventris*, we may well believe that there has been a misidentification in this case. The true *M. aureum* would then appear not to have been imported.

Steindachner has given an account of the young stages of *M. duriventris* (ref. *Denkschr. Akad. Wiss. Wien* Bd.93, Taf.VI, 1917).

Myloplus arnoldi *E. Ahl* 1936 (Fig. 105)
The genus *Myloplus* is distinguished from related genera mainly by the form of its dentition; dorsal fin long-based, adipose short.

Amazon R.; to 18 cm.

D 23–25; A 29–31; 33–39 scutes in ventral keel. Body disc-shaped, ventral keel toothed. The anterior part of the anal fin has a sickle-shaped prolongation. Body uniformly silvery with a delicate yellowish lustre, especially noticeable on the upper part of the flanks. Dorsal, adipose and caudal fins delicate yellowish to orange, sometimes with blackish margins. The sickle-shaped part of the anal is bright orange-red to blood-red. Pectoral and ventral fins colourless.

Sex-distinctions in coloration not described.

Care, as for *Metynnis roosevelti*; not yet bred in captivity. 1934/+.

Myloplus schultzei *E. Ahl* 1938 (Fig. 104)
Lower reaches of the Amazon and its southern tributaries (?); to 20 cm.

D 29; A 39; 46 scutes in ventral keel. Body disc-shaped, ventral keel toothed. The anal fin, behind the produced anterior rays, is emarginate; the middle and hinder part again convex. A very beautiful species. Body in healthy fishes often

Figs. 95–97

Fig. 95. *Serrasalmus rhombeus* (Spotted Piranha); half-grown, greatly reduced.
Fig. 96. *Rooseveltiella nattereri* (Natterer's Piranha); adult, greatly reduced.
Fig. 97. *Pygocentrus piraya* (Piraya, Piranha); adult, greatly reduced.

very dark in its entirety, sometimes quite black with a greenish lustre; usually, however, more grey-green, in part with handsome iridescent patches. Over the whole body are strewn numerous very large golden, orange and dark red spots; often the same colour-tones may be united in one spot, or the red spots may stand out within a golden margin. Some golden spots on the back are usually especially brilliant. In addition the body is covered with innumerable glistening spangles. Fins colourless to delicate blue-grey or blackish, sometimes with black margins.

♂ anal fin more strongly emarginate.

Care, as for *Metynnis roosevelti*; not yet bred in captivity. 1938/+.

Metynnis anisurus *E. Ahl* 1923 (Fig. 112)
The genus *Metynnis* comprises about 22 species of disc-shaped Characins with a sharp-toothed ventral keel. From the similarly-shaped genera *Piaractus, Colossoma, Myloplus, Serrasalmus*, etc., they are mainly separated by peculiarities of dentition. The species described here fall into two groups according to their body form. *M. hypsauchen, calichromus* and *schreitmuelleri* have a very deep body; the depth of the body in these cases is almost equal to the length without the head. In contrast the other *Metynnis* spp., at least when sexually ripe, are somewhat more elongate.
The sexes are usually distinguished by the form of the anal fin:–

♂ anal fin emarginate in the anterior part, produced to a sickle-shape, or at any rate more strongly prolonged than in the ♀.

All *Metynnis* spp. are quite peaceful shoaling fishes which feed mainly on plant materials. For further details, see under *Metynnis roosevelti*.
M. anisurus is a native of the Rio Tapajoz, a southern tributary of the R. Amazon; to 12 cm.
D 17; A 41; 36 teeth on ventral keel. Body in young disc-shaped, in older fishes somewhat elongate (see above). Anal fin not produced into a sickle-shape; lower

Plate 15

Fig. 98. The development of the European Eel (after Murray and Hjørt, from Brehm). Commencing at the top of the plate:

Stages 1–5: willow-leaf-shaped larval stages *(Leptocephali)*.
Stages 6–8: stages in metamorphosis from *Leptocephalus* to Glass-eel.
Stage 9: Glass-eel.
Stage 10: Elver.

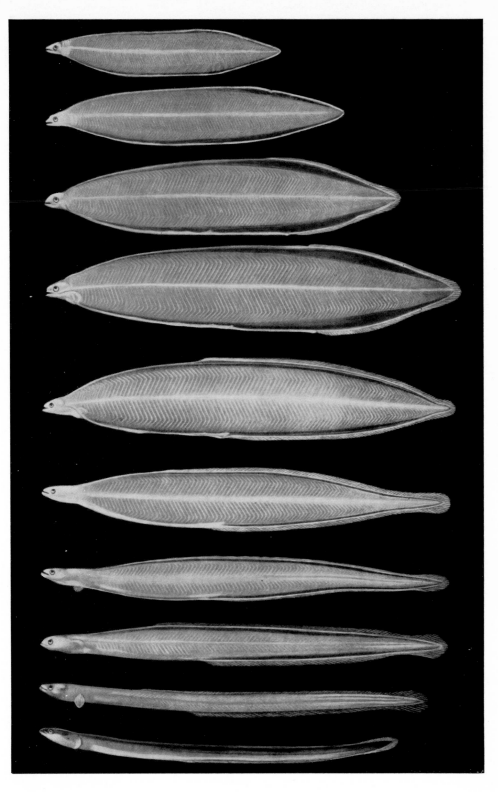

Plate 15

Plate 16

Plate 16

Fig. 99. *Umbra krameri* (Rihahal or Hundsfisch); adults, reduced. (Photo P. Unger)
Fig. 100. *Roeboides microlepis* (Small-scaled Glass-characin); half-grown, enlarged. (Original)

lobe of caudal somewhat longer than upper. Coloration, according to E. Ahl:–upperside delicate olive-green; flanks silvery with a bluish sheen; a dark shoulder-spot, usually inconspicuous; ventral fins with a narrow black margin; adipose fin reddish.

Care and peculiarities, as for *M. roosevelti*. 1914/–.

Metynnis calichromus *E. Ahl* 1923 (Figs. 106, 113)
Rio Jamundá (northern tributary of the middle Amazon) near the town of Faro; to 15 cm.

D 19; A 41–44; 27–29 scutes in ventral keel. Body at all stages very deeply disc-shaped (see above). Anterior end of anal fin with a sickle-shaped prolongation, posteriorly emarginate in the ♂; caudal fin slightly notched. Coloration, according to E. Ahl:–Upperside grey to delicate brownish-green; flanks pale, silvery, with pronounced bluish or greenish lustre, occasionally with a few narrow, dusky transverse bars which commence broadly on the back and taper to points at the level of the lateral line; dark spots on the lower half of the body. A dark shoulder-spot is at most faintly defined. Dorsal fin with numerous dusky streaks and a black margin. Anal fin ochre-yellow, anterior part red, anterior edge black. Caudal fin colourless with a broad red margin. Sometimes all the vertical fins have slightly dusky margins.

Care and peculiarities, as for *Metynnis roosevelti*. 1922/+.

Metynnis dungerni *E. Ahl* 1926 (Fig. 114)
Amazon R. and near Pará; to 12 cm.

D 18; A 40; 40 scutes in ventral keel. Body disc-shaped, somewhat elongate. Anal fin without sickle-shaped prolongation. Caudal fin symmetrical, notched. Coloration, according to E. Ahl:–upperside greenish-grey; flanks pale, silvery with a bluish lustre and, not always in evidence, dark spots of the size of the pupil which may run together into transverse stripes. On the other hand there is a fine dusky pigmentation on certain groups of scales, usually quite distinctly marked. Breast with a golden-red lustre. Dorsal fin blackish; anal fin clear wine-red, all other fins colourless. Iris orange.

Care and peculiarities, as for *M. roosevelti*. 1923/–.

Metynnis heinrothi *E. Ahl* 1923 (Fig. 121)

Amazon basin (more precise locality–data lacking); to 10 cm. (?)

D 16; A 38; 38 scutes in ventral keel. Similar to the foregoing species. Coloration according to E. Ahl:–upperside brownish-green; flanks and belly pale, silvery with a steely-blue lustre; throat golden red. A dark shoulder spot is quite prominent; similarly to the foregoing species isolated scales on the side of the body are darkly pigmented. Upper part of dorsal fin blackish; adipose fin and caudal with dark margins; anal fin bordered with deep black.

Care and peculiarities, as for *M. roosevelti.* 1913/ –.

Metynnis hypsauchen (*Müller* and *Troschel* 1845) (Fig. 107)

Guiana and Amazon basin, said to prefer standing water; to 14 cm.

D 18–19; A 38–41; 27–31 scutes on ventral keel. Very similar to *M. schreitmuelleri* in body-form and finnage; first rays of the anal fin somewhat elongate. Upperside delicate grey-green; flanks silvery with a delicate bluish lustre; occasionally in older fishes several transverse rows of dark spots or transverse bars are very prominent. Usually with 1–2 shoulder-spots. Fins pale yellow; anterior part of anal fin reddish.

Care and peculiarities, as for *M. roosevelti.* 1912/ +.

Metynnis maculatus (*Kner* 1859) (Fig. 122)

Guiana, Amazon, Rio Paraguay; to 18 cm.

D 17–21; A 37–40; 31–35 scutes in ventral keel. Body, at least in older fishes, somewhat elongate (see *M. anisurus*), strongly compressed (disc-shaped). Edge of belly serrate as in all *Metynnis* spp. Anal fin without sickle-shaped projection. Upperside fawn, often with a grey-blue lustre; flanks grey to delicate brownish or mud-colour, bearing numerous dark brown spots which are mostly not quite round but rather elongate-oval and in part arranged in rows; underside silvery. A shining orange-coloured spot on the gill-cover; usually behind this an extraordinary larger, often double, darker spot. All the fins are dark-bordered, except for the colourless pectorals. Caudal with orange-red inner margin; anal brick-red anteriorly.

Figs. 101–103

Fig. 101. *Serrasalmus hollandi;* adult, much reduced.
Fig. 102. *Serrasalmus niger;* adult, much reduced.
Fig. 103. *Serrasalmus spilopleura;* adult, much reduced.

♀ outer margin of anal fin straight.

♂ front part of outer edge of anal fin with a semicircular convexity.

Care and peculiarities, as for *M. roosevelti*. 1910/+.

Metynnis roosevelti *Eigenmann* 1915 (Fig. 75)

Amazon R.; to 14 cm.

D 15–18; A 36–43; LL about 80; 34–42 scutes in ventral keel. This species belongs to the more elongate group of *Metynnis,* the body-depth in sexually mature fishes being less than the body-length without the head. The caudal fin is hardly notched. Upperside delicate olive-colour; flanks whitish with silver reflexions and numerous more or less distinct brown to blackish round spots, which are arranged quite at random. Shoulder-spot orange-red to blackish, not always distinct. Vertical fins yellowish, front of anal reddish, caudal dark-edged (according to Rachow, in old individuals the upper lobe of the caudal may become quite black).

♀ anal fin bright orange-red on the free edge; outer edge straight, except first fin-ray which is often a little produced.

♂ especially at spawning-time the caudal and anal fins have a bright red inner border, on the former within an outer black margin. The free edge of the anal is anteriorly convex, whereby the hinder part appears emarginate.

All *Metynnis* spp. are shoaling fishes and for their comfort need more than anything else plenty of room to move about; in small tanks (100–150 cm. long) they remain persistently timid and nervous. They are predominantly herbivores which in their natural habitats look for richly-weeded pasturage, wherefore, of course, their tanks should not be planted, but root-systems offering suitable hiding-places should be provided. A dark bottom and subdued light further promote the fishes' well-being. As regards water-conditions for spawning they are not very sensitive, nevertheless hard, unmatured water should never be used. Temperature 24–27°C. Plant-food in large quantities, and above all lettuce, upon which the fishes will feed really heartily; in addition live animal food of various

Plate 17

Fig. 104. *Myloplus schultzei;* large adult, reduced. In the Hellabrunn Aquarium, Munich. (Original)

Fig. 105. *Myloplus arnoldi;* adults, reduced. The lower left-hand fish is a *Metynnis schreitmuelleri*. In the Hellabrunn Aquarium, Munich. (Original)

Plate 17

Plate 18

Plate 18

Fig. 106. *Metynnis calichromus;* large individual, reduced, in the Hellabrunn Aquarium, Munich. (Original)

Fig. 107. *Metynnis hypsauchen;* adults, somewhat reduced; above ♂, below ♀; in the Hellabrunn Aquarium, Munich. (Original)

kinds. As yet only the species *M. roosevelti* and *M. schreitmuelleri* have been bred in captivity. Concerning *M. roosevelti* H.J.Franke reports:—

'The fishes spawned for the first time in the late evening by artificial light. After vigorous driving mating took place in the usual Characin fashion, the fishes pressing against one another in *Myriophyllum* tufts or on the alga-covered rear wall of the tank, whereby altogether 150 eggs were expelled. These are more than 2 mm. in diameter and require 4 days to develop before the young emerge. The newly-emerged embryos are 8 mm. long and swim freely after 4–5 days. They feed from the first day on medium-sized *Cyclops* nauplii and grow very rapidly with good feeding. Six months later their size approaches that of the parents.'

Concerning the breeding of *M. schreitmuelleri* G.Schmidt says:—'Temperature 26°C.; pH 6·8. During mating the fishes keep close together with the heads somewhat raised; they quiver, the bodies striking against one another, and eject eggs and milt in the manner characteristic of all Characins. The eggs are 2 mm. in diameter and fall to the bottom; the egg-membrane is not adhesive. Observed number of eggs 2000. The parents do not interfere with the eggs; at 28°C., the young emerge after 70 hours. Initially they are 4 mm. long and lie on the bottom; after 2–3 days they attach themselves loosely to the glass and begin to feed (on nauplii) about the 4th–5th day. Growth rapid with good feeding.'

I once had the opportunity, in Wuppertal, to watch a shoal of about 200 *M. schreitmuelleri* and I should like to add that never since have I seen such a fascinating picture. The whole shoal behaved as one, moving in perfect unison; not one fish disturbed the harmony, not one attempt to swim an independent tack; hundreds of lovely, glittering fishes in graceful, silent, mutual understanding.

Metynnis schreitmuelleri *E.Ahl* 1922 (Figs. 74, 105)
Amazon basin; to 15 cm.

D 20; A 42; 26 scutes on ventral keel. Body disc-shaped, very deep, body-depth about equal to body-length without head (see *M. anisurus*). Caudal fin hardly notched. Upperside bright olive-colour; flanks and underside splendid shining silver, occasionally with a bluish or greenish shine. The hoop-like transverse markings mentioned by E. Ahl have not been confirmed despite repeated attempts to observe them. Dorsal fin with sparse but well-marked spots and streaks; caudal occasionally with faint dark edge; anterior part of anal brilliant brick-red.

Care, breeding, sex-distinctions, see under *M. roosevelti*. 1913/−.

Metynnis snethlageae *E. Ahl* 1923 (Fig. 123)
Amazon basin; to 12 cm. (?)

D 16–17; A 38–42; 36–37 scutes on ventral keel. Similar to *M. roosevelti*, but still more elongate. Caudal fin distinctly forked. Coloration, according to Schreit-müller: upperside brownish green to brown-yellow; flanks silver with numerous brownish spots which are, however, usually very indistinct or quite absent. A very large and clearly marked shoulder-blotch. Iris of the eye yellowish. Dorsal fin blackish above with a dark edge; caudal fin with a deep black margin.

♀ anal fin bluish-grey.
♂ anal fin faint reddish-brown with a black margin. Further distinguished by bluish-black pectoral fins, a nipple-shaped prolongation of the anterior part of the anal, and a region behind the pectoral fin which is finely sprinkled with dark.

Care and peculiarities, as for *Metynnis roosevelti*. 1913/−.

Aphyocharax alburnus (*Günther* 1869) (Fig. 128)
Marañon; according to Arnold from southern Brazil to the Paraná basin; to 7 cm.

D 10; A 20; LL 37. Body slim, *Danio*-like. Faint grey-green with a strong bluish sheen on the flanks which is particularly intense on 2–3 middle longitudinal series of scales. Back olive-coloured, belly silvery. Fins colourless; root of caudal fin and part of the lower caudal lobe near the root blood-red. A dark shoulder-blotch, according to Arnold, is usually rather indistinct.

Sex-distinctions unknown.

Care, as for *A. rubripinnis*. Apparently not yet bred in captivity. 1934/+.

Figs. 108–110
Fig. 108. *Piaractus nigripinnis;* young, about natural size.
Fig. 109. *Mylossoma duriventris;* adult, greatly reduced. Below, right, a young specimen of this species.
Fig. 110. *Mylossoma argenteum;* adult ♂, reduced.

Aphyocharax nattereri (*Steindachner* 1882) (Fig. 129)

Amazon R. (Villa Bella), La Plata (?); to 5 cm.

D 9–10; A 23; LL 30; TR 4/3. Body somewhat stockier and deeper than in *A. rubripinnis*. Faint grey-green with a strong bluish-silver sheen or a weak brassy sheen on the flanks; as in the foregoing species 2–3 middle longitudinal series of scales stand out, shining blue-green. Belly white. Vertical fins bright red at base, more yellow-red outside; anal fin with a black margin.

♂ (according to Praetorius) has lilac wine-red on the lower part of the caudal peduncle; otherwise sex-distinctions unknown.

Care, as for *A. rubripinnis*. Not yet bred in captivity. 1906/−.

Aphyocharax rubripinnis *Pappenheim* 1921 (Fig. 145)   Bloodfin

This species is apparently identical with *A. affinis* E. Ahl 1923.

Paraná, Argentine; to 5·5 cm.

D 9–10; A 20–21; LL 33–34. Body slim, *Danio*-like. Ground-colour yellow to grey-green, gleaming bright silvery by reflected light. Along the lateral line a faint dull bluish gleaming stripe. Except for the pectorals and upper lobe of the caudal, all the fins are blood-red.

♀ outside breeding season, very similar to ♂.

♂ slim and always more brightly coloured during the breeding season.

Peaceful, lively shoaling fishes, requiring large tanks with plenty of swimming-space. Fairly resistant to temperature variations; tolerates anything beyond 18°C., but flourishes best at 24–28°C. Omnivorous. For breeding provide a spacious tank, finely-divided plants, soft to medium-hard water and a temperature around 26°C. Spawns after vigorous driving in the early hours of the morning. The eggs are shed at random and fall to the bottom.

After spawning, remove the parents (spawn-eater!). Eggs glass-clear. Young hatch after about 30 hours and hang during the early days at or near the surface. Feed on smallest animals (later supplemented with dried food). Very rapid-growing. 1906/+.

Tetragonopterus chalceus *Agassiz* 1829 (Fig. 131)

Amazon R., Guiana; to 12 cm.

D 11; A 28–34; LL 29–34. Body very deep, strongly compressed. Lateral line turns immediately downwards anteriorly and then runs in a straight line to the root of the tail. Adipose fin present. Gleaming bright silver fishes. Upperside olive-green to yellow-brown; flanks silvery, exhibiting, according to lighting, bluish-green to faint copper-red or violet zones of reflexion; underside silvery-white. Two shoulder-blotches, one behind the other, are only distinctly present in young fishes; the second blotch is the first to vanish. Root of tail always with a transverse bar-like dark blotch. Fins colourless, dorsal usually finely dusted and with a white leading edge.

♀ more robust; dorsal fin-rays not prolonged.
♂ usually smaller; dorsal fin-rays prolonged in older fishes.

Care and breeding, as for *Hemigrammus* spp.
Very satisfying; larger individuals often unsociable. 1913/+.

Moenkhausia oligolepis (*Günther* 1864) (Fig. 119)   Glass Tetra
Amazon and Guiana, in small standing or sluggish waters; to 12 cm.

D 11; A 24–28; LL 28–31; TR 5/4. Body elongate and deep, strongly compressed. Lateral line running almost straight. Upperside olive-green to olive-yellow; flanks splendid gleaming silver with bluish sheen; underside silvery white. The large scales are often dark-edged. One or two indistinct shoulder-blotches. A weak longitudinal band from the hind end of the gill-cover to the root of the tail is not usually apparent. Root of tail black, often displaying two gold-gleaming blotches. Dorsal, caudal and anal fins faint yellow to reddish. Iris red above, otherwise golden.

♀ fins not prolonged; anal without prolonged rays.
♂ fins slightly prolonged; first rays of anal particularly long.

Unassuming and peaceful; young especially interesting and lively. Omnivorous; breeding not difficult.
Care and breeding, as for *Hemigrammus* spp. 1912/+.

Moenkhausia pittieri *Eigenmann* 1920 (Fig. 120)
Venezuela (Lake Valencia); to 6 cm.

D 11; A 26–29; LL 33–36. Body slimmer than in the foregoing species. Dorsal fin, especially in ♂, drawn out, banner-like. Ground-colour brassy yellow, back darker, belly yellowish-white. At the level of the dorsal fin a darker band commences which becomes broader behind and is lost in older fishes. Upper half of the body gleaming a splendid gold by reflected light; lower parts with metallic iridescence; flanks sprinkled with numerous shining green points. Vertical fins milky violet with white tips.

♀ coloration somewhat paler.
♂ coloration as above; dorsal fin longer.

This beautiful and unusually lively species should be treated like the *Hemigrammus* spp. It requires plenty of room to move about. Breeding not difficult (15–20 litre tanks). 1933/+.

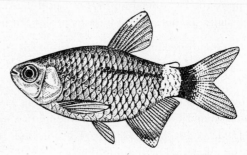

Fig. 111
Moenkhausia sanctae-filomenae;
slightly enlarged.

Moenkhausia sanctae-filomenae (*Steindachner* 1907) (Fig. 111)
Basin of the Paraguay and Paranahyba; to 7 cm.

D 9; A 22–23; LL 24 + 2 on the base of the caudal fin. Of similar form to *M. oligolepis* but somewhat deeper, with darker scales and with more distinct dark edges to these. Body shining bright silvery; upperside light brownish to greenish; underside delicate yellowish. A broad, deep black transverse bar at the root of the tail; in front of this a wide, shining yellow area. Upper part of eye bright blood-red. Fins to some extent smoke-grey; tip of dorsal and anterior rays of anal whitish.

Sex-distinctions in young unknown; sexually mature ♀♀ may be distinguished by the more robust convexity of the belly.

Care and breeding of this lively and very beautiful species, as for *Hemigrammus* spp. 1956.

Figs. 112–114

Fig. 112. *Metynnis anisurus;* drawn from a living specimen of 10 cm.
Fig. 113. *Metynnis calichromus;* adult ♂, reduced.
Fig. 114. *Metynnis dungerni;* adult ♂, reduced.

110

Gymnocorymbus ternetzi (*Boulenger* 1895) (Fig. 156)   Black Tetra; Blackamoor; Petticoat-fish.

Matto Grosso region of Rio Paraguay, Rio Negro; to 5·5 cm.

D 11–12; A 40–42; LL 32–36; TR 7–8/8–9. Body moderately elongate, deep. Dorsal and anal fins very large. Lateral line complete, almost straight. Back olive-green. Belly white with silver sheen. Head with dark transverse band extending over the eyes. Mouth black. Behind the gill-cover a constant black transverse bar, equal in depth to the height of the dorsal fin. Hinder part of the body, including the dorsal, anal and adipose fins, black in young fishes, grey in older ones. Pectoral and caudal fins pale, translucent, the last with whitish points.

♀ somewhat larger; body-cavity posteriorly rounded (when the fish is examined against the light!); caudal fin without white points.

♂ body-cavity posteriorly tapering; caudal with clear white spots.

Care, as for *Hemigrammus* spp. Breeding, at 27–28 °C., easy. 1935/+.

Markiana nigripinnis (*Perugia* 1891) (Fig. 130)
Region of the upper Paraguay, Paraná; to 10 cm.

D 11; A 44; LL 36 + 2 on the caudal fin. Elongate, strongly compressed, shoaling fishes with a very long, low, anal fin. Upper lobe of caudal fin pointed, lower rounded. Ground colour greenish, back darker, belly yellowish with silver sheen, flanks with rows of reddish-brown spots and a wide, silvery longitudinal band. Shoulder-blotch occasionally indistinct; blotch at root of tail, especially in young, dark brown to black. Dorsal and caudal fins yellowish; adipose fin yellow; anal fin greenish-blue at base, yellow distally with an orange border outlined in blue-green.

♀ all fins with more yellowish tones.

♂ all fins with more reddish tones.

Plate 19

Fig. 115. *Colossoma* sp. (Pacu). The Pacu is a rarely-imported species from northern South America, which in its natural habitat feeds mainly on fruit. Maximum length 70 cm. Back grey-green, sides of belly black. Photograph of a 40 cm. specimen in the Hellabrunn Aquarium, Munich. (Original)

Fig. 116. *Mylossoma argenteum;* adult, reduced, in the Hellabrunn Aquarium, Munich.

Fig. 117. *Arnoldichthys spilopterus* (Red-eyed Characin); somewhat enlarged.

Plate 19

Plate 20

Plate 20

Fig. 118. *Roeboides guatemalensis* (Guatemala Glass-characin); ripe adults, natural size. (Original)
Fig. 119. *Moenkhausia oligolepis* (Glass Tetra); ripe adults, natural size. (Original)
Fig. 120. *Moenkhausia pittieri;* left ♀, right ♂, natural size. (Original)

Care and breeding of this very robust, though not exactly predatory, species as given for the genus *Hemigrammus*. Omnivorous; supplementary plant food (lettuce) advised. Breeding not difficult. 1912/ −.

Thayeria obliquua *Eigenmann* 1908 (Fig. 159)   Penguin Fish
Amazon R.; to 8 cm.

D 10–11; A (15)16–17(18); LL 28–31. Body elongate, compressed. Lateral line incomplete. Lower lobe of caudal fin lengthened. The fishes carry themselves usually in a somewhat inclined position, head upwards. Back dark bronze-green; lower half of body yellowish-blue to delicate olive-green. From the hinder edge of the gill-cover to the root of the tail and thence into the lower caudal lobe there extends a broad deep-black band, bounded ventrally by a glittering golden line. Dorsal fin with a yellow-reddish base anteriorly, otherwise colourless; base of the upper caudal lobe also occasionally reddish; anal fin with a white leading-edge.

Sexes identical in coloration; ♀ substantially fuller at spawning time.

Care of this very beautiful, elegant species, as for the genus *Hemigrammus*. For breeding select a large 10–15 litre all-glass tank with *Myriophyllum* clumps and soft, slightly acid water. It is recommended that part of the water be removed after spawning and the tank topped up with suitable fresh water; if this precaution is omitted putrescence ensues through the decay of the very copiously produced milt. The eggs are brown in colour and the young sometimes hatch after only 12 hours. A spawning can produce over 1000 newcomers. 1935/ +.

Thayeria sanctae-mariae *Ladiges* 1949 (Fig. 132)
Near the village of St. Maria in Goyaz State (Brazil); to? (type specimen 47 mm.).

D 12; A 16–17; LL 28. Very similar in shape to the foregoing species, but easily distinguished by the substantially shorter lateral band. Coloration, according to Ladiges:–ground-colour, as in *T. obliquua*; the black lateral band commences rather hazily at the level of the hinder end of the dorsal fin and, becoming increas-

113

ingly prominent, extends to the root of the tail where it turns down into the lower caudal lobe; it is bounded, above and below, by pale stripes. Adipose fin yellow.

In other respects similar to *T.obliquua*. 1949/+.

Pristella riddlei (*S. E. Meek* 1907) (Fig. 157)   X-ray Fish, Water Goldfinch
Northern South America, Guiana, lower Amazon R.; to 4·5 cm.

D 11; A 20–24; LL 32, of which 6–8 are pierced. Body transparent, yellow-greenish; shining silver by reflected light. A clear black shoulder-blotch. Dorsal and anal fins lemon-yellow, each bearing a large deep black blotch. Tips of fins white; a similar but rather smaller blotch on the ventral fins. Caudal fin reddish.

♀ more robust; hinder end of body-cavity (viewed against the light) rounded.
♂ slimmer; hinder end of body-cavity drawn out, tapering to a point.

This favourite and very charming shoaling fish is similar to the *Hemigrammus* spp. as regards breeding and care. Selection of a pair requires a little skill; strangely enough not every pair will oblige! Breeding otherwise not difficult. The young hatch after 22–28 hours. One spawning can produce 300–400 young. 1924/+.

Genera Hemigrammus and Hyphessobrycon: Care and Breeding

To the genera *Hemigrammus* and *Hyphessobrycon*, natives of Central and South America, there belong almost exclusively small, decorative Characins, of tropical magnificence for the most part, which enjoy world-wide affection. These fishes, without exception lively and very peaceful, are shoaling fishes which in their native countries inhabit standing and flowing water right down to the smallest watercourses and bogs and feed upon small water-animals as well as drifting insects of the surface-film and, to a certain extent, aquatic plants. The body is usually moderately elongate, compressed and more or less deep. The almost square, upstanding dorsal fin is a fundamental character

Figs. 121–123

Fig. 121. *Metynnis heinrothi;* slightly reduced.
Fig. 122. *Metynnis maculatus;* adult ♂, reduced.
Fig. 123. *Metynnis snethlageae;* slightly reduced.

which places these genera in the subfamily *Tetragonopterinae* (= 'Square-fins'). A small adipose fin is usually present. Caudal fin deeply notched. Anal fin more or less elongate. The sexes are not easily distinguished, as the coloration of the ♂ and ♀ may be similar throughout. However, the ♂ is soon recognised by the observant student by his slimmer form. Another reliable sex-distinguishing character, one of several visible when the fishes are viewed against a strong light, is the shape of the swim-bladder as well as its position in the body-cavity. Thus, in the ♂ the swim-bladder is more tapered posteriorly than in the ♀. Further, in the ♂ there is nearly always a free space between the viscera and the hind edge of the swim-bladder; in the ♀ this space is filled by the ovary. The two genera are only very narrowly distinguished. However, in all *Hemigrammus* as here understood the base of the caudal fin is scaly; in all *Hyphessobrycon* it is completely scale-less.

Many of the species under consideration are undemanding and hardy, qualities which too often mislead aquarists into keeping the fishes under very poor conditions, a neglect which is by no means justified. Any fish, even the Red Tetra from Rio, for example, will develop its full intensity of life and brilliance of colour only under optimum conditions. The members of the genera *Hemigrammus* and *Hyphessobrycon* have the following require-ments:–aquaria which are not too small (at least 30 litres) with thick clumps of plants here and there, free space for swimming about, a dark background and some sunlight which may, with advantage, be dimmed in some places by floating plants. Above all, however, the water should be poor in lime. Old 'matured' water, or better still, slightly acid water filtered through peat, noticeably furthers the well-being of the fishes. As regards preferred tempe-ratures the various species have their own different requirements but in general 23–25°C. will suffice. A moderate fall in temperature generally does

Plate 21

Fig. 124. *Hyphessobrycon pulchripinnis* (Lemon Tetra); natural size. (Original)
Fig. 125. *Hyphessobrycon serpae;* young of a breed which is of an especially bright red-orange colour and lacks a shoulder-blotch; falsely known as '*H. minor*'. (Original)

Plate 21

Plate 22

Plate 22

Fig. 126. *Hyphessobrycon innesi* (Neon Tetra); adults, a trifle enlarged. (Original)
Fig. 127. *Hemigrammus erythrozonus* (Glowlight Tetra); adults; lower left, a ♂. (Original)

no harm; indeed many species, such as the Neon Tetra, are quite able to tolerate temperatures below 17 °C. Give live food of various kinds, at least a few midge-larvae or small insects now and then. Some species accept dried foods as well; a few, like the beautiful *Hemigrammus caudovittatus*, also nibble plants. All *Hemigrammus* and *Hyphessobrycon* spp. are quite peacefully inclined and may be kept quite well with one another as well as with other peaceful fishes; in fact, since they are shoaling fishes, several of a kind should always be kept together. All-glass aquaria are suitable for breeding the above fishes, and thick tufts of fine-leaved plants, e.g. *Myriophyllum*, *Amblystegium*, root-systems of *Pistia*, or artificial spawning tissue like green Perlon, should be provided. Soil on the bottom of the tank is not necessary. For breeding water use spring water, somewhat acid, clear and soft, which may further be filtered through peat or have tannic acid (0.1–0.3 gm. per 10 litres of water) added to it. Even softened tapwater is quite usable. It goes without saying that the glass of the breeding tank must be clean and the plants well rinsed. Willingness to spawn may be considerably heightened by correct setting-up of the tank; a situation which provides morning sunshine is particularly stimulating in this respect. The pairs should be put into the breeding tank in the evening (only ♀♀ which already show the onset of spawning should be chosen) and often spawn the next morning or on one of the subsequent days. Spawning is often a stormy business; ♂ and ♀ press their sides together after vigorous driving in a tangle of plants. The eggs are shed with a brief quivering and are freely fertilised in the water. In many species the eggs adhere firmly to water plants, in others they merely fall to the bottom. Since all these species are spawn-robbers the parents must be removed immediately after spawning. To protect the eggs on the floor of the breeding tank from being grabbed this may be covered with a single layer of dark, sloe-sized, glass beads or marbles.

The young hatch after only 20–28 hours and at first usually hang, like little glass-clear rods, on the plants or panes of glass. As soon as they begin to swim freely give them the finest food: rotifers, *Cyclops* nauplii, if necessary infusoria or micro-worms. Growth is generally rapid. The young fishes should be transferred to fresh water after feeding (later several times repeated); in doing this it is not necessary to use exactly the same kind of water, on the contrary, experience has shown that somewhat harder water may be advantageous. Many of the *Tetragonopterinae* are 'problem fishes' and require some experience for their successful breeding, as for example the Neon Tetra and the Glowlight Tetra. Breeding is easy in the Red Tetra from Rio, somewhat more difficult in *Pristella*. The beginner should therefore gain his experience with these species.

Hemigrammus armstrongi *Schultz* and *Axelrod* 1955 (Fig. 161)   Golden Tetra
Western Guiana; to 4·5 cm.

D 2/8–9; A 4/19–21; P 1/9–11; V 1/7; LL 31–33, 6–10 pierced. Form similar to the better-known *H. ocellifer*. Body of newly-imported fishes a beautiful shining gold, especially by artificial top-lighting. An intensely shining spot on the nape and another on top of the caudal peduncle. On the flanks a dark longitudinal streak which enlarges into a lozenge-shaped spot at the root of the tail. Caudal fin often faint reddish.

♀ more robust and with a less intense golden gleam.

Care and breeding, as for *Hemigrammus* above. Well-matched pairs spawn readily. Unfortunately the beautiful golden gleam disappears in the first-born generation in captivity; on the contrary, the reddish fin-colours are intensified. 1950.

Figs. 128–131
Fig. 128. *Aphyocharax alburnus;* adult, natural size.
Fig. 129. *Aphyocharax nattereri;* adult, natural size.
Fig. 130. *Markiana nigripinnis;* adult, natural size.
Fig. 131. *Tetragonopterus chalceus;* adult, reduced.

Hemigrammus caudovittatus *E. Ahl* 1923 (Fig. 146)   Buenos Aires Tetra
La Plata basin; to 7 cm.

D 11; A 26–27; LL 32–34 + 2–3, 7–10 pierced; TR 12–13. Yellow-brown, back olive-brown. Flanks with an iridescent metallic gleam. A bluish-black longitudinal stripe, by reflected light shining silver, begins at the level of the dorsal fin and broadens to the root of the tail-fin on to which it is continued tapering to a point; in the region of the caudal fin this lozenge-shaped longitudinal stripe has a pale margin above and below. A dark shoulder-blotch is evident only in certain conditions (reflected light): Upper half of the iris red. Dorsal and caudal fins yellowish to red. Base of anal fin bright brick-red.

♀ shape of body more rounded; fins almost colourless, at most a delicate pink.
♂ coloration as given above; slimmer.

Care and breeding, as given for *Hemigrammus* spp.

Unassuming, voracious (especially plants) and resistant to temperature variations. Breeding temperature 24°C.; easy to breed. 1922/+.

Hemigrammus erythrozonus *Durbin* 1909 (Fig. 127)   Glowlight Tetra
British Guiana; to 4·5 cm.

D 11; A 20–22; LL 31–34, 6–9 pierced; TR 5/3–3½. Shape similar to Neon Tetra. Grey-green. A broad, gleaming ruby-coloured longitudinal stripe extends, interrupted at the junction of the body-cavity with the tail, from the gill-cover to the root of the tail where it widens into a similarly gleaming spot. Anterior rays of the dorsal fin and upper half of the iris brilliant red. Tips of dorsal and ventral fins ivory-coloured. By artificial light a shining golden line shows up on the sparkling longitudinal band.

♀ somewhat larger and more stocky.
♂ slimmer, the belly-region appearing sunken.

Figs. 132–137

Fig. 132. *Thayeria sanctae-mariae;* adult, natural size.
Fig. 133. *Hemigrammus marginatus;* adult, natural size.
Fig. 134. *Hemigrammus rodwayi* (Rodway's Tetra); adult, natural size.
Fig. 135. *Hemigrammus ulreyi* (Ulrey's Tetra); natural size.
Fig. 136. *Hemigrammus unilineatus* (Feather Fin, One-line Tetra); adult, natural size.
Fig. 137. *Hemigrammus nanus* (Silver-tipped Tetra); natural size.

Care and breeding, as for *Hemigrammus* spp. generally (see above). Vies with the Neon Fish as one of the most beautiful of Characins. Breeding rather difficult. Soft, moderately acid water. The ♀♀ spawn readily at 28°C. The young hatch after 24 hours and, on a diet including *Cyclops* nauplii, grow very rapidly. During rearing frequent changes of water are necessary. 1939/+.

Hemigrammus marginatus *Ellis* 1911 (Fig. 133)
Venezuela to Argentine; to 8 cm.

D 11; A 20–24; LL 29–34, 5–14 pierced; TR 5/3–4. Grey-green to pale violet tints. Back olive-green, belly whitish. A dark, almost black, longitudinal band, its upper edge pale-bordered, extends from the gill-cover to the root of the tail. Root of tail often with a black blotch. Dorsal and anal fins yellow-green, tips shining white. Caudal fin lemon-yellow with broad black transverse bars. Eye golden yellow above.

♀ anal fin and base of dorsal fin yellowish.
♂ coloured as above. Dorsal and anal fins with brilliant white tips.

Care and breeding, as given for *Hemigrammus* spp. above. Temperature 25–27°C. 1933/−.

Hemigrammus nanus (*Lütken* 1874) (Fig. 137)　　　　　　　Silver-tipped Tetra
San Francisco basin; to 5 cm.

D 11; A 17–19; LL 30–32 + 3, 4–7 pierced; TR $3\frac{1}{2}/2\frac{1}{2}$–3. Shape similar to Glowlight Tetra. Outside the breeding season silver-grey to yellowish, strongly translucent. Flanks moderately brownish, belly silver. A narrow, dark longitudinal band begins about the level of the anal fin, becomes much broader towards the root of the tail and extends onto the middle caudal rays, sometimes reaching to the margin of the fin. Fins colourless, glassy, tips white. Scales of the upper half of the body often delicately edged with dark.

Figs. 138–144

Fig. 138. *Hyphessobrycon bentosi* (Bentos Tetra); adult, natural size.
Fig. 139. *Hyphessobrycon copelandi* (Copeland's Tetra); natural size.
Fig. 140. *Hyphessobrycon rosaceus* (Rosy Tetra, Black-flag Tetra); natural size.
Fig. 141. *Hyphessobrycon bifasciatus* (Yellow Tetra); natural size.
Fig. 142. *Hyphessobrycon maculicauda* (Tail-spot Tetra); natural size.
Fig. 143. *Hyphessobrycon erythrurus* (Red-tailed Tetra); natural size.
Fig. 144. *Hyphessobrycon luetkeni* (Lütken's Tetra); natural size.

♀ even at spawning-time, coloured as above.

♂ at spawning-time an intense brown-red, becoming paler behind. Root of caudal ink-red (according to Pinter).

Care and breeding, as given for *Hemigrammus* above. 1954.

Hemigrammus ocellifer (*Steindachner* 1883) (Fig. 162) Beacon Fish, Head-and-tail-Light Fish

Amazon basin and Guiana; to 4·5 cm.

D 10–11; A 22–28; LL 29–31 + 2–3, 6–8 pierced; TR 5/3–3½. Brown- to green-yellow. The dark shoulder-blotch with its shining green border is not always evident. A narrow dark longitudinal band commences at the level of the dorsal fin and extends to the root of the tail, where it is crossed by a dark transverse bar. In the angles of the cross are clear, shining golden-yellow spots, the one behind the adipose fin being particularly prominent. Upper half of iris red, lower half golden. Fins colourless, usually with bluish-white margins or at least with bluish tips.

♀ more robust; swim-bladder usually masked when viewed against the light.
♂ slimmer; swim-bladder clearly visible against the light.

Care and breeding, as for *Hemigrammus* above. Very prolific. 1910/+.

Hemigrammus pulcher *Ladiges* 1938 (Fig. 160)   Pretty Tetra

Middle Amazon; to 6 cm.

D 10–11; A 24–25; LL 31–34, 8–9 pierced; TR 10–11. Coloration very variable and depending on the angle of lighting. Back brownish-green, flanks pale grey-green, belly yellowish-white. Head dark green, blackish towards the snout; snout black. Iris crimson above, blue-green below. A few shining brassy-coloured patches on the throat. A gleaming coppery shoulder-blotch behind the gill-cover; a similar, elongate brightly-shining fleck on the caudal peduncle and below this

Plate 23

Fig. 145. *Aphyocharax rubripinnis* (Bloodfin); adults, natural size. (Original)
Fig. 146. *Hemigrammus caudovittatus* (Buenos Aires Tetra); young, natural size.
Fig. 147. *Hyphessobrycon heterorhabdus* (Flag Tetra); above ♀, below ♂, somewhat enlarged. (Original)

Plate 23

Plate 24

Plate 24

Fig. 148. *Cheirodon axelrodi* (Cardinal Tetra); adults, natural size. (Original)
Fig. 149. *Micralestes interruptus* (Congo Tetra); adults, natural size; left ♂, right ♀. The parts of the body which appear bluish in this photograph can change to iridescent green under a different lighting.

another, blue-black, wedge-shaped blotch. Dorsal, anal and caudal fins brilliant coppery; in a suitable light the whole body shines coppery to greenish.

♀ somewhat larger, more robust; swim-bladder only partly visible against the light.
♂ smaller, slimmer; swim-bladder easily and completely visible against the light.

Care and breeding, as for *Hemigrammus* above. Temperature 25–28 °C. In this very beautiful species it is rather difficult to find suitable partners for breeding; in case of failure one should try to replace the ♂. Fishes which have once spawned together are generally ready to do so again. 1938/+.

Hemigrammus rhodostomus *Ahl* 1924 (Fig. 166)   Red- or Rummy-nosed Tetra
Lower Amazon; to 4 cm.

D 10; A 14–15; LL 31–33, 7–14 pierced; TR 6/5. Back brownish to olive-green, belly greenish-white, head and iris blood-red. A light greenish gleaming spot on the nape. From the middle of the body to the root of the tail extends a dark longitudinal band which becomes broader posteriorly; this is accompanied above by a greenish gleaming line over which again, on the caudal peduncle, there is a further very prominent golden stripe; the last ends in a gold-gleaming fleck on the root of the tail. An oblique-oval dark blotch on each lobe of the caudal. In front of these blotches the caudal fin is yellow. All the other fins are colourless or faintly green. The intensive red colouring of the head unfortunately seldom develops in captivity.

♀ stockier and more robust.
♂ slimmer.

Care and breeding, as for *Hemigrammus* above. A somewhat sensitive species. So far breeding has been only moderately successful. 1925/+.

Hemigrammus rodwayi *Durbin* 1909 (Fig. 134)   Rodway's Tetra
Lower Amazon R., Guiana; to 5·5 cm.

D 11; A 22–24; LL 32–34, 9–12 (–15) pierced; TR 5/2½–3½. Coloration, according to Arnold, delicate grey-green to yellow-grey. Upperside olive-green, underside pale. A silvery lateral band begins about the level of the dorsal fin and extends into a large black blotch at the root of the tail; the latter may further extend as a stripe along the middle fin-rays. Scales on the upper part of the flanks dark-edged. No shoulder-blotch. Fins lightly tinted; each lobe of the caudal has a cherry-red spot at its base. Dorsal fin with a reddish base, anal fin reddish with a white leading edge.

♀ fins more yellowish; anal not white-edged.
♂ coloration as above.

Care and breeding, as for *Hemigrammus* above. Seldom imported; said to be rather delicate. 1930/−.

Hemigrammus ulreyi (*Boulenger* 1895) (Fig. 135)　　　　　Ulrey's Tetra
Matto-Grosso region and Paraguay R.; to 5 cm.

D 10; A 23–26; LL 30 + 2–3, 8–10 pierced; TR 5–6/3½. Very delicate green-grey to brown-green. Flanks and belly almost colourless, with a faint silvery iridescence by reflected light. The whole fish is moderately translucent. From a shoulder-blotch which is usually not prominent there extends to the root of the tail a triple band, bright red above, white-greenish in the middle and broad black below. Dorsal fin yellowish with a dark spot in its outer third, often with a black leading-edge as well. The other fins are faint yellowish to reddish.

♀ body stocky; adipose fin delicate orange.
♂ slimmer; adipose fin often reddish.

Care and breeding, as for *Hemigrammus* above. Very seldom imported and not yet bred in captivity. This species is not the same as the widely-distributed 'False-Ulreyi' (*Hyphessobrycon heterorhabdus*); the latter is in general somewhat slimmer and darker. 1905/−.

Hemigrammus unilineatus (*Gill* 1858) (Fig. 136)　　　Feather Fin, One-line Tetra
Trinidad and the whole of northern South America; to 5 cm.

D 11; A 23–27; LL 30–31 + 2–3, 5–8 pierced; TR 5/3–4½. Translucent; greenish-grey, by reflected light gleaming bluish-silver. Along the vertebral column, which is visible through the fish, is a gold-gleaming longitudinal band. A black shoulder-blotch is only occasionally present. Vertical fins reddish to red; the leading-edges and the tips of the dorsal and anal fins milky white. Dorsal with a dark triangular spot; pectoral and ventral fins colourless.

126

♀ body form more stocky.

♂ slimmer; often somewhat paler.

Care and breeding, as for *Hemigrammus* above. A very undemanding species. 1910/+.

Hyphessobrycon bentosi *Durbin* 1908 (Figs. 138, 168)   Bentos Tetra
(For classification and nomenclature, see p. 139.)
District around Bentos on the lower Amazon; to 6 cm.

D 11; A 27–30; LL 30–33. Shape similar to the better known *H. serpae*. Characteristic to this species is the scarcely-perceptible shoulder-blotch and the very weakly-marked longitudinal band. Arnold (*Taschenkalender für Aquarien- und Terrarienkunde*, Jg. 28, p. 124, 1936) mentions that on the introduction of *H. bentosi* Dr. Ahl determined the species with a certain hesitation. Even if the figured fish (see also Arnold and Ahl 1936, p. 76), with the exception of the shoulder-blotch – this appears, according to Arnold, only after killing in alcohol – agrees quite well with the true *H. bentosi*, in my opinion the correctness of the colour-description, at least in regard to the dorsal fin, is somewhat questionable. Since I have no further information from the literature concerning the life-colours for comparison, this question must here be left open.

Care and breeding, as for *Hemigrammus* above. Not yet bred in captivity. Allegedly 1934/–.

Hyphessobrycon bifasciatus *Ellis* 1911 (Fig. 141)   Yellow Tetra
South-eastern Brazil, in coastal districts; to 5 cm.

D 11; A 29–32; LL 33–36, 6–9 pierced; TR 6–7/5–6. Similar in shape to the Red Tetra from Rio. Delicately translucent, grey-yellow to green-yellow. Behind the gill-cover is a quite clear field in which two transversely-elongate dark shoulder-blotches appear, of which the first is always somewhat smaller but more distinct. From behind the second shoulder-blotch, and superimposed upon a dull silvery lateral band, there follows a long row of numerous dark chevrons (see Fig. 141). The fins are quite uniformly grey, markedly reddish in the young.

♀ more robust; anal fin somewhat concave.

♂ dorsal and anal fins with white leading-edges; anal often slightly reddish and convex.

Care and breeding, as for *Hemigrammus* above. Very contented; easy to breed. 1925/–.

127

Hyphessobrycon copelandi *Durbin* 1908 (Figs. 139, 168)   Copeland's Tetra
(For classification and nomenclature, see p. 139.)
Neighbourhood of Tabatinga in the upper basin of the Amazon; to 5 cm.

D 11; A 28; LL 24–27, 5–9 pierced; TR 5–7/3½. Shape similar to that of the better-known *H. serpae* and not unlike it with regard to colouring. Shoulder-blotch distinct. The olive-green upperside, the faintly clay-coloured flanks and clear underside are all tinged with faint reddish. Shoulder-blotch deep black, transversely elongate. Fins reddish to bright red; dorsal with a broad black centre and a white tip; anal faintly dark-edged, anterior corner white.

♀ more robust, particularly at spawning time; fins usually without white tips. ♂ somewhat slimmer.

Care and breeding, as for *Hemigrammus* above. 1934/+.

Hyphessobrycon eos *Durbin* 1909 (Fig. 150)   Dawn Tetra
Western Guiana; to 4·5 cm.

D 11; A 17–20; LL 33–34, 7–10 pierced; TR 6/4. Shape similar to that of the better-known *H. ocellifer*. Coloration, according to Arnold and Ahl:–olive-green to brownish, upperside rather dark. Scales on the upper part of the body with dark edges. Shoulder-blotch immediately behind the gill-cover and only weakly indicated. Lateral stripe narrow. A large, deep blue blotch on the caudal peduncle. The whole body is strewn with dark pigment-spots which are especially prominent on the gill-cover. Throat yellow. Dorsal fin yellow at the base; caudal bright yellow to orange, the lower lobe more strongly coloured; base and anterior part of anal fin reddish.

Sex-distinctions unknown.

Care and breeding of this very beautiful species, as for *Hemigrammus* above. Not yet bred in captivity. 1933/–.

Hyphessobrycon erythrurus *E. Ahl* 1928 (Fig. 143)   Red-tailed Tetra
Amazon R. (?); to 5 cm.

D 11; A 28; LL 34, 10 pierced; TR 6/5. Shape similar to that of the well-known *H. ocellifer*. Coloration, according to Arnold:–brownish-green with iridescent sheen. From the gill-cover there extends to the root of the tail a narrow longitudinal band which gleams bright silver to bluish, according to the direction of the light, and which merges posteriorly with the yellow periphery of a blue-black spot. Shoulder-blotch only weakly indicated. Caudal and anal fins red, the latter with a white leading-edge; dorsal and pectoral fins yellowish-grey.

128

♂ slimmer; the red colours of the fins are intense only when the fish is in good condition.

Care and breeding of these delightful fishes, as for *Hemigrammus* above. Not yet bred in captivity. 1928/ –.

Hyphessobrycon flammeus *Myers* 1924 (Fig. 77)　　　Red Tetra from Rio,
Flame Tetra

Neighbourhood of Rio de Janeiro; to 4·5 cm.

D 10; A 25; LL 33, 3–6 pierced; TR 7/5–6. Back grey-green; sides brassy-coloured; belly whitish; hinder part of the body gleaming red. Behind the gill-cover are two parallel transverse shoulder-blotches which taper below. The dark longitudinal stripe seldom materialises. Fins, with the exception of the pectorals, brilliant brick-red; dorsal with a white margin anteriorly; anal with a black leading-edge and tip.

♀ ventral and anal fins reddish, without black margin.
♂ ventral and anal fins blood-red, the latter with a black margin.

Care and breeding of this favourite species, as for *Hemigrammus* spp. above. Very undemanding. Breeding very easy, even in moderately hard water. Quite prolific. 1920/ +.

Hyphessobrycon gracilis (*Reinhardt* 1874) (Fig. 153)
From Guiana to Paraguay; to 4·5 cm.

D 10 (–11); A 17–24; LL 29–34, 6–13 pierced; TR 5/3½–4. Similar in shape to the Glow-light Tetra *(Hemigrammus erythrozonus)* but rather inconspicuously coloured a delicate grey-green. This not very striking fish is merely mentioned here because for a long time it was held to be identical with one of our most beautiful Characins. We owe the correction of this mistake to Fraser-Brunner (1955) who gave the Glow-light Tetra its proper name *Hemigrammus erythrozonus* Durbin 1909 (see p. 120).

Hyphessobrycon griemi *Hoedeman* 1957
Near Goyaz in Brazil; to 3 cm.

D 12–13; A 26–28; LL 32–34; TR 13. Similar in shape to *Hyphessobrycon flammeus* (Red Tetra from Rio), or *H. bifasciatus*, a species to which *H. griemi* is closely related. Two shoulder-blotches, coloured as in *H. flammeus*. Coloration, according to Hoedeman:– body translucent fawn to olive-brown. First shoulder-blotch merely indicated; second deep black with a light border. Dorsal, anal and

129

caudal fins intense cinnabar-red, the produced part of the anal milk-white and separated from the red part by a delicate black boundary. Likewise the longest anterior rays of the dorsal fin are milk-white with a black boundary behind. When excited the whole body is more or less cinnabar-red.

Care and breeding, as for *Hemigrammus* above. Very undemanding, easy to breed. 1956.

Hyphessobrycon heterorhabdus (*Ulrey* 1895) (Fig. 147)   Flag Tetra
Lower Amazon, Rio Tocantins; to 5 cm.

D 10; A 20–23; LL 32–34, 8–9 pierced; TR 5/3. Back red-brown; flanks yellow-brown; belly olive to bright silver. From the gill-cover to the root of the tail extends a broad tricoloured band, shining red above, whitish to golden in the middle and deep black below. Upper half of iris shining red. Fins colourless to faint yellowish, sometimes with white tips.

♀ the dark, shimmering body-cavity is rounded posteriorly.
♂ slimmer; body-cavity tapered to a point posteriorly.

Care and breeding, as for *Hemigrammus* above. This species is somewhat sensitive and not easy to keep in large numbers. Soft, acid water quickly leads to success. 1910/+.

Hyphessobrycon innesi *Myers* 1936 (Fig. 126)   Neon Tetra
Headwaters of the Amazon (Letitia-Tabatinga district); to 4 cm.

D 11; A 20–21; LL 32–33, 3 pierced; TR 9 between D and V. Back dark olive-green; belly yellowish-white. From the anterior edge of the eye over the upper edge of the orbit and as far as the level of the adipose fin there extends a beautiful green iridescent stripe which tapers to a point posteriorly; beneath this, beginning before the middle of the body, there runs an equally intensely-gleaming red band. The iris of the eye is a shining blue-green and exhibits, particularly in the upper part,

Figs. 150–155

Fig. 150. *Hyphessobrycon eos* (Dawn Tetra); natural size.
Fig. 151. *Hyphessobrycon* sp.; natural size.
Fig. 152. *Hyphessobrycon minimus* (Dwarf Tetra); adult, enlarged.
Fig. 153. *Hyphessobrycon gracilis;* natural size.
Fig. 154. *Hyphessobrycon nigrifrons* (Black-crowned Tetra); natural size.
Fig. 155. *Hyphessobrycon reticulatus* (Netted Tetra); somewhat reduced.

some golden points which sparkle like brilliants. Fins colourless; only the first rays of the dorsal a milky-white.

♀ more robust; profile of belly rounded.
♂ slimmer; the belly slightly sunken.

The perfect colour-harmony of this jewel among freshwater fishes is well matched by its liveliness and contentedness. Almost any well set-up aquarium is suitable for the care of the Neon Tetra, although its peak condition is attained in tanks which are not too light, have a dark background and soft to medium-hard water. The species may be kept with almost any peaceful fishes of the same size which have similar requirements. Preferred temperature 21–23°C. Small live food of all kinds, also dried foods. Concerning the very widespread 'Neon Disease' see my *Aquarienkunde*, Vol. 2.

Unfortunately the breeding of this beautiful fish is not everywhere simple and the fundamental difficulty is usually that of the water. Most suitable are small (8–10 litres) all-glass aquaria, very carefully cleaned, planted with clumps of *Myriophyllum* and filled with very soft, slightly-acid spring water, (pH 5·5–6·0). It is best to put in young pairs as soon as the ♀ shows the onset of spawning. Temperature not, repeat, not above 24°C. The eggs, which are laid among plants, are glass-clear and not very adhesive. The parents should be removed after spawning and the breeding-tank darkened. The young hatch after 22–26 hours and swim freely at about the fifth day; during the early days they are somewhat sensitive. Now change the water several times, preferably changing over to harder water. One spawning generally produces 60–130 young. (See also instructions for *Hemigrammus* above.) 1936/+.

Hyphessobrycon luetkeni (*Boulenger* 1887) (Fig. 144)   Lütken's Tetra
Rio Grande do Sul, Rio Paraguay basin; to 6·5 cm.

D 11; A 20–26; LL 30–35, 5–20 pierced; TR 5–6/4–5. Shape similar to that of the better known *Hyphessobrycon heterorhabdus*. Coloration, according to Arnold

Plate 25

Fig. 156. *Gymnocorymbus ternetzi* (Black Tetra, Blackamoor, Petticoat Fish); left ♂, right ♀, slightly enlarged. (Original)
Fig. 157. *Pristella riddlei* (X-ray Fish, Water Goldfinch); above ♂, centre ♀, natural size. (Original)
Fig. 158. *Prochilodus insignis;* half-grown fish, natural size. (Original)

Plate 25

Plate 26

Plate 26

Fig. 159. *Thayeria obliquua* (Penguin Fish); fine ripe adults, natural size; above ♀, below ♂♂. (Original)

Fig. 160. *Hemigrammus pulcher* (Pretty Tetra); adults, somewhat enlarged. (Original)

Fig. 161. *Hemigrammus armstrongi* (Golden Tetra); adults, somewhat enlarged. (Original)

and Ahl:—grey-green, shining silver by reflected light. Behind the gill-cover an irregular and not always distinct shoulder-blotch, immediately followed by a further smaller, darker, pale-bordered blotch. A shining silver band extends from the edge of the gill-cover to the dark root of the tail. Fins clear grey; anal base blackish.

Sex-distinctions not known; however, the ♀ may probably be distinguished by the more strongly convex profile of the belly. Care, as for *Hemigrammus* above.

Probably not yet bred in captivity. 1928/—.

Hyphessobrycon maculicauda *E. Ahl* 1936 (Fig. 142)   Tail-spot Tetra
Central Brazil; to 5 cm.

D 11; A 31; LL 32, 6 pierced; TR 6½–7/5½. Shape similar to that of *Hyphessobrycon pulchripinnis*. Coloration, according to Arnold:—upperside olive-brown, flanks delicate yellow-green, underside yellowish-grey. Characteristic of this species is a large, round, pale-bordered dark blotch at the root of the tail. Caudal fin brilliant red, all other fins pale reddish.

Sex-distinctions not known.

Care of this species, which has only once been imported, as for *Hemigrammus* above. Not yet bred in captivity. 1934/—.

Hyphessobrycon metae *Eigenmann* and *Henn* 1914   Loreto Tetra
Meta R., Loreto district in the Peruvian part of the Amazon; to 4·5 cm.

D 11; A 19–23; LL 30–36, 7 pierced; TR 5–6/4–3. Shape similar to that of the Neon Tetra *(H. innesi)*. Coloration of freshly-killed fishes preserved in formalin, according to Ladiges:—back pale brownish-yellow with dark edges to the scales; belly white. Shoulder-blotch only faintly indicated. Under the dorsal fin there begins quite abruptly a bold, dark longitudinal band which extends back into the lower half of a centrally positioned spot at the root of the tail. Gill-cover with a strong metallic shine. Dorsal fin of ♂ with a broad yellow centre, base colourless, tip white; adipose fin yellow; caudal fin shining orange-red, tips of the fin-lobes colourless; anal fin concave, in the ♂ milk-white anteriorly with a round yellow spot. Eyes silvery.

Arnold (*Wochenschrift für Aquarien- und Terrarienkunde*, 1938, p. 645) gives the following description of the living fishes:–Back grey-green to brown, belly grey-white. From the hind edge of the eye to the base of the caudal fin extends a slender, shining, grey-green to copper-coloured band, ventrally with a very broad blue-black region from the gill-cover to the root of the tail. Caudal fin brick-red; all other fins reddish with the exception of the pectorals; anal with a black edge and white inner margin. Iris yellow above, green below.

♀ dorsal fin with two yellow spots; profile of belly more strongly convex.

Care, as for *Hemigrammus* above. Not yet successfully bred in captivity. 1938/–.

Hyphessobrycon minimus *Durbin* 1909 (Fig. 152)   Dwarf Tetra
Guiana and lower Amazon basin; to 2·5 cm.

D 11; A 16–17; LL 30–33, 5–8 pierced; TR 5/3. Shape similar to that of *H. heterorhabdus*. Coloration, according to Arnold and Ahl:–delicate yellowish-green to grey; a bluish iridescence on the gill-cover and flanks by reflected light. Scales on the upper half of the body dark-edged. Shoulder-blotch absent. A narrow longitudinal band, becoming broader posteriorly, extends from the hinder edge of the gill-cover to a dark, round spot on the tail. Fins colourless, transparent.

Sex-distinctions not known. Profile of ♀ belly probably more strongly convex.

Care, as for *Hemigrammus* above. Not yet bred in captivity. 1932/–.

Hyphessobrycon nigrifrons *E. Ahl* 1936 (Fig. 154)   Black-crowned Tetra
Lower Amazon R.; to 6 cm.

D 9; A 18; LL 33, 6–8 pierced, TR 5½/4. Shape similar to that of *H. pulchripinnis*. Upperside delicate brownish to olive-coloured. Flanks very pale, somewhat silvery or, depending on lighting, bluish to greenish. Underside silvery white. On the top of the head a pale brown to deep black spot edged with gold. Root of tail with a large dark blotch with a narrow, brightly shining row of scales running forward from it. Fins delicate yellowish, dorsal and anal with white tips, the latter with a dark leading-edge. Eye yellowish.

The ♀ can only be recognised by the more strongly convex profile of the belly.

Care of this only rarely imported species, as for *Hemigrammus* above. Not yet bred in captivity. 1933/+.

Hyphessobrycon ornatus *E. Ahl* 1934 (Fig. 76)
Lower Amazon, Guiana; to 4 cm.

D 11; A 26–27; LL 33–34, 5–6 pierced; TR 5–6/3–4. Olive-yellow strongly tinged with carmine-red (especially in healthy individuals). Shoulder-blotch absent. The dorsal fin, especially in older ♂♂, may be drawn out into a sickle-shape, with a large, irregular, deep black blotch; tip and leading-edge white. Caudal fin yellowish with more or less reddish tones and a bright red area in the centre of each lobe. Anal fin yellowish-red with a black, white-bordered tip. The leading-edges of the yellowish ventral fins are likewise white.

♀ body robust; dorsal fin not drawn out.
♂ slim; dorsal fin drawn out, sickle-shaped.

Care and breeding, as for *Hemigrammus* above. Breeding is not very easy as not every ♂ seems to be capable of impregnation. Eggs brown-red. 1933/+.

Hyphessobrycon peruvianus *Ladiges* 1938 (Fig. 164)
Near Iquitos in the Peruvian part of the Amazon; to 4 cm.

D 11; A 22–24; LL 34–35, 8–9 pierced; TR 5–6/3. Shape similar to that of the Neon Tetra. Back grey-green to brown with a greenish lustre. From the hinder edge of the eye to the root of the caudal fin runs a thin, shining, green-yellow to copper-coloured line; this is ventrally bounded by a broad blue-black zone reaching down towards the whitish belly and extending from the tip of the snout over the lower part of the eye as far back as the root of the tail. Caudal fin brick-red; all other fins, with the exception of the pectorals, reddish. Anal fin with whitish outer and blackish inner margins. Eye large; iris orange above, dark below.

♀ more robust; swim-bladder, seen against the light, only partly visible.
♂ slimmer; swim-bladder, seen against the light, completely visible.

Care and breeding, as for *Hemigrammus* above. A very beautiful Characin. 1938/+.

Hyphessobrycon pulchripinnis *E. Ahl* 1937 (Fig. 124)   Lemon Tetra
(This species is sometimes incorrectly called *Hemigrammus erythrophthalmus*.)
South America, precise locality unknown; to 5 cm.

D 10; A 26–27; LL 32–33, 5–6 pierced; TR 10 between D and V. The body of this species is glass-clear, of a light yellowish tint throughout. Back brownish to greenish. Flanks silvery; a shining longitudinal band is scarcely recognisable. Anal fin yellowish, the first rays bright yellow, the remainder deep black, lower fin-edge black. Dorsal fin occasionally also black, more often with only a black tip. Eyes large, upper half of iris brilliant blood-red.

135

♀ anal fin without, or with only a very faint, black margin below.
♂ anal fin with a broad black margin.

Care and breeding, as for *Hemigrammus* above. Breeding is not very easy; the ♀ frequently becomes spawn-bound. 1932/+.

Hyphessobrycon reticulatus *Ellis* 1911 (Fig. 155)   Netted Tetra
La Plata basin; to 6 cm.

D 11; A 18–21; LL 31–34, 5–7 pierced; TR 6–7/4–5. Shape similar to that of the well-known *Hyphessobrycon pulchripinnis*. Coloration, according to Arnold and Ahl:–back grey-green, flanks yellow-green, belly yellowish with a bluish lustre. All scales dark-edged (body with a dark network). Shoulder-blotch dark, almost triangular. At the level of the dorsal fin a thin, dark longitudinal band commences which extends to a black, gold-edged blotch at the root of the tail. Vertical fins yellowish to orange, paired fins colourless.

Care, as for *Hemigrammus* above. This species, according to Arnold, is very resistant to low temperatures (15°C.), but also pugnacious and snappy. Only a single specimen so far imported. 1932/–.

Hyphessobrycon rosaceus *Durbin* 1909 (Fig. 168)   Rosy Tetra, Black-flag Tetra
(For classification and nomenclature, see p. 139.)
Western Guiana, Gluck Island in the Essequibo; to 4 cm.

D 11; A 26–27; LL 31–33, 6–7 pierced; TR 5/3. Shape similar to that of the better-known *Hyphessobrycon ornatus*. Not many fishes in the aquarium world have so many vague ideas associated with them as the Rosy Tetra whose very name, even, is forever being given to related species. Even Rachow (see Holly, Meinken and Rachow, *Deutsche Aquarien- und Terrarien-Zeitschrift*, Jg. 3, p. 19, 1950) will lay stress on providing a shoulder-blotch for his Rosy Tetra, and that despite the fact that the original description stresses the absence of a shoulder-blotch as being a diagnostic character of the species. The species described by

Plate 2?

Fig. 162. *Hemigrammus ocellifer* (Beacon Fish, Head-and-tail-Light Fish); young, somewhat enlarged. (Original)

Fig. 163. *Hyphessobrycon scholzei* (Scholze's Tetra, Black-line Tetra); young, somewhat enlarged. (Original)

Fig. 164. *Hyphessobrycon peruvianus;* ripe ♀, enlarged. (Original)

Plate 27

Plate 28

Plate 28

Fig.165. *Hasemania marginata;* ripe adults, somewhat enlarged. (Original)
Fig.166. *Hemigrammus rhodostomus* (Red- or Rummy-nosed Tetra); young, enlarged. (Photo Dr. Foersch)

Rachow may possibly have been *Hyphessobrycon copelandi.* As regards colouring the Rosy Tetra and *H.ornatus* are very similar; however, in the Rosy Tetra the dorsal fin of the ♂ is not elongated and the red spot on the caudal fin is lacking. The eggs are said not to be brown but on the contrary more yellowish. (Data according to Friesel, British Guiana.)

Care, as for *Hemigrammus* above. Probably not yet bred in Europe. In view of the constant confusion with *H.ornatus* and *H.serpae* the date of the first importation cannot be precisely ascertained.

Fig.167
Hyphessobrycon rubrostigma; natural size

Hyphessobrycon rubrostigma *Hoedeman* 1956 (Fig.167)
Colombia; to 3·5 cm.

D 11–12; A 29–32; LL 32; TR 11–12. Shape similar to that of *Hyphessobrycon ornatus,* i.e., body strongly compressed and relatively deep. Upper half of body delicate grey-green to brownish, with a light red bloom. Lower half of body reddish-silver, throat and belly region orange coloured. A large blood-red, pearly-margined spot on the middle of the flank on a level with the origin of the dorsal fin. Dorsal fin red with a wide, black, white-edged stripe along the anterior rays. A vertical black streak across the eye. The colouring of this species is strongly reminiscent of that of the Blood Characins (see p. 139) and it may, as Hoedeman suggests, be

137

no more than a subspecies of the *Callistus* group (see pp. 139–140). A very beautiful species.

Care and breeding, about as for *Hemigrammus* above. 1956

Hyphessobrycon scholzei *E. Ahl* 1936 (Fig. 163)   Scholze's Tetra, Black-line Tetra
Neighbourhood of Pará; to 5 cm.

D 11; A 25–26; LL 32–33. Back olive-green to brownish; flanks bluish-silver, with brassy reflexions by reflected light; belly silver; gill-cover with a golden gleam. Iris yellow. A black longitudinal stripe runs from the gill-cover to terminate in a lozenge-shaped blotch at the root of the tail and is accompanied along its upper edge by a shining metallic line. Pectoral fins colourless; all other fins light reddish; anal fin with a black leading-edge.

♀ more stocky, larger.
♂ slimmer, caudal fin more deeply forked.

Care and breeeding, as for *Hemigrammus* above; easy to breed. 1936/+.

Hyphessobrycon serpae *Durbin* 1908 (Figs. 76, 125, 168)
(For classification and nomenclature, see p. 139.)
Middle Amazon, southwards to Paraguay; to 4·5 cm.

D 10–11; A 25–30; LL 29–31, 5–6 pierced; TR 5/3½. Very variable in coloration and markings. Back dark olive; flanks grey-green; belly region yellowish with an iridescent lustre. The hinder part of the body becomes blood-red when the fish is excited. Shoulder-blotch indistinct. A narrow line, usually hardly visible, extends along the side of the body and broadens posteriorly. Dorsal fin clear at the base, occasionally somewhat milky; centre black, tip white. Anal fin red with a delicate black margin and a white tip. Caudal and ventral fins red.

♀ somewhat paler in colour.
♂ with especially prominent strong red tones.

Care and breeding, as for *Hemigrammus* above. 1924/+.

Recently a blood-red variety of the last-named species, lacking a shoulder-blotch or with only a very small one, has been wrongly given the name *minor* (Fig. 125). The fishes distributed in Europe under the name 'Serpasalmler' (Serpa Characins) belong not only to the species *Hyphessobrycon serpae* Durbin 1908, however, but also to *Hyphessobrycon callistus* Durbin 1908, which is almost identical in coloration. The latter, however, is distinguished from the true *H. serpae* by the very elongate, intense black shoulder-blotch, by the broad extension of the black centre of the dorsal fin almost to the tip, and by the broad black margin of the anal fin, especially in the hinder part (Fig. 168). Quite possibly these two species have hybridised in captivity.

The species *H. bentosi, serpae, callistus, copelandi, minor* (the last, according to Ladiges, also not yet imported), *rosaceus* and *ornatus*, which Pinter collectively terms 'Blutsalmler' (Blood Characins), have received especial systematic interest for some time past on account of their close similarity. Attempts have not been lacking to perceive, in the division of the species, subspecies which have arisen from a common stem-form through geographical isolation (see Hoedeman, *Die Aquarien- und Terrarien-Zeitschrift*, Jg. 7, p. 109, 1954).

Assuming these suggestions of Hoedeman's to be established, the classification of the Blood Characins would appear as follows:–

Hyphessobrycon bentosi	= *Hyphessobrycon callistus bentosi*
Hyphessobrycon serpae	= *Hyphessobrycon callistus serpae*
Hyphessobrycon callistus	= *Hyphessobrycon callistus callistus*
Hyphessobrycon copelandi	= *Hyphessobrycon callistus copelandi*
Hyphessobrycon minor	= *Hyphessobrycon callistus minor*
Hyphessobrycon rosaceus	= *Hyphessobrycon callistus rosaceus*

In this matter I agree with Pinter (1955) that *Hyphessobrycon ornatus* must obviously be removed from this series in any case as a clearly distinct, well-differentiated species. I cannot agree with the suggestion that all the Serpa Characins in Europe at present belong to *H. callistus callistus*. We often find, for example, in an individual brood, fishes with typical shoulder-blotches side by side with others in which they are very faint or completely lacking, and further displaying very considerable variation in the black of the dorsal fin, a phenomenon which points either to extreme variability in these characters or to the occurrence of hybridisation. Likewise it may perhaps be desirable to undertake further investigations with regard to the so-called *minor* (Ladiges, *Wochenschrift für Aquarien- und Terrarienkunde*, 1950, p. 39).

Hasemania marginata *Meinken* 1938 (Fig. 165)
Hasemania is distinguished from the very closely related *Hyphessobrycon* by little more than the absence of an adipose fin.

South-east Brazil; to 4 cm.

D 11; A 16; LL 32, 5 pierced. Body moderately elongate, strongly compressed. Yellowish-olive. Gill-cover and flanks shining silver, sometimes with a bluish

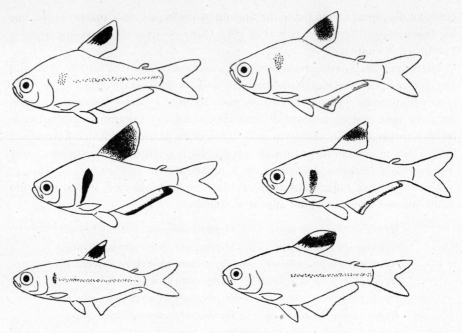

Fig. 168

Comparison of the forms which, according to Hoedeman, may possibly be merely sub-species of *Hyphessobrycon callistus* (after Hoedeman).

H. bentosi	*H. serpae*
H. callistus	*H. copelandi*
H. minor	*H. rosaceus*

sheen; belly white; scales dark-edged. A silver longitudinal band commences at the level of the pectoral fin and extends to the root of the tail. The yellowish to golden base of the caudal fin is divided into two fields by a dark band which begins on the caudal peduncle and there overlies the silvery band. Dorsal, anal and caudal fins deep brown with a porcelain-white margin; pectoral and ventral fins yellowish-white. Iris silvery.

♀ body more stocky; somewhat paler.

♂ slimmer; a beautiful copper-colour at spawning time.

Care and breeding, as for *Hemigrammus* above. This very beautiful and lively species exhibits its finest colouring only after a lengthy period of acclimatisation.

140

The fishes spawn among plants and are arrant spawn-robbers. Eggs brownish. 1937/+.

Hollandichthys multifasciatus (*Eigenmann* and *Norris* 1900) (Fig. 182)
South-east Brazil, widely distributed; to 12 cm.

D 11; A 28–31; LL 40; TR 5–6/3. Body spindle-shaped, compressed. Mouth large, upwardly directed. Adipose fin present. Scales on the flanks large. Upperside dark- or olive-brown; flanks light clay-yellow or grey-yellow with dusky to black zig-zag boundary lines between the longitudinal rows of scales. Underside white, often with a reddish lustre. Throat yellowish. Shoulder-blotch usually well-marked only in the young. Fins delicate grey-brown or clay-yellow; at the breeding season more or less bright orange-coloured. Dorsal fin with an indistinct dark blotch. Adipose fin, in fine fishes, intense orange rimmed with black. A dark transverse band over the eye.

♀ generally easily recognised by the convex profile of the belly.
♂ with anterior part of anal fin produced in a semicircle.

Care. A beautiful, lively, but unfortunately rather unsociable and snappy species which should be kept in large, unshaded and not too thickly planted aquaria; a warm, open-air position is best of all. Temperature 16–23 °C. Omnivorous, with a preference for smaller fish. The species has apparently not yet been bred in captivity. 1906/–.

Genus Astyanax: Care and Breeding

The genus *Astyanax*, which includes numerous species (about 75), is widely distributed from New Mexico and Arizona (USA) over the whole of Central America to Patagonia. Here belong small fishes of more or less elongate, fairly strongly-compressed shape. The upper and lower profiles are almost equally convex. Adipose fin present. Caudal fin deeply emarginate, anal with a long base. From the similarly-shaped genera *Hemigrammus* and *Hyphessobrycon* the species of *Astyanax* are distinguished mainly by the complete lateral line. The fishes inhabit very diverse types of water; many species are found from the mountainous headwaters right down to the estuary of the same river. The largest species, *A.maximus*, in Peru grows to 20 cm.

The care of the very lively and hardy *Astyanax* spp. presents few difficulties provided they are allowed sufficient space to cater for their urge for movement. Large, unshaded aquaria with moderate planting or loosely-hanging root-systems and a sandy bottom fulfil almost all their needs. Soft to medium-hard water; most of the species have no special requirements. The preferred temperatures of the various *Astyanax* spp. are very diverse in correspondence with their wide distribution; in general even quite wide fluctuations do no harm. The usual live-foods are willingly accepted throughout; some species will eat dried foods as well, and plant materials. (In the last instance supplementary lettuce may be fed.) Most of the species are relatively peaceful and make good community fishes.

Breeding easy. After vigorous driving the weakly-adhesive eggs are laid at random among plants, also in the open water. The young hatch after 24 to 36 hours and swim freely after about 5 days. Rearing is easy. Very prolific fishes. Brassy-coloured *Astyanax* produce only predominantly silvery offspring in the first generation bred in captivity. Descriptions of individual species are according to Eigenmann (The American Characidae, *Mem. Mus. Comp. Zool.*, XLIII/1–4, 1917–27).

Astyanax bimaculatus (*Linnaeus* 1758) (Fig. 169)   Two-spot Astyanax
Widely distributed through north-eastern and eastern South America, southward to the La Plata basin; to 15 cm.

D 11; A 21–43; LL 31–45; TR 6–8/5–7. Body-shape typical of genus, irregularly elliptical, becoming deeper with age. The wide distribution of this species has led

Figs. 169–171

Fig. 169. *Astyanax bimaculatus* (Two-spot Astyanax); adult, somewhat reduced.
Fig. 170. *Astyanax fasciatus fasciatus* (Banded Astyanax); adult, somewhat reduced.
Fig. 171. *Astyanax fasciatus jequitinhonhae;* adult.

(All figures on this page re-drawn, after Eigenmann)

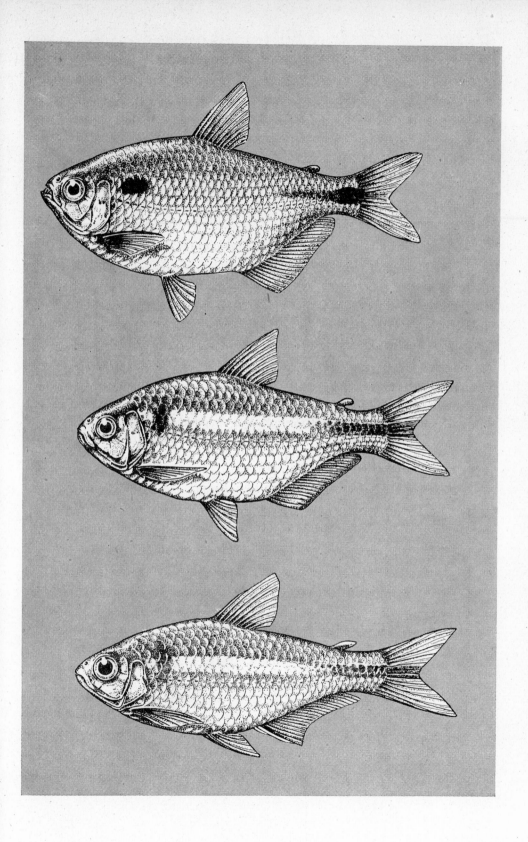

to the formation of several races and numerous colour-variants. The typical coloration is silvery or light brass-coloured; upperside olive-coloured. Behind the gill-cover and above the lateral line is an elongate-oval black blotch which is often surrounded by a pale zone. A second dark blotch at the root of the tail is often produced as a triangle on the middle rays of the caudal fin; occasionally a similar forward prolongation is exhibited. Behind the shoulder-blotch there is sometimes a blackish transverse mark. Fins colourless; anal and caudal fins of older ♂♂ often yellowish to faint reddish.

♀ considerably more robust when sexually mature.

Care, as given on p.141. Apparently not yet bred in captivity. Preferred temperature 19–24°C. 1907/ –.

Astyanax fasciatus fasciatus (*Cuvier* 1819) (Fig. 170)   Banded Astyanax
Very widely distributed, from Central America and the West Indies as far as the Argentine; common everywhere; to 17 cm.

Typical form (Fig. 170) from the Rio San Francisco and the Paraná.

D 11; A 25–34; LL 34–41; TR 7/6–7. Body gleaming silver to brassy; upperside olive-brown. Shoulder-blotch transversely placed and very weakly developed (in life often not apparent). A dull greenish-silver longitudinal band becomes blackish on the caudal peduncle and is rather broadly produced on the middle caudal rays. Fins delicate yellowish, according to Arnold also reddish (?). Anal fin often faintly dark on the free edge; leading-edge and tip usually milky-white. Specimens from the Rio Novo have black-edged caudal and anal fins and a spotted dorsal.

Astyanax fasciatus jequitinhonhae (*Steindachner* 1876) (Fig. 171)
Eastern Brazil.

D 11; A 25–30, usually 28; LL 34–37, usually 36. Shape similar to the foregoing species but somewhat more elongate. Eye large. Markings and coloration likewise similar but shoulder-blotch usually distinct. According to Arnold the body is

Plate 29

(These photographs have been considerably re-touched on account of shadows)

Fig. 172. *Ctenobrycon spilurus* (Silver Tetra); adults, somewhat reduced. (Original)
Fig. 173. *Anoptichthys jordani* (Blind Cave-fish); young, somewhat enlarged. (Original)
Fig. 174. *Hemigrammus* sp. (the so-called 'Neon Costello' or 'Green Neon'); young, somewhat enlarged. (Original)

Plate 29

Plate 30

Plate 30

Fig. 175. *Mimagoniates inaequalis* (Croaking Tetra); above ♂, below ♀, somewhat enlarged. (Original)

Fig. 176. *Microbrycon cochui* (?); above ♀, below ♂, about twice natural size. (Original)

Fig. 177. *Ephippicharax orbicularis;* young ♀, natural size. (Original)

bright brass-coloured and, except for the dull silvery longitudinal band, takes on a dark colouring immediately behind the shoulder-blotch (?). Fins colourless; the first two rays of the anal fin are usually white.

Astyanax fasciatus macrophthalmus *Regan* 1908 (Fig. 178)
Southern Mexico.

D 11; A 26–31; LL 37–38. Eye very large; the interocular width is distinctly smaller than the diameter of the eye. Similarly marked and coloured to the typical form, but the dark colour of the lateral band in this case begins at the level of the dorsal fin. Shoulder-blotch distinct.

The figure identified as *A. fasciatus jequitinhonhae* in Arnold and Ahl (1936, p. 48) represents a typical example of the subspecies *macrophthalmus.*

As well as the subspecies mentioned here there is a whole series more, which have not yet been imported. Furthermore, every now and again one or other species of *Astyanax* is regarded as a subspecies of *A. fasciatus;* the grouping given here is that of Eigenmann 1917–29 (The American Characidae, *Mem. Mus. Comp. Zool.* XLIII/1–4).

Care and breeding, as given on p. 141. Temperature 19–24°C.

Astyanax mexicanus (*Filippi* 1853) = *Astyanax fasciatus mexicanus* (?) (Fig. 179)
Texas to Panama; to 8 cm.

D 11; A 22–25, usually 24; LL 35–40. Body typical of the genus but somewhat more club-shaped and slimmer. Overall silvery to pale brassy-coloured. Upperside olive. At the level of the origin of the anal fin the very indistinct dull greenish-silver longitudinal zone takes on a dusky colour. Caudal blotch round, bordered in front and behind with pale yellow. Middle rays of anal fin black. Fins yellowish to pale reddish. Anal with a white anterior tip.

♀ more robust when sexually mature.

Care and breeding, as given on p. 141. Preferred temperature 18–24°C. 1913/−.

145

Astyanax poetzschkei *E. Ahl* 1932 (Fig. 180)
Eastern Brazil and Amazon R.; to 10 cm.

D 11; A 32; LL 45; TR 9/8. Shape similar to *A. bimaculatus* but somewhat slimmer. Coloration, according to E. Ahl: in general bright gleaming silver; back yellowish-brown. Shoulder-blotch at the most quite weakly indicated. A blotch at the root of the caudal fin is completely lacking. Fins colourless.

Sex-distinctions probably as in *A. bimaculatus.*

Care, as given on p. 141. Preferred temperature 22–24°C. The species is said to eat plants *(Vallisneria)*! 1917 (?)/ – .

Astyanax ruberrimus *Eigenmann* 1913 (Fig. 181)
Panama and Pacific slope of Colombia; to 12·5 cm.

D 11; A 23–28; LL 35–36. In body-form very similar to *A. bimaculatus.* Upperside fawn; flanks and belly silvery with yellow-green, often also delicate reddish or red-brown, sheen. At the level of the dorsal fin begins a dark longitudinal band which is crossed on the caudal peduncle by a transversely elongate blotch; the angles of the cross are light yellow. Longitudinal band not produced onto the middle rays of the caudal fin. Shoulder-blotch very slightly indicated, often absent. Base of dorsal fin and middle part of anal fin yellowish; outer parts of these fins, as well as the anal fin, brown-red to brick-red.

♀ more robust; fins yellowish.
♂ fins as described above.

Care and breeding of this very delightful species, as given on p. 141. Preferred temperature 20–24°C. 1934/ – .

Anoptichthys jordani *Hubbs* and *Innes* 1938 (Fig. 173)   Blind Cave-fish
Subterranean streams and pools near San Luis Potosi in Mexico; to 8 cm.

D 11; A 22–23; LL 37–39. *A. jordani* is similar in shape to *Astyanax fasciatus* (see p. 144), from whose Mexican subspecies *A. f. mexicanus* it has been directly derived.

Figs. 178–181

Fig. 178. *Astyanax fasciatus macrophthalmus;* somewhat reduced.
Fig. 179. *Astyanax mexicanus;* adult, somewhat reduced.
Fig. 180. *Astyanax poetzschkei;* adult, natural size.
Fig. 181. *Astyanax ruberrimus;* adult, reduced.

(Fig. 178 re-drawn, after Eigenmann)

This Characin is one of the few true cave-fishes. The eyes and orbits are vestigial and partly overgrown by skin. The young possess eyes which are small but normally functional. Orientation in space and perception of food in blind animals are accomplished exclusively through heightened senses of touch and smell; the former is here mainly localised in the well-developed lateral line.

Uniform flesh-colour with a strong silver sheen. Fins colourless to light reddish. Young fishes display a lozenge-shaped blotch on the caudal peduncle.

♀ more robust and bulky, usually somewhat more delicately coloured.
♂ slimmer.

A very interesting species. Provide a large tank with flat pebbles (the kind used for playing 'ducks and drakes') on the bottom. Although it lives as a cave-fish it is not absolutely necessary to keep it in darkness. Temperature 18–23 °C. Takes all kinds of food eagerly. The fishes usually swim restlessly about, in a slightly head-down position as though snuffling over the bottom. For breeding use clear, soft water, reasonably free of bacteria; temperature 18–20 °C. When mating the partners press their bodies together in the usual Characin fashion, ending in this position at the surface of the water where they expel the eggs and milt (according to Lüling). The sperm are said to be very long-lived. The young hatch after 3–4 days and swim freely on the 6th. On a diet of nauplii they grow very rapidly. 1949.

Opisthanodus haerteli *E. Ahl* 1935
Middle Amazon R.; maximum size unknown, imported specimens to 4 cm.

D 10; A 26–27; LL 34–35; TR 8/5–6. The genus *Opisthanodus* is closely related to *Astyanax* and is only distinguished by certain peculiarities of dentition. Body *Astyanax*-like. Origin of dorsal somewhat closer to the tip of the snout than to the root of the caudal fin; its hinder edge is produced, sickle-shaped, and its longest ray is nearly as long as the depth of the body. Caudal fin deeply forked. Back moss-green with metallic sheen, flanks bluish-silver, belly white. The lower part of the

Figs. 182–187

Fig. 182. *Hollandichthys multifasciatus;* adult, reduced.
Fig. 183. *Creagrutus beni* (Gold-striped Characin); natural size.
Fig. 184. *Hemibrycon guppyi* (Guppy's Characin); adult, somewhat reduced.
Fig. 185. *Hemibrycon taeniurus;* somewhat reduced.
Fig. 186. *Creatochanes affinis* (Orange-finned Characin); adult, somewhat reduced.
Fig. 187. *Creatochanes caudomaculatus;* adult, somewhat reduced.

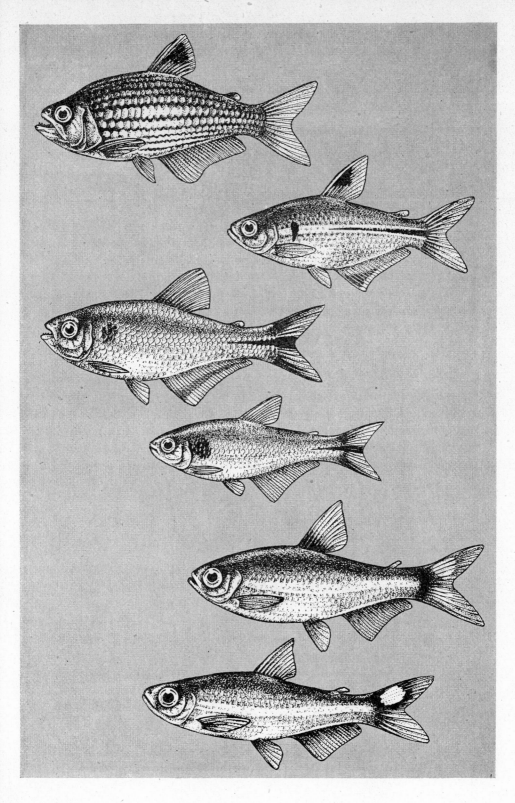

caudal peduncle has a strong violet and bluish iridescence. All fins pale, transparent; tip of anal blackish. Eye large; iris yellow, somewhat red posteriorly.

♂ dorsal fin substantially higher.

Care, as given for *Hemigrammus* above, p. 116. Breeding unknown. 1934/−.

Ctenobrycon spilurus (*Cuvier* and *Valenciennes* 1848) (Fig. 172)   Silver Tetra
Northern South America, in coastal districts; to 8 cm.

D 11; A 41–45; LL 41–50; TR 11–12/7–10. Body deep, strongly compressed. Ground-colour olive-green; flanks and belly pale with a bright bluish-silver lustre. From a large gleaming blue-black shoulder-blotch a shining green band extends to the root of the tail where it ends in a large shining metallic blue-black blotch which often covers the whole root. Gill-cover iridescent green. Dorsal and adipose fins yellow-green; caudal grey with a yellowish margin; anal fin long, low, lemon-yellow, often with a pale red border.

♀ ventral keel somewhat more strongly convex; generally paler in colour.
♂ coloration as above.

Care: provide a large, well-planted tank. Temperature 23–28 °C.; tolerates a temporary fall in temperature quite well and, what is more, is a contented inhabitant of unheated room-aquaria. Omnivorous, an eager feeder. Breeding easy. The eggs are shed after wild courtship among water plants. At a temperature of 26 °C. the young hatch after 24 hours and grow very rapidly. A very prolific species. 1912/+.

Creagrutus beni *Eigenmann* 1911 (Fig. 183)   Gold-striped Characin
Region of the upper Amazon and further northwards to Venezuela, but also in southern Brazil; to 8·5 cm.

D 10; A 11–13; LL 35–40; TR 4/3. Body moderately elongate, laterally flattened. Adipose fin present. Very variable in coloration in correspondence with its wide distribution. Upperside pale brown; flanks delicate lemon-yellow with a broad, shining, brilliant red-gold longitudinal band which extends to the root of the tail and, from about the level of the dorsal fin onwards, becomes divided into two lines by an intervening dark brown or deep black stripe. Shoulder-blotch dark, usually prominent. Dorsal fin with a pale leading-edge and triangular black blotch, yellow-red to red. Upper lobe of caudal reddish, lower yellowish. Anterior part of anal red, fin with pale border.

150

♀ more intensely and contrastingly coloured.

♂ dull; fins often merely yellowish.

Care of this attractive and peaceful species is similar to that described for *Hemigrammus* above, p. 116. Reproduction is interesting in that the eggs are not fertilised freely in the water but in the maternal oviducts. The sperm transferred to the ♀ is stored for some time so that at the actual spawning the presence of the ♂ is unnecessary. A spawning produces about 50–70 eggs, which the ♀ prefers to deposit on water plants. The young hatch in 24–28 hours (at 26 °C.). 1932/+.

Hemibrycon guppyi (*Regan* 1906) (Fig. 184)   Guppy's Characin
Trinidad, in clear brooks; to 10 cm.

D 10; A 28–32; LL 38–40; TR 7/5. Body elongate, compressed. Lateral line complete. The middle rays of the caudal fin are black, as in all *Hemibrycon* spp. Almost uniformly silver with a yellow or yellowish-green lustre. Shoulder-blotch usually inconspicuous and as a rule no better developed in older fishes. Upper and lower lobes of the caudal fin dark, the black middle region continuing as a stripe which diminishes anteriorly. Anal fin with a brownish margin.

Sex-distinctions in colouring cannot be given with certainty; however, the ♀♀ are easily distinguished by the more strongly convex profile of the belly.

Keep this very peaceful species in large aquaria with plenty of room to swim about and not too soft water. Temperature 17–23 °C. Live food, especially insect-larvae. Not yet bred in captivity. 1913/−.

Hemibrycon taeniurus (*Gill* 1858) (Fig. 185)
Trinidad (northern South America ?); to 7 cm.

D 10; A 29–31; LL 37–39. Very similar to the foregoing species in shape, markings and coloration. *H. taeniurus*, however, is more green-blue-silvery when in a healthy condition. An intense blue-green shining spot behind the gill-cover. The anal fin lacks a pale brownish margin.

Care and sex-distinctions, as given for the previous species. *H. taeniurus* has been repeatedly bred. The eggs are laid among water plants and are not delicate. The young hatch after 24–30 hours. 1911/−.

Creatochanes affinis (*Günther* 1864) (Fig. 186)   Orange-finned Characin
Widely distributed in South America, Guiana, Amazon basin, Paraguay; to 12 cm.

D 11; A 26–29; LL 44–47; TR 7/2½–3. Body spindle-shaped, hardly compressed. Lateral line complete, downcurved. Coloration of young fishes:–upper-

151

side brown to grey-brown; flanks bluish-grey above, lower down greenish with a silvery lustre. A broad, shining stripe, often with a rainbow iridescence, extends from the gill-cover to the root of the tail, which has a dark transverse band. Underside yellowish- to whitish-silver. Dorsal fin orange- to dark red near the body, rest yellow. Base of caudal fin yellow; upper lobe, and sometimes both lobes, blackish. Anal fin and paired fins opaque brownish, yellowish or light grey-green. Eye very large, orange-coloured. Even the metallic colours pale with age to a uniform silver-grey or brownish tone.

Sexes not easily distinguished. In ♂♂ the lobes of the caudal fin may taper to a point.

This species, which is very gaily-coloured and active in youth, but also predatory, does very well in captivity. Unfortunately even members of the same species are rather pugnacious with one another so that solitary confinement is practically essential. Temperature 22–26°C. Live food of all kinds, particularly smaller fishes. Not yet bred in captivity. 1913/ + .

Creatochanes caudomaculatus (*Günther* 1864) (Fig. 187)
Guiana, middle Amazon basin, at medium heights in Colombia; to 13 cm.

D 11; A (28)–31; LL about 45. Shape and colour similar to the foregoing species, but distinguished by the length of the pectoral fins which here reach to the origin of the ventrals (shorter in *C. affinis*), and the very distinct black-rimmed ocellus in the upper lobe of the caudal fin; according to Arnold this ocellus is golden yellow in youth and becomes brick-red with age. Lower lobe of caudal faintly blackish.

Sex-distinctions, care and breeding, as for the previous species. 1933/ − .

Phenacogaster suborbitalis *E. Ahl* 1936 (Fig. 194)
Eastern Brazil, in small coastal streams; to 7 cm.

D 11; A 37; LL 39–40; TR 7/5. Body deep, strongly compressed. Adipose fin present. Lateral line complete, slightly curved downwards. Belly with two lateral ridges before ventral fins. Translucent delicate olive or grey-green with a strong silver sheen, often with a greenish to violet sheen on the flanks. Fins colourless; vertical fins in large ♂♂ yellowish to reddish. Eye very large, iris black.

♀ free edge of anal fin slightly concave.
♂ anterior part of anal fin enlarged into a lobe.

Care, as for *Hemigrammus* above, see p. 116. A peaceful, shoaling fish. Temperature 23–26°C. Omnivorous. Not yet bred in captivity. 1926/ − .

Mimagoniates inaequalis (*Eigenmann* 1911) (Fig. 175)   Croaking Tetra
(Formerly known as *Glandulocauda inaequalis;* however, *Glandulocauda* has now
been shown by Dr. L. P. Schultz to be a synonym of *Mimagoniates*.)
Porto Alegro, Rio Grande do Sul; ♂ to 6 cm., ♀ to 4·5 cm.

D 10; A 27–33; LL 38; TR 7/6. Body spindle-shaped, compressed. Dorsal fin
inserted far back. Adipose fin present. Lateral line incomplete, short (6–7).
Upperside olive-brown to dark brown; flanks bluish-white, shining a beautiful
green-blue by reflected light; underside silver-white. Shoulder-blotch drop-shaped,
light blue to metallic dark blue. At the level of the pectoral fins there begins
a light longitudinal band (accompanied by a light blue zone below) which becomes
denser and narrower posteriorly and is produced onto the caudal fin. Dorsal fin
with a colourless base, outside this greenish-blue or whitish-blue with a fawn
longitudinal band. Caudal fin yellowish, bordered above and below with dark. Anal
fin colourless with a clay-yellow longitudinal band.

♀ with symmetrical caudal fin, both lobes equal.
♂ with lower caudal lobe broader, obliquely truncate.

This lively, very contented and peaceful species is a very rewarding pet. Like
the representatives of all the related genera (*Gephyrocharax*, etc.) *M. inaequalis*
should be kept in a roomy, well-planted aquarium. Indirect sunlight, or sunlight
screened here and there by floating plants, is beneficial. Even at spawning time it
is not exacting in the matter of water-conditions but should not be kept at too high
a temperature: 19–23 °C. (no more!). Live food of all kinds, also occasional dried
food.

The eggs are fertilised in the oviduct of the ♀ (see also *Corynopoma riisei*, p. 156)
and are usually laid on the undersides of the leaves of water plants (up to 70 eggs
at a spawning). The young hatch after 24–30 hours. This species is also interesting
for its accessory breathing-organ, from which air can be expressed to produce long-
drawn-out grasshopper-noises which are distinctly audible. 1926/+.

Mimagoniates barberi *Regan* 1907 (Fig. 209)
Northern Argentine, Paraguay; to 4·5 cm.

D 10; A 30–34; LL 42–45. Nearly-related to the foregoing species. Body
elongate, compressed. Lateral line very short. Dorsal fin inserted far back. Upperside delicate to shining brownish-silver. Flanks light brownish-yellow, iridescent
dull bluish to greenish by reflected light, with a broad, deep-blue longitudinal
band which arises below the eye and extends into the lower caudal lobe; this band
is accompanied above by a narrow iridescent greenish to copper-red stripe.

153

Underside brown-yellow to yellowish. Gill-cover greenish. Fins delicate red-brown to yellow-brown. Dorsal fin often a pure red-yellow with a dark longitudinal band.

♀ dorsal fin rounded, caudal lobes almost equal.
♂ dorsal fin pennon-like, acute; lower caudal lobe distinctly broader.

Care and breeding, as for the foregoing species. *M. barberi* is rather sensitive and soft water is apparently indicated. Extraordinarily lively. The ♂♂ carry out peculiar courtship dances; in these the ♂ shoots up to the ♀, turns about and in an elegant arc closes the swum figure-of-eight, tirelessly repeating the same figure many times over. During the extraordinarily short pairing the ♂ lies across and encircles the ♀ and ejects a spermatophore into her cloaca. The spermatophore is taken up into the oviduct where it subsequently disintegrates and thus enables the ♀ to lay fertilised eggs at leisure without the presence of a ♂. It is therefore recommended that the ♀♀ be isolated after pairing. Egg-laying may take place several hours, days or even weeks after pairing and the ♀ then carefully sticks the eggs onto the undersides of leaves of small water plants. The young hatch after 24–30 hours and are not difficult to rear. However, *M. barberi* has not been very successfully propagated as yet. 1907/+.

Mimagoniates microlepis (*Steindachner* 1876) (Fig. 190)   Blue Tetra
Southern Brazil; to 7 cm.

D 10; A 30–34; LL 43–46. Yellowish-brown, shimmering bluish by reflected light. Along the flanks extends a very broad band, indistinct in its anterior part but showing a deep blue-black on the caudal peduncle, where it tapers to a point and is produced onto the middle rays of the caudal fin. Dorsal shining green with a distinct blue longitudinal band along the middle of the fin. Base of anal fin dark with a broad black band.

♀ anal fin without white margin; caudal lobes of equal size.
♂ anal fin with a white margin, shining greenish; lower caudal lobe broader.

Care and breeding, as for *M. inaequalis* above. This species, too, exhibits peculiar courtship dances during which the transmission of the spermatophore is attempted several times. 1907/+.

Gephyrocharax atracaudatus (*Meek* and *Hildebrand* 1912) (Fig. 195) Platinum Tetra
Panama Republic, with the exception of the Rio Chane; to 6 cm.

D 9; A 26–33; LL 37–43; TR 6/6. Body elongate, strongly compressed. Dorsal fin inserted far back. Lower supporting ray of caudal fin detached, spine-like in the ♂. Upperside delicate olive-green; flanks bluish with a whitish longitudinal stripe, bordered below with light blue; underside yellowish to white. Root of tail with a deep black blotch enclosing two gleaming vivid spots, the blotch extending into the fin like a forked tail. Fins colourless; ventrals in fine specimens sometimes light reddish.

♀ body more stocky; without a delicate spine under the caudal fin; free edge of anal fin straight.

♂ with small spine under caudal fin; free edge of anal fin slightly convex in the middle.

Care and breeding of this lively species, as for *M. inaequalis* above. 1933/−.

Gephyrocharax valencia *Eigenmann* 1920 (Fig. 196)
Lake Valencia, Venezuela; to 5 cm.

D 9; A 30–32; LL 40–43; TR 6–6½/5. Shape as in the foregoing species. Back olive- to blue-green; flanks and belly lighter with a strong silver sheen. Fins colourless or faintly yellowish. Dorsal fin with white upper margin and sometimes also with white fin-rays. Mouth edged with black. A very indistinct dark longitudinal band ends in a black blotch at the root of the caudal fin.

♀ with the edge of the anal fin evenly curved.
♂ with the edge of the anal fin lobed.

Care and breeding, as for *Mimagoniates inaequalis* above. 1932/−.

Microbrycon cochui *Ladiges* 1949 (Fig. 176)
Near Ramon Castillo on the upper Amazon; to 3·5 cm.

D 9; A 19–21; LL 35–36. Body club-shaped, compressed. Dorsal fin small. Upper lobe of caudal (according to Ladiges) somewhat larger. Translucent, delicate bluish-violet. Flanks with a slight, rather dull, silver sheen and a silvery blue longitudinal band which is accompanied from the level of the ventrals by a dark and usually very indistinct stripe. The gill-arches appear very dark through the gill-cover. Dorsal and anal fins dull orange, broadly edged with milky-white. Caudal fin blackish-orange, the two lobes with clear tips. The pale colours of this very beautiful species give the observer the impression of reflected moonlight.

♀ more robust; a dark lateral stripe is scarcely evident.
♂ slimmer; the dark lateral stripe is usually distinctly developed.

The sexes are further distinguished by peculiar structures in the region of the caudal and anal fins.

Care and breeding, as for *Mimagoniates inaequalis* above. This species, however, is somewhat more delicate and requires soft, slightly acid (peat-filtered) water. Temperature around 22–24°C. 1949.

Corynopoma riisei *Gill* 1858 (Fig. 189)   Swordtail Characin
Trinidad and northern Venezuela; to 7 cm.

D 9–11; A 24–30; LL 38–44; TR 6–7/5. A slimmer, daintier fish whose trunk is strongly compressed. Gill-cover in ♀ produced into a backwardly-directed spine; in ♂ distinguished by a long, movable spoon-shaped appendage extending as far as the anal fin. The lower part of the caudal fin and the dorsal are particularly long in the ♂. Translucent; by reflected light with a bronze to green-brown back and silvery belly. Fins colourless, at the most with a reddish tinge. A dark longitudinal band, present only in the young, is continued into a blackish-brown blotch at the root of the tail. Gill-cover appendage of ♂ porcelain-white in breeding season; during excitement the spoon-shaped end is deep black.

Care. An undemanding species; provide richly-planted tanks in full sunlight at 22–28°C. Live foods of all kinds. The reproductive biology is particularly interesting since fertilisation is internal and egg-laying considerably delayed.

Pairing is accompanied by a dainty love-play. The ♂ strokes the ♀ repeatedly with his gill-cover appendage, the end of which is now deep black with excitement. This black, slightly-quivering point must probably appear to the ♀ as a food-object, for she makes a lightning-quick dart for it. The ♂ uses this instant to reach the side of the ♀ partner. The sperms are not produced singly but are enclosed in a capsule (spermatophore) in the ♂ body which is transferred to the oviduct of the ♀ and there retained until the laying of the eggs. Once mated a ♀, even when she is kept alone, may spawn many times without the presence of the ♂; indeed, in most cases, the spermatophore lasts her whole lifetime. At each egg-laying some sperms escape

Plate 31

Fig. 188. *Alestes longipinnis* (Long-finned Characin); ripe adults, natural size; above ♂, below ♀. (Original)
Fig. 189. *Corynopoma riisei* (Swordtail Characin); adults, natural size; left ♂, right ♀. (Original)
Fig. 190. *Mimagoniates microlepis* (Blue Tetra); adults, natural size; left ♂, right ♀. (Original)

Plate 31

Plate 32

Plate 32

Fig. 191. *Prionobrama filigera* (Glass Bloodfish, Translucent Bloodfin); ripe adults, somewhat enlarged; left ♂, right ♀. (Original)

Fig. 192. *Pyrrhulina vittata* (Striped Pyrrhulina); ripe adults, natural size; left, below ♂, left, above and right, below ♀♀. (Original)

Fig. 193. *Copeina guttata* (Red-spotted Copeina); ripe adults, natural size; above ♂, below ♀. (Original)

from the reservoir container and fertilise the eggs while still in the oviduct. The young hatch after 20–36 hours and may be reared without difficulty. 1932/+.

Pseudocorynopoma doriae *Perugia* 1891 (Fig. 215)   Dragon-finned Characin
South Brazil and La Plata State; to 8 cm.

D 10–11; A 32–37; LL 40–43; TR 7/6. Body elongate, compressed. Throat and belly trenchant. Dorsal and anal fins in ♂ with considerable nipple-like prolongations. Adipose fin present. Uniformly olive-green to brownish-green; flanks and belly lighter, translucent. Light gleaming silver with steel-blue to greenish sheen by reflected light. Fins grey. Caudal fin with dark points.

♀ without prolonged dorsal and anal fin-rays.

Care and breeding, as given for *Corynopoma riisei* above. Very undemanding and hardy. This species tolerates transitory temperatures between 16–18°C. Omnivorous. 1905/+.

Pseudocorynopoma heterandria *Eigenmann* 1914 (Fig. 216)
Central Brazil, neighbourhood of São Paulo (?); to 9 cm. (?)

D 10; A 40–44; LL 40–45; TR 7/6. Shape similar to that of foregoing species. Only ♂♂ imported up till now and described by Arnold as follows:–coloration olive-yellow on the flanks, passing into orange-yellow on the belly. Back dark brown. A dark lateral stripe, becoming broader posteriorly, extends from the hind edge of the gill-cover to the root of the tail, terminating posteriorly in a lozenge-shaped blotch which is produced onto the base of the caudal fin and has a bright rim. Fins translucent yellowish (*Taschenkalender*, Jg. 28, 1936, p. 114).

Sex-distinctions, care and breeding, as for the previous species. 1935/−.

Iguanodectes tenuis *Cope* 1871 (Fig. 222)
Middle and lower Amazon R., Guiana; to 9 cm.

D 10–11; A 33–38; LL 54–64; TR 6–8/3½–5. Body very elongate, strongly compressed. Dorsal fin origin about the middle of the body. Lateral line complete. Upperside light brown to olive-brown; flanks light clay-colour with a tricolour longitudinal band (upper edge narrow but brilliant red, middle clear to pure white, lower edge broad and black), extending from the gill-cover to the root of the tail. Fins colourless, glass-clear. Base and upper lobe of caudal fin sometimes blackish.

♀ anal fin of almost even depth.

♂ anterior rays of anal elongate, so that the free edge of the fin appears to be semicircularly emarginate.

Care of this peaceful, lively species, as given for *Hemigrammus* above (p. 116). Accepts live food of all kinds. Not yet bred in captivity. 1912/−.

Piabucus dentatus (*Kolreuter* 1761) (Fig. 223)
Middle and lower basin of the Amazon R., Guiana; to 20 cm.

D 10–11; A 42–46; LL 79–95. Body elongate, strongly compressed. Head small. Anal fin-base very long. Adipose fin present. Upperside olive; flanks delicate grey-green, dull silver with a delicate blue to violet lustre by reflected light. From the gill-cover to the dark root of the tail extends a very bright brownish metallic stripe. Underside grey-white. Fins colourless, glassy, occasionally delicate brownish at the base.

Sex-distinctions have not yet been described.

Care of this interesting species, as for *Roeboides* spp. (see p. 90). Temperature 22–26°C. *P. dentatus* is a very active swimmer, which frequents the lower layers of the water and seeks its food mainly on the bottom. Feed worms, insects, etc. 1912/−.

Stethaprion innesi Myers 1932 (Fig. 197)
Lower Amazon and tributaries; to 12 cm.

D 12; A 40; LL 62. Body disc-shaped. Dorsal fin high; in front of it a small spine lying horizontally in a groove. Anal fin-base long; fin anteriorly produced

Figs. 194–197

Fig. 194. *Phenacogaster suborbitalis;* half-grown, natural size.
Fig. 195. *Gephyrocharax atracaudatus* (Platinum Tetra); adult, natural size.
Fig. 196. *Gephyrocharax valencia;* adult, reduced.
Fig. 197. *Stethaprion innesi;* adult, reduced.

into a lobe. Caudal fin deeply emarginate. Lateral line complete. Scales small. Uniform silvery with bluish or violet sheen on the flanks and caudal peduncle; upperside olive-green to brown. Fins delicate grey-green or colourless. Anal fin light reddish anteriorly in older fishes.

Definite sex-distinctions not yet described.

Stethaprion spp. are, without exception, active, peaceful shoaling fishes which mainly inhabit the layers of water near the bottom. Their needs are best met by large tanks, having dark soil on the bottom and some light screened by floating plants. They feed on tender leaves of water plants. Adult fishes are not sensitive to hard water. Temperature 23–25°C. Live food of all kinds, especially midge-larvae. Not yet bred in captivity. 1935/−.

Ephippicharax orbicularis (*Cuvier* and *Valenciennes* 1848) (Fig. 177)
Widely distributed in South America, Guiana, Amazon basin, etc.; to 12 cm.

D 11–12; A 30–34 (–36); LL 34–36. Nearly related to the previous species and similarly shaped. Scales fairly large. Upperside blackish-green; flanks silvery, gleaming greenish, bluish, violet or yellowish according to lighting. Two indistinct transverse bands in front of the dorsal fin, and a dark longitudinal stripe, are only occasionally distinctly displayed. Fins colourless. Vertical fins with slightly dusky spots at the base. Leading-edge of anal fin brown.

Reliable sex-distinctions unknown.

Care, as for the previous species. 1934/+.

Plate 33

Fig. 198. *Copeina arnoldi* (Spraying Characin); embryos immediately prior to hatching; about X12. (Photo Dr. Foersch)

Fig. 199. *Copeina arnoldi;* young, ready to commence feeding; about X15. (Photo Dr. Foersch)

Fig. 200. *Petersius occidentalis;* large, ripe adults; above ♀, below ♂. (Original)

Plate 34 (overleaf)

Fig. 201. *Hepsetus odoë* (Pike Characin); 50 cm. specimen, in the Hellabrunn Aquarium, Munich. (Original)

Fig. 202. *Alestes macrophthalmus;* young, natural size. (Original)

Fig. 203. *Alestopetersius caudalis* (Yellow Congo Characin); ripe adults, natural size; left ♀, right ♂. (Original)

160

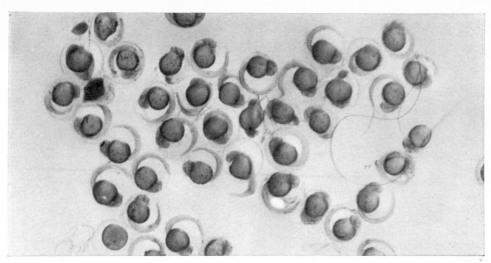

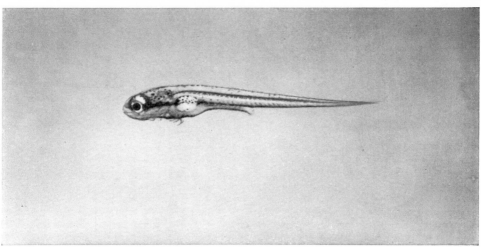

Plate 33

Plate 34 (see page 160)

Plate 35 (see page 161)

Plate 36

Plate 35 (overleaf)

Fig. 204. *Abramites microcephalus* (Headstander); 12 cm. specimen in the Hellabrunn Aquarium, Munich. (Original)

Fig. 205. *Neoborus ornatus;* ripe adult, natural size. (Photo Dr. Foersch)

Fig. 206. *Anostomus trimaculatus* (Three-spot Anostomus); 18 cm. specimen in the Hellabrunn Aquarium, Munich. (Original)

Plate 36

Fig. 207. *Characidium fasciatum* (Darter Characin); half-grown, somewhat enlarged. (Original)

Fig. 208. *Chilodus punctatus* (Spotted Headstander); half-grown, somewhat enlarged. (Original)

Cheirodon arnoldi *Boulenger* 1909 (Fig. 217)

The genus *Cheirodon* comprises shoaling fishes which exhibit a likeness to the genera of the sub-family *Tetragonopterinae* (*Hemigrammus, Hyphessobrycon, Pristella,* etc.). The shape of the body is uniform throughout, elongate and compressed. The upper and lower profiles are about equally convex. Teeth in jaws always in a single row (uniseriate). Lateral line incomplete. Adipose fin always present. The underside of the caudal peduncle is provided with spinous platelets which originate developmentally from transformed scales.

Cheirodon arnoldi is a native of Mexico and Central America.

D 11; A 22; LL 32, 4–5 pierced; TR 11. Back grey-green, sides and belly metallic silver. The root of the caudal fin is covered by a large blotch which is light-edged in young fishes. A narrow dark longitudinal band is not always visible. Vertical fins yellow-red; ventral fins and anal with white tips. Iris vivid red.

♀ body more stocky, fins yellowish.

♂ body slimmer.

Care and breeding, as given for *Cheirodon interruptus* below.

Rachow (*Handbuch der Zierfischkunde*, 1928, p. 11) believes – if I understand him rightly – that the *C. arnoldi* handled by Arnold (*Wochenschrift für Aquarien- und Terrarienkunde*, 1911, 1912, 1913) were *Astyanax mexicanus*, a determination which can hardly be correct since Arnold sent his specimens to London with a request for determination and Boulenger actually described the new species on the basis of this (type) material. 1909/–.

161

Cheirodon axelrodi *Schultz* 1956 (Fig. 148)   Cardinal Tetra

The name *Hyphessobrycon cardinalis* Myers & Weitzman 1956 was proposed on the day following the publication of *C. axelrodi*, and there has consequently been some confusion in the literature. The International Commission on Zoological Nomenclature has since ruled in favour of Schultz's species as having priority.

Upper Rio Negro, in forest pools; to 4 cm.

D 11; A 19; LL 32–33, 4–6 pierced. Similar to the Neon Tetra as regards form and colouring. The Cardinal Tetra, however, is altogether rather slimmer and a considerably brighter red. Whereas in the average Neon Tetra the brilliant red band under the iridescent blue-green longitudinal band only reaches from the root of the tail to the middle of the body, in the Cardinal Tetra it reaches all the way to the tip of the snout and spreads, a shining cardinal-red, onto the throat and belly. Back fine red-brown; edge of belly silvery.

Sex-distinctions, care and breeding, as given for *Hyphessobrycon innesi* (see p. 132). 1956.

Cheirodon interruptus (*Jenyns* 1842) (Fig. 220)

Uruguay basin and the region between this and the coast; to 6 cm.

D 11(–12); A 17–24; LL 32–36, 7–12 pierced. Shape of body as in *C. arnoldi*. Upperside delicate light brown to olive; in younger fishes often gleaming brassy-coloured. Flanks faint bluish on a silvery ground, greenish on the gill-cover, with a lead-coloured longitudinal band which becomes distinctly broader posteriorly and ends in a dark, often almost triangular, blotch at the root of the caudal. (Occasionally this band is continued, much narrowed, onto the middle rays of the caudal fin.) Fins colourless to faint yellowish; dorsal and caudal fins in fine specimens tinged with reddish.

♂ anal fin strongly convex anteriorly.

The active *Cheirodon* spp. require large aquaria in a sunny position and not too thickly planted. In general all the species are quite easily satisfied; however, their temperament, which is quite often agressive and pugnacious towards other fishes, allows them to be kept in the company only of larger species. Temperature 20–25 °C.; not sensitive to temporary cooling. Live foods of all kinds in large quantities.

The breeding of *Cheirodon* spp. is generally quite easy and they seem to prefer medium hard water. The eggs are laid among water plants but the greater part fall to the bottom. Arrant spawn-robbers. The young hatch after 24–30 hours. Rearing quite easy and the young grow rapidly. 1935/–.

Cheirodon leuciscus *E. Ahl* 1936 (Fig. 218)
Lower course of the Paraná R.; to 8 cm.

D 10–11; A 19–20; LL 32–35, 7–9 pierced; TR 5/3½–4. Upperside olive, particularly brown on the head; flanks delicate grey-green with a bluish sheen. The blue-green iridescence of the longitudinal series of scales is particularly marked on the caudal peduncle. Underside silvery. A rather vague dark blotch at the root of the caudal fin. Fins colourless.

Sex-distinctions not certainly known; ♂ with the anal fin produced anteriorly into a lobe (?).

Care, as for *C. interruptus* above. Not yet bred in captivity. 1934/+.

Cheirodon meinkeni *E. Ahl* 1928 (Fig. 219)
Eastern coastal streams and waters of Brazil between Bahia and Rio de Janeiro (according to Arnold); to 5 cm.

D 11; A 17–19; LL 35, 5–7 pierced; TR 12–13. Upperside olive-green to brown-green; flanks gleaming silvery with a delicate olive-green tone. A dark metallic gleaming line, which broadens on the caudal peduncle and merges into a dark blotch on the root of the tail, only appears by reflected light. Fins a delicate translucent yellowish. Eye yellowish-silvery.

Sex-distinctions unknown, but apparently the anal fin of the ♂ is more strongly convex in front.

Care, as for *C. interruptus* above. Not yet bred in captivity. 1928/–.

Cheirodon piaba *Lütken* 1874 (Fig. 221)
Eastern Brazil; to 5 cm.

D 11; A 19–27; LL (31–)33 or 34(–36), 9–12 pierced. The coloration of this species is strongly reminiscent of that of *C. interruptus*, with which this fish was often formerly confused; it is, moreover, rather variable in correspondence with the wide distribution. Upperside delicate brownish-green to olive-green; flanks silvery with an underlying greenish tone. A dark longitudinal band, broadening posteriorly, merges on the caudal peduncle into a large blue-black to lead-coloured blotch from which, also, a narrow black stripe may extend onto the middle caudal rays. Fins colourless, translucent or slightly yellowish.

♂ anal fin strongly convex anteriorly; lower lobe of the caudal often red.

Care and breeding, as for *C. interruptus* above. *Cheirodon piaba* is said to be very peaceful. 1911/–.

Prionobrama filigera *(Cope* 1870) (Fig. 191) Glass Bloodfish, Translucent Bloodfin
Catchment-area of the Rio Madeira (a tributary of the Amazon); to 6 cm.

D 10(–11); A (31–)34–35(–39); LL 38–41. Body elongate, compressed, not
unlike the well-known Bloodfin *(Aphyocharax rubripinnis)*. The first rays of the
large anal fin are often produced into filaments. Glass-clear. Light grey-yellow;
by reflected light delicately iridescent bluish to greenish. Root of caudal reddish
to blood-red, the colour often radiating out into the fin. Leading-edge of anal fin
cream-coloured to white.

♀ without a black stripe on the anal fin.

♂ with a black streak behind the white leading-edge of the anal fin.

Care and breeding, as given for *Aphyocharax rubripinnis* above (p. 108). A very
beautiful shoaling fish. 1931/+.

Rachoviscus crassiceps *Myers* 1926 (Fig. 224)
Neighbourhood of Rio de Janeiro; to 4·5 cm.

D 11; A 29; LL 42. Body stocky, head large and stout (carp-like). Mouth large.
Ground-colour weak blue-green; back brownish, belly yellowish-white. From the
gill-cover to the root of the tail extends a dark band, broadening behind, dull red
by reflected light but vivid dark red posteriorly. The whole body is sprinkled with
blue-green spots. Fins colourless; dorsal and anal fins with a brown zone along
the outer edge. Adipose fin wine-red.

♀ more dully coloured; dorsal and anal fins smaller than in the ♂.

♂ coloured as described above. In fine ♂♂ the caudal fin is edged above and below
with yellowish brown.

Rachoviscus requires spacious tanks with dense groups of plants and soft water.
Temperature 20–23 °C. Live food. The courtship is said to be very vigorous but
nothing is known about rearing. A very beautiful but rather aggressive species
which must be kept alone. 1926/–.

Plate 37

Fig. 209. *Copeina arnoldi* (Spraying Characin); fine imported specimens, natural size;
above ♀, below ♂. (Original)

Fig. 210. *Tanichthys albonubes* (White Cloud Mountain Minnow); young, natural size.
(Original)

Fig. 211. *Nannostomus marginatus* (One-lined Pencilfish); ripe adults, natural size. (Original)

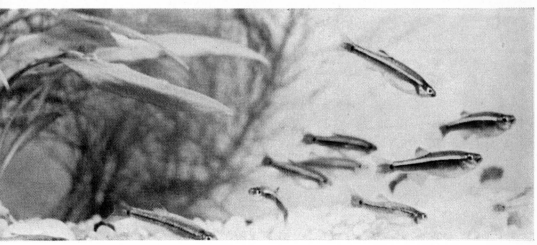

Plate 37

Plate 38

Plate 38

Fig. 212. *Leporinus affinis*; large, 20 cm. specimen, in the Hellabrunn Aquarium, Munich. (Original)

Fig. 213. *Chilodus punctatus* (Spotted Headstander); young, natural size. (Original)

Phoxinopsis broccae (*Myers* 1925) (Fig. 226)

Hinterland of Rio de Janeiro; to 2·5 cm.

D 9–10; A 16–17; LL 32–33. Body moderately elongate, compressed. Upper and lower profiles about equally convex. No adipose fin. Delicate clay-yellow, upperside brownish-yellow, belly silvery. Scales, especially near the back, dark-edged. From the gill-cover to the root of the caudal and thence, much narrowed, onto the middle rays of the fin, extends a broad, dark- to yellow-brown band. A second similar band begins over the ventral fins and ends in the hinder part of the anal. It is interesting to note that the band-marking can almost completely fade out while at the same time an angular blotch at the root of the tail becomes distinctly marked. Vertical fins in healthy fish delicate reddish.

The sexes are distinguished by the shape of the anal fin, which in the ♂ is more strongly convex in front.

Care of this very small yet beautifully-coloured species, as for *Hemigrammus* above (p. 116). Single fishes or small groups are rather timid; larger shoals, on the other hand, quite lively. Lives in the lower water-layers. Preferred temperature 23–25 °C. Small live food, mealworms, *Tubifex*, *Cyclops*, etc. Breeds only in soft water. The fishes spawn quite quietly among fine-leaved water plants and the young hatch after 24–30 hours. Rearing rather difficult; feed the smallest nauplii. 1923/–.

Leptagoniates steindachneri *Boulenger* 1887 (Fig. 225)

Marañon and tributaries; to 10 cm.

D 10; A 70; LL 47; TR 7/7. Body very elongate and strongly compressed (*Notopterus*-like), fairly strongly translucent. Anal fin-base very long. Adipose fin present. Lateral line complete, straight. Upperside delicate brownish. Flanks yellowish, provided with a broad, silvery, bluish to greenish iridescent metallic stripe which extends from the gill-cover to the greenish caudal peduncle. The fins are glass-clear.

Sex-distinctions not yet described.

This very rare, elegant and active species is best accommodated in tanks which are not too well lighted (although older accounts, on the contrary, state that *Leptagoniates* needs sunshine). Temperature 20–22°C. Care should be taken in putting this with smaller species. Not yet reared in captivity. 1909/−.

Brycon falcatus *Müller* and *Troschel* 1845 (Fig.227)
The genus *Brycon* includes many species and consists almost entirely of larger river fishes, some of which are esteemed food-fishes. They are distinguished from other groups by the form and arrangement of the teeth in the jaws. The genus inhabits the whole of South America as far south as the La Plata basin.

Brycon falcatus is distributed through the Guianas; to 25 cm.

D 11; A 19–24; LL 47–53. Body elongate, compressed. Adipose fin present. Lateral line complete, almost straight. Upperside blue-grey to olive-grey; flanks silvery-bluish by reflected light. The dark round shoulder-blotch is not always distinct. On the caudal peduncle there is a broad, deep black blotch which also extends onto the fin and there parallels its shape. Dark longitudinal stripes are said to be sometimes present on the upper region of the flanks. Vertical fins orange to red (in older specimens). Base of anal fin dark.

Sex-distinctions not yet described.

This robust, very hardy species is suitable for domestic aquaria only when young. Generally it is not at all demanding under such conditions and even temporary cooling is well tolerated. Preferred temperature 20–22°C. Greedy and very omnivorous. Grows very rapidly when well fed. 1923/−.

Chalceus macrolepidotus *Cuvier* 1817 (Fig.228)   Pink-tailed Characin,
Guianas; to 25 cm.

D 11; A 11–12; LL 20–25. Body elongate, compressed. Fins small. The very large scales on the upper half of the body are particularly characteristic. Upperside dark blue-grey. Flanks a considerably lighter grey, silvery with a beautiful greenish sheen on the middle series of scales. Underside almost white-silver. Shoulder-blotch brown, usually distinct. Fins grey-yellow to delicate reddish-yellow; caudal fin red. Eye yellowish.

Sex-distinctions not yet described.

Figs.214–216

Fig.214. *Mimagoniates barberi;* somewhat enlarged.
Fig.215. *Pseudocorynopoma doriae* (Dragon-finned Characin); ♂, with a sketch of the ♀ below; natural size.
Fig.216. *Pseudocorynopoma heterandria;* ♂, natural size.

Care. Keep this lively and not at all predatory species in well-lighted, clear-standing tanks with sufficient room to move about. (Shoaling fish!) Temperature about 24–26 °C. Greedy and omnivorous; large specimens will even take earthworms and pieces of meat. Not yet bred in captivity. *C. macrolepidotus* can jump extra-ordinarily well and far, so caution must be exercised when capturing it for transfer from one tank to another.

Arnold gives a further account of the introduction of a *Chalceus erythrurus* Cope 1870 (*Wochenschrift für Aquarien- und Terrarienkunde*, Jg. 36, p. 322, 1939). As Rachow has already opined (Holly, Meinken & Rachow, 7 1/I, 40), the species introduced in 1939 was *Chalceus macrolepidotus. Plethodectes (Chalceus) erythrurus* Cope 1870 (*Proc. Amer. Phil. Soc.* 1870) from the Marañon has therefore not yet been imported.

Lebiasina bimaculata *Cuvier* and *Valenciennes* 1846 (Fig. 229)

Two-spotted Lebiasina

Peru and Ecuador, west of the Andes; to 20 cm.

D (9–)10; A 10–12; LL 25–29; 6½ between D and V. Body elongate, cylindrical. Fins relatively small. Scales very large. Base of caudal fin, with the exception of a median stripe, scaled. Adipose fin usually absent, occasionally present as a vestige. Upperside olive-grey to grey-brown; flanks light clay-coloured, according to the direction of the light, with a delicate violet or reddish sheen; underside light yellow to whitish. Scales with red-brown to red spots, dark edged. Shoulder-blotch vivid red. Vertical fins orange to faint reddish; paired fins yellowish.

♀ usually easily recognised by the strongly convex profile of the belly.
♂ during breeding season considerably more vividly coloured.

This very robust and strong-swimming species is very easily satisfied and hardy. Only the young are normally suitable for room aquaria. Temperature around 25 °C.; not sensitive to cooling. Live food of all kinds in great quantities, also earthworms. Only equally large or larger fishes are suitable as companions. Not yet bred in captivity. *Lebiasina* possesses an accessory breathing-organ in the shape of a specially-modified portion of the swim-bladder adapted to air-breathing when living in poorly-oxygenated waters. 1914/ –.

Lebiasina intermedia *Meinken* 1936 (Fig. 230)
Middle Amazon near Santarem; to 15 cm.

D 10; A 11; LL 32. Shape similar to that of the previous species, but with a slimmer caudal peduncle. Upper lobe of caudal fin enlarged. Coloration, according to Meinken:—upperside blackish olive-green; a shining grass-green row of scales on the flanks whose yellowish colour becomes increasingly paler ventrally until finally it becomes whitish. A dark round blotch behind the gill-cover from which an increasingly broad, dark longitudinal band with blurred edges runs back to a black spot at the root of the tail. The scales on the lower half of this band have red spots. Gill-cover brilliant brass-colour. Edges of mouth black. Fins delicate orange-red to reddish. Dorsal fin with a deep black blotch at the base. Eye red above, orange below.

Sex-distinctions presumably as in the previous species.

Care, as given for *L. bimaculata* above. 1936/—.

Crenuchus spilurus *Günther* 1863 (Fig. 249)　　　　　　　Sailfin Characin
Western Guiana, middle Amazon R. and tributaries; to 6 cm.

D 17–18; A 11; LL 29–32. Body elongate, strongly compressed, upper and lower profiles almost equally convex. Edge of ♀ dorsal fin cut short, horizontal; in the ♂ the fin is large and flag-like. Caudal fin deeply notched. Anal fin of ♂ likewise greatly enlarged. Mouth large.

Bright red-brown, belly yellowish-white. Scales dark-edged, especially on the back. From the gill-cover to the root of the tail extends a dark band with a yellow upper edge. A large, rectangular, deep black blotch at the root of the tail. The upper part of the iris is blood-red. Vertical fins with a magnificent mosaic-like pattern in brown-red and orange colours. Ventral fins orange; pectorals colourless.

♀ with weaker colouring; dorsal and anal fins short.
♂ coloured as above.

This beautiful species, somewhat suggestive of a predator in appearance, is relatively peaceful. Provide it with a not-too-bright aquarium, partly planted with thick clumps of plants, and soft, slightly peat-filtered water. Preferred temperature probably around 25°C. Live foods of all kinds, especially worms and eventually small fishes. Not yet bred in captivity. *Crenuchus spilurus* is considered to be rather delicate. 1912/+.

Genera Pyrrhulina and Copeina: Care and Breeding

The species of the very closely-related genera *Pyrrhulina* and *Copeina*, natives of South America, are all small fishes which mostly live in the upper water layers and frequently obtain their food from the surface film. Their shape is reminiscent of that of the egg-laying tooth-carps (Cyprinodonts) of the genera *Rivulus* and *Fundulus*, with which they also have in common a flattened head and a more or less upwardly-directed gape. The fins, with the exception of the pectorals, are not particularly large but in ♂♂ occasionally the dorsal fin and often too the upper lobe of the caudal are strongly elongated. The adults always lack an adipose fin. Almost all the species are quite gaily coloured.

For the care of these species, some of which are rather delicate, large aquaria are suitable, furnished with large-leaved plants which do not grow too densely, and if possible so placed that some sunlight can penetrate. Soft, slightly acid water (pH 6·5–7) which has been filtered through peat. Insect food (midge-larvae, vinegar flies, plant aphides, etc.) together with other live foods. The not infrequently somewhat timid and fearful character of these fishes is greatly mitigated by a few floating plants and a dark bottom. Preferred temperature very high, 26–28 °C. All the species are very good jumpers.

The reproduction of *Pyrrhulina* and *Copeina* is very interesting. With the exception of *Copeina arnoldi* (see p. 177) the pairs spawn preferably on large, submerged leaves or, if these are absent, in shallow pits in the sand. (For exceptions see under individual species.) The places chosen for spawning are cleaned by the ♂ for hours beforehand and finally the ♀ is enticed there for

Figs. 217–221

Fig. 217. *Cheirodon arnoldi;* adult; somewhat reduced.
Fig. 218. *Cheirodon leuciscus;* somewhat reduced.
Fig. 219. *Cheirodon meinkeni;* natural size.
Fig. 220. *Cheirodon interruptus;* adult, natural size.
Fig. 221. *Cheirodon piaba;* adult, natural size.

170

egg-laying. Thereupon the ♂ whirls about with butterfly-like swimming movements but also drives the ♀ with bites and gentle prods. The spawn is looked after by the ♂ and is fanned so that eggs initially laid upon leaves mostly fall off onto the bottom. (The place of the ♂ can be taken by a weak aerator-diffuser, so placed that the air bubbles do not actually strike the eggs.) The very small young generally hatch after only 24 hours. At first they lie near the water surface but as soon as they swim freely they should be reared on the finest foods (nauplii and rotifers). Change the water during rearing.

The species of *Pyrrhulina* are distinguished from those of *Copeina* by the teeth on the premaxillaries, which are in two rows in the former and in only one row in the latter.

Pyrrhulina brevis *Steindachner* 1875 (Fig. 235)   Short Pyrrhulina
Amazon, Rio Negro; to 9 cm.

D 9–10; A 11–12; LL 20–22. Shape somewhat stocky. Caudal fin only moderately emarginate. Back brown to bronze-green; flanks with a slight bluish sheen; throat and belly silvery tinged with reddish. A blackish band extends from the anterior edge of the lower jaw over the middle of the eye to the level of the dorsal fin. Flanks with four series of red spots. A dark blotch on the leading-edge of the dorsal fin.

♀ fins yellowish, not black-edged; lobes of caudal fin equal in size.

♂ fins fiery red; dorsal, anal and ventrals black-edged; blotch on dorsal rimmed with white; upper lobe of caudal somewhat longer.

Care, as given above. This species is said to spawn on large leaves, but no successful breeding has been recorded. The ♂♂ are ruffians at spawning time. 1910/–.

Pyrrhulina nattereri *Steindachner* 1875 (Fig. 236)   Natterer's Pyrrhulina
Middle Amazon, Rio Negro(?); to 5 cm.

D 10; A 11; V 8; LL 20. Body very elongate and lower than in other *Pyrrhulina*

Figs. 222–226

Fig. 222. *Iguanodectes tenuis;* adult, natural size.
Fig. 223. *Piabucus dentatus;* adult, reduced.
Fig. 224. *Rachoviscus crassiceps;* natural size.
Fig. 225. *Leptagoniates steindachneri;* adult, natural size.
Fig. 226. *Phoxinopsis broccae;* adult, somewhat enlarged.

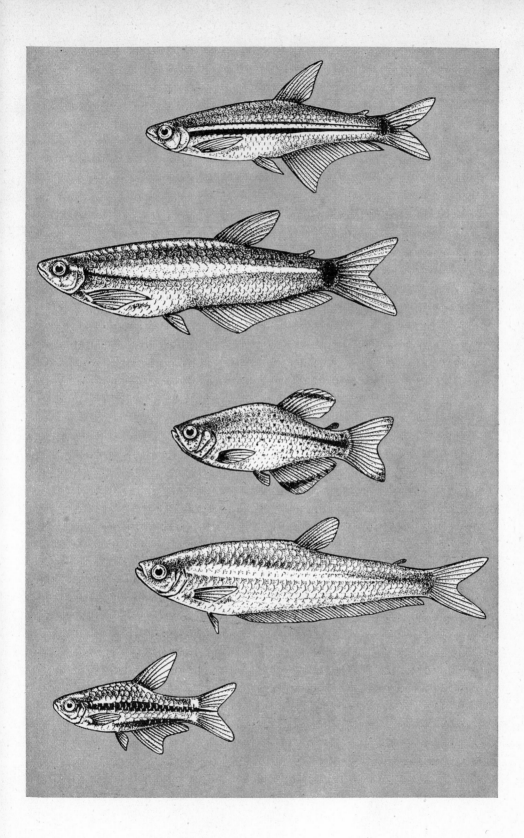

spp. Caudal peduncle long. Upperside dark gold-brown; flanks delicate olive-yellow, each scale with a distinct light brown spot and a dark edge. A dark brown streak runs from the snout, over the eye and onto the gill-cover or even (somewhat diluted) onto the flanks. Fins delicate yellowish; the dorsal with a reddish or bright red base and a large black blotch. The sexes are easily recognised by the caudal fin, the upper lobe of which is distinctly elongate in the ♂.

Care, as given on p. 170. Very rarely imported. Not yet reared in captivity. 1913/−.

Pyrrhulina nigrofasciata *Meinken* 1952 (Fig. 237) Black-banded Pyrrhulina
Exact locality unknown, probably Middle Amazon; to 6 cm.

D 10; A 11; V 8; LL 22–23. Shape similar to that of *Copeina arnoldi*. Back fawn-coloured; flanks brownish; belly yellowish-white. A broad, coffee-brown, longitudinal band, sometimes giving place to a zig-zag band, extends from the mouth across the eye and on to the root of the tail. Every scale with a blood-red spot, those on the anterior part of the body being brighter. All fins yellowish to red-brown, the dorsal with a black blotch bounded at the base by white.

♀ somewhat smaller; colouring of the fins more subdued.
♂ fins larger, more acutely produced; upper lobe of the caudal longer; anal fin edged with black-brown.

Care and breeding, as given on p. 170. First bred by H. J. Franke in 1951. This beautiful species proved to be very delicate and has unfortunately vanished from aquarium stock. 1950.

Pyrrhulina rachoviana *Myers* 1926 (Fig. 238) Rachow's Pyrrhulina,
Fanning Characin

Lower Paraná and La Plata (Rosário de Santa Fé); to 5 cm.

D 10; A 11; LL 21. Shape as described for the genus (p. 170). Back gleaming dark brown; belly yellowish-white. A gleaming golden longitudinal band extends from the head to the root of the tail and is bordered ventrally by another brown

Figs. 227–230

Fig. 227. *Brycon falcatus;* adult, greatly reduced.
Fig. 228. *Chalceus macrolepidotus* (Pink-tailed Characin); adult, greatly reduced.
Fig. 229. *Lebiasina bimaculata* (Two-spotted Lebiasina); adult, reduced.
Fig. 230. *Lebiasina intermedia;* somewhat reduced.

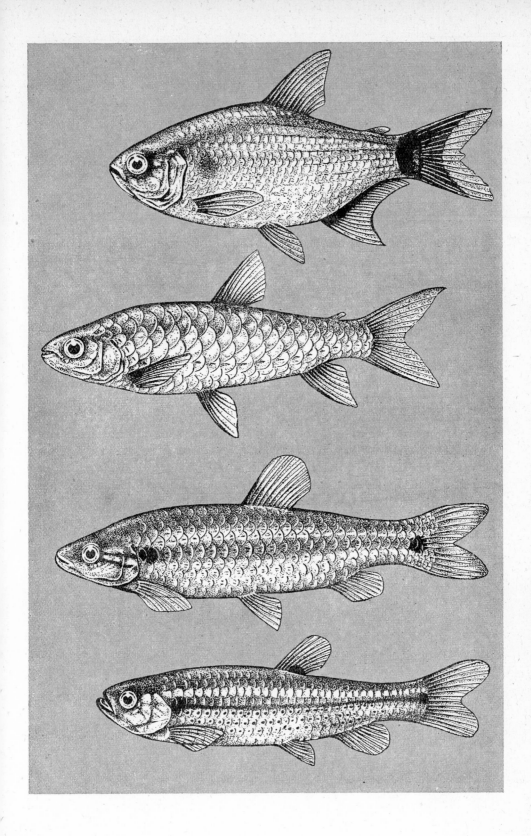

longitudinal band which runs around the tip of the jaw and over the eye, subsequently merging gradually into the yellowish-white of the belly. A shining light green blotch on the gill-cover. Two longitudinal series of large reddish spots or blotches on the anterior third of the body. Fins yellowish-green, the dorsal with an oval black blotch; by reflected light the fins have a delicate bluish border.

♀ both caudal lobes equal in length; longitudinal bands merely indicated.
♂ upper caudal lobe longer; anal and ventral fins with brick-red borders.

Lively, active fishes, somewhat quarrelsome but undemanding and hardy.
Care and breeding, as given on p. 170. This species spawns readily, on leaves or in the bottom-soil. 1906/+.

Pyrrhulina laeta (*Cope* 1871) (Fig. 239)　　　　　　Half-banded Pyrrhulina
Guiana, Middle Amazon R. (hinterland of Cayenne, said to be abundant); to 8 cm.

D 10; A 11; LL 22–23. Shape typical of genus, but head somewhat more pointed than in the other species. Upperside dark brown, occasionally with two almost black blotches between the head and the dorsal fin; flanks delicate grey-brown with light bluish sheen; underside yellowish to white. Some of the scales dark-edged. A dark brown band, which on the body may be quite indistinct or broken into spots, extends from the lower jaw across the eye and gill-cover to about the level of the dorsal fin. Particularly characteristic of this species, however, is the fact that this band runs slightly obliquely across the body in the direction of the anal fin. Fins yellowish to reddish, the dorsal with a large round blotch which is often pale-margined.

The sexes are clearly distinguished by the generally longer upper lobe of the caudal fin in the ♂.

Care, as given on p. 170. Apparently not yet bred in captivity. 1910/−.

Plate 39

Fig. 231. *Neolebias ansorgei*. The fish illustrated is one of the greenish variety which has been imported several times in recent years. Adult ♂, about twice natural size. (Photo Dr. Foersch)
Fig. 232. *Anostomus anostomus* (Striped Anostomus); specimens 12 cm. long, in the Hellabrunn Aquarium, Munich. (Original)

Plate 39

Plate 40

Plate 40

Fig. 233. *Carnegiella strigata vesca* (Marbled Hatchetfish); ripe young, natural size. (Original)

Fig. 234. *Exodon paradoxus;* young, natural size. (Original)

Pyrrhulina vittata *Regan* 1912 (Fig. 192)　　　　　　　Striped Pyrrhulina
Amazon R., near Santarem, Rio Tapajoz; to 7 cm.

D 10, A 11; LL 20–22. Shape typical of genus. Upperside grey-green or brownish; flanks dull silvery with bluish or greenish sheen; underside whitish, often faintly tinged with delicate reddish (according to Rachow occasionally bright red in older ♂♂). Scales on upper half of body with a light spot and delicate dark edge. A black or dark brown band runs from the lower jaw to a little behind the gill-cover. Very occasionally 2–3 narrow transverse bars appear. Fins glass-clear to delicate reddish, often with a bluish-white edge. Dorsal fin with a large, black, light-edged blotch.

♀ fins all colourless, at the most with bluish margins; more robust.

♂ often with yellowish or reddish fins when full grown; upper caudal lobe somewhat elongate.

Care and breeding, as given on p. 170. A very lively, peaceful species, and easily bred. 1912/ + .

Arnold (1939) reports (*Taschenkalender* Jg. 31, p. 80) a single specimen of a *Pyrrhulina* sp. from the Middle Amazon which he tentatively identifies as '*Pyrrhulina filamentosa* Cuvier and Valenciennes 1846'. Since no subsequent scientific data can be traced, no description of this species is given here.

Copeina arnoldi *Regan* 1912 (Figs. 198, 199, 209)　　　　　Spraying Characin
Lower Amazon, Rio Pará; ♂ to 8 cm., ♀ to 6 cm.

D 10; A 11; LL 23–24. Body elongate, only slightly compressed. Gape wide, horizontal. Back dark brown-yellow; flanks and belly yellowish to greenish with a rust-brown sheen. Edges of the scales dark-edged, forming a fine network over the body. A greenish-gold blotch on the gill-cover. A dark band across the mouth, extending laterally to the eye. Dorsal fin very beautiful, yellow with a black blotch and a red tip. Caudal with a greatly elongate upper lobe, yellow with a red edge and the tips often black. Ventral and anal fins yellow with red tips.

♀ fins less well developed.

♂ with all fins produced to a point; more gaily coloured.

Care of this very beautiful species, as given on p. 170. Breeding temperature 28°C. The fishes prefer to spawn above the water, on the cover-glass or on over-hanging leaves. After vigorous driving the pair lie side by side, rising slowly to a position under the water-surface previously chosen, accelerate, still lying side by side, so that they shoot out of the water and arrive with the belly against the cover-glass where they pause a moment and then fall back singly into the water. Spawn-ing is achieved after a series of such preparatory exercises. At each spawning 5–12 eggs are laid, to a total of 50–200. At the conclusion of spawning the ♂ rests under the water surface, sprinkling the spawn with his caudal fin. The young hatch after 36 hours, fall into the water, and must then be reared on the finest food. 1905/+.

Copeina callolepis *Regan* 1912 (Fig. 240)   Beautiful-scaled Characin
Region of the lower Amazon R.; to 6 cm.

D 10; A 11; LL 21. Body very elongate and low, similarly shaped to that of *Pyrrhulina nattereri*. Upperside dark yellow-brown; flanks light yellow to yellow-grey with a greenish sheen; underside yellowish to white. Scales with rust-red or shining red dots which align themselves into longitudinal series of spots and, par-ticularly on the upper half of the body, have dark edges. A narrow dark band, distinct only on the head, extends from the lower jaw across the eye and onto the flanks.

♀ fins less developed, colourless; dorsal with a dark spot.
♂ fins, at sexual maturity, delicate yellowish-brown; dorsal prolonged, with a dark blotch edged with white below; upper caudal lobe strongly elongate.

Care and breeding, as given on p. 170. This very peaceful, warmth-requiring species spawns on large submerged leaves. 1908/+.

Figs. 235–240
Fig. 235. *Pyrrhulina brevis* (Short Pyrrhulina); somewhat reduced.
Fig. 236. *Pyrrhulina nattereri* (Natterer's Pyrrhulina); adult, slightly reduced.
Fig. 237. *Pyrrhulina nigrofasciata* (Black-banded Pyrrhulina); somewhat enlarged.
Fig. 238. *Pyrrhulina rachoviana* (Rachow's Pyrrhulina, Fanning Characin); somewhat enlarged.
Fig. 239. *Pyrrhulina laeta* (Half-banded Pyrrhulina); natural size.
Fig. 240. *Copeina callolepis* (Beautiful-scaled Characin); adult, somewhat enlarged.

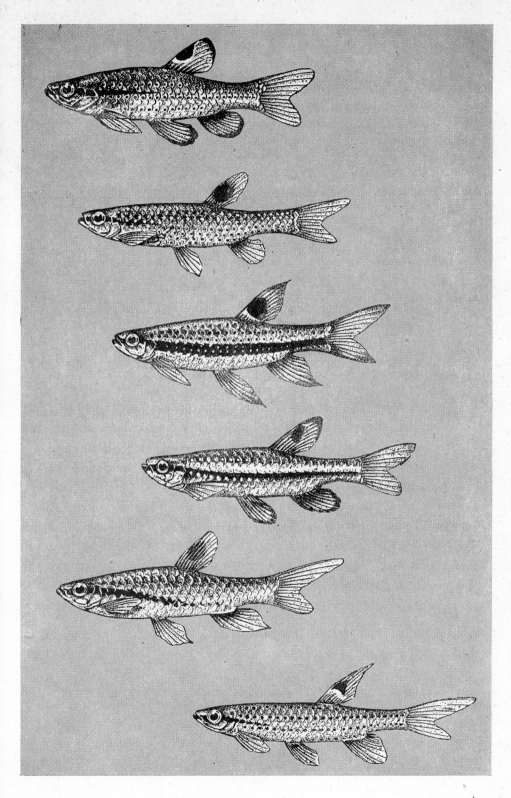

Copeina guttata (*Steindachner* 1875) (Figs. 193, 248)   Red-spotted Copeina
Middle Amazon R. and tributaries; to 15 cm., but mature at 6–7 cm.

D 10; A 12; LL 23–24. Body more stocky than in the previous species. Fins in ♂ scarcely prolonged. Scales quite large. Back greenish-brown; flanks shining sky-blue; belly white. Each scale bears a blue to violet-red spot at its base, causing the fish to appear marked with longitudinal series of spots. Upper half of iris red. Dorsal fin with a black, drop-shaped blotch, otherwise translucent yellowish-white. Anal, caudal and ventral fins bright yellow with broad orange-red margins.

♀ coloration in general paler; fins yellowish-grey; blotch on the dorsal usually distinct.

♂ coloured as described above; upper caudal lobe somewhat prolonged.

Care and breeding of this robust, undemanding species, as given on p. 170. The fishes spawn in pits in the sand and are very prolific. The eggs will develop even in medium hard water. 1912/+.

African Characidae

The Characidae are one of four families of freshwater fishes which inhabit both South America and Africa. In Africa they range from the large, sharp-toothed Tiger-fish *(Hydrocynus)* and the pike-like *Hepsetus* (fish-predators, not suitable for domestic aquaria) to the dainty *Micralestes* spp., none of which, however, matches the splendour of the Neon Tetra and other South American Characins. In *Arnoldichthys* and *Alestes* the teeth of the upper jaw are in two series, while those of the lower jaw are in one series with an inner pair; most of the teeth are stout and many-cusped. In *Micralestes*, which remains small, the teeth are similar but flattened instead of being thick and molariform. The body is generally moderately elongate and strongly compressed. The dorsal fin is inserted at the level of the ventrals. In ♂♂ the fin-rays are often greatly elongate and in some species the anal fin has prolonged middle rays. These fishes inhabit the most diverse bodies of water.

Arnoldichthys spilopterus (*Boulenger* 1909) (Fig. 117)   Red-eyed Characin
Tropical West Africa, Lagos to Niger estuary; to 7 cm.
(*Arnoldichthys* is distinguished from the following genera by the enlarged scales on the upper half of the body.)

D 12; A 14; LL 28–30. Body spindle-shaped, compressed. The lateral line runs along the lower half of the body, even on the caudal peduncle. Adipose fin present. Caudal fin deeply emarginate. A very beautiful species.

♂ upperside delicate brownish with green sheen; flanks with bright grass-green to blue-green iridescence. A dark band runs from the gill-cover to the middle rays of the anal fin and is accompanied, above by an equally broad band shining with all the colours of the rainbow, and below, by a very splendid light band. Belly golden yellow, often with a reddish sheen. Vertical fins yellowish; dorsal with a large dark blotch, anal with a dark marking parallel to the long axis of the body. Eye red to brown-red.

♀ somewhat less brilliantly coloured; anal fin, in contrast to that of the ♂, only very slightly convex.

This active, peaceful species should, like the other smaller African Characins, be kept in roomy aquaria which are not too densely planted. Soft, slightly acid water which has been filtered through peat, and the darkest possible bottom are essential. Temperature 24–27°C. Live food of all kinds, especially *Drosophila*, and small cockroaches. This species also accepts dried food. Not yet bred in captivity. 1907/ –.

Alestes chaperi *Sauvage* 1882 (Fig. 250)   Chaper's Characin
Tropical West Africa, Ghana to Niger; to 9 cm.

D 10; A 21–23; LL 26–29. Body elongate, fairly deep, compressed. Scales large. Adipose fin present. Lateral line complete, somewhat curved. Upperside light olive-green; flanks beautiful grass-green with a deep black longitudinal band on the caudal peduncle. In the young a dark shoulder-blotch is distinctly exhibited, also a fine line between this and the posterior longitudinal band. Dorsal and caudal fins brick-red with a broad yellow margin; all other fins yellowish. Eye large, shining red above, yellowish below.

Sex-distinctions in coloration not known.

All the very beautiful and lively *Alestes* spp. remain rather shy in captivity, like many species with good eyesight. They require large aquaria with moderate plant growth, a dark bottom, and soft, acid water which has been filtered through peat. The fishes are not altogether light-shy and like a little sunshine. They prefer to swim in the middle water-layers. For intense coloration, growth and sexual maturation, and especially for the inducement of spawning, correct food is essential. Like many other African Characins *Alestes* spp. need insect food, at least as a supplement to

181

other live food; flies, vinegar flies, cockroaches, beetles, etc. Temperature 23–25°C. *A.chaperi* has apparently not yet been bred in captivity. 1911/+.

Alestes longipinnis (*Günther* 1864) (Fig. 188)　　　　　Long-finned Characin
Tropical West Africa, Sierra Leone to Congo; to 13 cm.

D 10; A 22–24; LL 24–29. Very similar to the previous species; the ♂, however, has a greatly produced dorsal fin. Upperside olive-green to olive-yellow; flanks clay-yellow with a strong silvery sheen. A broad black longitudinal band on the caudal peduncle is continued, much narrowed, onto the middle caudal rays; above this band is a beautiful golden, strongly iridescent zone. Underside silvery-white. Dorsal and caudal fins yellowish, in the ♂ often reddish; the prolonged dorsal fin-rays are often clear to white. Anal fin delicate yellowish. Eye a beautiful red.

Care, as given for the previous species. Not yet reared in captivity. 1928/+.

Alestes macrophthalmus *Günther* 1867 (Fig. 202)
Congo, Lake Tanganyika, Lake Mueru and other localities, widely distributed; to 45 cm.

D 2/8; A 14–18; LL 26–33. Body slim and strongly elongate. Lateral line complete and curved. Strikingly silver; upperside somewhat greenish. Caudal fin wholly delicate reddish. Sex-distinctions unknown. 1956.

Alestes nurse (*Rüppel* 1832) (Fig. 251)
Widely distributed through tropical Africa, from the Nile to Senegal; to 25 cm.

D 10; A 14–18; LL 26–33. Similar in shape to the previous species, but somewhat deeper in the body. The lower profile rises at the beginning of the anal fin almost vertically towards the adipose fin, then passes immediately into a slender caudal peduncle. In younger fishes the lower profile is more even and not as angular as described above. Body yellowish-brown to olive-brown, with a bright brassy iridescence, particularly on the lower reaches of the flanks and caudal peduncle. Underside yellowish to white. A vague black blotch over the origin of the pectoral fin; another, larger and always more distinct, on the caudal peduncle. Fins grey, in young fishes yellowish to reddish.

Sexes distinguished by the form of the adipose fin, the free edge being straight in the ♀, convex in the middle in the ♂.

Care, as given for *A.chaperi*, but *A.nurse* is decidedly more exacting in regard to water conditions and food. For domestic aquaria only young fishes are suitable, which, like other *Alestes* spp., delight the observer with their elegant swimming movements. 1911/−.

Alestopetersius caudalis (*Boulenger* 1899) (Fig. 203)   Yellow Congo Characin
Lower Congo and tributaries; to 7 cm.

D 2/8; A 3–4/19–20; LL 29–30; TR $5\frac{1}{2}/3\frac{1}{2}$. Shape similar to that of the better known *Micralestes interruptus*, but scales smaller, body more translucent and middle rays of ♂ caudal never so greatly prolonged. Translucent yellowish to yellowish-grey; underside almost pure white. A brownish longitudinal stripe is only occasionally distinct. Dorsal and caudal fins light yellow. Dorsal fin of ♂ with prolonged, distally black, fin-rays; caudal fin of ♂ with a deep black median stripe, bordered above and below by white; anal fin of ♂ with a broad white margin.

Care and breeding, as given for *Micralestes interruptus*, see p. 185. 1954.

Hepsetus odoë (*Bloch* 1794) (Fig. 201)   Pike Characin
Tropical Africa, from Senegal to the Zambesi; to 35 cm.

D 9; A 11; V 9; LL 60. Body pike-like, elongate, slender, scarcely compressed. Upperside of head flat. Dorsal fin inserted far back. Pectoral and ventral fins well developed. Mouth large, with very powerful conical teeth. Jaw with sail-like appendages (? sense-organs). Upperside brownish to clay-coloured; flanks and belly silvery with a buff metallic sheen. Rays of dorsal fin brown-red; adipose, caudal and anal fins grey, spotted with dark brown; pectoral and ventral fins brownish. Eye large; iris brass-coloured.

Sex-distinctions not so far described.

This extraordinarily predaceous species is unfortunately rather delicate and often succumbs to the slightest damage, even in transit. Acclimatised fishes are among the most interesting rarities in public aquaria. Roomy tanks and plentiful feeding with living fishes (according to Heck horseflesh and *Tubifex* as well) are essential. Preferred temperature 26–28 °C. Not recommended for domestic aquaria. 1913/+.

Micralestes acutidens (*Peters* 1852) (Fig. 252)
Widely distributed through Africa, Nile, Niger, Zambesi; to 6·5 cm.

D 10; A 17–19; LL 23–28. Anal fin relatively short. Caudal deeply emarginate. Upperside light brown; flanks and body silvery, with zones of bluish sheen, particularly on the caudal peduncle. A broad, lead-grey to black, longitudinal band extends from the gill-cover to the root of the tail. Fins colourless or light grey; dorsal fin with a black stripe.

Anal fin of ♂ produced anteriorly into a lobe.

Care, as given for *M. interruptus*. Seldom imported. 1932/+.

183

Micralestes hilgendorfi (*Boulenger* 1899) (Fig. 253)

Congo Basin; to 10 cm.

D 10; A 23–26; LL 23–26. Shape similar to that of the previous species. Caudal fin deeply emarginate, its middle rays not prolonged. Upperside yellow-brown; flanks strongly silver, gleaming, according to light, delicate yellowish or greenish. A dark, often elongate, transverse blotch behind the gill-cover. A broad, dark, blurred-edged longitudinal band begins at the level of the ventral fins and extends to the root of the tail. Fins translucent yellowish-grey or colourless. Dorsal fin and lobes of caudal with blackish tips.

Sex-distinctions not certainly known; the dorsal fin of older ♂♂ is often prolonged like a flag.

Care, as given for *M. interruptus*. Not yet reared in captivity. Rachow (in Holly, Meinken & Rachow, 7 g, 25 a) remarks that the '*Petersius ubalo*', imported in 1913, was wrongly determined and was really a *Micralestes hilgendorfi*; for various reasons I do not agree with this opinion. 1913/—.

Micralestes interruptus *Boulenger* 1899 (Fig. 149)   Congo Tetra

Congo Basin; ♂ to 8 cm., ♀ to 6 cm.

D 11; A 23–24, LL 23. Body elongate, strongly compressed. Middle caudal rays of ♂♂ prolonged, nipple-like. By reflected light the fishes gleam with all the colours of the rainbow. Back and nape blackish brown-olive; upper part of caudal peduncle gleaming gold. Towards the belly the colour pales to a red to light brown longitudinal band which, further ventrally, is bordered by a beautiful brass-yellow band; then there follow, proceeding towards the belly, a golden, then a green-yellow and then a green series of scales. The belly gleams pale to violet-blue. These several bands are not sharply separated from one another, and are sometimes accompanied by black zig-zag lines. A beautiful light blue blotch behind the metallic green gill-cover. Fins smoke-grey to reddish; anal and caudal fins edged with white. Prolonged middle rays black, white-edged. Pectoral fins colourless.

Plate 41

Fig. 241. *Nannostomus beckfordi anomalus* (Golden Pencilfish); adults, somewhat enlarged; above ♂, below ♀. (Photo Dr. Foersch)

Fig. 242. *Nannostomus beckfordi beckfordi* (Golden Pencilfish); adults, enlarged. (Original)

Fig. 243. *Nannostomus espei;* ripe young, somewhat enlarged. (Original)

Plate 41

Plate 42

Plate 42

Fig. 244. *Nannostomus unifasciatus;* adults, somewhat enlarged; above ♀, below ♂. (Original)

Fig. 245. *Nannostomus bifasciatus;* adult ♀, somewhat enlarged. (Original)

Fig. 246. *Nannostomus trifasciatus;* adult ♂♂, somewhat enlarged; note the distinctly visible adipose fins. (Original)

♀ uniformly paler; dorsal fin and middle part of caudal fin hardly prolonged.

♂ larger, coloured as described above; dorsal fin much prolonged.

This beautiful and elegant shoaling-fish has similar requirements to the *Alestes* spp., i.e., plenty of room to move about, soft, slightly acid peaty water, insect food and occasional changes of water. Unfortunately really fine Congo Tetras are already – only a few years after their introduction – quite rare, but one often sees fishes with short fins and short middle caudal lobes; the latter, in fine specimens, should be 20 mm. long and a good 8 mm. broad. Much has been written concerning the cause of this deterioration in captivity. A considerable role seems to be played by the nitrogenous compounds dissolved in the water. Furthermore, it is important to allow this species time to develop; it is better to underfeed it than to force its growth by overfeeding. Temperature 25–26°C. First bred in 1951 by Meder (Neustadt). The pairs generally spawn on sunny days. The large, light brownish eggs are laid after vigorous driving and, being non-adhesive, sink to the bottom. Up to 300 eggs and more at a spawning. The egg-membrane swells considerably. The young hatch after 6 days and may be fed at once. 1949.

Petersius occidentalis *Günther* 1899 (Fig. 200)

Ghana and Congo; to 6·5 cm.

D 3/8; A 3/18–21; LL 24–27; TR $4\frac{1}{2}/2\frac{1}{2}$. Body elongate, strongly compressed. Lateral line complete, curved. Uniformly bright shining silver. A dark longitudinal band is usually quite indistinct. Especially characteristic of this species is the blackish dorsal fin which in the ♂ shows a broad, shining yellow band; in the ♀ there is only a pale tip. Ventral and anal fins in ♂ with white tips.

Care and breeding, as for *Micralestes interruptus*. 1956.

Family Anostomidae

The *Anostomidae*, which are distributed through South and Central America, including the West Indies, are sometimes very beautifully marked and coloured. They are almost exclusively inhabitants of standing or sluggish, weedy waters in which, gathered in small troops, they glide quietly over the bottom, continually seeking their food. Many species have the habit of stand-

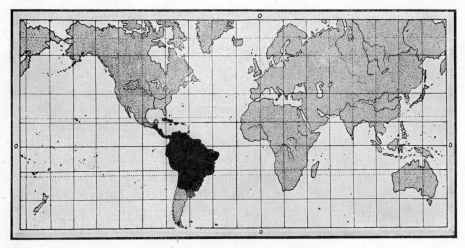

Fig. 247
Distribution of the *Anostomidae*

ing on their heads. Apart from a few forms which are wholly carnivorous or herbivorous, most of the species are omnivorous. The narrow mouth, which is characteristic of almost the entire family, may be variously modified; thus in *Anostomus* spp. it is vertically cleft and surrounded by folded lips, while in

Figs. 248–249

Fig. 248. *Copeina guttata* (Red-spotted Copeina); adult ♂, somewhat reduced.
Fig. 249. *Crenuchus spilurus* (Sailfin Characin); ♂, natural size. A sketch of the ♀ is given below.

Prochilodus spp. it may be turned back as a sucking-disc, or in some other genera have thick, swollen lips, and so on. Many *Anostomidae* remain relatively small and are thus well-suited to the domestic aquarium. Larger forms are often esteemed as food-fishes in their native countries and are prized exhibits in foreign public aquaria. For care, see under individual species.

Abramites microcephalus *Norman* 1926 (Fig. 204)   Headstander
Lower Amazon; to 13 cm.

D 2/10; A 2/11; LL about 36. Body elongate, compressed. Upper and lower profiles fairly strongly convex, and approximately equally so. Head small; snout acute. A head-stander. Coloration rather variable; dark brown or grey to yellow-brown, with irregular broad brown transverse bars. Caudal, anal and pectoral fins clay-yellow to pure yellow; anal fin further with a broad black base and a black margin. Adipose fin bright yellow with a broad black margin. Pectoral fins black.
Sex-distinctions unknown.

This head-stander, which is very rare in its native home and therefore only rarely imported, is rather similar in behaviour to the Spotted Headstander *(Chilodus punctatus)* and should be similarly cared for (see p. 193). Larger specimens are often quite quarrelsome among themselves. Reproduction unknown. 1949.

Anostomus anostomus *(Linnaeus* 1758) (Fig. 232)   Striped Anostomus
The exclusively South American genus *Anostomus* comprises fishes of elongate, strongly compressed form in which the head is often somewhat flattened above and the gape directed slightly upwards. The fishes swim in an oblique position, with the head down. *A.anostomus* occurs in western Guiana and in the Amazon from Manaõs upwards; to 14 cm.

D 11–12; A 10; LL 40–43. Older specimens with three dark green or brown to brownish-black longitudinal stripes, which extend to the caudal fin. The upper stripe begins on the head, the middle one on the mouth and the lowest in the

Figs. 250–253

Fig. 250. *Alestes chaperi* (Chaper's Characin); adult, natural size.
Fig. 251. *Alestes nurse;* young, natural size.
Fig. 252. *Micralestes acutidens;* natural size.
Fig. 253. *Micralestes hilgendorfi;* ♂, natural size.

throat region. The parts of the body lying between the stripes are shining ochre-yellow to red. Throat and region above the pectoral fins lilac to purple. The bases of all the fins are reddish or red-violet, becoming yellowish to colourless towards the free ends. Bases of dorsal and caudal fins often blood-red. The anal fin occasionally has a black leading-edge. One of the most beautiful South American fishes.

Sex-distinctions unknown.

Care of this quite hardy species: large aquaria, not too densely planted but, if possible, with root-systems and dark bottom-soil. Preferred temperature 24–27 °C. Not particular about its food; prefers small worms which are sucked up from the bottom. Generally peaceful with other species of the same size. The peculiar mode of swimming is of special interest; the fishes glide head-downwards looking for food on the bottom, or stand among water plants. For quick forward movements, as in flight, they assume a horizontal position and are then very nimble. It is recommended that these fishes should be kept in small troops. Not yet bred in captivity. 1924/+.

Anostomus fasciatus *Spix* and *Agassiz* 1829 (Fig. 254)   Six-barred Anostomus
Widely distributed through northern South America, east of the Andes; to 40 cm. (A food-fish.)

D 10–11; A 11; LL 38–42. Similar in shape to the previous species. Coloration of larger specimens shining greenish-silver; upperside somewhat darker; underside almost white, often light yellowish. On the flanks are six broad brownish transverse bands which gradually fade out towards the back and belly; in the third and fifth transverse bands, at about the level of the middle line, a very intense black spot is inset. Fins colourless, often yellowish at their bases. Unfortunately younger fishes are often quite uniformly coloured.

Sex-distinctions unknown.

Care, as for *A. anostomus*. 1907/−.

Figs. 254–258

Fig. 254. (Above, left) – *Anostomus fasciatus* (Six-barred Anostomus); young, natural size.
Fig. 255. (Above, right) – *Curimatopsis maculatus;* natural size.
Fig. 256. *Curimatopsis saladensis;* natural size.
Fig. 257. *Curimatus argenteus;* adult, somewhat reduced.
Fig. 258. *Curimatus mivarti;* adult, reduced.

Anostomus trimaculatus (*Kner* 1858) (Fig. 206)   Three-spot Anostomus
Guiana and Lower Amazon R.; to 20 cm.

D 11–12; A 10–11; LL 40–43. Body form and finnage as in *A. anostomus*, but head somewhat blunter. Upperside dull olive-brown; flanks clay-coloured to brownish liike a walnut-shell); underside pale, faintly yellowish. A deep black blotch on the gill-cover, another below the dorsal fin and a third on the caudal peduncle; the first two blotches have a silver to faint golden edging. Quite faintly marked longitudinal series of spots are usually only visible on the lower flanks. Vertical fins faint yellowish at their bases, outside reddish to bright red; paired fins colourless. According to Rachow vague transverse bands appear occasionally, especially in pale specimens.

Sex-distinctions unknown.

Care, as for *A. anostomus*. Not yet bred in captivity. 1913/+.

Chilodus punctatus *Müller* and *Troschel* 1845 (Figs. 208, 213)   Spotted Headstander
Widely distributed through northern South America, Orinoco, Rio Negro, middle and upper Amazon Basin; to 7 cm.

D 11; A 12–13; LL 25–27. Body moderately elongate, the upper part more strongly compressed than the lower. Back rather elevated. Mouth small, somewhat upwardly directed with a thick upper lip. Lateral line complete. Scales large. A head-stander. Ground-colour delicate to strong grey or brown; back dark brown; flanks paler; throat and belly silvery. A black longitudinal band extends from the tip of the mouth, over the eye, to the middle of the caudal fin origin. Each of the large scales, with the exception of those on the chest, has a large brown blotch at the base, causing the fish to appear marked with series of spots. Dorsal fin spotted with dark brown, with a dark brown leading-edge and a very dark tip.

♀ at spawning time considerably more robust.

Plate 43

Fig. 259. *Nannostomus ocellatus* (Tail-eye Pencilfish); adults, somewhat enlarged; above ♀, below ♂. (Original)

Fig. 260. *Nannostomus eques* (Tube-mouthed Pencilfish); adults, somewhat enlarged; above ♀, below ♂. (Original)

Fig. 261. Hybrid *Nannostomus beckfordi anomalus* x *N. b. aripirangensis*, as kept in various more or less fine forms in Central Europe; somewhat enlarged. (Original)

Plate 43

Plate 44

Plate 44

Fig. 262. Nocturnal coloration of various *Nannostomus* spp. (Original) From above downwards: –

Nannostomus unifasciatus (One-lined Pencilfish)
Nannostomus bifasciatus (Two-banded Pencilfish)
Nannostomus trifasciatus (Three-banded Pencilfish)
Nannostomus beckfordi anomalus × *O.b. aripirangensis*
Nannostomus eques (Tube-mouthed Pencilfish)
Nannostomus ocellatus (Tail-eye Pencilfish)

This interesting, active species requires plenty of room to move about. It should therefore be kept only in large aquaria with a dark bottom, sparse planting, branch-systems and, here and there, a patchy cover of floating plants. Corresponding to its natural occurrence in shallow, sometimes very marshy, waters this species requires soft, slightly acid water which has been filtered through peat. Preferred temperature 25–27 °C. Live food of all kinds, also supplementary plant food (lettuce, rolled oats). Breeding can only be achieved in tanks fitted as described above. Some sort of spawning-medium is required, such as flattened mats of algae, *Nitella* tufts or a synthetic substitute such as Perlon. According to Feigs these fishes exhibit a special coloration during the breeding period; the dark longitudinal band and the dark markings of the dorsal fin regress and two blotches the size of peas become distinctly visible behind the gill-cover, while the anal and adipose fins take on a quite dark tint. The eggs are laid on the plant clumps provided. As in *Nannostomus marginatus*, *Micralestes interruptus* and others, the egg-membrane swells up so that the eggs attain a diameter of 2·5 cm. The egg itself is brownish. The young hatch after 3–4 days and are not easily reared (feed with Rotifers). Special structures on the fourth gill-arch are developed as accessory breathing-organs. 1912/ + .

Curimatopsis maculatus *E. Ahl* 1934 (Fig. 255)
Northern Argentine; to 6 cm.

Body shape typical of the genus (see following species). Coloration, according to Arnold: – upperside olive-grey; flanks paler in their upper parts with large dark grey spots; underside yellowish to white. Gill-cover with metallic blotch. Interorbital space black. A lozenge-shaped black blotch on the caudal peduncle. Fins colourless, transparent.

Sex distinctions, apparently as in the following species, which also see for care and breeding. 1914 (?)/ – .

Curimatopsis saladensis *Meinken* 1933 (Fig. 256)

The species of *Curimatopsis* are small *Anostomidae* of *Barbus*-like form. Especially characteristic are the toothless mouth, long tongue and very short lateral line. Adipose fin present. The sexes are clearly distinguishable when full grown. A few species in the northern Argentine.

C. saladensis occurs in the Rio Salado system and in the Paraná (?); to 6 cm.

D 11; A 9; V 1/7; LL 32. Body form typical of the genus. Coloration of adult ♂, according to Meinken:– upperside blackish-olive; flanks shining with bands of grass-green to metallic green. Region behind the dorsal fin blue-green. Chest and belly faintly reddish. Gill-cover a beautiful brass-colour. Scales distinctly dark-edged. A dark longitudinal band extends from the gill-cover to a deep black, copper-edged blotch on the caudal peduncle. Fins, with the exception of the pectorals, bright yellow-red. Anterior rays of the dorsal fin bright orange. A further characteristic of the ♂♂ is the deepening with age of the caudal peduncle.

♀ with slender caudal peduncle; colouring in general plainer.

This very easily satisfied species should be kept in richly planted aquaria in a rather sunny position and benefits appreciably from not too hard, clear water and a varied diet. Preferred temperature 20–23 °C. Like many Barbels these fishes continually search for all kinds of food on the bottom, but they do not grub for it. Breeding quite easy, and should be provided for as in *Hyphessobrycon* spp. (see p. 116). The young hatch after 26–32 hours and are quite easily reared. 1932/–.

Curimatus argenteus *Gill* 1858 (Fig. 257)

To the genus *Curimatus*, rich in species and widely distributed through South and Central America, belong moderately elongate, relatively deep and only slightly compressed fishes. Adipose fin present. Caudal fin deeply emarginate. Mouth narrow. Many species, as well as eating all kinds of small prey which they mostly dig out of the mud, also feed on plants.

C. argenteus occurs in Trinidad, Colombia and Venezuela; to 15 cm.

D 10–11; A 8–9; LL 36–37. Shape typical of the genus. Uniformly silvery; upperside somewhat olive-green and flanks often with a strong blue sheen. A prominent pip-shaped black spot on the caudal peduncle. Fins yellowish; vertical fins reddish at the base. Dorsal fin with a broad black band at the base.

♀ said to be considerably more robust and even gross at spawning time.

The species of *Curimatus* are best cared for in aquaria with stony or coarse gravel bottoms (basalt chips). Instead of plants provide plenty of root-systems, pieces of wood, pendant *Monstera* aerial roots, and other such things. The water should be not too fresh and somewhat peaty. Preferred temperature 22–24 °C. Not particular about food; supplementary plant food should be given. Not yet bred in captivity. 1920/ – .

Curimatus latior (*Spix* and *Agassiz* 1829) (Fig. 274)
Middle and lower Amazon region; to 20 cm.

D 12; A about 15; LL 100–110. Shape typical of the genus, but distinguished from other *Curimatus* spp. by the very small scales and sharp ventral keel. Body uniformly light brown (walnut-shell colour); flanks and belly more or less brightly shining silver, often with a light bluish sheen. Fins colourless. Especially characteristic of this species is the large eye, whose iris is a bright shining yellow inside and black outside.

Sex-distinctions not so far described.

Care, as given for *C. argenteus*. Very rarely imported. 1913/ – .

Curimatus mivarti *Steindachner* 1879 (Fig. 258)
R. Magdalena basin; to 20 cm.

D 12; A 13; V 10; LL 69–70. Shape typical of the genus. Scales small. Anterior rays of anal fin prolonged. Uniformly silvery, with a very pronounced and beautiful steel-blue sheen, especially on the back and the upper parts of the flanks. Lower half of the body more grey-silver; belly white. A fine green-silver longitudinal band is scarcely apparent. A grey blotch at the root of the caudal fin only rarely present. Fins colourless, with the exception of the anal whose centre may be a strong red colour. Outer part of the dorsal fin, as well as the ends of the caudal lobes, usually dark-spotted.

Sex-distinctions in coloration not known.

Care, as given for *C. argenteus* above. Not yet bred in captivity. 1926/ – .

Laemolyta taeniata (*Kner* 1858) (Fig. 263)
Middle Amazon and tributaries; to 25 cm.

D 12–13; A 10–11; LL 41–45. Body form and finnage, as given for *Anostomus anostomus*. Cleft of mouth more strongly inclined upwards. Upperside chocolate-brown; flanks light brown above, faint yellow-brown towards the belly, with a bluish or violet sheen by reflected light; underside yellowish to white. Especially characteristic of this species are a broad, dark longitudinal band running from the

195

snout to the root of the tail and four broad, very vaguely delineated transverse bands. (These markings appear only weakly by day but more strongly by night.) Fins colourless, adipose fin usually brownish.

Older ♂♂ have the upper lobe of the caudal fin somewhat enlarged.

Care, as given for *Anostomus anostomus*. Not yet reared in captivity. 1913/+.

Leporinus affinis *Günther* 1884 (Fig. 212)

The genus *Leporinus*, exclusively confined to South America east of the Andes, comprises fishes with an elongate, torpedo-shaped body which is only slightly compressed. Especially characteristic is the conical head, tapering to a point, with the relatively small and meagrely-toothed mouth whose hare-lipped form is indicated in the generic name *Leporinus* (= a young hare). Lateral line present. Most of the species are herbivores and inhabit gravelly sluggish streams. In many species the very attractive coloration of the young is progressively replaced by a more inconspicuous garb with increasing age. Almost all the species are head-standers.

L. affinis is widely distributed through South America, from the Orinoco to the Rio Paraguay region; to 25 cm.

D 12; A 11; V 11; LL 43. Coloration of younger fishes: clay-yellow to brilliant emon or golden-yellow with nine complete, deep black transverse bars. The first of these passes over the head between the eyes. There is also a black band following the edge of the lower jaw. Fins delicate grey or quite colourless.

Sex-distinctions in coloration are not known.

Care, as given for *Anostomus anostomus* (see. p. 190), but a gravelly bottom is more appropriate for *Leporinus*. The fishes require supplementary plant-food (lettuce, algae, rolled oats) and very frequent changes of fresh water. In general very hardy and peaceful. Not yet bred in captivity. 1912/+.

Leporinus fasciatus (*Bloch* 1795) (Fig. 264)

Widely distributed through South America, from Guiana and the Orinoco region to the La Plata basin in the far south; to 30 cm.

Figs. 263–266

Fig. 263. *Laemolyta taeniata;* adult, reduced.
Fig. 264. *Leporinus fasciatus* (Black-banded Leporinus); adult, greatly reduced.
Fig. 265. *Leporinus leschenaulti;* adult, greatly reduced.
Fig. 266. *Leporinus frederici;* adult, very greatly reduced.

D 12; A 11; V 11; LL 42. Very similar to the previous species, but with ten somewhat more slender black transverse bars. In this case too there is a dark band running along the edge of the lower jaw and between the eyes. According to Arnold and Ahl (1936) the ♂♂ are distinguished by their more slender build and more orange-yellow coloured snout and throat.

Care and peculiarities, as given for the previous species. 1912/+.

Leporinus frederici (*Bloch* 1795) (Fig. 266)
From Guiana to the Amazon; to 35 cm.

D 12; A 11; V 9; LL 38–39. Shape as given for *L. affinis*. Upperside grey; flanks yellow-grey with a slight silver sheen; caudal peduncle bright yellow; underside yellowish. From the back numerous irregular dark transverse bars extend to the lower part of the flanks. More dark spots on the midline of the body, of which the first (on the lower half of the hind end of the dorsal fin) and last (at the root of the tail) are especially large and prominent. A black band between the eyes and along the lower jaw. Fins colourless; adipose fin dark-edged. Anal fin, according to Arnold and Ahl (1936), coloured blackish.

Sex-distinctions in coloration not so far described.

Care and peculiarities, as given for *L. affinis*. 1913/+.

Leporinus leschenaulti *Cuvier* and *Valenciennes* 1848 (Fig. 265)
Very widely distributed through South America, Guiana, Amazon Basin, Rio Paraguay; to 25 cm.

D 12–13; A 11–12; LL 37–39. Body somewhat stockier than in other *Leporinus* spp. Coloration, according to Arnold and Ahl:–ground-colour grey blue, with four sharply contrasted large black spots. A black lozenge-shaped blotch at the root of the tail. Fins colourless.

Sex-distinctions in coloration not so far described.

Care and peculiarities, as given for *L. affinis*. 1912/–.

Leporinus megalepis (*Günther* 1863) (Fig. 275)
Northern South America, including the Amazon system; to 20 cm.

D 12; A 11 (–12); V 9; LL 33–36. Shape as given for *L. affinis*. Scales strikingly large. Young fishes of about 10 cm. length are very brilliantly coloured: according to Arnold:–upperside dark green; flanks golden-yellow, shining strongly by reflected light; underside yellowish. A black transverse bar over the head between the eyes; another running bridle-like from the eyes around the lower jaw. Three vermiform bands on the gill-cover. Darker transverse bands between the head and the dorsal fin; behind these three large, round, pale-margined spots. Vertical fins ochre-yellow with dark bands and streaks; adipose fin bright red.

Sex-distinctions in coloration not so far described.

This species swims in an almost normal attitude, only slightly inclined forward.

Care and peculiarities, as given for *L. affinis*. 1934/+.

Leporinus melanopleura *Günther* 1864 (Fig. 276)
West Brazil, between the Amazon R. and Rio de Janeiro; to 20 cm.

D 12; A 11; LL 35–37. Body somewhat less elongate than in other *Leporinus* spp. Upperside olive-brown; flanks delicate brownish, yellowish-brown towards the belly; underside yellowish. Caudal peduncle with a reddish-violet sheen and numerous fine brown dots. A shining greenish to brownish longitudinal band extends from the gill-cover to the root of the tail. Fins delicate yellowish or colourless. Dorsal and anal fins of large fishes occasionally dark-edged; according to Rachow this characterises ♂♂.

Care and peculiarities, as given for *L. affinis*. 1926/−.

Leporinus striatus *Kner* 1859 (Fig. 277)
Matto Grosso, Marañon, R. Magdalena, also in other localities; to 25 cm.

D 10–12; A 9–10; LL 35–37. Shape typical of genus. Back and flanks brownish (like a walnut-shell); underside yellowish. Of the longitudinal stripes (see Fig. 277) the middle dark brown one always stands out conspicuously; the upper and the lowest stripes, being of a paler brown colour, are not very striking. Fins colourless; base of anal fin occasionally brown.

Sex-distinctions in coloration not known.

Care and peculiarities, as given for *L. affinis*. 1935/+.

Prochilodus insignis *Schomburgk* 1841 (Fig. 158)
To the genus *Prochilodus*, widely distributed through South America, belong larger fishes which in many places are valued as food. Many species exhibit a very brilliant colouring in youth. Body elongate, strongly compressed, deep anteriorly. Caudal peduncle long. The large, deeply-forked caudal fin often bears striking markings. The distensible mouth, modified to form a suctorial disc-like structure with which the fishes can graze on algae on the bottom, is characteristic. The lips are thick and beset with fine papillae.

Prochilodus insignis lives in Guiana and the Amazon basin; to 35 cm.

199

D 9–10; A 9–10; LL about 45. Body typical of the genus. Young silvery with bluish to greenish sheen. Lower part of the body and belly delicate reddish or violet. Numerous dark streaks on the flanks, which are arranged in longitudinal rows and are generally prominent on the caudal peduncle. Fins delicate yellow-green. Dorsal fin with dark blue curved stripes. Caudal fin with 5–7 dark blue parallel bars. Anal fin likewise with longitudinal bars. Pectoral and ventral fins reddish. Older fishes essentially self-coloured.

Sex-distinctions in coloration not yet described.

This species, unfortunately never so lovely as when young, should be kept in large aquaria, well-covered (the fish is a good leaper and loves it!) and provided with root-systems and pieces of wood which offer possible hiding-places. Peaceful and very lively, especially in shoals. Temperature 22–26 °C. Plant food is of primary importance, such as algae, cooked spinach, lettuce, soaked rolled oats, but animal food should also be given, especially waterfleas. Not yet bred in captivity. 1910/ –.

Prochilodus taeniurus (*Valenciennes* 1847) (Fig. 283)
Amazon region; to 30 cm.

D 10; A 10; LL about 76. Similarly shaped and coloured to the previous species. Scales very small. *P. taeniurus* is altogether more yellowish and the belly is not reddish. Flanks with a dark longitudinal streak, which begins about the level of the dorsal fin and runs to the caudal fin. Longitudinal rows of streaks absent (see above). Dorsal fin with a large, dark blotch at its base. Anal fin without markings. Eye golden yellow.

Sex-distinctions not so far described.

Care, as given for the previous species. 1912/ –.

Tylobranchus maculosus Eigenmann 1912 (Fig. 285)
Guiana, in coastal waters, Rio Negro; to 15 cm.

D 12; A 9; V 10; LL 26–27. The general appearance of this species is suggestive

Plate 45

Fig. 267. *Distichodus lusosso;* 30 cm. specimen in the Hellabrunn Aquarium, Munich. (Original)

Fig. 268. *Distichodus sexfasciatus;* 20 cm. specimen in the Hellabrunn Aquarium, Munich. (Original)

Fig. 269. *Distichodus altus;* 16 cm. specimen in the Hellabrunn Aquarium, Munich. (Original)

Plate 45

Plate 46

Plate 46

Fig. 270. *Nannaethiops tritaeniatus* (Three-striped African Characin); adults, enlarged; above ♂, below ♀. (Original)

Fig. 271. *Nannaethiops unitaeniatus* (One-striped African Characin); adults, somewhat enlarged; above ♀, below ♂. (Original)

Fig. 272. *Nannaethiops geisleri;* ripe fishes, somewhat enlarged; left ♂, right ♀. (Original)

of *Chilodus punctatus*, but a sound distinguishing character is provided by the very different shape of the anal fin (Fig. 285). *T. maculosus* also cannot be said to be a typical head-stander. Upperside light brown to chestnut brown; flanks delicate clay-colour or grey-yellow, with a dull silver sheen; underside yellowish to white. From the tip of the snout onto the middle caudal rays extends a blackish longitudinal band, above and below which run parallel rows of coarse spots. Fins yellowish. Dorsal fin with a black leading-edge and tip. Adipose fin bright brown.

A marking-variant of *T. maculosus* has the longitudinal band broken into spots at the level of the pectoral fin. According to Arnold the ♂♂ are characterised by a slimmer form and more intense coloration.

Care, as given for *Chilodus punctatus*. Not yet bred in captivity. 1924/+.

Family Hemiodontidae

Characin-like *Ostariophysi* of South America which are separated from the typical Characins by their dentition; in fact in most of them the lower jaw is toothless. The scientific name *Hemiodontidae* (= half-toothed ones) is given in allusion to this peculiarity. Many of the smallest and at the same time most brilliantly coloured species are favourite pets which are very hardy in captivity. In the older classification the *Hemiodontidae* were ranked as a sub-family of the *Characidae*.

Characidium fasciatum *Reinhardt* 1866 (Fig. 207)
Widely distributed through South America, from the Orinoco region to the La Plata basin; to 10 cm.

D 11; A 7–8; LL 35–36. Body elongate, compressed. Lateral line complete. Very variable in regard to markings and coloration, in correspondence with its

201

wide distribution. Clay-yellow to olive-brown. Upperside scarcely darker; underside very pale. A conspicuous broad dark longitudinal band usually extends from the snout to the root of the tail, where it runs into an almost always very dark blotch; frequently this longitudinal band is regularly interrupted. Very irregular brown transverse bands extend from the back to the middle of the side. Fins translucent, colourless.

♀ more robust; dorsal fin without any markings.
♂ slimmer; dorsal fin often with fine brown spots at the base.

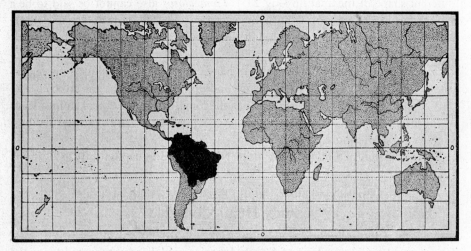

Fig. 273
Distribution of the *Hemiodontidae*

This lively, peaceful fish, remarkable for its jerky movements, does very well in captivity. Its principal requirements are a partly soft, partly stony bottom, clear, not too old, water and the provision of suitable hiding-places. Not very warmth-loving, 18–22 °C. Live food of all kinds, especially worms. Breeding not

Figs. 274–277

Fig. 274. *Curimatus latior;* young, natural size.
Fig. 275. *Leporinus megalepis;* half-grown, with characteristic markings.
Fig. 276. *Leporinus melanopleura;* adult, reduced.
Fig. 277. *Leporinus striatus;* adult, reduced.

difficult. After vigorous driving the minute eggs are shed indiscriminately among plants and usually fall to the bottom. The young fishes hatch in 30–40 hours and swim freely after 3–4 days, when they must be given a plentiful supply of the finest live food (nauplii). 1913/+.

Characidium rachovi *Regan* 1913 (Fig. 286)
Southern Brazil, neighbourhood of Curitiba; to 7 cm.

D 13–15; A 8–9; LL 32. Not so strongly compressed and deeper than the previous species. Upperside brown to yellow-brown. Flanks clay-yellow, with a narrow dark longitudinal band ending in a transverse blotch at the root of the tail, and further usually quite indistinct transverse bars on the upper half of the body. Underside pale yellowish. Fins, with the exception of the caudal, transparent colourless. Dorsal, anal and ventral fins in part with rows of reddish spots. Caudal fin yellowish to delicate reddish.

♀ more robust; dorsal and anal fins without dark margins.
♂ slimmer; dorsal and anal fins often dark margined.

Care and breeding, as given for the previous species. 1912/–.

Hemiodus gracilis *Günther* 1864
Amazon R., Guiana; to 16 cm.

D 11; A 10; V 11–12; LL 42. Very similar to the following better-known species in shape and coloration. In life only distinguished from *H. semitaeniatus* by its somewhat slimmer body and an orange-red to blue-red stripe near the corner of the lower caudal lobe. The upper lobe of the caudal is often tinted light orange as well.

Care and peculiarities, as given for the following species. 1935/+.

Hemiodus semitaeniatus *Kner* 1859 (Fig. 284)
Widely distributed through South America, Guiana, middle and lower Amazon and its southern tributaries; to 20 cm.

Plate 47

Fig. 278. *Distichodus rostratus;* 35 cm. specimen in the Hellabrunn Aquarium, Munich. (Original)
Fig. 279. *Citharinus congicus;* 7 cm. young. (Photo Dr. Foersch)
Fig. 280. *Gasteropelecus sternicla* (Common Hatchetfish); adult, natural size. (Original)

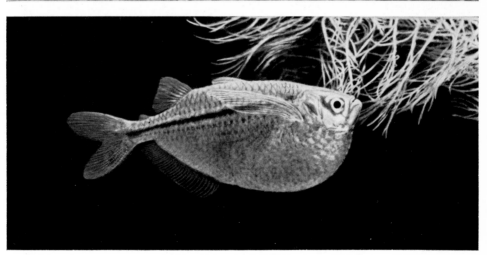

Plate 47

Plate 48

Plate 48

Fig. 281. *Leucaspius delineatus* (Moderlieschen); adults, somewhat reduced. (Photo P. Unger)

Fig. 282. *Abramis sapa* (Zobel); young, somewhat reduced. (Photo P. Unger)

D 11; A 9–11; V 11; LL 56–58. Body symmetrically slim, compressed. Anal fin relatively small. Caudal fin large, deeply forked, the lobes very divergent. Uniformly shining silver. Upperside olive-brown to silver. Flanks shining brilliant greenish to steel-blue, according to the lighting. Underside white-silver. From a usually very distinct round black blotch on the flank a fine dark line extends to the root of the tail and thence, much broadened, into the lower caudal lobe. Fins transparent, glass-clear. Upper caudal lobe often slightly blackish; tips of both lobes occasionally delicate red.

Sex-distinctions in coloration have not been described.

This very elegant and extraordinarily swift and agile shoaling fish only prospers in really large aquaria which give it room to move about. It is not a very delicate species and will accept a variety of live foods and, above all, plant material (lettuce); very voracious. Preferred temperature around 23 °C. A shoal of *Hemiodus* makes a lovely picture. Not yet bred in captivity. 1912/+.

Genus Nannostomus (including Poecilobrycon): Care and Breeding

The Pencilfishes have often been the subject of systematic investigations in recent years, without any substantially satisfactory result having been attained. Even the comprehensive and interesting study by Hoedeman (*The Amsterdam Naturalist, I,* 1951) is painfully unconvincing. From the genus *Nannostomus* described by Günther in 1872, Eigenmann (1909) removed a species with an adipose fin for which he erected the genus *Poecilobrycon.* It is apparent, however, that the adipose fin in both these nominal genera is by no means a constant and always distinctly diagnostic character; on the contrary, it occasionally appears in *Nannostomus* spp. or is absent in so-called *Poecilobrycon* spp.

For various reasons, above all in the effort not to anticipate the urgently necessary definitive study of the Pencilfishes, all the species are here referred

18 Sterba

205

to *Nannostomus*, thereby essentially sustaining the generic definition of Steindachner (1876).

The Pencilfishes, exclusively native to Central and northern South America, are interesting fishes and, owing to their small size and attractive colours, very popular aquarium pets. In their natural haunts almost all the species inhabit small, slow-flowing, weedy or shaded waters of a soft peaty quality, rather like the dark water of our moorland streams, or even the marshy shallows of the larger rivers. Many species are fishes of the surface layers, which obtain their prey – predominantly insects – from the surface film. As an adaptation to this habit of feeding some Pencilfishes take up an oblique position in which they swim quietly with the head upward, as for example *Nannostomus eques*. The motion of many species, alternating between sudden forward sallies and equally unexpected pauses in the inclined position, is very suggestive of the progress of a mouse. Almost all *Nannostomus* spp. exhibit a specifically-characteristic dark-adapted coloration (nocturnal coloration).

These fishes should be kept in richly-planted aquaria, either small or large. Of paramount importance is the quality of the water, which should be soft, peaty and not too fresh. Almost all Pencilfishes are very warmth-loving and demand temperatures between 25–28°C. and a varied diet of live food.

According to H. J. Franke the sexes of almost all the imported species may by recognised with certainty by the shape of the anal fin which, in the ♂♂, is always rounded below or evenly waved, in the ♀♀ straight or emarginate. In species having a white-edged anal fin and light tips to the ventral fins, the characters are always more strongly shown in the ♂♂. Ripe ♀♀ can often be

Figs. 283–286

Fig. 283. *Prochilodus taeniurus;* young, natural size.
Fig. 284. *Hemiodus semitaeniatus;* reduced.
Fig. 285. *Tylobranchus maculosus;* somewhat reduced.
Fig. 286. *Characidium rachovi;* about natural size.

easily recognised by the eggs in the oviduct which, when the fishes are viewed against the light, shine through the body-wall like rows of yellow pearls.

For breeding, use small all-glass tanks (4–6 litres) and very soft, well-matured spring water which has been filtered through peat for a short time; alternatively, softened tapwater or rainwater in which several *Myriophyllum* tufts have stood for 3–4 weeks. *Nannostomus beckfordi beckfordi, N. b. anomalus, N.b.aripirangensis, N.harrisoni, N.bifasciatus,* and *N.marginatus* all spawn among fine-leaved plants and are great spawn-robbers; pairs of *N.marginatus* have occasionally been seen to go so far as to devour their own newlaid eggs. For the species named above, the breeding tank should be providedwith dense *Myriophyllum* and must not be placed in too light a position.

N.trifasciatus likes to spawn in sunshine, among *Riccia* or among the submerged leaves of *Salvinia,* without specially lying in wait for the eggs. *N.eques* and *N.ocellatus,* on the other hand, spawn on broad-leaved plants, preferably on *Hygrophila.*

The pairs are put into the breeding tank in the evening and often spawn, after numerous false pairings, the following morning. After each mating, in which the fishes quiver slightly with their flanks firmly approximated, 1–3 eggs are laid to a total of rarely more than 80–100. The pairs may, if they are well fed *(Enchytraeidae),* often be put together again after 2–4 days. At 26–28°C. the young hatch after 18–26 hours and at first lie on the bottom, later hanging vertically on the water plants or from the sides of the tank and swimming freely after 4–5 days. Feed them with the smallest nauplii or rotifers. Growth not very rapid. The usually dark juvenile coloration, which appears very early, remains for quite a long time. A peculiarity of the young is the 'oar' or embryonic adipose fin which lies, like a little flag, in front of the originally somewhat downwardly directed caudal fin and serves for locomotion.

According to Hoedeman (1951), the variability of *Poecilobrycon eques* (Steindachner 1876) is so great that *P.unifasciatus* (Steindachner 1876), *P.ocellatus* Eigenmann (1909) as well as *P.auratus* Eigenmann (1909) may all be included as synonyms. Perhaps Hoedeman has been misled by Rachow's figures (Holly, Meinken & Rachow, 1937, 529/30) which also show *P.eques* under the name *P.unifasciatus*, or by other contributory circumstances; at any rate these opinions certainly cannot be sustained. *Nannostomus* (or *Poecilobrycon*) *unifasciatus* and *N.eques* are very distinctly separated species which are well distinguished, not only morphologically but also in their behaviour, and do not interbreed. I have never been able to observe, like Hoedeman (1951), typical *N.* (or *P.*) *ocellatus* present in a brood of *N.* (or *P.*) *eques*. It is important always to make the comparison between full-grown animals, for young fishes may exhibit certain similarities. The genus *Nannobrycon* was established under assumptions which cannot be accepted.

Nannostomus beckfordi beckfordi *Günther* 1872 (Fig. 242) Golden Pencilfish
West Guiana; to 6·5 cm.

I consider the form distributed as 'Gold Anomalus' (Meinken 1951, *Die Aquarien- und Terrarien-Zeitschrift 4*, p. 147) to be *N. beckfordi beckfordi*. Imported specimens, and also bred specimens, exhibit on the gill-cover a more or less strong and usually downwardly-directed blotch-like broadening of the dark longitudinal band; that is, the marking which is always given as the most important distinguishing character between *N. beckfordi* and *N. anomalus*. By the term 'Gold Anomalus' Meinken wished to indicate that these fishes were typical *N. anomalus* in their body-form but had a stronger gold sheen. Nedl (1951) was the first to announce that the 'Gold Anomalus' was not only distinct from typical *N. anomalus* but also exhibited a distinct mode of behaviour. Platz (1953) extended these observations to the breeding behaviour. According to H.J.Franke, in the 'Gold Anomalus' the post-embryonic hair-stripe marking appears considerably later than in *N. anomalus*.

D 8–10; A 10–11; LL 22–23. Body elongate, torpedo-shaped, moderately compressed. Head rather acute. Adipose fin absent. Lobes of caudal fin equal. The dorsal fin arises exactly over the ventral fins. Back fawn; sides yellowish to yellow-silvery, belly white. A blackish to deep black longitudinal band extends from the tip of the snout over the eye to the root of the tail, and is accompanied above by a golden, and this again by an iridescent greenish, zone. Scales, at least above the middle of the sides, dark-edged. Fins yellowish to reddish; anal fin and lower lobe of caudal a beautiful brick-red.

209

♀ more stocky; general coloration paler. Anal fin with an angular emargination below. At spawning time the eggs can be recognised in the long, produced oviduct when the fish is viewed aginst the light.

♂ slimmer; red colouring stronger. Anal fin rounded below. Hinder half of body ink-red at spawning time.

Care and breeding, see p.206. The ♂♂ stand obliquely facing one another during threat-display. 1951.

Nannostomus beckfordi anomalus *Steindachner* 1876 (Fig.241)   Golden Pencilfish
Guiana, Paraná, Rio Negro, middle and lower Amazon; to 4·5 cm.

D 9–10; A 10–11; LL 22–24. Distinguished from the previous form only by the certainly very variable coloration and by the behaviour. Upperside grey-green to yellow-brown; flanks yellowish; belly whitish to delicate yellow. Scales delicately dark-edged. From the tip of the mouth, over the eye to the root of the tail and thence occasionally onto the middle caudal rays (!) there extends a brown-black band, accompanied above by a golden band and, in fine animals (usually only in ♂♂), sometimes further accompanied to some extent by a red stripe. At night two dark transverse bars become prominent.

♀ all fins colourless.
♂ lower lobe of caudal fin and the anal fin carmine-red; when excited, blood-red. Ventral fins without bluish tips.

Care and breeding simple, see p.206. Rival ♂♂ rest horizontal and strike one another rapidly, at the same time quivering with their bodies together. 1911/+.

Nannostomus beckfordi aripirangensis *Meinken* 1931   Golden Pencilfish
Aripiranga Island in the lower Amazon; to 4 cm.

D 10–11; A 9–10; LL 23–24. This subspecies is very similar to the previous one, with which it very readily hybridises. Indeed, in my opinion, no new wild stock has been imported since the War. All the fishes bred in captivity and so designated have been the results of crosses with *N. beckfordi anomalus*, the hybrids being practically as viable as the genuine form. Wild stock may be distinguished from the true *N.b.anomalus* by the following characters (partly taken from Meinken):–

1. Red stripe over the golden longitudinal band continuous and brilliant.

2. A fine red line extending from the insertion of the pectoral fin to the anal fin.

3. Ventral fins blood-red with bluish tips.

4. In the ♂♂ at spawning time the whole caudal peduncle is blood-red.

♀ with a delicate red blotch on the dorsal fin.

Care and breeding, see p. 205. Behaviour as in *N. beckfordi anomalus*.

Nannostomus bifasciatus *Hoedeman* 1954 (Figs. 245, 262)   Two-banded Pencilfish
Surinam; to 6 cm.

D 9; A 9 (10); LL 23–24. Body elongate, torpedo-shaped. Adipose fin at most developed in the form of a single fin-ray. The dorsal fin is inserted opposite the ventrals. *N. bifasciatus* swims in a horizontal position. Ground-colour silver-white to delicate yellowish. Two dark, usually almost pure black, longitudinal bands are present, of which the lower is substantially denser and runs from the tip of the snout, over the eye, to the root of the tail; this band is often turned downwards in older fishes. The upper longitudinal band, often condensed into a spot, runs from the upper edge of the eye to the upper edge of the caudal peduncle and may be very indistinct against the dark colour of the back. Bases of the caudal and anal fins delicate red throughout. For nocturnal coloration, see Fig. 262.

♀ ventral fins without bluish-white tips; a shining green-gold stripe on each side
   of the snout.

♂ ventral fins with bluish-white tips; zone between the longitudinal bands golden;
   snout with a shining green-gold blotch.

Care and breeding, see p. 205. According to H. J. Franke, spawning takes place among fine-leaved plants, as in most other species. 1953.

Nannostomus marginatus *Eigenmann* 1909 (Fig. 211)   Dwarf Pencilfish
Surinam, West Guiana; to 4 cm.

D 10; A 11–12; LL 21. Body shorter and more stocky than in other *Nanno-stomus* species. Adipose fin absent. *N. marginatus* swims in a horizontal position. One of the most beautiful members of the genus. Back olive-green to brown with a black mid-line; underside yellowish to silver-white. Three dark brown to black longitudinal bands, the middle and at the same time broadest of these accompanied above by a brilliant red stripe. The zones between the longitudinal bands are yellow to golden. Dorsal fin with a black leading-edge and a crimson blotch. Anal fin orange with a red and black margin. Ventral fins with a red blotch. Nocturnal coloration:–a larger, darker blotch on the dorsal fin and a small dark spot on the gill-cover.

211

♀ anal fin cut straight posteriorly, pointed. At spawning time the eggs are distinctly visible in the protracted oviducts when the fish is viewed against the light.

♂ anal fin rounded posteriorly, completely black-edged.

Care and breeding, see p. 206. The ravenous appetite of the adults toward even the freshly-spawned eggs makes the economic breeding of Dwarf Pencilfishes a far from easy matter. Very thick *Myriophyllum* clumps among which the eggs can fall, a not too light position and the prompt removal of the parents after spawning are precautions which all attempts at breeding must observe. With nourishing food the pairs can be brought to breed every 3–4 days. In slightly acid, soft water the egg-membranes swell up very strongly. 1928/+.

Nannostomus trifasciatus *Steindachner* 1876 (Figs. 246, 262) Three-banded Pencilfish West Guiana, middle Amazon, Rio Negro; to 6 cm.

D 9–10; A 9–12; LL 24–27. Body very slim. The adipose fin may be distinctly developed or quite absent; when present it is always situated behind the level of the anal fin. *N. trifasciatus* swims in a horizontal position. The most beautiful member of the genus. General pattern of markings and coloration similar to those of *N. marginatus*. Back olive-brown; belly white. A black longitudinal band from the tip of the snout to the lower part of the caudal root, with a further thinner black longitudinal band running back from the eye parallel with this. A broader, only weakly-indicated, black longitudinal band from the pectoral fin to the anal. A row of golden scales between the middle and upper longitudinal bands. A dark red blotch behind the gill-cover. Dorsal, ventral and caudal fins likewise with red blotches. Upper part of the tip of the snout gleaming gold. Ventral and anal fins with bluish-white tips. Nocturnal coloration greenish-grey to yellowish-grey with three broad, dark, transverse bars (Fig. 262).

♀ body-form more rounded; coloration somewhat paler.

♂ as described above.

Care and breeding, see p. 206. Old water from woodland ponds is best for breeding. No special breeding conditions have so far been specified. 1912/+.

Plate 49

Fig. 287. *Alburnus alburnus* (Bleak); young, somewhat enlarged. (Original)

Fig. 288. *Aspius aspius* (Rapfen); large, 65 cm. specimen in the Hellabrunn Aquarium, Munich. (Original)

Fig. 289. *Leuciscus virgo* (Frauenerfling), a relation of the Roach; 6 cm. young. (Original)

Plate 49

Plate 50

Plate 50

Fig. 290. *Cyprinus carpio* (Common Carp); adult Mirror Carp, about 80 cm. long, in the Hellabrunn Aquarium, Munich. (Original).

Fig. 291. *Cyprinus carpio;* adult specimen from the Danube, about 1 m. long, in the Hellabrunn Aquarium, Munich. (Original)

Fig. 292. *Abramis brama* (Bream); half-grown specimens, about 20 cm. long, in the Hellabrunn Aquarium, Munich. (Original)

Nannostomus espei (*Meinken* 1956) (Fig. 243)
(*Poecilobrycon* of some authors) (as below, N. harrisoni)
South America, without any precise locality; to 4 cm.

Exact fin-formula not so far described.

LL about 35; TR about 5–6 between D and V. Body slim, spindle-shaped. Mouth narrow. Snout pointed. Adipose fin present. Ground colour delicate grey-brown, very pale towards the underside. Belly white. From the snout, over the eye to the root of the tail extends a golden longitudinal band which, in the head region, is underlined by a black stripe. All scales, especially those on the upper half of the body, dark-edged. Four very prominent oblique black bars on the lower half of the body. Underside of caudal peduncle black. Fins glass-clear or delicate red-brown, the lower lobe of the caudal occasionally with dark longitudinal stripes.

♀ rather more stocky, profile of belly more strongly rounded.
♂ golden longitudinal band as a rule somewhat brighter. Anterior rays of anal lightly pigmented.

Care and breeding of this very attractive species, as given on p. 205. No details of any special peculiarities have yet been noted. At night an additional bar appears between the first two oblique bars, extending from the dorsal fin to the edge of the belly. The species rests slightly obliquely in the water with the head up. 1955.

Nannostomus harrisoni *Eigenmann* 1909
(*Poecilobrycon* of some authors)
West Guiana, near Christianburg; to 6 cm.

D 9–10; A 10; LL 26–27(–29). Body elongate, torpedo-shaped. The distinct adipose fin arises behind the level of the anal fin; the dorsal fin somewhat behind the level of the ventrals. *N. harrisoni* swims in a horizontal position. The yellow-brown to chocolate-brown upperside is here sharply delimited by a broad straw-yellow longitudinal band which extends from the tip of the snout into the upper lobe of the caudal fin. Along the lower half of this band is a nearly black longitudinal band, which runs from the lower jaw over the eye onto the middle caudal rays. Underside yellowish to silvery, spotted between the ventral and anal fins. Caudal and anal fins light reddish. The last anal ray is occasionally black.

Sex-distinctions unknown.

Care, see p. 206. Probably not yet imported.

Nannostomus unifasciatus *Steindachner* 1876 (Figs. 244, 262)   One-lined Pencilfish
(*Poecilobrycon* of some authors)
Middle and lower Amazon and tributaries; to 6·5 cm.

D 9; A 11; V 8; LL 25–26. This is the most elongate of all the *Nannostomus* spp.; in full-grown animals the body-depth is contained 4–$4\frac{1}{2}$ times in the body-length without caudal fin (= Standard Length). Dorsal fin inserted somewhat behind the level of the ventrals, about an eye-diameter behind the middle of the Standard Length. Lobes of caudal fin similarly shaped (!). The adipose fin arises about the level of the hinder end of the anal. The species swims rather obliquely and keeps near the bottom. Yellow-brown to golden brown with a dark brown margined longitudinal band from the mouth to the lower part of the caudal peduncle; a golden zone above this. Scales dark-edged. Base of caudal fin reddish, lower lobe in particular dark towards its edge. Anal fin reddish. Ventral fins red with whitish or bluish tips. A brilliant iridescent reddish-yellow blotch on the snout. For nocturnal coloration, see Fig. 262.

♀ anal fin margin cut straight.
♂ anal fin rounded below; anterior edge more brilliantly coloured.

Care, see p. 206. Not yet bred. A very beautiful, elegant species. 1953.

Nannostomus ocellatus (*Eigenmann* 1909) (Figs. 259, 262)   Tail-eye Pencilfish
(*Poecilobrycon* of some authors)
Guiana, Amazon; to 6 cm.

D 10; A 10–11; LL 28. Body-form somewhat like that of *N. unifasciatus*, but the lower lobe of the caudal is distinctly enlarged. The adipose fin arises at the level of the hinder end of the anal. The species carries itself obliquely when swimming quietly (the long axis of the body making an angle of about 30° with the bottom). Clay-yellow to pale brown or even grey-brown. The dark longitudinal band becomes pale-edged below and extends into the lower lobe of the caudal fin

214

where, with the addition of white and red colours, it forms a large peacock ocellus. Especially characteristic (in dead specimens as well) is a small, dark, white-edged stripe in the middle of the caudal fin. Belly clear white. Anal fin with a brilliant white leading-edge, the hinder part occasionally blackish. A shining blotch at the tip of the snout. For nocturnal coloration, see Fig. 262.

♀ more robust. Anal fin margin cut straight.
♂ slimmer.

Care, see p. 206. To a modest degree already bred. This peaceful, elegant species is among the most beautiful Pencilfishes. 1949.

Nannostomus eques *Steindachner* 1876 (Figs. 260, 262)   Tube-mouthed Pencilfish
(*Poecilobrycon* of some authors)
Middle Amazon, Rio Negro (?); to 5 cm.

D 9; A 9–11; V 8; LL 22–23. *N. eques* is more stocky than *N. unifasciatus* or *N. ocellatus*. Head pointed. Lower lobe of caudal distinctly enlarged. The adipose fin is very small or quite absent; it arises somewhat behind the level of the hinder end of the anal. When swimming quietly this species carries itself very obliquely, often almost vertically. Pale grey-brown to dirty silver with five longitudinal rows of dark blotches, or longitudinal bands, on the back (a median one and two lateral ones on each side). A broader and very striking, anteriorly dark, posteriorly dark wine-red, longitudinal band runs from the snout over the eye into the lower lobe of the caudal which it quite fills; this band sometimes breaks up, especially anteriorly, into isolated blotches. The edges of the scales within the band are often pale. Caudal fin:–upper lobe glass-clear, lower lobe wine-red at the base and black distally. The lower lobe of the caudal is often delimited from the upper by a white curved line (Fig. 260). Anal fin red and black, with a white margin. Ventral fins in fine ♂♂ with brilliant blue-white tips. Nocturnal coloration: two broad, somewhat oblique blurred transverse bars. (Fig. 262).

♀ usually not so brightly-coloured; more robust.
♂ substantially slimmer; profile of belly almost straight.

Care and breeding, see p. 206. This species spawns for preference on *Hygrophila* or *Ludwigia* leaves; well-matched pairs spawn very readily. 1910/+.

Family Citharinidae

Ostariophysi, exclusively confined to Africa, which were formerly classed with the true Characins but now, in the modern classification, become separated off as a family by themselves. The major feature of the whole group is the straight lateral line, a character which sharply separates the *Citharinidae* from the true African Characins in which the lateral line is downcurved.

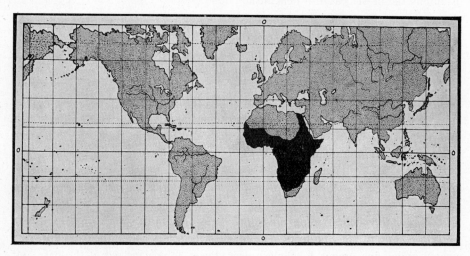

Fig. 293
Distribution of the *Citharinidae*

Among other diagnostic characters are the ctenoid scales. Some of the individual genera are quite distinctive, being, like *Phago* and *Neoborus*, quite extraordinarily shaped. Only the smaller species are suitable for the domestic aquarium; many of the larger ones, on the other hand, are fine exhibits for public aquaria.

Distichodus noboli *Boulenger* 1899 (Fig. 297)
The members of the genus *Distichodus*, exclusively native to Africa, are active river fishes which mainly dwell in the lower water-layers. Body robust, moderately

elongate to stocky, strongly compressed; back high. In most species the relatively small head is characteristically shaped, more or less conical or drawn out into a funnel-shape. Adipose fin and caudal fin partly covered with small scales.

D. noboli lives in the Congo system; to 8 cm.

D 20; A 16; LL 45; TR 9/10. Body-shape typical of the genus; head conical. Lobes of caudal fin rounded. Upperside olive- to chocolate-brown; flanks grey-silvery or even pure silver; underside silvery; chest dark. Scales dark-edged, especially in the lower half of the body. A round dark blotch at the root of the tail. Vertical fins and ventral fins orange to brick-red. Anterior part of dorsal black.

Sex-distinctions unknown.

The peaceful *Distichodus* spp. should be kept only in spacious aquaria. Planting is not recommended since the fishes have a penchant for devouring fine leaves and shoots; moreover different species, and even members of the same species, behave quite individually in this respect. The aquarium may be given a natural appearance by providing hanging roots or branch-systems and in this way the shyness of the fishes can be noticeably diminished. Not too hard water. Preferred temperature 24–27°C. Live food of all kinds in large quantities; occasionally dried foods (rolled oats) are also accepted. Not yet bred in captivity. 1911/+.

The following have also been imported:

Distichodus affinis *Günther* 1873 (Fig. 294)
Mainly in the lower Congo; to 12 cm.

D 16; A 19–21; LL 37–39; TR 7/10. Uniform silver with a light green-blue back. Leading-edge of dorsal fin black, at least in the young. 1935/−.

Distichodus altus *Boulenger* 1899 (Fig. 269)
Mainly in the middle Congo and tributaries; to 20 cm.

D 17–18; A 21–22; LL 40–42; TR 9/11–12. Uniform light bronze colour; a strong golden sheen on the back. Fins often dark. 1953.

Distichodus antonii *Schilthuis* 1891 (Fig. 295)
Whole Congo basin; to 55 cm.

D 22–25; A 13–15; LL 60–66; TR 10–12/12–13. Grey-green to grey-blue with numerous narrow, usually weakly-indicated, transverse bars. Dorsal fin with dark spots. 1953.

217

Distichodus atroventralis *Boulenger* 1901
Congo basin, Stanley Pool; to 42 cm.

D 22–24; A 13–15; LL 68–77; TR 14/14–15. The young are grey-silver or quite delicate rust-red and show 6–10 dark transverse bars. Dorsal fin with dark spots. Ventral fins black. Older fishes uniformly brown-silver. Belly light yellowish. 1953.

Distichodus fasciolatus *Boulenger* 1901 (Fig. 296)
Congo basin; to 30 cm.

D 25–27; A 14–16; LL 68–80; TR about 14/14–16. Brown- to greenish-silver; upperside rather dark, underside pale. Numerous fine, dark transverse bars. Caudal peduncle in young with dark spots or blotches. 1953.

Distichodus lusosso *Schilthuis* 1891 (Fig. 267)
Upper and middle Congo, Stanley Pool; to 40 cm.

D 25–26; A 13–14; LL 70–85; TR 15/15–17. A very lovely species; uniformly more or less brilliant orange with 6–8 dark transverse bars. Dorsal fin in young with dark spots. 1953.

Distichodus rostratus (*Günther* 1864) (Fig. 278)
Nile region, Lake Chad, Senegal and Niger basin, Congo (?); to 60 cm.

D 22–27; A 12–14; LL 80–98; TR about 15/18. Grey to grey-green with a slight silver sheen, occasionally delicate reddish-brown. Young with numerous fine transverse bars. Adults often with fine dark zig-zag lines, formed from the dark edges of the scales. Dorsal fin with dark spots.

Distichodus sexfasciatus *Boulenger* 1897 (Fig. 268)
Whole Congo basin with the exception of the upper reaches; to 25 cm.

D 24–25; A 12–14; LL 60–68; TR 14–16/14–16. More or less reddish-yellow to delicate red-brown; underside pale. 6–7 broad dark transverse bars. Mainly distinguished from the similarly-coloured *D. lusosso* by the substantially blunter snout. 1953.

Figs. 294–297

Fig. 294. *Distichodus affinis;* adult, reduced.
Fig. 295. *Distichodus antonii;* much reduced.
Fig. 296. *Distichodus fasciolatus;* much reduced.
Fig. 297. *Distichodus noboli;* slightly reduced.

Nannaethiops geisleri *Hoedeman* 1956 (Fig. 272)

Lower Congo near Leopoldville; to 2·5 cm.

D 2–3/10–11; A 2/6–7; LL 29–32; TR 10. Like all *Nannaethiops* spp., *N. geisleri* is distinguished from the very similar *Neolebias* spp. (whose caudal fins are not scaly) by the partial scaliness of this fin and by the toothed upper jaw. From the other species of its own genus *N. geisleri* is easily distinguished by its lack of an adipose fin. Coloration of spirit specimens, according to Hoedeman:–back brownish, belly yellowish. On the flanks, occupying the breadth of three scale-rows, a broad deep black longitudinal band running from the hinder edge of the eye over the gill-cover to a deep black vertical ocellus at the end of the caudal peduncle. The back region is thickly sprinkled with melanophores (= black pigment-cells). Fins yellowish, the membrane with scattered melanophores.

Sex-distinctions not known.

Care, as for other *Nannaethiops* spp., see under *N. unitaeniatus* below. 1951.

Nannaethiops tritaeniatus *Boulenger* 1913 (Fig. 270)   Three-striped African Characin

Upper Congo; to 4 cm.

D 3/10–11; A 3/7; LL 34–35; TR 10. Shape similar to that of the next species. Back brownish-olive to fawn, scales dark-edged. Flanks paler. Belly silver, tinged with reddish. Three blackish to deep black, well-nigh parallel, longitudinal bands, of which the median one commences on the snout and runs over the eye straight to the root of the tail; this band becomes broadened to form an elongate oval blotch on the gill-cover and again at the root of the tail. The caudal blotch is edged with gold and never extends onto the middle part of the fin as it does in *Neolebias trilineatus*. The zones between the longitudinal bands are golden. Ventral fins reddish, with blue leading-edges. Dorsal fin yellow-red. Caudal and anal fins reddish to delicate red-brown.

Plate 51

Fig. 298. *Barbus barbus* (Barbel); ripe specimen, 60 cm. long, in the Hellabrunn Aquarium, Munich. (Original)

Fig. 299. *Squalius cephalus* (Chub); 50 cm. specimen, in the Hellabrunn Aquarium, Munich. (Original)

Fig. 300. *Chondrostoma nasus* (Näsling); very large specimen, 50 cm. long, in the Hellabrunn Aquarium, Munich. (Original)

Plate 51

Plate 52

Plate 52

Fig. 301. *Abramis vimba* (Zährte); 20 cm. specimen, in the Hellabrunn Aquarium, Munich. (Original)
Fig. 302. *Tinca tinca* (Tench); half-grown, 12 cm. long. (Original)
Fig. 303. *Carassius carassius* (Crucian Carp); half-grown, deeply-pigmented specimen. (Original)

♀ larger; shining gold all over at spawning time.
♂ smaller; dorsal fin higher; with blood-red longitudinal bands and red fins at spawning time.

Care and breeding, as given for the following species. 1949.

Nannaethiops unitaeniatus *Günther* 1871 (Fig. 271) One-striped African Characin
Widely distributed throughout the whole of Equatorial Africa, from the White Nile to the West Coast; to 6·5 cm.
D 3/10–12; A 3/7; LL 35–38. Body moderately elongated, moderately compressed. Mouth small. Adipose fin quite large. Caudal deeply forked. Lateral line complete. (Maxillary teeth fine.) Back dark brown to brownish-olive; belly and throat yellowish to white with a silvery sheen. From the mouth over the eye to the root of the tail and thence onto the middle caudal rays extends a fine, dark-brown to blue-black longitudinal band which is accompanied above by a gleaming golden or coppery band. The lower half of the caudal peduncle is often reddish. Fins yellowish-grey to green-whitish. Dorsal fin with a black leading-edge and black tip.

♀ somewhat more soberly coloured; body stocky.
♂ coloration as given above; slim. At spawning time the anterior part of the dorsal fin and the upper lobe of the caudal are a magnificent blood-red.

This peaceful, hardy, but almost always somewhat timid species should be kept in large, not too thickly planted aquaria which receive occasional sunshine. It lives almost exclusively in the lower water-layers and fine sand is almost indispensable as bottom-soil. Live food, not choosy. Temperature 23–26 °C. Very large aquaria (40–50 litres) are required for breeding, since this species is very prolific. According to Pinter it is advisable to strew the bottom of the breeding-tank with fine scalded sand; the fishes will not breed on a clean glass bottom (?). The eggs are scattered indiscriminately among plants and over the bottom-soil. Breeding pairs should be removed after spawning. Morning sunshine greatly stimulates willingness to spawn. The young fish hatch after 26–32 hours at 25°C. and swim freely after 5 days. Rearing not difficult.

These fishes only display their beautiful colours in suitable tanks. 1931/+.

Neolebias ansorgei *Boulenger* 1912 (Fig. 231)

The genus *Neolebias* comprises very small *Citharinidae* of moderately elongate to stocky, compressed form. The mouth is small. The adipose fin is usually absent. The caudal fin is not scaly.

The maxillary is often said to be toothless, and Boulenger did indeed use this as a principal generic character. However, a paratype of *N. unifasciatus*, the type species of the genus, in the British Museum (Natural History) does have teeth on the maxillary. This species should probably be referred to *Nannaethiops*, although the remaining species now listed under *Neolebias* do undoubtedly belong to a distinct genus.

Neolebias ansorgei is mainly found in Central Africa, Tschiloango; to 3·5 cm.

D 3/8; A 2/6; LL 29–32; TR 9. Back brownish to green. Flanks delicate grass-green to greenish-blue, iridescent, often with a light violet tinge. Belly yellowish. Occasionally a dark green, pale-bordered shoulder-blotch is clearly visible. A dark green, yellow-bordered transverse bar on the caudal peduncle. A wide, dark, only seldom distinct, longitudinal band, with a brilliant pale green stripe above it. Dorsal, caudal and anal fins pale yellow to red, often margined with black. Ventral fins reddish.

♀ more robust, profile of belly rounded. At the onset of spawning the eggs in the oviduct are clearly visible when the fish is viewed against the light.

♂ profile of belly level. At spawning time all the fins, with the exception of the pectorals, are blood-red.

This very beautiful species is somewhat sensitive, especially to hard water and changes in the water, and always remains very timid and pale in community tanks. It is therefore recommended that the fishes be kept in isolated pairs. *Neolebias*

Figs. 304–308

Fig. 304. *Phago loricatus;* adult, somewhat reduced.
Fig. 305. *Phago maculatus* (Pike Characin); adult, somewhat reduced.
Fig. 306. *Citharinus latus;* greatly reduced.
Fig. 307. *Citharinus citharus;* greatly reduced.
Fig. 308. *Neolebias unifasciatus;* adult, enlarged.

spp. keep to the water-layers over the bottom. Preferred temperature 24–28°C. Small live food. Small, thickly-planted, all-glass tanks are satisfactory for breeding. Temperature 30°C. With butterfly-like movements the ♂ entices the ♀ to a previously selected place in a plant thicket where they remain quivering while 5–10 eggs are laid. Grand total of eggs 300 or more. The young hatch after 20–24 hours and should be reared on the finest food; they grow rapidly and are sexually ripe in 6–7 months. Rearing not easy. 1924/+.

Neolebias landgrafi *E. Ahl* 1928
Cameroons; to 3·5 cm.

D 3/8–9; A 2–3/6–7; LL 33–34; TR 10. Very similar to the previous species as regards the body-form and finnage. The two species also have a great deal in common in their coloration at markings. Upperside olive-brown, often with a rust-red sheen; flanks paler; belly silver with a reddish tinge. From the tip of the snout to a dark transverse band at the root of the tail extends a broad blue band which, according to Ahl (1928), in its anterior third has a series of thickenings (?). In healthy fishes the flanks have a delicate wine-red lustre. The brilliant red colour of the caudal fin base gradually fades out across the caudal lobes. According to Arnold the fins are also dark-edged in *N. landgrafi*. Entirely blood-red at spawning time. Certain discrimination between *N. ansorgei* and *N. landgrafi* is often difficult, owing to the fact that the extension of the red colour and the general coloration and markings depend very much on the state of health, reproductive phase and age of these fishes. Assuming, however, that no confusion is present in the literature, the colours of the broad longitudinal bands (pale brown, dark brown or even deep black in *N. ansorgei;* sky-blue to steel-blue in *N. landgrafi*) afford a reliable distinguishing character in the living animals.

Sex-distinctions, care and breeding, as given for the previous species. 1929/ −.

Neolebias unifasciatus *Steindachner* 1894 (Fig. 308)
Tropical West Africa; to 4·5 cm.

D 3–4/7–8; A 3/6–7; LL 32–36; TR 10. Shape similar to that of the previous species. No adipose fin. Coloration, according to Rachow:–more or less reddish overall, back reddish-brown. From the tip of the snout to a round, dark, orange- or reddish-edged blotch at the root of the tail extends a dark brown band, accompanied above by a shining golden stripe. Vertical fins reddish to bright red, with dark to blackish borders.

Sex-distinctions, care and breeding, as given for *N. ansorgei*. 1911/ −.

Phago loricatus *Günther* 1865 (Fig. 304)

The genus *Phago*, native to tropical West Africa, comprises fishes which are extraordinarily elongate, hardly at all compressed, with a very long, slender snout and a deeply cleft, strongly toothed mouth whose upper jaw can be moved upwards. Very strong ctenoid scales, provided with bristles and a comb-edge. Fins partly composed of hard rays. Adipose fin very small.

Phago loricatus lives in the Niger basin; to 15 cm.

D 3/9; A 3/8; LL 47; TR 5. Shape typical of the genus, exceptionally elongate. Upperside dark brown. Flanks delicate reddish-brown with at least two, usually three, dark longitudinal bands of which the one lying along the middle of the body is always the most strongly developed. Fins colourless, at most delicate yellowish. Dorsal and anal fins with dark brown to blackish band-like markings, arranged as shown in Fig. 304.

Sex-distinctions not yet described.

The interesting but unfortunately very timid *Phago* spp. are said to be predators. They are not easy to keep and it is essential that they be provided with suitable hiding-places between plants or among root-systems; a reasonably dark position for the aquarium is also recommended. As regards the composition of the water they are anything but sensitive. Very warmth-loving, 26–28°C. Food animals consist almost exclusively of small fishes, but if occasion arises large insect-larvae may also be given. When greatly alarmed the fishes refuse to accept food. Not yet bred in captivity. 1912/+.

Phago maculatus *E. Ahl* 1922 (Fig. 305)　　　　　　　　　　Pike Characin

Niger basin; to 14 cm.

D 3/8–9; A 3/7–8; LL 47–48; TR 5. Shape typical of the genus, but not quite so slender as the previous species. Upperside marbled fawn to black-brown; flanks delicate yellowish-brown with numerous fine brown transverse stripes; underside yellowish to white-silver. Upper jaw brown. Fins transparent yellowish. Dorsal, adipose and caudal fins with dark brown or blackish bands.

Sex-distinctions unknown.

Care, as given for the previous species. 1913/−.

Neoborus ornatus *Boulenger* 1901 (Fig. 205)

Upper Congo, Stanley Pool; to 20 cm.

D 3/13–15; A 3–4/14–15; LL 98–100; TR 25–28. Body elongate, but not so much drawn-out as in the *Phago* spp.; also the snout is in this case somewhat shorter

225

although no less deeply cleft. Scales very small. Lateral line complete. The genera *Phago* and *Neoborus* are also distinguished, among other differences, by their dentition. Upperside grey to red-brown; flanks green-silver; underside usually pure white. Three vague-edged, olive-coloured longitudinal bands. Dorsal and caudal fins grey, in older fishes often light orange-colour; the latter also have 6–7 deep black longitudinal stripes.

Sex-distinctions unknown. Care, as given for *Phago loricatus*. 1955.

From time to time isolated specimens representing the genus *Citharinus* are imported, such as:–

Citharinus citharus (*Geoffroy* 1809) (Fig. 307)
Throughout tropical Central Africa; to 50 cm.
  D 19; A 28–30; V 11; LL 77–90; TR 40–50.

Citharinus congicus *Boulenger* 1901 (Fig. 279)
Upper Congo, Stanley Pool; to 45 cm.
  D 18–21; A 25–30; LL 60–66; TR 31–35.

Citharinus latus *Müller & Troschel* 1845 (Fig. 306)
Throughout the whole of tropical Central and East Africa, as well as the lower Nile; to 42 cm.
  D 22; A 26; V 11; LL 63–71; TR 34–38.

These fishes are uniformly silver, Bleak-like and noteworthy for their stocky, deep, strongly-compressed form. They are very active fishes, suitable only for large public aquaria, and feed readily on live food and on rolled oats, of which they take large quantities. Growth very rapid. Temperature of their natural waters said to be 22–26 °C.

Family Gasteropelecidae (Hatchetfishes)

Fishes *(Cyprinoidea)* with a deep, strongly-compressed head and body. The profile of the back forms a nearly horizontal straight line. On the other hand, the profile of the lower jaw, together with the conspicuously trenchant ventral keel, forms a semicircular arc which, from the origin of the anal fin, is continued directly to the caudal fin. This protrusion of the breast-region is filled out by the enlargement of the shoulder-girdle to which the powerful musculature of the pectoral fins is attached.

These fishes have the power, through rapid beating of the pectoral fins, to shoot out of the water and glide for distances of up to 3–5 m. over the surface. The lateral line is upwardly arched from the gill-cover and ends about the level of the anal fin origin.

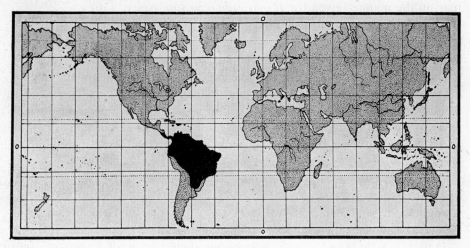

Fig. 309
Distribution of the *Gasteropelecidae*

The range of the *Gasteropelecidae* extends from Panama to La Plata. The fishes are best kept in long, well-covered aquaria, with a dark bottom and soft, slightly acid water. The planting can be scanty, but there is no need to exclude individual broad-leaved floating plants and hanging root-systems. Temperature 23–30 °C. Live food, especially midge-larvae, vinegar flies and small cockroaches, as well as Enchytraeids and small crustaceans. Peaceful fishes, which inhabit the lower water-layers, are well-suited as companions to these in community tanks.

Sex-distinctions are not yet certainly known. In smaller species it is possible to recognise the ♀ by her eggs. *Carnegiella marthae* and *C. strigata*, as well as *Gasteropelecus levis*, have already flourished in captivity but little has been

227

FAMILY GASTEROPELECIDAE

learned about them. The first-mentioned species spawns among thick root-systems, and has strongly adhesive eggs; Kluge (1956), however, reports to the contrary. *C. strigata* spawns in *Myriophyllum* clumps near the surface. The extrusion of the eggs is said to follow a butterfly-like courtship dance by the ♂, accompanying the ♀ along a parallel course. According to the author already quoted the young hatch after up to 30 hours and are not difficult to rear, in the manner given for *Hyphessobrycon* spp. (see p. 116).

Carnegiella marthae *Myers* 1927 (Fig. 315) Black-winged Hatchetfish
Venezuela, Peru, Brazilian Amazon, Rio Negro, Orinoco; to 3·5 cm.

 D 10–11; A 22–23; V 5–6; LL 26. The smallest of the Hatchetfishes. Adipose fin absent. Coloration in a dark aquarium:–middle portion of wing-like pectorals black. A dark stripe, with a silvery or golden upper edge, extends from the gill-cover to the root of the tail. Breast and ventral keel black. A fine line or row of spots on the flanks which rises obliquely posteriorly. Two black stripes on the cheeks.

 Care, as given in the family description; a delicate species. 1935/+.

Carnegiella strigata *Günther* 1864 (Fig. 233) Marbled Hatchetfish
Amazon and Guiana, in small forest pools; to 4·5 cm.

 D 10–11; A 25–28; LL 27–32. Adipose fin absent, as in all *Carnegiella* spp. Shade-loving. Ground colour greenish to yellowish or light violet with a pronounced silver sheen when viewed at the right angle. Back dark olive-green with blackish spots and stripes. A dark stripe, with a silver margin above, extends from the gill-cover to the lower edge of the caudal peduncle. Over the belly extend three black, irregular, saw-edged bars, rising obliquely posteriorly. Fins colourless. The colours fade when the fishes are kept in too strong a light. In contrast to *Carnegiella marthae* the ventral keel in this species is yellowish, not black.

Plate 53

Fig. 310. *Barbus tetrazona tetrazona* (Sumatra Barb, Tiger Barb); adults, natural size. (Original)
Fig. 311. *Barbus oligolepis* (Checkered Barb, Iridescent Barb, Island Barb); ripe young, natural size; left ♂♂, below, right ♀. (Original)

228

Plate 53

Plate 54

Plate 54

Fig. 312. *Barbus stoliczkanus* (Stoliczka's Barb); adults, somewhat enlarged; left ♀, right ♂. (Original)

Fig. 313. *Epalzeorhynchus kallopterus;* adult, somewhat enlarged. (Original)

Care, as given in the family description. Harmless, very greedy fishes, hardy in aquaria.

Recently (Fraser-Brunner, 1950. *Annals & Magazine of Natural History*, Ser. 12, Vol. 3, p. 959) two subspecies have been recognised, mainly on the grounds of distribution and coloration:

Carnegiella strigata strigata – Amazon R.

Carnegiella strigata vesca – West Guiana and lower Amazon.

Weitzman (1961) regards these as distinct species.

Bred in captivity with excellent results, but details have not yet been published. 1912/+.

Gasteropelecus levis (*Eigenmann* 1909)   Silver Hatchetfish
Lower Amazon region; to 6 cm.

D 10–11; A 31–35; LL 29–32. As in all *Gasteropelecus* spp. the profile of the back ascends only slightly towards the dorsal fin. Adipose fin absent. Premaxillary with a single row of teeth. This species is often very difficult to distinguish from the very similar and better-known *Gasteropelecus sternicla*. In *G. levis* there is often a dark blotch at the base of the dorsal fin, also, occasionally, a black streak along the base of the anal.

Care, as given in the family description. 1933/?

Gasteropelecus maculatus *Steindachner* 1879 (Fig. 316)   Spotted Hatchetfish
Western Colombia to Panama; to 9 cm.

D 10–11; A 30–36(37); LL 31–33. Shaped like the previous species (see above). Upperside pale grey-green to brown-green, sometimes silvery, often with a delicate bluish sheen. From the gill-cover to the root of the tail there extends a dark longitudinal stripe which is bordered above by a metallic silver line; above this again there is often a longitudinal row of spots. More or less prominent dark brown blotches and spots appear on the flanks in a transverse band-like arrangement. Fins colourless; dorsal dark-edged.

Care, as given in the family description. 1910/−.

Figs. 314–316

Fig. 314. *Thoracocharax stellatus;* adult, natural size.
Fig. 315. *Carnegiella marthae* (Black-winged Hatchetfish); natural size.
Fig. 316. *Gasteropelecus maculatus* (Spotted Hatchetfish); natural size.

Gasteropelecus sternicla (*Linnaeus* 1758) (Fig. 280)   Common Hatchetfish
Amazon region, Guiana; to 6·5 cm.

D 10–11; A 31–33(–34); LL 30–35. Shaped like *Gasteropelecus levis*. Ground-colour yellowish to grey-silver, silver by reflected light. From the hinder edge of the gill-cover there extends to the root of the tail a narrow dark stripe, accompanied on either side by a pale stripe. Fins colourless; dorsal fin occasionally with a dark leading-edge.

Care, as given in the family description. A hardy species. 1912/+.

Thoracocharax securis (*Filippi* 1853)
Central South America east of the Andes, Amazon and its right-bank tributaries, Paraná; to 9 cm.

D 13–16; A 38–42; LL 18–22. The members of the genus *Thoracocharax* are distinguished from those of the genera *Carnegiella* and *Gasteropelecus* by peculiarities of dentition, the large scales with their radiating striae, and the numerous dorsal and anal fin-rays. Dorsal profile anterior to the dorsal fin nearly straight. The pectoral fins reach to the origin of the dorsal or a little beyond. Yellow-brown or pale olive-colour with a strong silver reflection. From the gill-cover to the root of the tail extends an increasingly broad band which shines blue or greenish by reflected light. Fins colourless. Old fishes are often as deep as they are long.

Care, as given in the family description. 1910/+.

Thoracocharax stellatus (*Kner* 1859) (Fig. 314)
From Central Brazil to the Argentine, very common; to 7 cm.

D 14–16; A 39–44 LL 19–22. *Thoracocharax stellatus* is distinguished from the previous species by the shorter pectoral fins and by the presence of a blackish blotch or stripe on the anterior edge of the dorsal fin. Here, too, the breast-belly profile is somewhat less trenchant.

Specimens imported from the Argentine should not be kept too warm. First import doubtful /+.

Family Cyprinidae (Carps and Carp-like Fishes)

Most of the *Cyprinidae* are the embodiment of the conventional bony fish shape. The body is usually only moderately compressed and the upper and lower profiles are, with few exceptions, equally convex. The belly is seldom strongly keeled. There is no adipose fin. The caudal fin is, as a rule, emarginate, with equal lobes. The mouth is usually more or less protractile and always toothless. Barbels absent, or one or two pairs present. Lower pharyngeal teeth large, sabre-shaped to molariform, usually in several rows. Head scaleless; body, with few exceptions, evenly scaled. The family *Cyprinidae* is world-wide, being absent only from Madagascar, Australia, New Zealand, South America, southern Central America, northern Canada and Alaska,

231

Greenland and Iceland. (In some of these areas the fishes have been deliberately introduced by Man, as in Madagascar, or have accidentally escaped from fishponds and established themselves in local rivers, such as the Amazon.) About 1450 species are known, some of which are very valuable economically. Many *Cyprinidae* are small and very strikingly coloured. The largest species, *Barbus tor* (one of the Indian Mahseers), may grow to a length of 250 cm.

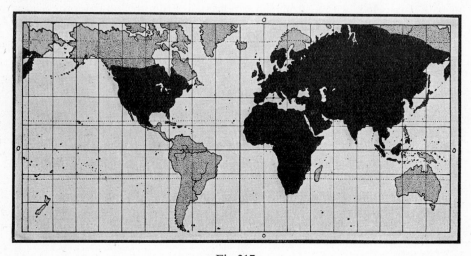

Fig. 317
Distribution of the *Cyprinidae*

European Cyprinidae

Almost all the European *Cyprinidae* can be acclimatised in large aquaria and kept successfully for long periods. Many interesting species, and also some prettily coloured ones, are suitable for unheated domestic aquaria. This is especially true of those which live mainly in quiet lowland waters, such as:–

Bitterling, small Carps, Tench especially Golden Tench, Crucian Carp and Goldfish, and the Moderlieschen *(Leucaspius delineatus)*.

No difficulty is presented, moreover, in acclimatising such species as live in slow-flowing waters or in clear, standing waters. These include:–

Minnow, Bleak, Orfe (especially Golden Orfe), Rudd, Roach, Chub and Dace.

It is rather more difficult to acclimatise species from mountain streams or lowland brooks or swift rivers, and in a domestic aquarium these often need to be provided with a water circulation. These include:–

Barbel, Gudgeon *(Gobio gobio)* and Danubian Gudgeon *(G.urano-scopus)*.

Some *Cyprinidae* can be bred successfully in domestic aquaria and many valuable observations have been published upon these. In comparison with the breeding behaviour of the Bitterling and the Moderlieschen *(Leucaspius)* the reproduction of the well-known tropical Characins or Barbs is quite a dull performance.

In setting up a domestic aquarium for *Cyprinidae* a position should be chosen which can be sheltered in summer from too much heat. Admittedly all *Cyprinidae*, except the Bitterling and Moderlieschen, are far more resistant to high temperatures than, for example, most of the *Salmonidae*, and even Carp and Tench can support temperatures up to 28 °C. if provided with good aeration. In general, however, an upper limit of 21 or 22°C. should not be exceeded. On the other hand, winter cooling down to 4°C. is well supported by all species. As bottom-soil soft river-sand should be provided, at least for species in which bottom-feeding is the habit, such as Carp, Tench, Barbel, Gudgeon and Danubian Gudgeon. For forms from standing waters stones covered with algae or willow moss, branches and root systems, even reed-stalks, provide a natural environment. Among our native water-plants such should be selected as remain green throughout the winter in the coldwater aquarium, or only seldom die down:–Canadian Pondweed *(Elodea canadensis)*, Moneywort *(Lysimachia nummularia* forma *submersa)*, Water Starwort *(Callitriche* spp.*)*, Water Soldier *(Stratiotes aloides)*, Willow Moss *(Fontinalis antipyretica)*. Note, in the care of these plants, that in winter they need a good deal of light. Almost all *Cyprinidae* from ponds prefer matured water,

233

or tapwater mixed with rainwater. For species from lakes and brooks freshwater with frequent additions is indicated. Here it is also important to use chlorine-free water, well-aerated; good aeration is almost indispensable, at least in the summer months. With fishes which like to grub about on the bottom the water can only be kept clear with the aid of a filter.

Feeding European *Cyprinidae* scarcely presents any difficulty. Almost all the species take the most varied food-animals, such as *Daphnia*, insect-larvae, water lice (*Asellus* spp.), freshwater shrimps (*Gammarus* spp., etc.), copepods, maggots, worms and so on. Many will also take dried foods of various kinds, softened rolled oats and even small pieces of bread or cooked spinach. Admittedly one should try out various foods and see which are accepted. The feeding of large specimens is rather more difficult (see below).

In big public aquaria, as well as the species mentioned, even large rarities have been kept such as the Lau *(Chondrostoma genei)*. Usually such public aquaria set great store by very large, old examples which are often of no little value. Insofar as temperature, water-conditions and the renewal of water are concerned, the same principles generally apply as in domestic aquaria, but the care of large specimens is accompanied by many additional difficulties, especially in species such as the Carp which grub about a great deal but will not tolerate a continuous water-circulation. One of these problems is the fouling of the water through feeding. Ladiges 1952 (*Die Aquarien- und Terrarien-Zeitschrift*, Jg. 5, p. 37) reports on the difficulties which arise in the feeding of large Carp. A recommended food which provokes the least turbidity of the water is a mixture of well-cooked rolled oats with chopped meat or fish. Further, from time to time a fattening period with softened maize or soya-meal must be arranged. Large *Cyprinidae* understand how to hunt small fishes cleverly. Chub like to eat cherries and May-bugs. Large Barbel should be cared for like Carp. Valuable information on the keeping of European fishes in exhibition aquaria is given by Ladiges in *Die Aquarien- und Terrarien-Zeitschrift* for 1951 and 1952. Finally, it must be noted that many *Cyprinidae* are good jumpers and that their tanks should therefore be carefully covered.

Abramis brama (*Linnaeus* 1758) (Fig. 292)　　　　　　　　　　　　Bream

Central, Northern and Eastern Europe, not south of the Alps, in slow-flowing waters and lakes; to about 70 cm.

D 3/9; A 3/23–28; P 1/15; V 2/8; LL 50–57. Body stocky, strongly compressed, deep (very deep in older fishes). Head small. Lateral line complete. Upperside dark blue-grey, often blackish, rarely greenish; flanks pale, gleaming dull silver. Vertical fins dark grey, paired fins pale blue-grey. Outside the breeding season the sexes are not easily distinguished. At spawning time the ♀ is substantially more robust; the ♂ develops rows of white tubercles on the head and body, and on all the fins except the dorsal.

The Bream mainly lives in deep water and feeds on watersnails, worms, small mussels and detritus; large ones also take small fishes. At spawning time (May to July) they move into thickly-weeded places against the banks where, usually at night, they lay their eggs. These are yellowish and adhere firmly to the water plants.

Care, as given on p. 233. Young Bream are very hardy in aquaria, but they do stir up the bottom a great deal. It is essential to select only perfectly undamaged specimens, since this species appears to be very susceptible to fungus diseases. Closely related to the Bream are two Continental species, the Zobel *(Abramis sapa* (Pallas)*)* (Fig. 282) which mainly lives in the River Danube from Donauwörth upwards, and the Zährte (*A. vimba* (Linnaeus)) (Fig. 301).

Alburnus alburnus (*Linnaeus* 1758) (Fig. 287)　　　　　　　　　　　Bleak

Europe, north of the Alps, in standing or slow-flowing waters, eastern Baltic; to 20 cm., usually smaller.

D 3/8; A 3/17–20; P 1/15; V 2/8; LL 46–53. Body elongate, slim, compressed. Gape upwardly directed. Lateral line complete. Uniformly bright shining silver. Upperside bluish-green. Fins colourless, glassy, occasionally tinted delicate orange at their bases. Dorsal and caudal fins often pale grey.

Sexes not easily distinguished. ♀ at spawning time (April to July) more robust; ♂ at spawning time with rows of white tubercles.

Care, as given on p. 233. The Bleak, like two other, exclusively Continental, relatives, the Schneider (see following species) and the Schiedling (*Alburnus mento* (Agassiz)), are shoaling fishes which mainly frequent the upper water-layers and obtain their food from the surface film. At spawning time the fishes gather in very large shoals and move upstream in search of places with a stony bottom. The eggs are laid on stones. Pearl-essence (Essence d'Orient) is obtained from the silvery scales, though less often now than formerly. The insides of small glass beads are coated with the essence and subsequently filled with wax; the glass 'pearls' made in this way can achieve a very close resemblance to true pearls. In aquaria these species are very hardy and attractive with their bright silver colour and general liveliness. Sudden temperature-changes should be avoided. Very undemanding as regards food; a proportion of dried food is accepted together with live food of all kinds.

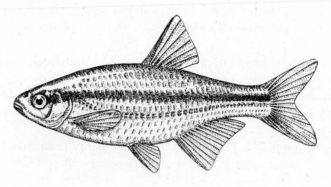

Fig.318
Alburnus bipunctatus (Schneider); adult, slightly reduced.

Alburnus bipunctatus (*Linnaeus* 1758) (Fig.318) Schneider
The whole of Europe north of the Alps and Pyrenees (but not the British Isles), in flowing, clear or not too turbid, waters; to 16 cm., usually smaller.

D 3/7–8; A 3/15–17; P 1/14; V 2/7–8; LL 47–51. Shape rather like that of the previous species, but deeper and not quite so elongate. Lateral line complete, quite strongly down-bowed. Upperside olive- to brown-green. Flanks paler, with a strong silver sheen, especially in the lower parts. Underside whitish. A broad, dark band

Plate 55

Fig.319. *Barbus pentazona pentazona* (Five-banded Barb); maximum size. The pair of yellowish fishes below are *Barbus phutunio* (Dwarf Barb, Pigmy Barb); the blotches are usually bluish-brown, especially in the ♂ (left). (Original)
Fig.320. *Barbus conchonius* (Red Barb, Rosy Barb); half-grown fishes; below, left, a ♀. (Original)

Plate 55

Plate 56

Plate 56

Fig. 321. *Barbus titteya* (Cherry Barb); imported specimens, somewhat enlarged. (Photo Dr. Foersch)

Fig. 322. *Barbus arulius;* adult ♂, somewhat enlarged. The blue-green iridescence is generally more pronounced. (Original)

from the eye to the root of the tail. Lateral line darkly pigmented. Fins delicate orange. During the breeding season altogether more brilliantly coloured. Sexes mainly distinguished by the more robust body of the ♀.

Care, as given for previous species.

Aspius aspius (*Linnaeus* 1758) (Figs. 288, 323)   Rapfen

Eastern Europe, westwards to the Elbe, Danube region, in rivers and lakes (also in brackish water in the Baltic); to 100 cm., usually smaller.

D 3/7–8; A 3/12–15; P 1/16; V 2/8–9; LL 65–70. Body elongate, only moderately compressed. Gape large, somewhat upwardly directed. Upperside very dark, usually black-olive. Flanks yellowish-silver. Underside pure silver. Fins delicate grey, occasionally tinged reddish. ♂ at spawning time with a considerable rash of white tubercles.

Large individuals of this species are predatory fishes, feeding chiefly on small Cyprinid fishes and amphibians. Spawns during the months April–July, in flowing waters with a sandy bottom. This predatory species is well suited only to exhibition tanks, for which large specimens are worthwhile rarities. Unfortunately very delicate, especially during the settling-in period. According to Ladiges, good aeration and frequent renewal of the water are indispensable.

Barbus barbus (*Linnaeus* 1758) (Fig. 298)   Barbel

The whole of Central Europe, Britain, France, Bulgaria, Rumania, Hungary; in clear running waters with a sandy or gravelly bottom; to about 90 cm., but usually substantially smaller.

D 3/8–9; A 3/5; P 1/15–17; V 2/8; LL 58–61. Body elongate, slim, compressed, low. The snout overhangs the mouth, which has thick lips. Two pairs of barbels on the upper jaw. Typical coloration:–upperside grey-green; flanks delicate greenish to grey-yellowish; gill-cover shining golden; underside very pale. Dorsal and caudal fins colourless or delicate grey-green; lower lobe of caudal often reddish, especially at the edge. Paired fins and anal fin often light reddish towards their edges.

♀ at spawning time substantially more robust.

♂ at spawning time with white tubercles arranged in rows on the upper surface of the head and the nape.

Barbel are gregarious, holding station against the current over the bottom by day and only going in search of food (mussels, water snails, worms, young fishes, detritus) at night. At spawning time (May to July) the fishes gather in large shoals and migrate upstream to a suitable headwater where there is a stony or coarse gravel bottom. The eggs adhere firmly to the bottom. The fishes winter in large flocks, in quiet parts of the rivers or under root-stocks. It is not uninteresting to mention that the hard roe (eggs) of the Barbel is poisonous, especially before the spawning season.

Small specimens are well suited to domestic aquaria. Frequent renewal with fresh water is necessary. Large specimens are fine exhibits for public aquaria. Yellowish or light golden colour-varieties of the Barbel are also known, but these are of very infrequent occurrence.

Blicca björkna (*Linnaeus* 1758) (Fig. 324)   Silver Bream
Europe (excluding Britain) north of the Alps and Pyrenees, also in southern Scandinavia; to 40 cm., usually smaller.

D 3/8; A 3/19–23; P 1/14–16; V 2/8; LL (44) 45–48. Body-form strongly reminiscent of the Bream *(Abramis brama)*. Snout, however, more strongly rounded. Mouth somewhat downwardly directed. As regards coloration and other peculiarities very similar to the Bream.

Carassius carassius (*Linnaeus* 1758) (Fig. 303)   Crucian Carp
Widely distributed throughout Europe, but absent from Spain, Switzerland, southern Italy and northern Finland; very rarely to 75 cm., but usually very much smaller, around 20 cm.

D 3–4/14–21; A 3/5–8; P 1/12–13; V 2–3/7–8; LL 19–20. Body carp-like, the back especially high in old individuals. Mouth forwardly directed. Dorsal fin relatively long and high. Upperside dark olive-green; underside yellowish to brilliant golden yellow. An elongate transverse dark blotch at the root of the tail is quite distinct in the young. Dorsal and caudal fins yellow-red, in young fishes quite a beautiful reddish colour.

♀ sexually-ripe adult more robust.

The Crucian Carp mainly inhabits quiet, sometimes really turbid, waters and feeds on various small animals, plant remains and detritus. Spawning season from May to June. The eggs are laid among water plants. Very prolific (up to 300,000 eggs). An uncommonly hardy and easily-satisfied species, eminently suited to the unheated domestic aquarium. Anyone who did not know the Crucian Carp would think this beautifully coloured fish must be some tropical species.

Carassius auratus gibelio (*Bloch* 1782)   Prussian Carp
Widely distributed through Europe and Asia; generally remains somewhat smaller than the Crucian Carp.

Shape similar to the Crucian Carp, from which it is distinguished by the rather less deep and rather less compressed body, larger scales, peculiarities of the gill-arches (more gill-rakers), lack of a blotch on the caudal peduncle, and above all by the different coloration.

Prussian Carp are almost purely grey-yellowish or grey-silver, the yellowish to brassy-yellow tones of the Crucian Carp being absent.

The Prussian Carp is the western subspecies of the Chinese Goldfish and its varieties. All else as in the Crucian Carp.

Chondrostoma nasus (*Linnaeus* 1758) (Fig. 300)   Näsling
Central Europe north of the Alps, especially in the Danube and Rhine districts; to 50 cm., usually smaller.

D 3/9; A 3/10–11; P 1/15–17; V 2/9; LL 56–62. Body elongate, slim, spindle-shaped. The snout overhangs the mouth like a nose. Lips horny, sharp-edged. Lateral line complete. Upperside olive-green to grey; flanks grey-silver; underside delicate yellow to whitish. Dorsal and caudal fins dark, occasionally with a reddish lustre. Paired fins and anal fin delicate yellowish to brilliant red or brown-red.

Sexes not easily distinguished outside the breeding season. At spawning time both sexes have white tubercles on the head and flanks. The ♂, however, is easily recognised by the generally darker, on the anterior part of the body often even blackish, coloration.

This species inhabits richly-weeded flowing waters where it feeds on plant materials and small animals, with a preference for the algal growths on stones and plants which it grazes with its sharp lips. At spawning time (March to June) the fishes congregate in large parties and spawn in small streams having a gravelly bottom. According to old accounts young individuals of this species behave quite well toward other and prudent inhabitants of the aquarium for quite a long time.

They should be given algae now and then to feed upon and provided with a soft bottom; the Näsling likes to be able to grub around sometimes.

Cyprinus carpio *Linnaeus* 1758 (Figs. 290, 291)   Common Carp
Original home Japan, China, Central Asia; today distributed throughout the whole of Europe. To 100 cm., usually considerably smaller, 30–40 cm.

D 3–4/17–22; A 3/5; P 1/15–16; V 2/8–9; LL 35–39. Wild form elongate, moderately deep, slightly compressed. Squamation complete. Mouth directed forwards, protrusible, surrounded by fleshy lips. 2 pairs of barbels on the upper lip. Lateral line complete.

Domesticated breeds: stocky with a high back, squamation very much reduced (Mirror Carp), or almost completely reduced (Leather Carp).

Upperside olive-green to yellow green; flanks greenish clay-yellow or brassy-yellow; underside yellowish. Fins opaque grey-green or brownish, sometimes slightly reddish.

♀ dumpy before spawning time.
♂ at spawning time with only a weak development of tubercles.

Carp similar to the wild form are found today mainly in the larger rivers. Almost all Carp in standing waters are artificially bred. In Central Europe Carp are sexually mature during about the 3rd or 4th year. Natural food: small animals and parts of plants; large individuals also take fishes.

The first reliable report of Carp derives from the sixth century, when Cassiodorus wrote of this food-fish as follows:–'The ordinary man may eat what opportunity affords him; on the princely table belong such rare delicacies as the Carp which lives in the Danube.' In the year 1512 the Carp reached England; in 1560 Denmark; in 1585 it was settled in Prussia and thence, in 1729, brought to the then St. Petersburg. Peter the Great introduced it finally to Moscow. The Carp first arrived in North America in 1872 and acclimatised itself extraordinarily well in California. History also records some very large Carp. Frederick II once caught one of 76 lb.; another of 140 lb. is said to have been caught at Frankfurt on

Figs. 323–326
Fig. 323. *Aspius aspius* (Rapfen); adult, greatly reduced.
Fig. 324. *Blicca björkna* (Silver Bream); adult, reduced.
Fig. 325. *Gobio uranoscopus* (Steingressling); adult, slightly reduced.
Fig. 326. *Telestes agassizi* (Strömer); adult, reduced.

Oder. Reports of 400 lb. are doubtless exaggerated. Small carp can easily be kept in domestic aquaria.

For particulars of care, see p. 233.

Gobio gobio (*Linnaeus* 1758) (Fig. 370)   Gudgeon
Europe, excepting southern Italy, Norway and Scotland; Asia to China; to 15 cm.

D 3/7; A 3/6; P 1/14–15; V 2/8; LL 40–44. Body elongate; somewhat compressed posteriorly, not compressed anteriorly. Mouth ventral. A pair of short barbels at the corners of the mouth. Upperside grey-green to blackish-grey; flanks lighter with dark spots; underside silver, tinged a delicate reddish. Dorsal and caudal fins yellowish with rows of dark spots. All other fins pale yellow, rarely reddish.

Sexes distinguished with difficulty. ♂ at spawning time with white tubercles.

The Gudgeon is a shoaling fish which chiefly frequents the beds of swift-flowing rivers or the shallow margins of larger lakes, rarely fens or the brackish waters of the Baltic. It feeds on smaller animals and parts of plants and also has a partiality to fish-spawn. At spawning time (April to June) the fishes frequent flat-bottomed shallows where groups of ♂♂ and ♀♀ rush towards the shore, shedding the spawn and milt as they go. This species accommodates itself very well to the domestic aquarium. Clean, clear water and good aeration are essential, of course, and the water level should be kept low. Readily bred in aquaria. The young develop rapidly (see also p. 233). In France popular as food.

Gobio uranoscopus (*Agassiz* 1828) (Fig. 325)   Steingressling
In isolated areas in the Danube and Dniester basins; to 15 cm.

D 2/7; A 2/5–6; P 1/13; V 1/6; LL 40–42 (43). Shape similar to that of the previous species, but slimmer. Upperside leaden-coloured; flanks and belly very pale. 5 indistinct, broad, dark transverse bars from the back to the lateral line. Fins yellowish, dorsal and caudal fins occasionally with rows of brown blotches. In all other respects similar to the previous species.

Idus idus (*Linnaeus* 1758) (Fig. 327)   Silver Orfe, Ide
Widely distributed through Europe north of the Alps and Pyrenees, also in brackish water in the Baltic; western Siberia; to 75 cm., usually substantially smaller.

D 3/8–9; A 3/9–11; P 1/15–16; V 2/8; LL 52–59 (60). Body elongate, somewhat compressed, broad. Mouth small, forwardly directed; no barbels. Lateral line complete. Upperside olive-brown to blackish; flanks pale, in the posterior region

242

a lovely silver colour with a bluish sheen; underside silvery. Dorsal and caudal fins opaque grey; all other fins light reddish (red at spawning time).

♀ in sexually-ripe adults more robust.
♂ with white tubercles at spawning time.

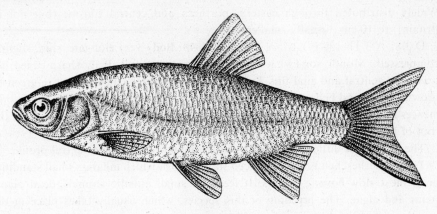

Fig. 327
Idus idus (Silver Orfe); adult, greatly reduced.

The Silver Orfe lives in the upper layers of flowing waters and lakes and feeds mainly on such small animals as crustacea, small water snails and mussels, worms, etc. Breeding season April to July. The eggs are laid on plants and stones. The young adapt themselves very well to aquarium life. For further particulars concerning care (in large aquaria) see p. 233.

Idus idus (*Linnaeus* 1758) (golden variety)   Golden Orfe
A golden variety of the Silver Orfe occurs under natural conditions in various places in south Germany and is bred in vast numbers as an ornamental fish for garden pools and decorative fountains. Little is known concerning the origin of this form, but in this regard the Dinkelsbühl district of Bavaria, where almost all the young Silver Orfe metamorphose into Golden Orfe, is celebrated. The Golden Orfe is very hardy and on this account for the purposes mentioned above better suited than the true Goldfish *(Carassius auratus)*.
The upper half of the body of this beautiful fish is red-golden, the lower part of the flanks more orange-coloured and the belly a delicate golden-white silver. The majority of Golden Orfe seen, however, have a uniform orange-yellow colouring.

243

Young Golden Orfe adapt themselves very well to the unheated domestic aquarium. The fishes are plentiful, lively and put up with almost any food. Their growth in aquaria is slow.

Leucaspius delineatus *Heckel* 1843 (Fig. 281)   Moderlieschen
Widely distributed through eastern, northern and central Europe (but not in Britain); to 10 cm., usually smaller.

D 3/8; A 3/11–13; P 1/13; V 2/8; LL 44–48. Body very elongate, slim, slightly compressed. Mouth somewhat upwardly directed, small. Belly sharp-edged between the ventral and anal fins. Lateral line incomplete. Upperside olive-green to brown; flanks and belly a lovely silver-white. A steel-blue longitudinal band commences in the posterior third of the body and ends, considerably broadened, at the root of the tail. Fins glassy, colourless or delicate yellowish.

The ♀♀ are not difficult to distinguish by the more trenchant ventral profile.

The Moderlieschen is a pronounced shoaling-fish which inhabits small standing, or at most slow-flowing, waters. It feeds on small aquatic animals, dead plant-stems and algae. The breeding of this species, which usually takes place in the months of April and May, is especially interesting. The eggs are deposited in annular rows on plant-stems, such as reeds and rushes, and then fertilised by the ♂.

The Moderlieschen is excellently suited to aquarium life. The lovely, silver-coloured, lively fishes are very contented and also resistant to higher temperatures. Good aeration of the water must be provided for. Plentiful clumps of plants and a dark bottom-soil with plenty of mulm are obviously beneficial. It puts up with any sort of food. After a cold hibernation it willingly proceeds to breed, at least in large aquaria.

The scales of this species, like those of the Bleak (see p. 235) are used in the manufacture of pearl essence.

Leuciscus leuciscus (*Linnaeus* 1758)   Dace
Widely distributed through the whole of Europe north of the Alps and Pyrenees; to 30 cm., usually remaining smaller.

Plate 57

Fig. 328 *Scardinius erythrophthalmus* (Rudd); half-grown, somewhat reduced. (Original)
Fig. 329. *Rutilus rutilus* (Roach); half-grown, somewhat reduced. (Original)
Fig. 330. *Phoxinus phoxinus* (Minnow); adults, slightly reduced. (Original)

Plate 57

Plate 58

Plate 58

Fig. 331. *Rhodeus sericeus* (Bitterling); breeding-behaviour.
Above, left. The ♀ has introduced her ovipositor into the exhalant siphon of a swan-mussel and now lays 1–2 eggs between the valves of the shell. The ♂ stays behind the ♀.
Above, right. The ♀ has now left the mussel and swum in an arc to take up a position behind the ♂, who now sheds milt over the inhalant siphon of the mussel.
Below, left. Hard-pressed by the ♂, the ♀ prepares for a further spawning. The tip of the stiffened ovipositor lies ready over the exhalant siphon and in a moment will be re-inserted with lightning speed. (Photos G. zu Klampen)
Below, right. Bitterling out of the breeding-season; about natural size. (Original)

D 3/7–8; A 3/7–9; P 1/16–17; V 2/8; LL 47–53 (54). Body spindle-shaped, only a little compressed. The small mouth is downwardly directed. Lateral line complete. Upperside leaden-grey to blackish; flanks and belly a splendid gleaming silver, often with yellowish tones. Dorsal and caudal fins opaque grey; all other fins delicate yellowish, occasionally even reddish.

♀ sexually-ripe adult with more strongly convex ventral profile.
♂ with white tubercles at spawning time.

The Dace inhabits flowing lowland waters as a rule and spends most of its time in the upper water-layers. It feeds on small aquatic animals of all kinds. Breeding season March to May. The eggs are laid on water plants.

Young specimens are well suited to the unheated aquarium. A large shoal of adults is hardly a commonplace spectacle in public aquaria. (See also p. 233.)

Rutilus rutilus (*Linnaeus* 1758) (Fig. 329)   Roach
The whole of Europe north of the Alps and Pyrenees, but not in Ireland; to 45 cm., usually smaller.

D 3/9–11; A 3/9–11; P 1/15; V 2/8; LL 40–45. Body elongate, compressed. Back high, especially in older specimens. Mouth downwardly directed. Lateral line complete. Upperside olive-green to grey-green; flanks gleaming bright silver; underside whitish. Dorsal and caudal fins grey, fawn or blackish; all other fins a beautiful yellow to blood-red. Eye red.

♀ sexually-ripe adult, especially at spawning time, appreciably more robust.
♂ with white tubercles at spawning time.

The Roach frequents slow-flowing and standing waters and spends most of its time in the deeper water-layers. It feeds on various small animals, also on water plants; large individuals capture small fishes as well.

For care in domestic and in public aquaria, see p. 233.

Closely related to the above is the Frauennerfling (*Leuciscus virgo* Heckel, Fig. 289).

Phoxinus phoxinus (*Linnaeus* 1758) (Fig. 330)   Minnow

The whole of Europe, with the exception of southern Spain and Iceland; to 14 cm.

D 3/7; A 3/7; P 1/15; V 2/8; LL 80–90. Body elongate, hardly compressed apart from the caudal peduncle. Mouth forwardly directed, small. Scales small. Lateral line incomplete.

The coloration is very changeable. Back olive- to grey-green, often with dark blotches; flanks yellow-green with metallic glints. Corners of mouth carmine-red. Throat black. Breast often scarlet. Belly white-yellowish. A gleaming gold longitudinal stripe extends from behind the eye to the root of the tail. Dorsal, anal and caudal fins more or less dirty yellow; anal occasionally crimson. Pectoral and ventral fins grey to crimson. The coloration depends very much upon the condition of the fish; now and then vague transverse bars appear. At spawning time pointed whitish tubercles appear from the nape backwards. The sexes can hardly be distinguished, but at spawning time the bellies of the ♀♀ are rounder.

The Minnow is a shoaling-fish which principally inhabits the upper layers of clear waters. As food it takes mainly insect-larvae and small crustacea. Breeding season April to July. It gathers in great shoals to spawn in the shallows, mainly on stones.

Very well suited to the unheated aquarium. Tanks with coarse, sandy bottom-soil and fresh water provide the best imitation of its preferred natural habitat. Aeration essential. It prefers to eat red midge-larvae, Enchytraeids and other worms, also beetles and other insects.

Breeding in captivity not very difficult. When morning sunshine is expected, several breeding pairs can be placed in the breeding tank the previous evening. This should contain crystal-clear fresh water and have large stones on the bottom on which the animals will spawn; the water level should not exceed 15 cm. and vigorous aeration must be provided. The young hatch after 6 days and should be fed with sifted small crustacea. They grow very slowly and are first sexually ripe at 3–4 years old. The Minnow possesses excellent senses of hearing and smell, properties which have many times been scientifically studied. The capacity to discriminate between fine differences of pitch is as well developed in the Minnow as it is in Man.

Rhodeus sericeus (*Pallas* 1776) (Figs. 331)   Bitterling
Central and Eastern Europe, Asia Minor; rarely to 9 cm.

D 3/9–10; A 3/8–10; P 1/11; V 2/6–7; LL 34–38. Shape carp-like, but strongly compressed. The small mouth is forwardly directed. Lateral line incomplete (piercing 5–6 scales).

The loveliest and most interesting of European freshwater fishes, very well suited to the domestic aquarium and in its beautiful coloration at spawning time excelled by few exotic species. Outside the breeding season both sexes are similarly coloured. Back grey-green; flanks and belly gleaming silver. Under the dorsal fin begins a shining grey-green stripe which ends at the root of the tail. Dorsal fin blackish; all other fins delicate reddish or yellowish.

♂ at spawning time. Nape and back olive- to grass-green; flanks iridescent with all the colours of the rainbow, violet and steel-blue especially predominating. Throat and belly orange to blood-red. Dorsal and anal fins bright red and black-edged. Caudal fin greenish at its base, distally yellow. Pectoral and ventral fins yellowish. Large whitish tubercles above the upper lip and eye.

♀ at spawning time, more yellowish, less iridescent. A pink ovipositor 45–50 mm. long projects from the anal fin.

Care in well-planted tanks with a layer of mulm and without aeration. Temperature up to 22°C. Omnivorous, with a preference for Enchytraeids and midge-larvae. It is important to keep Swan-Mussels (*Anodonta* spp.) in the tanks as well, as the Bitterling needs these for spawning. Spawns readily in April after a cold wintering. The ♀ inserts her long ovipositor between the valves of the mussel and there deposits the eggs. The ♂ sheds his milt over the mussel and this becomes drawn in with the respiratory current and fertilises the eggs. Before inserting the ovipositor the Bitterling conditions the mussel to the stimulus by repeated nudgings with the mouth, and thus insures against closing of the valves during the insertion of the ovipositor. The young leave the host mussel after 4–5 weeks and must then be reared on the finest food. After spawning the ovipositor quickly shortens and the fine colouring of the ♂♂ fades. Mating is often repeated. (See p. 233.)

Scardinius erythrophthalmus (*Linnaeus* 1758) (Fig. 328)   Rudd
The whole of Europe, with the exceptions of the Iberian Peninsula, Scotland and southern Italy; also in Asia Minor; to 40 cm., usually remaining smaller.

D (2)–3/8–9; A 3/9–11; P 1/15–16; V 2/8; LL 41–43. Body stocky, somewhat egg-shaped, compressed. The narrow mouth is directed forwards. Belly, between the ventral fins and the vent, strongly keeled. Upperside brown-olive, sometimes with a brassy sheen; flanks brassy-coloured; belly silver-white. Ventral, anal, caudal, and rarely also the dorsal, fins with a dark base and brilliant golden-red outer part. Iris gleaming gold.

The keeled belly in this species serves to distinguish it from the very similar Roach, in which the belly is rounded. Furthermore, the colour of the eyes is different; in the Roach, red, and in the Rudd, golden.

Sexes difficult to distinguish; ♂ with spawning tubercles.

The Rudd is a shoaling-fish which dwells mainly in waters with a soft bottom and strong plant growth, especially where there are reedy margins. It feeds on small animals and plants and is particularly partial to insects from the surface. Breeding season April to June. The eggs adhere to water plants. Very prolific. These beautiful fish are quite suitable for the domestic aquarium when young.

For care, see p. 233.

Squalius cephalus (*Linnaeus* 1758) (Fig. 299)   Chub

From central and southern Europe to Asia Minor; to 65 cm., usually remaining smaller.

D 3/8–9; A 3/7–8; P 1/16–17; V 2/8; LL (44) 45–46. Body elongate, hardly at all compressed. Mouth large, forwardly directed. Scales coarse. Lateral line complete. Upperside leaden-grey with a greenish or brownish sheen; flanks and underside gleaming silver, often slightly yellowish; belly whitish. Scales dark-edged. Sides of head gleaming gold. Dorsal and caudal fins reddish to red. A sex-distinction is provided by the greater convexity of the profile of the belly in the ♀. ♂ at spawning time with spawning tubercles.

The Chub inhabits waters of various kinds and prefers the upper layers. A shoaling-fish. Feeds when young on all kinds of small organisms; larger individuals are voracious predators. The partiality of the Chub to cherries and May-bugs is well known. Spawning season April to June. The eggs are laid at random on water plants or stones.

Plate 59

Fig. 332. *Balantiocheilus melanopterus;* 15 cm. specimen in the Hellabrunn Aquarium, Munich. (Original)
Fig. 333. *Barilius christyi;* half-grown specimens, natural size. (Original)
Fig. 334. *Barbus dunckeri* (Duncker's Barb); young, natural size. (After Meinken)

Plate 59

Plate 60

Plate 60

Fig. 335. *Barbus cumingi* (Cuming's Barb); ripe young, somewhat reduced; above ♀, below ♂. (Original)

Fig. 336. *Barbus fasciatus* (Striped Barb, Zebra Barb); ripe young, natural size; above ♀, below ♂. (Original)

Fig. 337. *Barbus 'schuberti'* (Golden Barb, Schubert's Barb); adults, natural size; above ♂, below ♀. (Original)

The young are suitable for the domestic aquarium.

For care, see p. 233. Large specimens make fine show-exhibits which, unfortunately, are somewhat delicate.

Telestes agassizi (*Cuvier* and *Valenciennes* 1842) (Fig. 326)   Strömer

Danube, Rhine, Switzerland; to 24 cm., usually smaller.

D 2/8; A 3/8–9; P 1/13–14; V 2/8; LL 48–55(56). Elongate, only slightly compressed. Mouth directed downwards. Lateral line complete. Upperside blue-grey; flanks and underside bright gleaming silver. A dark, often iridescent violet, longitudinal band extends from the eye to the upper part of the root of the tail. Lateral line marked out in orange. All fins are yellowish to orange-yellow at the base, outside colourless.

♀ with longitudinal band usually indistinct.

♂ coloured as described above, with tubercles during the spawning season.

Telestes is a shoaling-fish which mainly inhabits the deeper layers of large lakes and there feeds on all kinds of small animals.

For care, see p. 233.

Tinca tinca (*Linnaeus* 1758) (Fig. 302)   Tench

Europe, widely distributed; to 70 cm., almost always remaining substantially smaller.

D 4/8–9; A 3–4/6–7; P 1/15–17; V 2/8–9; LL 95–100. Body stocky, only slightly compressed; caudal peduncle deep. Mouth directed forwards and surrounded by thick lips. 1 pair of barbels, at the corners of the mouth. Scales very small, deeply embedded in the slimy skin. Caudal fin squarely truncated. Olive-green; upperside generally blackish; belly somewhat paler with a warm golden sheen on the flanks. Fins opaque grey to greenish.

Sexes not easy to distinguish. ♀♀, at least when older, with a considerably more convex ventral profile.

Tench mainly inhabit standing waters with thick plant growth and there feed on small animals and plants. Very peaceful. Spawning season May–July. The eggs are laid on plants. Young Tench are very suitable for unheated domestic aquaria and may be treated in the same way as the Crucian Carp (see p. 238).

Tinca tinca (*Linnaeus*), golden form   Golden Tench
The Tench, too, produces golden colour-varieties which in many places are specially bred. Since they are considerably more tolerant of low temperatures they are often preferred to the true Goldfish. Golden Tench are a beautiful yellow-red on the upper half of the body, more yellowish on the lower half. The whole body and the fins are usually strewn with dark spots.

Cyprinidae of Tropical and Sub-Tropical Africa and Asia

Aphyocypris pooni *Lin* 1939 (Fig. 414)   Red-finned Wonder Fish, Venus Fish
China, east of Canton, Hong Kong; to 4 cm.
   D 3/6; A 3/7; V 1/6; LL 30–32; 15–16 scales between the back of the head and the dorsal. Body elongate, moderately compressed. The small mouth is deeply cleft and directed forwards (terminal). Gape horizontal. No barbels. No lateral line. Caudal fin emarginate. 1938/–.
   Since this species is very similar to the following one, the colours of both will be presented in a table. The opinion that these forms, which from the outset were regarded as species, are in fact only local races is not to be accepted.

Tanichthys albonubes *Lin* 1932 (Figs. 210, 413)   White Cloud Mountain Minnow
China, Canton in the gorges of the White Cloud Mountains; to 4 cm.
   D 2/7; A 3/8; LL about 30; 13–14 scales between the back of the head and the dorsal. Similar in shape to the previous species, but the cleft of the mouth is very oblique and the caudal fin is scarcely or only very slightly emarginate. 1938/–.
Hybrids are often met with in Central Europe. Pure *Aphyocypris pooni*, according to Meinken, probably no longer exist in captivity.
   The ♀♀ are usually not difficult to recognise by their greater girth.
   These beautiful fish can be cared for like *Danio* spp. Temperature, between 20–22°C.; for wintering, not more than 16–18°C.! Frequent additions of fresh water are beneficial. Omnivorous. They spawn on plants and should be provided

with dense clumps of *Myriophyllum*. Many pairs devour the eggs; others, again, leave the spawn and even the freshly-hatched young unmolested. The young hatch after 48 hours and should be reared on the finest living and dried foods. Many ♀♀ spawn very frequently but not prolifically; others spawn seldom but lay 250 or more eggs when they do. For the furnishing of the tank and other information, see p. 233.

Aphyocypris pooni	Features common to both species	*Tanichthys albonubes*
Altogether more yellowish. Dorsal fin red at the base, yellow outside, with a delicate blue margin in fine specimens. Anal fin yellow-green.	Upperside brown-olive or yellow-brown. Flanks substantially paler. Belly whitish. A brilliant band, gleaming greenish or golden according to the lighting, extends from the snout to the root of the tail; in the young this band has a brilliant blue-green iridescence.	Altogether more brownish. Dorsal and anal fins yellow at the base, brilliant red outside.

Amblypharyngodon microlepis (*Bleeker* 1853) (Fig. 338)
Eastern India; from Orissa to Madras; to 10 cm.

D 2/7; A 2/5; P 14; V 9; LL 55–60. Body elongate, *Barbus*-like. Upper lip absent. Barbels absent. Dorsal fin very short. Scales very small. Lateral line incomplete (a characteristic of the genus). Upperside bronze-colour; flanks brass-colour to golden, with a dull greenish-silver longitudinal band from the gill-cover to the root of the tail; belly whitish. Fins colourless to yellowish.

Sex-distinctions not yet described; the ♀♀ however are probably more robust and plumper.

Care of this active and peaceful species, as given for *Barbus* spp. (see p. 279). Probably not yet bred in captivity. 1913/ – .

Balantiocheilus melanopterus (*Bleeker* 1850) (Fig. 332)
Thailand, Borneo, Sumatra: in ditches and flowing waters; to 35 cm.

D 4/8–9; A 3/5; P 1/15; V 2/8–9; LL 34–35; TR 7/5½. Body *Barbus*-like, slim and very elegant. Mouth somewhat ventral. Upper lip thick, granular. No barbels. Lateral line complete. A very lovely species. Body silvery or yellowish-silver, underside paler. Fins a gorgeous yellow with broad, deep black outer parts.

251

Sex-distinctions not yet described.

Only young specimens are suitable for domestic aquaria; large ones make magnificent showpieces. The species is very hardy and, as well as living food of all kinds, also eats rolled oats and other prepared foods greedily. When seeking their prey on the bottom they rest head-downward, sucking at the surface of a stone here or grubbing about there. Supplementary plant food is recommended from time to time. Nothing is known about the reproduction. Temperature 23–26 °C. 1955.

Barilius christyi *Boulenger* 1920 (Fig. 333)

The range of the genus *Barilius* extends from China and Japan over the whole of southern Asia and into Africa. The fishes in question are more or less elongate to torpedo-shaped, and more or less compressed. Mouth large, deeply cleft. Lateral line, when complete, deeply depressed towards the belly. The majority of the species are very peaceful, active and elegant swimmers which, usually gathered together in shoals, prefer to pass their time in the upper water-layers. Many species are very beautifully coloured.

Barilius christyi is a native of the Congo region; to 13 cm.

D 3/7; A 3/13; LL 54. Body slim, torpedo-shaped. Lateral line complete. Back blackish-olive with a blue-green glint. Flanks silvery, with green reflexions by oblique light, with 16–18 narrow, vertical transverse bars of a brownish to deep blackish colour (conspicuous in older fishes). Upper jaw with a striking shining red-gold blotch. An oval to triangular deep black blotch at the root of the tail. Dorsal, anal and caudal fins yellowish to orange with blackish tips. Eyes reddish above and yellow.

Sex-distinctions in colour not known. These nimble, restless, shoaling fishes are very reminiscent of the *Danio* spp.

Large, at the most thinly-planted, tanks. Soft, slightly acid water. Temperatures around 24 °C. All *Barilius* spp. like to feed on live food, especially on insects from the surface film. Very peaceful. Not yet bred in captivity.

Figs. 338–342

Fig. 338. *Amblypharyngodon microlepis;* somewhat reduced.
Fig. 339. *Barilius neglectus;* natural size.
Fig. 340. *Oxygaster oxygastroides* (Glass Barb); adult, reduced.
Fig. 341. *Chela laubuca* (Indian Glass Barb); maximum size.
Fig. 342. *Cyclocheilichthys apogon* (Indian River Barb); young, natural size.

Barilius neglectus *Stieler* 1907 (Fig. 339)
Japan; to 7 cm.

D 3/7; A 2/9; LL 33. Body-shape typical of the genus, resembling an elongate *Barbus*. No barbels. Coloration very plain. Upperside brownish with a metallic greenish glint. Flanks yellowish with two bluish longitudinal stripes along the middle enclosing a row of fawn to dull greenish spots; further rows of spots outside these (each scale with a dark spot). Fins colourless, occasionally delicate yellowish.

♀ (sexually-ripe adult) more robust with a silvery ground-colour.
♂ slimmer, ground-colour more yellowish.

This active, unassuming species is best accommodated in a large aquarium with dark bottom-soil and standing in a sunny position. Temperature 22–24°C., wintering at a cooler 15–18°C. Omnivorous; also accepts dried foods. Breeding easy, similar to that described for *Danio* spp.; the ♂♂, however, should be settled in the breeding tank first. The ♀♀ usually spawn in the early morning. Prolific. 1907/−.

Beirabarbus palustris *Herre* 1936
South-east Africa; to 7 cm.

D 2–3/8; A 3/5; LL 26–27; TR $3\frac{1}{2}/3\frac{1}{2}$. Approximating to typical *Barbus*-shape. Head small, snout rounded. Belly rounded. The dorsal fin origin is over the 9th lateral line scale and is substantially nearer to the snout than to the caudal fin. Lateral line complete. Caudal fin deeply forked, lobes pointed. Altogether reddish to delicate olive-brown, with a very strong violet, blue or purple lustre. A narrow black lateral stripe extends from the tip of the snout to the root of the tail.

Concerning the sex-distinctions, care and breeding of this very beautiful shoaling fish nothing is known. 1938/−.

Caecobarbus geertsi *Boulenger* 1921 (Fig. 347)   Blind Barb
Subterranean waters in the region of the lower Congo (caves near Thysville); to 8 cm.

Fig. 343

The main domesticated varieties of Goldfish. Above, left: Standard Measurements for the Veiltail. (a) Comet; (b) Egg-fish; (c) Shubunkin; (d) Celestial; (e) Telescope-Veiltail; (f) Lionhead.

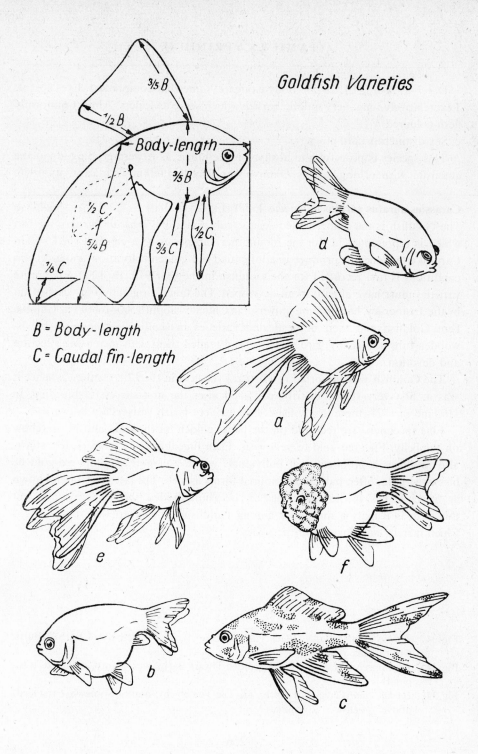

Goldfish Varieties

3/5 B

1/2 B

Body-length

3/5 B

1/2 C

5/4 B

3/5 C

1/2 C

1/6 C

B = Body-length
C = Caudal fin-length

a

b

c

d

e

f

D 3/7–8; A 3/5; LL 28–29. Body elongate, somewhat compressed. Eyes absent. Two relatively long, very mobile barbels which serve as feelers. Almost uniformly flesh-coloured.

Sex distinctions unknown.

This species is peaceful and always on the move, as it were groping about the aquarium with its long barbels. Omnivorous. Breeding unknown in captivity. 1956.

Carassius auratus auratus (*Linnaeus* 1758) (Figs. 343, 380)   Goldfish
The Goldfish is the domesticated Asiatic subspecies of *Carassius auratus*, the fish which is represented in Europe by another subspecies, *C.a.gibelio*. The Crucian Carp-like tendency to produce unadulterated red-golden coloration under certain conditions is first recorded for the Goldfish in the year 970. By 1200 A.D. more varieties must have already been developed. The fancy, originally only carried on by the aristocracy, had become universal in China by about 1500–1600. The Chinese kept Goldfish and their domesticated varieties in shallow earthenware bowls, wooden tubs and shady garden pools, and tended them with increasing affection and devotion.

The Goldfish was imported to Portugal via Java in the 17th century, whence it was at first very slowly distributed. Soon after the first successful breeding, in Holland in 1728, these lovely fishes became very nearly universally known.

Fine specimens are red-gold on the back, golden on the sides and brass-yellow on the belly. Fins red-gold to yellowish. Each breeding, even from perfect stock, also produces a proportion of individuals which are mottled white-red-gold or black-red-gold, often pale pink-coloured forms as well. The latter are often known as 'Silver Fishes' in the trade; they are occasionally described as 'scale-less', but this term is usually a misnomer among Goldfishes, being applied to specimens which merely lack guanine in the scales.

Plate 61

Fig. 344. *Barbus nigrofasciatus* (Black Ruby, Nigger Barb, Purple-headed Barb); adults, natural size. (Original)
Fig. 345. *Barbus gelius* (Golden Barb, Golden Dwarf Barb); half-grown, enlarged. (Original)
Fig. 346. *Barbus ticto* (Two-spot Barb, Tic-Tac-Toe Barb); adults, somewhat reduced; above ♀, below ♂. (Original)

Plate 61

Plate 62

Plate 62

Fig. 347. *Caecobarbus geertsi* (Blind Barb); adult, somewhat enlarged.
Fig. 348. *Barbus fasciolatus* (African Banded Barb); natural size.
Both photographs from blocks (provided by courtesy of Prof. Dr. Max Poll, Musée Royale d'Afrique Centrale, Tervuren) subsequently retouched. (Photos P. Favresse)

These fishes need large tanks, with moderate planting and good aeration. The traditional fish-globes are quite unsuitable, as also are large jampots and tall bell-jars. Omnivorous, including vegetable food. Goldfish develop very well in open-air ponds, but wintering outdoors is not generally successful in Continental Europe. (It is sometimes possible in southern England, the main requisite being a relatively deep region in the pond which insures against freezing to the bottom.) In America, southern France, Portugal and the island of Mauritius the Goldfish has now established itself as a wild species and may occur in thousands in ponds and streams.

The largest breeding-establishments are found in southern France. In Germany the following method is most successful. The fishes are kept in a large tank at 22–23 °C. and are well fed. Eventually, when they commence courtship, the fishes should be caught and carefully stripped of their roe and milt. First a deep plate, or even a fruit-dish, is carefully cleaned and placed ready (without water!). The ♀ is held in a damp napkin in the left hand, in such a way that the head and back lie in the hollow of the hand but the belly and vent region are exposed. Now stroke the fish carefully, using only moderate pressure with the right thumb, beginning at the gill-cover and stroking towards the vent while the remaining fingers give a gentle supporting pressure to the opposite side of the body. The movement is repeated (5–8 times) until no more eggs are extruded. Repeat the same process with the ♂, taking care that the viscous white milt drops onto the eggs. With practice it is possible to strip both fishes simultaneously, holding one in each hand. Finally, using a glass rod or a *blunt*-ended glass tube, the milt and roe are carefully stirred together in the dish and transferred to water. The fertilised eggs are best put into a large all-glass tank, where care must be taken to use only approximately neutral, crystal-clear, matured water. By this method it is possible to produce up to 10,000 or more at a spawning. The young hatch after 5–7 days and at first hang on the sides of the tank and on plants. After the absorption of the yolk-sac they should be fed with fine live food, or, if necessary, with fine egg-yolk and shredded lettuce leaves. The young are uniformly grey-green to begin with and only change colour after about 8–12 months.

All varieties of the Goldfish may be bred in the same way.

Goldfishes sometimes exhibit grotesque deviations from the normal fish shape. This peculiarity has been exploited by the Chinese and Japanese in the breeding' of various fancy varieties. The best known are:–

Veiltail (Figs. 343, 380)
Body shortened, thick, roundish. Fins greatly elongate. Especially sought-after are perfect golden specimens, whose caudal fins consist of two equally long, lobed or, in highly-bred forms, truncate, halves. The anal fin should be long and double. The dorsal fin must stand upright like a flag. The pectoral and ventral fins should be long and narrow. The whiter the tips of the flag-like fins are, the more valuable is the fish. As well as scaled, red-gold Veiltails, there are also scale-less and mottled ones of various kinds, and any brood also includes various colour-varieties, Comets, and other throw-backs to the wild type which are unsuitable for further breeding. As with all artificial breeds, the fundamental problem in the breeding of Veiltails is that of selecting the best parents. Only by repeated expert selection of the strongest and most beautiful fishes for breeding can the quality of the stock be improved, and only by repeated evaluation of the characters desired can a particular type be fixed.

Temperature, even in winter, not much below 15°C.; deep tanks. Vaguely outlined scarlet, often striped, spots on the edges of the fins of the Veiltail are small haemorrhages which can often be quickly healed by the addition of fresh water. (Allow tapwater and spring water to stand for a few days before using.) The haemorrhages are caused by bacterial damage to the fins.

Telescope-Veiltail (Fig. 343 e)
Similar to the foregoing, but with eyes which project strongly along the optic axis. Colouring generally blue-green to gold-red, mottled; pure black specimens are especially prized. Care, as for the previous form.

Comet (Fig. 343 a)
Altogether similar to the cultivated form of Goldfish, from which it differs merely in the very strongly elongated caudal fin. Care, as for the previous forms.

Egg-fish (Fig. 343 b)
Body stocky, egg-shaped. Fins only moderately developed. Dorsal fin absent. Caudal fin short, often double.

Shubunkin (Fig. 343 c)

A pale to deep blue-red-white-black-golden variegated, scale-less form of the Goldfish.

Celestial (Fig. 343 d)

Body-form as in the Egg-fish. The pupils of the prominent, globular eyes are upwardly directed.

Lionhead (Fig. 343 f)

Egg-fishes in which the head is distended with numerous swollen, blister-like excrescences, this proliferation appearing in older individuals.

All cultivated varieties of Goldfish are delicate and require warmth. Their value depends not only on the coloration and body-form but also on the size, proportions and symmetry of the finnage. First-class specimens command a substantial price and the standards are internationally determined.

The standard book on the subject, a work of quite outstanding scholarship, is:– *The Goldfish*, by G. F. Hervey and J. Hems (London: The Batchworth Press, 1948).

Chela laubuca (*Hamilton-Buchanan* 1822) (Fig. 341)   Indian Glass Barb

The genera *Chela*, *Oxygaster*, etc., are widely distributed through South-east Asia (inclusive of the islands) and comprise fishes which, at a casual inspection, are somewhat suggestive of the *Danio* and *Esomus* spp. They are distinguished from the latter, however, by the at least partly sharply-keeled edge to the belly and by the short dorsal fin. Body elongate, more or less deep, strongly compressed, the lower profile substantially more convex than the upper. Mouth somewhat ventral. No barbels. Pectoral fins stout; ventral fins, when present, as a rule with a strongly produced fin-ray. Lateral line complete, bowed down. The majority of the species are shoaling-fishes which inhabit the upper water-layers and are coloured rather like the Bleak.

Chela laubuca occurs throughout India and in Ceylon, Burma, the Malay Peninsula and Sumatra.

D 2/8; A 2/19; P 1/11; V 1/6; LL 32/34. Shape of body as described above. Interorbital region not scaly. Caudal fin moderately forked. Ventral fins well developed, the first fin-ray strongly produced. Translucent, shining silver to greenish-grey, with a violet lustre on the caudal peduncle. Back somewhat darker, often with a bright brassy gleam. A green to deep black longitudinal stripe begins somewhat before the level of the dorsal fin and runs along the vertebral column to

259

the root of the tail, where it may terminate in a deep black, golden-edged blotch. Above the dark longitudinal stripe lies a further fine golden band which extends forward to the gill-cover, where it surrounds a deep black blotch. Iris silver with a fine brassy-coloured periphery. Fins colourless, in fine specimens light orange to delicate brownish.

Sex-distinctions in coloration not known. ♀ more robust.

Care, as given for *Danio* spp. (see p. 265). This very beautiful shoaling fish prefers the upper water-layers and proves to be very hardy and undemanding in aquaria having a large surface-area. Greedily accepts any food provided, even dried food. Temperature, not less than 24°C. Not exacting as regards character of water; breeds in soft to medium hard, at most slightly acid water. Spawns at twilight.

Concerning the breeding of *Chela laubuca* and *Oxygaster atpar*, Mayburg reports as follows:–The breeding tank should be arranged as for *Danio* spp. By contrast, however, these fishes commence their courtship at the onset of twilight and often carry out their first spawning in full darkness. In spawning the ♂ tries to swim over the ♀ and to press her downward (especially in *Oxygaster atpar*). In the actual sex-act the ♀ awaits the ♂, who pushes himself against her left side and embraces the ridge of her back behind the dorsal fin with his caudal peduncle. The eggs and milt are then ejected with a quivering action (about 30–40 eggs at each mating). Thereupon the ♀ frees herself from the embrace with a twisting movement, in doing so scattering the eggs in all directions. The spawn is said to be little interfered with. Eggs glass-clear, very small. At 25–26°C. the young hatch after 20–24 hours. The young fishes swim freely after 3–4 days and should at first be reared on fine Rotifers (dried food too, according to Mayburg); later Nauplii. A very large number of batches of eggs are laid. 1925/+.

Chela mouhoti *Smith* 1945 (Fig. 368)
Central Thailand; to 6 cm.

D 3/10; A 3/23; LL 31. Body deep, strongly compressed. Lateral line complete, bowed down. Insertion of dorsal fin well back, exactly over the anal fin. Uniform bluish-silver, upperside fairly dark, especially between the dorsal and caudal fins.

Plate 63

Fig. 349. *Barbus filamentosus* (Black-spot Barb); young, natural size. (Original)
Fig. 350. *Barbus filamentosus;* adult ♂, somewhat reduced. (Original)
Fig. 351. *Barbus lateristriga* (Spanner Barb); 6 cm. young. (Original)

Plate 63

Plate 64

Plate 64

Fig. 352. *Barbus everetti* (Clown Barb, Everett's Barb); young, somewhat enlarged. (Original)

Fig. 353. *Barbus schwanenfeldi* (Schwanenfeld's Barb); 20 cm. specimen in the Hella-brunn Aquarium, Munich. (Original)

Fig. 354. *Rasbora daniconius* (Slender Rasbora); somewhat reduced.

A large deep black blotch behind the gill-cover. Dorsal and pectoral fins with dark spots.

Mature ♀ considerably more robust.

Care, as given for *Chela laubuca* above. A good jumper. Breeding in captivity unknown. 1956.

Oxygaster atpar (*Hamilton-Buchanan* 1822)
Southern India and Bengal, in flowing waters; to about 6 cm.

D 1/8; A 2/20; LL 53; TR 10/4. The species of *Oxygaster* are mainly distinguished from those of the closely related genus *Chela* by the forward extension of the scales of the nape; in *Oxygaster* the interorbital region is scaly, in *Chela* it is naked. Body elongate, as in *Chela*, deep, strongly compressed. Ventral fins small, the second fin-ray strongly produced. Translucent, shining brilliant silver by reflected light. Back light olive; belly whitish. A shining greenish longitudinal band begins at the level of the dorsal fin and broadens posteriorly. Fins delicate yellowish. Iris of the eye brass-coloured.

The sexes may be distinguished by the greater girth of the ♀.

Care and breeding, as given for *Chela laubuca* above. 1956.

Oxygaster bacaila (*Hamilton-Buchanan* 1822) (Fig. 367)
Throughout India, with the exception of Malabar, Mysore and Madras; to 18 cm.

D 2/7; A 3/10–15; LL 86–110. Body-shape typical of the genus (see *O. atpar* above). Scales very small. Upperside grey-green, sometimes uniformly silver. A broad, gleaming white-green band extends from the gill-cover to the root of the tail. Fins colourless.

The sexes may be distinguished only by the greater girth of the ♀.

Care, as given for *Chela laubuca* above. Not yet bred in captivity; breeding certainly not difficult, however. 1905/−.

261

Oxygaster oxygastroides (*Bleeker* 1852) (Fig. 340)   Glass Barb
Thailand, Greater Sunda Is., common in standing waters; to 20 cm., remains
considerably smaller in captivity.

D 2/7; A 3/28; LL 40–43. Body-shape typical of the genus (see *O. atpar* above).
Anal fin-base long. Upperside yellow-brown; flanks whitish-silver with a greenish
to bluish lustre; belly white. A beautiful broad shining silver stripe, often with a
black edge above it, extends from the gill-cover to the root of the tail. Now and
then there is a further black longitudinal stripe along the lower half of the body.
Fins colourless, glassy, with fine black spots. Young fish, especially, very translucent (Glass Barb).

♀ similarly coloured, but considerably more robust.

Care and breeding, as given for *Chela laubuca* above. 1929/ –.

Crossochilus oblongus (*Cuvier* and *Valenciennes* 1842) (Fig. 369)
Greater Sunda Is., Malay Peninsula, Thailand; to 16 cm.

D 3/8; A 3/5; P 1/14–15; V 1/8; LL 33–36. Body elongate, little compressed,
upper and lower profiles almost equally convex. Snout rounded, mouth ventral.
Upper lip fringed. Upper and lower jaws sharp-edged. 2 pairs of short barbels.
Lateral line complete, long. Upperside olive-grey to pale grey. Flanks delicate
yellowish with a broad black longitudinal band from the tip of the snout to the
root of the tail and thence onto the middle caudal rays; in the ♂♂ this band often
has a pale margin above and below. Fins colourless with a very delicate milky
tinge. Dorsal fin often pink.

♀ when sexually mature, considerably more robust.
♂ at spawning time, with a white film on top of the head (nuptial tubercles).

Care of this very peaceful and interesting species: large, well-planted aquaria
with dark bottom-soil and, if possible, hollow branches. Soft, slightly acid or

Figs. 355–360
Fig. 355. *Rasbora daniconius* (Slender Rasbora); somewhat reduced.
Fig. 356. *Rasbora leptosoma*; ♂, natural size.
Fig. 357. *Rasbora meinkeni* (Meinken's Rasbora); natural size.
Fig. 358. *Brachydanio kerri*; adult ♂, somewhat enlarged.
Fig. 359. *Esomus danrica* (Flying Barb); natural size.
Fig. 360. *Esomus lineatus* (Striped Flying Barb); somewhat enlarged.

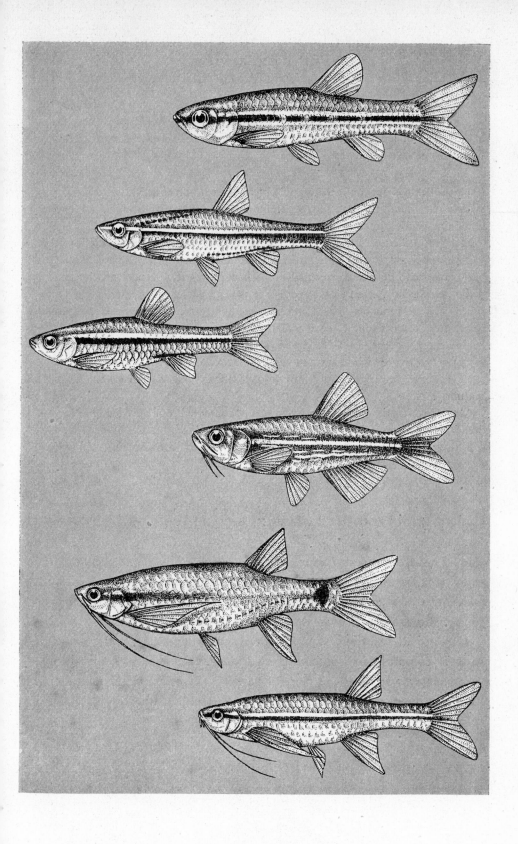

peat-filtered water. Temperature 22–25°C. Omnivorous, but with a preference for worms from the bottom and algal felt ('blanket weed'; also lettuce). These fishes like to hide; at feeding-time they come scurrying out like mice from their holes. Not yet bred in captivity. 1932/+.

Cyclocheilichthys apogon (*Cuvier* and *Valenciennes* 1842) (Fig. 342)
Widely distributed through Further India and the Malay Archipelago; to 25 cm., remaining smaller in captivity.

D 4/8; A 3/5–6; P 1/16–17; V 2/9; LL 34–35. Body stocky, strongly compressed. Mouth somewhat downwardly directed. Lateral line complete. Upperside olive to brass-coloured. Flanks greenish-silver with a pearly iridescence, on the caudal peduncle especially often with a reddish or delicate violet lustre. Underside white-silver. Top of head blackish. Gill-cover metallic green. Numerous longitudinal rows of dark spots (one to each scale). A small round black blotch immediately behind the gill-cover; another, larger, at the root of the tail. Vertical fins in part bright red, with grey-white margins. Ventral fins yellowish. Iris blood-red above.

Sex-distinctions in coloration not yet described; ♀ more robust when sexually mature.

Lively, attractive, peaceful and very easily contented, but only suitable for the domestic aquarium when young. Omnivorous. Temperature 22–24°C. This species loves shady resting-places among plants or hanging root-systems. Apparently not yet bred in captivity. 1934/–.

Genera Danio and Brachydanio: Care and Breeding

The fishes of the genera *Danio* and *Brachydanio* are native to the whole of India (with the exception of the northern part), Burma, the Malay Peninsula and Sumatra, where they inhabit both standing and flowing waters and in some districts often occur in vast numbers in the paddy fields.

They are all small and slim, very lively, shoaling-fishes. Body elongate, strongly compressed. Mouth directed forwards (terminal) or slightly upwards (superior); usually 2 pairs of barbels. The origin of the anal fin always lies opposite the dorsal. Many of the species are very attractively coloured.

Care: large, long tanks with thick clumps of plants as well as substantial spaces which give the fishes plenty of room to move about. Temperature 22–24°C., in winter 18–21°C. Lower temperatures should be avoided if possible, since the fishes then become pale and apathetic. Not-too-old water. Very easily contented omnivores, even accepting dried food.

For breeding use small, long, all-glass tanks (about 30 × 25 × 25 cm.) with fresh water. The hardness of the water and the pH values are of little consequence. In the dark corners of the breeding tank dense clumps of algae, *Nitella* or *Myriophyllum* should be provided; some species, such as the Zebra Danio, will spawn over gravelly bottoms even when there are no plants present. The plants should be anchored with a glass rod or small chips of stone, and somewhat loosened above. Spawning is stimulated by sunshine or reflected sunlight. The ♀ should be placed in the breeding tank by herself first; a day or two later one or two ♂♂ can be put in with her in the evening if there is a reasonable chance of sunshine on the following day. Spawning takes place in the early morning. The ♂♂ entice the ♀♀ into a plant thicket where they embrace or press against one another. Numerous large eggs are shed at one time. The parents may advantageously be fed with Enchytraeids during the spawning-act, since they are notorious spawn-robbers. The young hatch after 20–24 hours and at first hang on the sides of the tank and on plants; later, after the absorption of the yolk-sac, they should be provided with the finest live food (also dried food). The breeding pair can be mated again after a lapse of 3–4 weeks. Growth rapid. Very prolific.

In contrast to *Brachydanio*, the genus *Danio* has a complete lateral line and a greater number of fin-rays in the dorsal and anal fins:–

Danio . . . . D:8–17 soft rays; A:11–17 soft rays.
Brachydanio . . . D:6–7   soft rays; A:10–13 soft rays.

Brachydanio albolineatus (*Blyth* 1860) (Fig. 377)   Pearl Danio
Further India and Sumatra, in flowing waters; to 5·5 cm.
  D 2/7; A 3/13; LL 31–33. Body elongate, slim, moderately compressed. Mouth somewhat upwardly directed. Lateral line incomplete.

265

Coloration, seen against the light:–translucent grey-green, back darker, belly paler. Caudal peduncle dark olive. A flesh-coloured longitudinal band, broadening posteriorly, commences at the level of the pectoral fins and is bordered above and below with blue-violet. Dorsal fin and tips of caudal yellow-green. Anal fin yellow with a row of dark spots.

Coloration by reflected light:–very changeable. Body with a shining blue to violet iridescence, grass-green in sunlight. Back deep blue, belly bluish-silver, longitudinal stripe cherry-red with a blue-green border. Vertical fins grass-green with a reddish tinge. Base of anal fin cherry- to orange-red, centre cherry-red. Pectoral and ventral fins reddish.

♀ more soberly coloured, larger.
♂ coloration as given above.

Care and breeding, as given on p. 265; loves sunshine. Breeding temperature 26–28°C. A ♀ is best accompanied by two ♂♂. Very various and beautiful races are offered in the trade. 1911/+.

Brachydanio kerri (*H. M. Smith* 1931) (Fig. 358)
Islands of Koh Yao Yai and Koh Yao Noi (Thailand); to about 4 cm.

D 2/7; A 2/12–13; LL 28–30. Body not quite so slim as in the Zebra Danio. 2 pairs of barbels; the maxillary barbels reach to beyond the gill-opening. Lateral line absent. Coloration of this very beautiful species, according to Roloff:– Ground colour brilliant blue. Back grey-blue; lower part of belly whitish. An intense golden line extends from the gill-cover to the root of the tail; below this line runs a shorter, usually somewhat wavy, line of like colour whose first half as a rule is composed of small irregular streaks and which peters out about over the hinder end of the anal fin-base. Between the lines mentioned – with the exception of the last third–and below the same are found small streaks, spots and curved markings which are again of a golden colour. The blue colour of the flanks extends right through the middle portion of the caudal fin.

Figs. 361–366

Fig. 361. *Barbus binotatus* (Spotted Barb); adult, reduced.
Fig. 362. *Barbus chola* (Swamp Barb); adult, reduced.
Fig. 363. *Barbus dorsimaculatus;* adult, slightly enlarged.
Fig. 364. *Barbus sachsi* (Sachs' Barb, Gold-finned Barb); about natural size.
Fig. 365. *Barbus terio* (One-spot Barb); adult, somewhat reduced.
Fig. 366. *Barbus stigma;* adult.

Ripe ♂♂ are distinguished from ♀♀ by their slimmer bodies and by a turquoise-blue lustre extending over the whole body and caudal fin. The fins of ripe fishes in good condition are yellowish to yellow.

Care and breeding, as given on p. 265; simple. 1956.

Brachydanio nigrofasciatus (*Day* 1869) (Fig. 371)   Spotted Danio
Upper Burma, in rivers and still waters down to the tiniest pools; to 4 cm.

D 2/7; A 2/11; P 15; V 7; LL 28–32. Shape similar to that of the previous species (see also genus description on p. 264), but with only one pair of barbels. Lateral line absent.

Nape and back pale to olive-brown; belly orange to yellowish-white. From the gill-cover to the middle caudal rays extends a golden to brownish longitudinal band, bordered above and below by a blue-black band. Below the lower dark band a number of blue spots. Vertical fins yellow-brown to yellowish. Anal fin with blue spots and streaks.

♀ belly yellowish-white, plumper.
♂ belly orange.

Care and breeding, as given on p. 265. Breeding temperature 26–28 °C. A ♀ should be accompanied by two ♂♂. The sexes should be kept apart when not breeding. The ♀♀ are faithful to their mates. 1911/+.

Brachydanio rerio (*Hamilton-Buchanan* 1822) (Fig. 375)   Zebra Danio
Eastern part of India; to 4·5 cm.

D 2/7; A 2/13; LL 26–28. Shape typical of the genus, very slim, only slightly compressed. 2 pairs of barbels. Back brownish-olive; belly yellowish-white; flanks

Plate 65

Fig. 367. *Oxygaster baicala* (?); young, 4 cm., enlarged. (Original)
Fig. 368. *Chela mouhoti;* natural size. (Original)
Fig. 369. *Crossochilus oblongus;* young, somewhat enlarged. (Original)

Plate 66 (overleaf)

Fig. 370. *Gobio gobio* (Gudgeon); young, 4 cm., enlarged. (Original)
Fig. 371. *Brachydanio nigrofasciatus* (Spotted Danio); young, about twice natural size. (Original)
Fig. 372. *Danio regina;* young ♀, natural size. The shining lines on the flanks, arranged similarly to those on *Danio malabaricus*, are barely indicated in the photograph. (Original)

Plate 65

Plate 66 (see page 268)

Plate 67 (see page 269)

Plate 68

Plate 67 (overleaf)

Fig. 373. *Danio devario;* ripe specimens, natural size. (Original)

Fig. 374. *Danio malabaricus* (Giant Danio); ripe specimens, natural size; above, a ♂, below, two ♀♀; in the Erfurt Aquarium. (Original)

Plate 68

Fig. 375. *Brachydanio rerio* (Zebra Danio); natural size. (Original)

Fig. 376. *Esomus malayensis* (Malayan Flying Barb); natural size; above ♀, below ♂. (Original)

Fig. 377. *Brachydanio albolineatus* (Pearl Danio); adults, somewhat enlarged; above, a ♀, below, two ♂♂. (Original)

shining prussian blue, traversed by 4 beautiful shining gold bands from the gill-cover to the caudal fin. The two outer bands sharply delimit the blue of the sides above and below. The blue-gold stripes show up quite clearly on the anal fin as well. Dorsal fin yellow-olive at the base, otherwise blue with a white tip. Pectoral and ventral fins colourless. Iris golden-red. Gill-cover blue with golden blotches and transverse bars.

♀ more soberly coloured. The longitudinal bands are more silvery to yellowish. More robust.

♂ smaller; coloration as described above.

A favourite and undemanding species. Care and breeding, as given on p. 265. For breeding choose only dark ♂♂; the stripes should be shining gold and the tips of the fins white. Breeding temperature not above 24°C. The ♀♀ are very faithful to their mates and readily spawn again with the same partner. 1905/+.

Danio devario (*Hamilton-Buchanan* 1822) (Fig. 373)

India, in the following regions: N. W. Provinces, Orissa, Bengal, Assam; to 10 cm.

D 3/15–16; A 3/15–16; P 1/12; V 1/7; LL 41–48. Similarly shaped to the following species, but the ventral profile is still more strongly convex. Barbels absent. Lateral line complete. Ground colour pale greenish-silver; back grey- to blue-green; belly dull silver; shoulder region shining blue with several vertical yellow stripes. Three blue longitudinal bands, separated by yellow lines, begin gradually under the dorsal fin and unite at the root of the tail into a single blue band which runs up into the upper caudal lobe. Dorsal fin grey-brown with whitish bands on the upper edge. Ventral and anal fins brownish-red.

269

♀ plumper, more dully coloured.

♂ slimmer, more brilliantly coloured.

Care and breeding, as given on p. 265. 1939/+.

Danio malabaricus (*Jerdon* 1849) (Fig. 374)   Giant Danio
West coast of India, Ceylon, in clear flowing waters; to 12 cm., but mature at
6–7 cm.

D 2/10–13; A 3/12–16; P 1/14; V 1/7; LL 35–37. Body elongate. In contrast to
the *Brachydanio* spp., the *Danio* spp. are usually strongly compressed and, from
the caudal peduncle forward, relatively deep. The lower profile is more strongly
convex than the upper, and the head pointed. Mouth upwardly directed (superior).
One pair of barbels, on the snout. Maxillary barbels usually vestigial. Lateral line
complete.

Back steel-blue to greenish-grey. Head silvery. Belly pale pink. 3 to 4 steel-blue
longitudinal bands along the flanks, beginning over the pectoral fins and shining
indigo-blue by reflected light. The blue bands are separated from one another by
more slender golden longitudinal stripes. Gill-cover with a golden to greenish
blotch. A number of transverse golden stripes on an indigo ground on the hinder
part of the gill-cover. Iris golden. Pectoral fins colourless; the other fins delicate
bluish to pink, occasionally reddish at the base.

♀ more dully coloured; the middle blue stripe turns upward markedly at the base
  of the caudal fin.

♂ coloration as above; the middle blue stripe is straight.

Care and breeding, as given on p. 265. Breeding tank at least 50 × 25 × 30 cm.
Breeding temperature 25–28 °C. 1909/+.

Danio regina *Fowler* 1934 (Fig. 372)
Southern Thailand; to 12·5 cm.

This species is very similar to the better-known *D. malabaricus* and was probably
previously imported under this name. *D. regina* is altogether somewhat deeper than
D. malabaricus; with regard to its outline the species is somewhat reminiscent of
D. devario. It is further characterised by a black blotch at the upper end of the
gill-opening as well as by a somewhat different pattern of lines. (Lacrymal bone
with a backwardly-directed spine, which is absent in *D. malabaricus*.)

Care and breeding, as given on p. 265. Import data unknown.

270

Epalzeorhynchus kallopterus (*Bleeker* 1850) (Fig. 313)

Sumatra, Borneo; not common; to 14 cm., at most to 10 cm. in aquaria.

D 3/8; A 2/5; LL 34–36. Body elongate, slim, scarcely compressed. Head pointed; the snout far overhangs the mouth. 2 pairs of barbels. Upper lip fringed. Lateral line complete. Back, according to condition, golden-brown to dark olive-green, against the flanks delimited by a broad golden-yellow longitudinal band which extends from the tip of the snout to the root of the tail. In the middle of the flanks the golden-yellow band is bordered below by a broad dark longitudinal band which also begins at the tip of the snout and is continued onto the middle caudal rays. The deep black edges of the row of scales adjacent to this band simulate a zig-zag marking. Belly region white. Dorsal fin red-brownish to pink at its base, over that a band extending from the upper to the hinder tip of the fin; ventral and anal fins marked likewise. Caudal fin pink at its base. Pectoral fins wholly pink or reddish-brown. Upper part of iris red, inner edge golden. Often the whole fish is tinged with reddish.

Sex-distinctions not certainly known.

Care: large tanks with locally rich planting, twigs and a soft bottom-soil. Temperature 23–26 °C. Soft water. All kinds of live food. This undemanding species spends most of its time near the bottom. The resting position is peculiar: the fishes support themselves on the bottom with their pectoral fins, or seek large plant leaves on which to rest in the same position. They much prefer to hide in hollow tree-stumps or branches. The upper lip, with its fringe-like processes, is especially adapted to grazing on algal felts. A planarian-eradicator! Peacefully disposed towards other fishes, but on the other hand often quarrelsome with its own kind. Breeding unknown. 1935/ −.

Garra spp. (formerly Discognathus)

The members of the genus *Garra* are very interesting *Cyprinidae*, predominantly adapted to life in swift-flowing waters, and in their general appearance somewhat reminiscent of the European Loach although, of course, quite unrelated. Behind the ventral mouth there is a sucking-disc which enables the fish to hold fast in a strong current; in addition to this the fish presses its body firmly against the bottom and further increases the surface in contact by the large paired fins. By virtue of these peculiarities the *Garra* spp. are enabled to live even in mountain streams and rapids. Food is mainly a matter of the algal felts on stones. Most

271

of these fishes are native to Africa, but there is one species in Borneo and several in India and the Middle East. The species figured here (Fig. 418) comes from the Congo and is apparently still undescribed. (Import by Werner, Munich.) A related blind species, *Typhlogarra widdowsoni* Trewavas 1958, inhabits underground waters near the Euphrates and has been kept, but not bred, in captivity in England and Iraq.

Esomus danrica (*Hamilton-Buchanan* 1822) (Fig. 359)   Flying Barb
India, Ceylon, Thailand, Singapore; to 15 cm., remaining smaller in captivity.

D 2/6; A 3/5; P 1/14–15; V 1/7; LL 30–34. Body elongate, slim, especially strongly compressed posteriorly. Back almost straight. Head pointed. Mouth upwardly directed. 2 pairs of barbels, the pair on the snout short and fleshy. The maxillary barbels, when laid back, reach to about the middle of the body. Lateral line incomplete, very short, piercing 4–6 scales. Pectoral fins pointed, enlarged, sail-like; laid back they reach to the insertion of the ventrals and are usually widely spread out from the body. Back olive-green to grey-green with a pearly iridescence and sprinkled with fine dark spots. Flanks silvery-violet to delicate reddish, shining red-violet by reflected light. Belly silver-white. A broad dark brown band extends from the mouth to the root of the tail and in young fishes is bordered dorsally by a fine gold stripe. The dark band broadens out on the caudal peduncle to form a striking dark brown triangular blotch. Ventral fins reddish; all other fins brownish to orange-coloured.

♀ the blotch on the caudal peduncle is indistinct. Belly profile more rounded.
♂ the blotch on the caudal peduncle is a shining rust-red. Smaller.

Large tanks with large-leaved plants. Temperature 22–24°C. Very lively and undemanding. Omnivorous. For further particulars, see *E. malayensis*. 1904/ –.

Esomus goddardi *Fowler* 1937
Central Thailand, common; to about 8 cm.

D 3/6; A 3/5; LL 25–26 – 5–6 on the base of the caudal fin. The characteristics of this species are, according to H. M. Smith, the incomplete lateral line which usually only reaches to the anal fin, the long barbels (maxillary barbels reach to the anal fin when laid back) and a dark grey line from the head to the root of the tail.

The import of this species is very doubtful.

Esomus lineatus *E. Ahl* 1925 (Fig. 360)
Delta at the mouths of the Ganges; to 6 cm.

D 2/6; A 3/5; LL about 30. Similarly shaped to the following species and also not unlike it as regards coloration. *E. lineatus* may be recognised by the somewhat longer maxillary barbels which, when laid back, reach to about the middle of the pectoral fins. The dark blotch on the caudal fin of *E. malayensis* is either completely absent in the present species or only very vaguely indicated. A silver line from the gill-cover to the root of the tail.

Sex-distinctions, care and breeding, as given for the following species. 1911/−.

Esomus malayensis (*Mandée* 1909) (Fig. 376)   Malayan Flying Barb
Malay Peninsula and southern Viet-Nam; to 8 cm.

D 2/6; A 3/5; LL 29–30; TR 6 between D and V. Similarly shaped to the previous species, but with an indistinct longitudinal band. Maxillary barbels long, when laid back reaching to the origin of the pectoral fins. Back greenish to moss-green, steel-blue by reflected light; flanks greenish- to bluish-silver; belly silver-white. Along the middle of the side runs an indistinct dark longitudinal band which merges with a rectangular, deep black, golden-edged blotch at the root of the tail. A less prominent blotch over the anal fin. Iris pale yellow. Gill-cover with a shining golden blotch. Fins colourless. The whole fish often has a brassy gleam in sunshine.

♀ larger. Ventral profile more strongly convex.
♂ smaller and slimmer.

Care: large, long aquaria with clumps of plants and open spaces for swimming. These fishes swim at best in a loose shoal, tending to remain in certain favourite parts of the aquarium where they rest with body easily poised beneath the leaves of floating plants. Temperature 23–25°C. Live food. In preparation for breeding, midge-larvae, *Tubifex* and Enchytraeids are especially suitable and frequent changes of diet are desirable.

Breeding tanks should be generously provided with masses of algae, *Nitella* or Willow Moss; plants must be firmly anchored! Quite freshly arranged tanks with fresh water which has been allowed to stand are most suitable. When a sunny day is expected the ♀ should be put into the breeding-tank the previous morning, and followed by the ♂ the same evening. The fishes prefer to breed in a corner of the tank; after a brief embrace and a vigorous slap with the caudal fin some 10–30 eggs are sent whirling to the bottom. Good ♀♀ produce up to 700 eggs, but are, unfortunately, arrant spawn-robbers. The young hatch in 16–20 hours at 24–26°C. and at first hang from the plants and sides of the tank, swimming freely after 2–3 days. They should be fed with the very finest food, such as Rotifers and Nauplii; no Infusoria. After 5–6 days the very rapidly growing young fishes are ready to take a coarser grade of fine food. They become sexually mature after 15–20 weeks. Breeding not difficult. 1925/+.

Labeo bicolor *Smith* 1931 (Fig. 404)   Red-tailed Black 'Shark'
The members of the genera *Labeo* and *Morulius*, natives of Africa, South and South-east Asia inclusive of the islands, are *Cyprinidae* with strongly developed lips which unite to form a sucking-organ internally provided with sharp ridges and horny tubercles. Mouth ventral. 1 or 2 pairs of barbels.

L. *bicolor* inhabits Thailand (Menam Chao Phya and also near Bangkok) and is found mainly in streams; to 12 cm.

D 3/11–13; A 3/5; P 1/14–15; V 1/8; LL 30–35. Body elongate, somewhat compressed. Ventral profile rather straight. Dorsal fin notably flag-like, inserted somewhat anteriorly to the ventral fins. 2 pairs of barbels. Healthy fishes are velvety black with a sharply contrasting orange-red to blood-red caudal fin. Dorsal, anal and ventral fins likewise velvet black, pectorals more or less orange-red. Unsettled or poorly treated fishes are grey-brown to black-brown with a yellow-red caudal, although less beautiful local races do occur.

♀ when sexually mature, considerably more robust.

This extraordinarily handsome *Labeo* develops its full beauty in soft, slightly peaty water which is regularly partly replenished. The tank should not stand in too light a position and the very nimble but somewhat timid fishes must be provided with suitable hiding-places. Hollow tree-roots, inverted flower-pots or coconut-shells are evidently preferred. Besides live food of all kinds they very much like to graze on coatings of algae and will also accept lettuce. Very hardy and active at a temperature of 24–27°C. Unfortunately the fishes are very quarrelsome among themselves and continually drive one another. Already bred to my knowledge, although details are not available. 1952.

Labeo erythrura *Fowler* 1937 (Fig. 477)
Thailand, Mekong River near Kemarat; to 12 cm.

D 3/11–12; A 3/5; P 1/15; V 1/9; LL 27–30, 3–4 on the base of the caudal fin. Somewhat slimmer than L. *bicolor*. Ventral profile almost straight, back arched. In full-grown fishes the origin of the dorsal fin is anterior to the ventrals. 2 pairs of barbels. At a glance easily mistaken for a slim, not very finely coloured *L. bicolor*. Body pale brown, dark or even black-blue, becoming brighter on the underside, often somewhat blotchy. A dark bridle-like marking from the snout to the eyes and a dark transverse streak at the root of the tail. Ventral fins colourless or grey. Caudal fin orange to red. A dark blotch on the pectoral fins, which is smaller than the eye and is also present in *L. bicolor*.

Sex-distinctions unknown. Care, as given for *Labeo bicolor* above. 1956.

Labeo frenatus *Fowler* 1934 (Fig. 478)
North Thailand (Chiengmai); to 8 cm.

D 3/11; A 3/5; P 1/15; V 1/8; LL 29–30, 2–3 on the caudal peduncle. Distinguished from the previous species by the somewhat slimmer body, which is equally convex above and below. 2 pairs of barbels. Grey-olive to brownish-olive, underside bronze-colour to whitish. A black, bridle-like band from the tip of the snout over the eye to the gill-cover. A black triangular blotch at the root of the tail. Fins, especially the ventrals and anal, brilliant brick-red to blood-red. According to D. Vogt the anal fin in the ♂♂ has a black border.

Care, as given for *L. bicolor*, but not so quarrelsome among themselves. An excellent alga-eradicator. 1953.

Labeo forskali (*Rüppel* 1853) (Fig. 460)
Nile Basin and tributaries of the Blue Nile; to 36 cm.

D 2/(9)–10–(11); A 3/5; LL 38–42. Body elongate, very low. Origin of the dorsal fin well in front of the ventrals; the first and last dorsal rays produced in the ♂. Uniformly grey-green; underside paler to silvery. Fins grey to yellowish.

Care easy. This species is also resistant to lower temperatures and willingly accepts any kind of food. Peaceful towards other species but very quarrelsome with its own kind. 1935/−.

Labeo wecksi *Boulenger* 1909 (Fig. 406)
Upper and middle Congo; to 23 cm.

D 3/12; A 3/5; LL 36; TR 10–11. Body elongate, somewhat compressed. One pair of very small barbels; groups of small tubercles on the snout. Scales dark-edged; collectively the scales give the impression of an overall honeycomb-pattern. Yellow-green with narrow brownish longitudinal stripes. Flanks with a bronze-coloured lustre. Fins greenish to reddish-brown.

Sex-distinctions unknown. Care very easy. An interesting subject for large aquaria. Omnivorous. 1954.

Morulius chrysophekadion (*Bleeker* 1849) (Fig. 405)   Black 'Shark'
Thailand, Greater Sunda Islands; to 60 cm.

D 3/15–18; A 3/5; P 1/15–17; V 1/8; LL 41–43; TR 8/8½–9½. Body elongate, somewhat compressed; ventral profile in older specimens straight. Snout with numerous pores. 2 pairs of barbels. The very large sail-like dorsal fin is inserted well in front of the ventrals. Uniform black to blue-black; each of the scales on the flanks with a more or less distinct yellow to reddish spot. All fins velvet black.

Sex-distinctions not known.

Care, as given for the nearly-related *Labeo bicolor*. This species is very hardy and is partial to any kind of food. When hungry the fishes restlessly suck up the bottom-soil. Plants and tank-sides are sucked clean of algae. A lovely exhibit for large aquaria. Not yet bred. 1932/+.

Luciosoma spilopleura *Bleeker* 1855 (Fig. 461)
Thailand, Indo-China, Sumatra, Borneo; to 25 cm.

D 2/7; A 3/6–8; P 1/14–15; V 2/8; LL 41–42; TR 5½/4½–3½. Body elongate, little compressed. 2 pairs of barbels; the pair on the snout are relatively long. Lateral line complete. Upperside olive-green to yellow-green. Flanks delicate clay-colour. A broad, bluish-silver longitudinal band, which commences in a large, round, black shoulder-blotch and contains large black to dark violet blotches; shining iridescent golden zones between the blotches. Underside whitish. Fins yellowish to delicate reddish; in older individuals with rows of dark spots on the dorsal and anal fins.

Sex-distinctions unknown.

Care, as given for the genus *Rasbora* (see p.310). This very lively species frequents the upper water layers and requires soft, slightly acid water and some sunshine. Temperature 23–26 °C. It feeds chiefly on flying insects, such as flies,

Plate 69
Fig. 378. *Rasbora heteromorpha* (Harlequin Fish, Red Rasbora); natural size. (Original)
Fig. 379. *Rasbora maculata* (Pigmy Rasbora, Spotted Rasbora); adults, enlarged. The brick-red colouring is usually appreciably stronger. (Original)

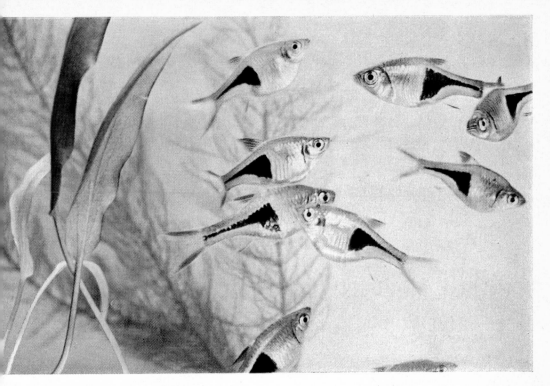

Plate 69

Plate 70

Plate 70

Fig. 380. Young Veiltail Goldfish in various swimming-positions. (Original)

moths, beetles and similar food and only takes other live food as a makeshift, although it does accept small fishes. Unfortunately somewhat frail. Only young specimens are suitable for the domestic aquarium. Not yet bred in captivity. 1924/–.

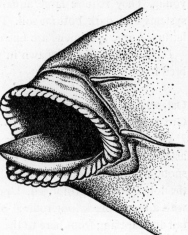

Fig. 381

The mouth of *Osteochilus hasselti* with the broad, protrusible, papilla-bearing upper and lower lips. The sharp-edged lower jaw projects over the lower lip. Above the upper lip the snout- and maxillary barbels of the left side are shown. (After M. Weber)

Osteochilus hasselti (*Cuvier* and *Valenciennes* 1842) (Figs. 381, 408)

Hasselt's Bony-lipped Barb

The genus *Osteochilus* is confined to the East Indies. The body is stocky or elongate, compressed. The mouth is upwardly directed, protrusible, bordered with papillae and characteristically shaped; the upper lip is covered by a fold of skin and the lower jaw forms a sharp projecting edge within the lower lip (Fig. 381). Dorsal fin large, beginning between the pectoral and ventral fins. Anal fin small. Lateral line complete, straight. Several species are very beautifully coloured.

O. hasselti is widely distributed in Thailand and through the larger, and many of the smaller, islands of the Malay Archipelago; to 32 cm.

D 3/12–18; A 3/5; P 1/13–15; V 1/9; LL 33–36. Body-shape typical of the genus, relatively deep. 2 pairs of barbels (1 pair on the snout and 1 pair of somewhat longer maxillary barbels). Ground colour olive-green, with a brassy gleam, especially on the flanks. Young specimens with 6–8 longitudinal rows of brown spots, each scale having a dark spot at its base. In the subspecies *O. hasselti microcephalus* a further, finer, dark longitudinal stripe is prominent, commencing at the level of the ventral fins. A deep black blotch at the root of the tail. Fins bright red, the dorsal and caudal being more yellowish. Old fishes unfortunately lose this very attractive colouring almost completely and become almost uniformly yellow-green to grey with greenish fins.

♀ easily recognised by her greater girth.

These active shoaling-fishes are suitable for the domestic aquarium only when young. They require large aquaria, loose plant growth, twigs or hanging root-systems and dark bottom-soil. Temperature 22–25°C. Live food, also algae or lettuce. Large specimens are fine exhibits for public aquaria.

O. hasselti is said to spawn in waters where there is a strong current. Not yet bred in captivity. 1931/+.

Osteochilus vittatus (*Cuvier* and *Valenciennes* 1842) (Fig. 407)   Bony-lipped Barb Greater Sunda Islands, chiefly in rivers; to 26 cm.

D 3/10–11; A 3/5; P 1/13–16; V 1/8; LL 33–34. Shape typical of the genus, as in the previous species, but relatively elongate and low. Middle of the rounded snout with large pores or wart-shaped tubercles. Caudal fin deeply emarginate, the lobes acutely prolonged. Upperside olive-coloured. Flanks beautiful silvery with a broad black longitudinal band from the tip of the snout to the root of the tail and tapering from here to the deepest part of the edge of the fin. Young fishes with longitudinal series of spots (each scale with a black spot?). Fins colourless, glass-clear. Dorsal fin occasionally with two series of black spots.

Sex-distinctions unknown.

Care, as given for previous species. Not yet bred in captivity. More frequent imports are much to be desired. 1954.

Genus Barbus: Small Species of Asia and Africa: Care and Breeding

Although these little fishes contrast with the large European Barbel *(Barbus barbus)*, which is the type-species of the genus, we do not here follow some authors who place them all in another genus *Puntius*. The limits and definition of *Puntius* cannot be understood without a great deal of further research, and we therefore continue meanwhile to use the genus *Barbus* in the broad sense for the little 'Barbs' as well as the great Barbel.

278

The *Barbus* spp. are exclusively native to the Old World. We meet representatives of this genus of many species in India, Ceylon, South-east Asia (including the East Indies), China and Africa. They inhabit the most varied kinds of water and often occur in large shoals. All the species are egglayers (oviparous), even *Barbus viviparus* from South-east Africa having been named under a misapprehension. *Barbus* spp. should, by reason of their active habits, be kept only in large aquaria (at least 50 litres) and especially require a soft and not too pale bottom-soil and often a loose screen of floating plants (*Riccia, Salvinia* and other plants with floating leaves). The planting should not be too thick, so as to leave plenty of room for freedom of movement. The majority of the species prefer to occupy the water-layers near the bottom. The quality of the water is quite unimportant to these fishes, but in general water which has been well matured by plants is to be preferred. Furthermore, if the fish are to prosper, the addition of fresh water from time is very desirable. Species from the warmer climates naturally require warmth, but they are not very sensitive to temperature reductions down to 17°C. *Barbus* spp. are easily contented and peaceful, and are therefore suited to community life with other peaceful fishes. Many of them become very tame. Feeding is simple; as well as live food all kinds of dried food are greedily devoured. The gluttony of these fishes is really quite remarkable; many of them pass their time chewing continuously through the upper layers of the soil. Young fishes like to associate in loose shoals.

Breeding is generally not difficult and in some species even very easy. Most Barbs spawn quite willingly even in large all-glass tanks without soil. Only some need a well-furnished aquarium for courtship.

All fine-leaved plants, which should not be too closely set, are suitable as spawning-substrate. Almost all species prefer soft, mature water for spawning (pH about 7·0) and spawning is often stimulated by the addition of fresh water. The prospective parents should be placed in the breeding tank during the evening; they generally spawn the very next morning. The position of the breeding tank should, if possible, be so chosen that it is caught by the first rays of the morning sun. After vigorous driving, which is often initiated

279

by the ♀, the fishes press against one another in the tufts of plants and, with violent quivering, emit the eggs and milt. The fertilised eggs adhere to the plants or fall to the bottom. The spawning process is repeated many times in succession. The young hatch usually after 24–36 hours, lie 1–2 days on the ground and then hang on the sides of the tank and on water plants. The parents are enthusiastic spawn-robbers and must be removed at once after spawning. Since the young are easily damaged by *Cyclops* and by Ostracods one should not feed the breeding pair with crustacea once they have entered the breeding tank. Rearing not difficult. The young grow quickly and in large tanks they are ready to spawn after 9–12 months. One breeding can produce many hundreds of offspring. If well-fed the mature fishes will spawn several times a year.

The Asiatic and African representatives of the genus will be dealt with separately.

Asiatic Barbus species

Barbus arulius (*Jerdon* 1849) (Fig. 322)
South-east India, Travancore, Cauvery; to 12 cm.

D 3/8; A 2/5; P 1/14; V 1/8; LL 21–23. Shape typical of the genus, only moderately compressed. 1 pair of relatively long maxillary barbels at the corners of the mouth. Lateral line complete, level. A very lovely species. Upperside delicate brownish. Flanks silvery with a reddish lustre, the scales over the lateral line, especially, with numerous tiny green shining spots. Throat and belly yellowish. Gill-cover with an iridescent green dot. The pattern of dark blotches is best indicated by Fig. 322; here we need only stress that the transverse bars at the level of the dorsal fin origin, at the level of the anal fin and on the caudal peduncle are extremely prominent. Caudal fin yellowish to reddish with bright red tips. Anal fin with a carmine-red outer margin. Ventral fins whitish. Iris dark with glittering green dots.

Figs. 382–385
Fig. 382. *Barbus orphoides;* adult, reduced.
Fig. 383. *Barbus vittatus;* natural size.
Fig. 384. *Barbus lateristriga* (Spanner Barb); young.
Fig. 385. *Barbus tetrarupagus;* adult, somewhat reduced.

♀ dorsal fin, in sexually mature fishes, with an entire edge.

♂ dorsal fin very beautiful, fin-rays strongly produced, dark to dark red.

Care and breeding, as given on p.279. Temperature 24–25°C. Not very prolific. 1954.

Barbus binotatus *Cuvier* and *Valenciennes* 1842 (Fig.361)　　　　Spotted Barb
Further India, Greater Sunda Islands, Banka, Biliton, Bali, widely distributed and common; to 18 cm., remaining very much smaller in aquaria.

D 4/8; A 3/5; P 1/15–17; V 1/8–9; LL 23–27. Shape typical of the genus. 1 pair of barbels on the snout and 1 pair of maxillary barbels, both pairs relatively long. Uniform silvery; back somewhat olive-coloured; flanks with a bluish lustre. The arrangement of the black blotches is very variable, depending on age and locality of origin. Young fishes usually display a large blotch underneath the anterior part of the dorsal fin, another over the first rays of the anal, a third and very conspicuous blotch on the caudal peduncle and four further blotches on the flanks. At sexual maturity the blotch over the anal fin disappears; instead a longitudinal stripe linking the blotches on the flanks stands out more prominently. Old individuals (according to Meinken) lack blotches. Dorsal and caudal fins salmon-pink with dark borders. Anal fin milky, often with reddish blotches.

♀ more robust, quite gross at spawning time. Fins more yellowish.

♂ slimmer. Coloration as described above.

Care and breeding, as described on p.279. Very prolific. 1907/ – .

Barbus chola (*Hamilton-Buchanan* 1822) (Fig.362)　　　　Swamp Barb
Eastern India, widely distributed and usually common; to 15 cm., remaining substantially smaller in domestic aquaria.

D 3/8; A 2/5; P 15; V 9; LL 26–28. Shape typical of the genus, but somewhat stockier. 1 pair of short maxillary barbels. Lateral line complete. Uniform silky

Figs.386–391

Fig.386. *Barbus callipterus;* natural size.
Fig.387. *Barbus camptacanthus* (African Red-finned Barb); adult, reduced.
Fig.388. *Barbus holotaenia;* adult, slightly reduced.
Fig.389. *Barbus nigeriensis;* young.
Fig.390. *Barbus viviparus;* maximum size.
Fig.391. *Barbus paludinosus;* somewhat reduced.

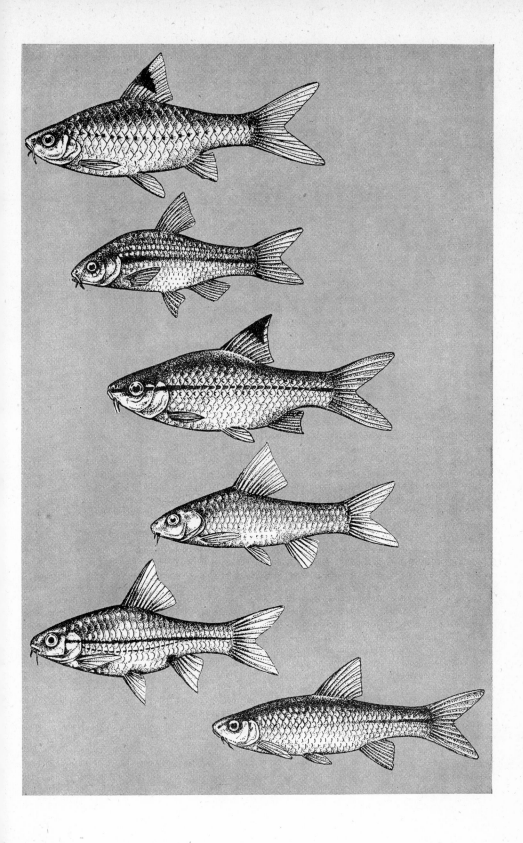

silvery with a strong olive-green tone on the back and a delicate yellowish sheen on the flanks. Underside whitish. Gill-cover with a large, blurred-edged, yellowish to golden blotch. A deep black blotch, often framed in gold, at the root of the tail. Dorsal fin, in fine specimens, yellow to orange, occasionally with brown spots in older individuals. All other fins delicate yellowish. Eye iridescent orange-red.

♀ more robust, fins only yellowish at spawning time.
♂ slimmer, fins reddish at spawning time.

Care and breeding, as given on p. 279. Very accommodating as regards temperature; can be wintered at 17–20 °C. 1904/+.

Barbus conchonius (*Hamilton-Buchanan* 1822) (Fig. 320)   Rosy Barb, Red Barb
Northern India, Bengal, Assam; to 14 cm., mature at 6 cm.

D 3/7–8; A 2/5–6; V 8–9; LL 24–28. Shape typical of the genus. It is best to describe the coloration as seen by reflected light. Back shining olive-green; flanks and belly silvery tinged with reddish, shining ink-red at spawning time. A deep black, golden-yellow-bordered blotch the size of a pea on the caudal peduncle at the level of the hinder end of the anal fin.

♀ fins colourless; tip of dorsal fin with only a dark tinge.
♂ slimmer; fins pink; tip of dorsal fin deep black.

One of the most undemanding and beautiful tropical fishes and a great favourite Care and breeding, as given on p. 279. 1903/+.

Barbus cumingi *Günther* 1868 (Fig. 335)   Cuming's Barb
Ceylon, in mountain forest streams; to 5 cm.

D 3/8; A 3/5; LL 21. Shape typical of the genus. Ground colour grey-white with a strong silver gleam, the anterior part of the body with a golden gleam. Each scale dark-edged. The flanks are embellished with two very large, transverse-oval dark blotches, of which the first runs from the nape to behind the pectoral fin-insertion and the second from the ridge of the caudal peduncle to the origin of the

Plate 71

Fig. 392. *Acanthophthalmus semicinctus* (Half-banded Coolie Loach); adults, natural size. (Original)
Fig. 393. *Botia macracanthus* (Clown Loach, Tiger Botia); young, natural size. (Original)

Plate 71

Plate 72

anal fin. Dorsal and ventral fins orange-red, pectorals colourless, anal and caudal fins pale yellow. Iris golden.

♀ more robust when mature, ventral profile more strongly convex.
♂ slimmer. Fin coloration usually more brilliant.

Care and breeding, as given on p. 279. A peaceful, undemanding species. Omnivorous. Temperature 25–27 °C. 1936/+.

Barbus dorsimaculatus *E. Ahl* 1923 (Fig. 363)
Sumatra; to 3·5 cm.

D 3/8; A 3/5; LL 24–26. Body slimmer than in the previous species. 1 pair of rostral, 1 pair of short maxillary barbels. Almost uniformly silvery, a brownish tone on the upperside. A very thin black stripe from the gill-cover to the root of the tail. Fins colourless, glassy. According to Ahl the dorsal fin has a large triangular blotch on the leading-edge.

Sex-distinctions probably similar to those prevailing in the other Barbs.

Care, as given on p. 279. Presumably not yet bred in captivity. 1913/−.

Barbus dunckeri *E. Ahl* 1929 (Fig. 334)   Duncker's Barb
Singapore, in jungle streams; to 30 cm., remaining considerably smaller in domestic aquaria but sexually ripe at 7–8 cm.

D 4/8; A 3/5; LL 23–24. Shape typical of the genus. 2 pairs of barbels. Beautifully coloured. Back yellow-brown, often with a greenish lustre; ridge of caudal peduncle iridescent pale green. Flanks a lovely shining golden yellow with large black-green blotches (for arrangement see Fig. 334). Underside orange-coloured. Gill-cover brass-coloured. Eye shining golden with tiny blood-red spots. All fins blood-red, externally more wine-red or violet, often with a milky tinge.

♀ very similar to the ♂ in colouring, but not quite so brilliant at spawning time; older mature ♀♀ are usually very gross.
♂ tinged all over with reddish-violet at spawning time.

Care and breeding, as given on p. 279. Warmth-loving, temperature 23–26°C. Needs frequent changes of water, likes fresh water; liable to be sickly in matured water. 1905/+.

Barbus everetti *Boulenger* 1894 (Fig. 352)   Clown Barb, Everett's Barb
Singapore, Borneo; to 13 cm.

D 4/8; A 3/5; P 1/13; V 1/7; LL 22–25. Shape typical of the genus. 2 pairs of barbels. Coloration not unlike that of the previous species. Back brown to brown-red, also orange-coloured. Rarely delicate golden to reddish with very large blue-green blotches arranged like transverse bars (see Fig. 352). No bars across the eyes. Fins reddish to poppy-red.

♀ altogether paler in colour.

Care, as given on p. 279. Breeding of this very beautiful Barb is unfortunately not exactly simple. It is essential to separate the sexes for 2–3 weeks and feed them up very generously with various worm-foods and midge-larvae as well as green lettuce, etc. For spawning use only large tanks, planted with *Myriophyllum* and as far as possible arranged so that the early morning sunshine can pour in on them. Temperature 25–27°C. 1913/+.

Barbus fasciatus *Bleeker* 1853 (Fig. 336)   Striped Barb, Zebra Barb
Sumatra, Borneo, Banka, Malay Peninsula (Johore); to 12 cm.

D 3–4/8; A 3/5–6; P 1/14–16; V 2/8; LL 27–30. Body somewhat compressed in comparison with the majority of other Barbs. Caudal peduncle slim. Typical form with 2 pairs of barbels. Uniformly yellowish- to brownish-silver with a light violet lustre by reflected light. 4–6 sharply separated dark blue to blue-black longitudinal stripes run back parallel to one another from the hinder end of the gill-cover. Dorsal and anal fins light yellowish to delicate rust-red; remaining fins almost colourless.

♀ considerably more robust; lateral stripes much paler.
♂ distinctly slimmer.

Breeding and care of this very active and easily-managed species, as given on p. 279. In Europe, in addition to the typical form, a barbel-less form from Johore State (Malaya) has been distributed under the name *Barbus* (or *Puntius*) *lineatus*. The latter is very easily bred and very prolific. 1934–35/+.

Barbus filamentosus (*Cuvier* and *Valenciennes* 1844) (Figs. 349, 350)

Black-spot Barb

South-west India (Further India, Thailand?); to about 15 cm.

D 3/8; A 2/5; P 1/15; LL 21. Shape, when mature, typical of the genus. Young somewhat slim. Dorsal fin of adult ♂♂ with produced fin-rays. The coloration at various ages is startlingly different. Adult fishes are uniformly silvery to greenish-silver, somewhat darker (olive-coloured) above, with a dull rainbow sheen by reflected light. A large, dark blotch on the flank above the anal fin. Fins delicate yellow-greenish. Fin-rays of dorsal partly dark violet. Young fishes are very brilliantly coloured, with broad, deep black transverse bars and orange-red to brick-red fins. Caudal fin of half-grown fishes reddish with a black blotch on each lobe, tips whitish.

♀ when mature, distinctly more robust; dorsal fin-rays not produced.

Care, as given on p. 279. Very prolific. 1950.

When it was first imported this species was wrongly identified as *Barbus* (or *Puntius*) *mahecola*, to which it is indeed very similar. The barbels, however, serve as a very simple distinguishing character; *B. mahecola* has one pair of maxillary barbels at the corners of the mouth, while *B. filamentosus* has no barbels at all.

Barbus gelius (*Hamilton-Buchanan* 1822) (Fig. 345)

Golden Barb,
Golden Dwarf Barb

Bengal and Central India, in still waters; to 4 cm.

D 2-3/8; A 3/5; V 9; LL 23-24. Shape typical of the genus. No barbels. Rather transparent. Back olive-green to brownish; throat and belly silvery-white. Shining golden by reflected light. Fine healthy specimens, especially ♂♂, display a broad longitudinal band which commences as a red-golden stripe and posteriorly becomes broader and increasingly copper-coloured until it ends in a shining coppery blotch at the root of the tail. The flanks are further embellished with irregular blotches and streaks of dark to deep black. Pectoral fins colourless. Caudal fin delicate reddish, all other fins yellowish. Iris pale green. Mouth edged with black.

♀ fuller, somewhat larger, with a gold-reddish lateral band.
♂ slimmer, with a coppery lateral band.

An ideal aquarium fish. Very plentiful and undemanding. Temperature about 20°C.; for breeding 21-22°C. (no higher!); for wintering 16-18°C. is sufficient. Not a spawn-robber, although the removal of the breeding pair is still to be recommended. The eggs adhere to the leaves of water plants. The young hatch after 24 hours and at first hang from the leaves and are later very difficult to see, since

287

they press their bellies or backs against the leaves or the glass sides of the tank and creep about in this fashion. Give the very finest live foods (Rotifers, Nauplii), also pulverised dried foods. See also p.279. 1907/+.

Barbus halei *Duncker* 1904   Hale's Barb
Malay Peninsula; to 10 cm.

D 3/9; A 1/5–6; LL 31. Body elongate, compressed; lower profile less convex than the upper. 2 pairs of short barbels. Scales large. Coloration, according to Schreitmüller:–Upperside brownish-green. Flanks silver with a bluish lustre, with a rainbow iridescence by reflected light. Underside whitish. A pale stripe along the middle of the side is seldom apparent. Fins delicate reddish to red. Tips of dorsal fin and caudal lobes black.

Sex-distinctions not yet described, but certainly in the ♀♀ the ripe fishes may be recognised by the more robust body.

Care, as given on p.279. Warmth-loving: temperature 22–26°C. Probably not yet bred in captivity. 1934/–.

Barbus lateristriga *Cuvier* and *Valenciennes* 1842 (Figs.351, 384)   Spanner Barb
Malay Peninsula, Singapore, Greater and Lesser Sunda Islands; to 18 cm., remaining considerably smaller in the domestic aquarium.

D 4/8; A 3/5; P 1/14–15; V 1/8; LL 23. Young fishes have the typical shape but the older ones are usually high-backed. 2 pairs of barbels. Very variable in form, markings and colour, owing to the wide distribution. Fine young specimens:–back greenish-orange, flanks golden-yellow, belly bright orange. In the anterior half of the body are two blue-black saddle-like bars which taper ventrally. A black blotch above the anal fin. A broad, black-blue, zig-zag longitudinal band extends from the middle of the body over the caudal peduncle and onto the caudal fin. Fins reddish, becoming paler towards the edges and sometimes with a bluish border.

♀ dorsal fin reddish.

♂ dorsal fin deep red at the base, otherwise with a rainbow iridescence.

Care and breeding, as given on p.279. Very prolific. *Barbus zelleri* Ahl is, according to Klausewitz (1957), identical with the juvenile form of *B. lateristriga*. 1914/+.

Barbus nigrofasciatus *Günther* 1868 (Fig.344)   Black Ruby, Nigger Barb,
                                           Purple-headed Barb
Southern Ceylon, in shallow, quiet-flowing waters; to 5 cm.

D 3/8; A 2–3/5; LL 20–22. Body deep. Head pointed. Barbels absent. Outside the breeding-season yellowish-grey with 3–4 blackish, wedge-shaped transverse bars which have blurred edges and in the ♀♀ often appear only as blotches. Head in both sexes a fine crimson. The silver edges of the scales give the impression of longitudinal rows of glittering spots. While in the ♀♀ only the basal portions of the vertical fins are dark-coloured, the ♂♂ display a deep black dorsal fin, a black-red anal and reddish ventral fins. At spawning time the whole anterior part of the body of the ♂ is a magnificent crimson, the caudal peduncle dark and the back velvet green and the rows of spots glittering greenish; a colour-scheme which can hardly be excelled.

Care: large tanks with as many floating plants and as much sunshine as possible. Breeding temperature 25–28°C. This species likes to spawn in morning sunshine and is very prolific (feed with Enchytraeids from time to time). For further details see p.279. The Nigger Barb is very suitable for the community tank. 1935/+.

Barbus oligolepis (*Bleeker* 1853) (Fig. 311)   Island Barb, Checkered Barb, Iridescent Barb

Sumatra; to 5 cm.

D 4/8; A 3/5; V 1/7–8; LL 17 + 2–4. Shape typical of the genus. A pair of small maxillary barbels at the corners of the mouth; rarely a pair of tiny rostral barbels on the snout as well. Ground colour delicate red-brown to ochre-brown. Back darker. Belly ochre-yellow. Flanks with a greenish, back with a bluish, pearly lustre. Each scale on the flanks with a bluish blotch at the base and a dark edge. A number of large dark irregular blotches on the sides which disappear with age; the last blotch, situated at the root of the tail, is preserved in the adults.

♀ vertical fins without black edges, ochre-yellow.
♂ vertical fins with black edges, reddish to brick-red.

Care and breeding, as given on p.279. 1925/+.

Barbus orphoides *Cuvier* and *Valenciennes* 1842 (Fig. 382)
Java, Borneo, Madura, Thailand; to 25 cm., remaining considerably smaller in captivity.

D 4/8; A 3/5; P 1/14–16; V 1/8; LL 31–34. Shape typical of the genus. 1 pair of barbels. Lateral line complete. Scales relatively large. Overall silvery. Upperside with a greenish or brownish lustre. Flanks iridescent bluish. A red blotch with a blurred edge on the gill-cover. Young fishes with a dark blotch at the root of the tail. Caudal fin reddish or colourless, with a deep black margin above and below. All other fins red. Iris brilliant red above.

Sex-distinctions in coloration not known.

Care: keep this very beautiful species in a large aquarium with plenty of room to move about, a light bottom-soil and clumps of plants. Omnivorous; grows very rapidly with good feeding. Only young fishes are suitable for the domestic aquarium; large specimens are magnificent showpieces. Not yet bred in captivity. (See also p.279.) 1951.

Barbus pentazona pentazona *Boulenger* 1894 (Figs. 319, 409)　　Five-banded Barb
Malay Peninsula, Singapore, Borneo, Sumatra; to 5 cm.

D 3/8; A 3/5; P 1/14; LL 22–25. Shape typical of the genus, but with a somewhat slimmer caudal peduncle. Back brown-red; flanks brilliant reddish; underside yellowish. 6 blue-black transverse bars, whose arrangement is best indicated by reference to Fig. 409. Scales in these bars with glittering green edges, the bars themselves often with yellowish edges. Fins dark red at the base, becoming paler outwardly with the edges almost colourless. Ventral fins colourless. Dorsal often with a black blotch at its base. According to Meinken this species may be distinguished from the other Banded Barbs by the following characters: from the nape over the eye, and there ending almost immediately, is a brilliant thin stripe. 5 bars on the flanks, 2 of them on the anterior part of the body and the remaining 3 on the caudal peduncle. The bar beginning on the back at the level of the leading-edge of the dorsal fin reaches to the insertion of the ventral. 2 pairs of barbels. Lateral line complete.

♀ fuller, more soberly coloured.
♂ slimmer, coloration as given above.

Care and breeding, as given for *B. tetrazona partipentazona*. Shy and not such a pronounced shoaling-fish as *B. t. partipentazona*. Breeding, at a temperature of 27–30°C., not exactly easy. 1911/−.

Figs. 397–402

Fig. 397. *Barbus setivimensis* (Algerian Barb); adult, greatly reduced.
Fig. 398. *Barbus trispilos* (African Three-spot Barb); natural size.
Fig. 399. *Barbus unitaeniatus* (Slender Barb, Red-finned Barb); natural size.
Fig. 400. *Barbus usarambarae;* adult.
Fig. 401. *Barbus wöhlerti;* enlarged.
Fig. 402. *Barbus sp.;* adult, slightly reduced.

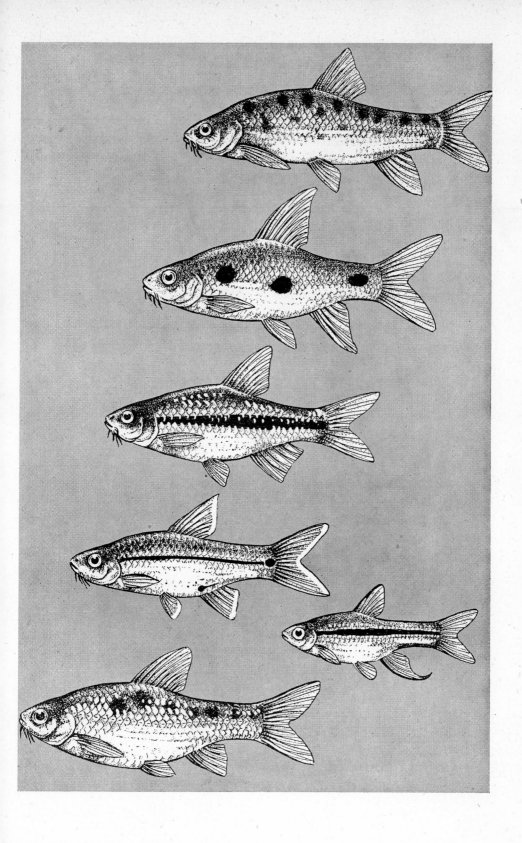

Barbus pentazona hexazona *Weber* and *De Beaufort* 1912 (Fig. 409)   Tiger Barb
Central Sumatra; to 5·5 cm.

Very similar to the typical form *B. pentazona pentazona*, from which, according to Meinken, it differs in the following characters: The bar across the eye is broad and rounded and extends over the orbit so as to enclose the whole eye; the second bar completely girdles the body; the third bar does not extend as far as the ventral fin. The coloration shows no substantial differences to that of the previous form, except that in the present case the dark bars are edged with grass-green or blue-green.

Sex-distinctions and care, as given for the typical form. ?/ — .

Barbus pentazona kahajani *Hoedeman* 1956 (Fig. 409)
Borneo, Kahajan and Kapuas Rivers; to 6 cm.

Somewhat slimmer than the typical form and with the head more pointed. Silvery-white with a red-brownish to greenish back and a brilliant reddish lustre on the flanks. Not counting the one over the eye there are four bars, whose arrangement is best indicated by reference to Fig. 409. Dorsal and anal fins brick-red at the base, outwardly paler; remaining fins reddish.

According to Meinken this subspecies is distinguished from the others by the following characters: the bar over the eye only extends slightly over the lower margin of the orbit. The second bar (first on the flanks) reaches from the nape to the insertion of the pectoral fin. The third bar, descending from the dorsal fin, broadens out under the lateral line and usually ends in a club-shaped expansion (rarely extending to the edge of the belly). The fourth bar extends ventrally onto the middle of the anal fin. The fifth bar is often merely a transverse oval blotch just before the root of the caudal. Two pairs of barbels. Lateral line complete.

This subspecies has been known as *B. p. tetrazona* Bleeker 1857, having originally been described as *Barbus tetrazona* Bleeker 1857. However, with the removal of *Capoeta tetrazona* Bleeker 1855 to *Barbus* (see following species), that name becomes pre-occupied and is therefore taxonomically invalid.

Puntius rhombo-ocellatus Koumans 1940 has a similar disposition of transverse bars to *B. p. tetrazona*, but the bars are said to have light centres instead of light

Plate 73

Fig. 403. *Gyrinocheilus aymonieri;* 7 cm. specimen. (Photo Dr. Foersch)
Fig. 404. *Labeo bicolor* (Red-tailed Black 'Shark'); ripe adult, natural size. (Original)
Fig. 405. *Morulius chrysophekadion* (Black 'Shark'); young, natural size. (Original)

Plate 73

Plate 74

Plate 74

Fig. 406. *Labeo wecksi;* ripe fish, 20 cm. long, in the Hellabrunn Aquarium, Munich. (Original)

Fig. 407. *Osteochilus vittatus* (Bony-lipped Barb); 20 cm. specimen, in the Hellabrunn Aquarium, Munich. (Original)

Fig. 408. *Osteochilus hasselti* (Hasselt's Bony-lipped Barb); 25 cm. specimen, in the Hellabrunn Aquarium, Munich. (Original)

edges. Koumans also describes a dark spot at the hind end of the base of the dorsal, as in *B. pentazona pentazona.* If Koumans' form does eventually prove to be identical with the present one, then *Barbus pentazona rhombo-ocellatus* (Koumans 1940) will have nomenclatorial priority over *Barbus pentazona kahajani* Hoedeman 1956.

Sex-distinctions, care and breeding, as given for *B. tetrazona partipentazona.* 1930/+.

Barbus tetrazona tetrazona (*Bleeker* 1855) (Figs. 310, 409)   Sumatra Barb,

Sumatra, Borneo (Thailand?); to 7 cm.   Tiger Barb

D 4/8–9; A 3/5–6; P 1/12; V 2/8; LL 21. Shape similar to that of *B. tetrazona partipentazona*, but somewhat more high-backed. Mouth obtuse. Silverwhite. Upperside brownish to olive-colour; flanks with a delicate reddishbrown lustre. Scales splendidly edged with shining gold. Four transverse black bars, including the one over the eye, whose arrangement is best indicated by reference to Fig. 409. Dorsal and anal fins blood-red; remaining fins more or less reddish. The ventral fins are occasionally black.

According to Meinken this species is distinguished from the other Banded Barbs by the following characters: the bar over the eye extends down to, or nearly down to, the lower edge of the gill-cover. The third bar is directly joined to a very large blotch which takes in the whole base of the dorsal fin although at most extending only slightly onto the back. No barbels. Lateral line incomplete. (The second bar is very variable and occasionally entirely absent.)

Sex-distinctions, care and breeding, as given for *B. tetrazona partipentazona*, below. 1935/+.

Barbus tetrazona partipentazona *Fowler* 1934 (Fig. 409)
South-east Thailand, Cambodia (?); to 6 cm.

D 3/8; A 3/5; LL 19–20 + 1–2. Body stocky, deep, compressed. Ground colour silvery with a yellowish, often too a reddish, lustre. Back brownish to brown-red. Belly white. Scales dark-edged, especially on the upper half of the body. Five deep black transverse bars, whose arrangement is best indicated by reference to Fig. 409. Underneath the third short transverse band which runs down from the back there occasionally occurs, usually on the right side of the body, a round dark blotch. The second bar may fork broadly towards the belly. (Description given by Meinken.) Scales within the transverse bars edged with shining green or gold. Upper part of dorsal fin brick-red; all other fins pale red to brilliant carmine, especially at the base.

According to Meinken this form is distinguished from the other Banded Barbs by the following characters: the bar across the eye extends to the lower edge of the gill-cover. The fourth bar is sharply (!) separated from the bar on the dorsal fin, and extends like a wedge down to the middle of the body. The fifth bar is usually a scale's breadth away from the root of the caudal. A pair of barbels at the corners of the mouth. Lateral line incomplete.

♀ distinguished by the greater girth of the body.

A brilliantly coloured fish, peaceful and easily contented. Not to be kept with long-finned fishes *(Pterophyllum)* because it likes to nibble the ends of their fins.

Care and breeding, as given on p. 279. The ♂ goes pale while driving. Very prolific; 600–1000 eggs. The breeding pairs should not be kept isolated beforehand, since isolated individuals often become quarrelsome and snappish; they are best kept in community tanks with other fishes. It is further recommended that the fishes be fed with Enchytraeids while spawning. The young hatch after 24–30 hours and swim freely after 6 days at the latest. Fine-grade food. Rearing easy. 1933/+.

Barbus phutunio *(Hamilton-Buchanan* 1822) (Fig. 319)   Dwarf Barb, Pigmy Barb Eastern India, north-eastern Bengal, Ceylon; to 4 cm.

D 2–3/8; A 3/5; P 15; V 9; LL 20–23. Shape typical of the genus, somewhat deep in old individuals. Lateral line complete. Back brownish-green to grey-green with a brilliant emerald-green shine on the scales of the nape, head and gill-cover. Flanks silver with a delicate violet or bluish lustre; each of the large scales with a dark base and glittering edge. Belly silver-white. Five steel-blue transverse bars appear, especially when the fish is excited, which usually fade into three dark blotches. Pectoral fins colourless; all other fins orange-red. Dorsal fin often with an oblique dark bar.

♀ blotches on the flanks quite pale.

♂ blotches more brilliant; slim.

Fig. 409

Diagram of the Banded Barbs (partly after Klausewitz)

left: *Barbus tetrazona partipentazona*　right: *Barbus tetrazona tetrazona*
Barbus pentazona pentazona　　　　　　*Barbus pentazona kahajani*
　　　　　　　　　　　　　　　　　　　Barbus pentazona hexazona

Care and breeding, as given on p. 279. Breeding temperature 24–25 °C. The young hatch after 24–30 hours. A successful spawning can produce 100 offspring. 1906/+.

Barbus roloffi (*Klausewitz* 1957)　　　　　　　　　　　Roloff's Barb
Thailand; to 4 cm.

D 3/8; A 3/5; P 13; V 1/8; LL 23; only 4 scales pierced. Shape typical of the genus. No barbels. Lateral line incomplete. Uniform silvery. Upperside olive green;

295

each scale, especially the lateral line scales, with a black transverse streak. A black blotch at the root of the caudal, with an intensely silver iridescent spot above it. Anal fin with a black crescent-shaped blotch.

♀ somewhat larger; anterior part of dorsal fin delicate yellow-orange, its anterior tip slightly blackish.

♂ altogether somewhat slimmer, often with more of a golden shine; ventral fins likewise brilliant red; dorsal and anal fins in healthy fishes yellowish.

Care and breeding, as in most other Barbs, not difficult. According to Klause-witz (1957) the fishes keep together in pairs and likewise in the wild live together in pairs in definite territories. Courtship very interesting; according to Roloff (1957) the ♂ swims close under the ♀. During the actual spawning the fishes turn on their backs, pressing their ventral surfaces against one another and setting the spawn either individually or in small groups on the undersides of large-leaved water plants. In soft, slightly acid water at a temperature of 24–26°C. the young hatch after 24 hours, at first hanging from the water plants, and swim freely after 5 days. Eggs relatively large; total small (50–70). 1956.

Barbus sachsi *E. Ahl* 1923 (Fig. 364)   Sachs' Barb, Gold-finned Barb
Singapore (South Viet-Nam?); to 7 cm.

D 3/8; A 3/5; LL 22 + 2. Body rather deep, caudal peduncle long and slender. Golden yellow to light greenish-yellow. Belly paler, brass-colour to yellowish-white. Young fishes with 5–7 vertical black-green stripes on the flanks and pale, trans-lucent fins. Older specimens without such stripes and with gold-red fins.

♀ duller in coloration; more robust.
♂ more intensely coloured; slimmer.

Care and breeding, as given on p. 279. The young should hatch after 3–6 days. 1895/−.

Barbus 'schuberti' (name not valid in scientific taxonomy) (Fig. 337)
                                        Golden Barb, Schubert's Barb
A form of *Barbus* which has not yet been properly determined, but which is probably closely related to *B. sachsi* E. Ahl. The Golden Barb suddenly appeared in America and was at first said to be a hybrid. As Ladiges has already emphasised, this has not been established.

Ground-colour golden yellow; belly with some silver reflections. A very prominent black blotch at the root of the tail. A single similar black spot, or a row of such spots, beneath the dorsal fin. Flanks in older fishes occasionally dark spotted.

♀ larger and more robust.
♂ slimmer, colours brighter.

Care and breeding, as given on p.279.

Barbus schwanenfeldi *Bleeker* 1853 (Fig. 353)   Schwanenfeld's Barb
Sumatra, Borneo, Malacca, Thailand; to 34 cm.

D 3/8; A 3/5–(6); P 1/14–15; V 2/8; LL 35–36. Body stocky, strongly compressed. Back high, especially in older fishes. Two pairs of barbels. Lateral line complete. Uniform silvery, occasionally with brilliant yellowish or even golden tones. Dorsal and caudal fins brilliant carmine, the former with a larger black spot on the outer part or a black tip, the latter often with a dark longitudinal band in each lobe. All other fins yellow-orange. Iris golden. In young specimens the fins are usually yellow.

Sex-distinctions in coloration not yet described.

Care: keep this lovely species in a large aquarium, with as much swimming-space and as soft a bottom-soil as possible. Growth rapid with good feeding. Omnivorous. Temperature 22–25°C. Large specimens make magnificent show-pieces for public aquaria. 1951.

Barbus semifasciolatus *Günther* 1868   Chinese Barb, Half-striped Barb,
                                                            Green Barb
South-east China; to 7 cm.

D 3/8; A 2/5–6; LL 22 + 2. Body moderately elongate. Back high, especially in old fishes. One pair of very short maxillary barbels at the corners of the mouth. Back pale- to reddish-brown. Flanks metallic green to shining olive-green towards the back, shining golden yellow to brassy-yellow towards the belly. Belly whitish, a beautiful orange-red during courtship. 5–7 large, more or less prominent dark streaks on the flanks in both sexes. A black blotch at the root of the tail. Dorsal, anal and caudal fins delicate brown-red to brownish brick-red. Ventral fins brownish to yellow. Pectoral fins colourless. All scales dark-edged.

♀ altogether more soberly coloured; very plump at spawning time.
♂ slimmer.

Care: a large tank in a sunny position, well-planted but also allowing clear space in which to swim. Temperature 22–24°C. Stands lower temperatures very well. Needs no aeration (oxygen sufficient).

297

Breeding: not too small a tank, at least $50 \times 25 \times 25$ cm. The ♂ approaches the ♀ with a dancing motion, the body being held obliquely, then darts at her flank and, nudging her with his wide-open mouth or, if she refuses, with blows with his caudal fin, drives her into a clump of plants. Pairing is generally tempestuous. Eggs medium-sized, yellowish. The young hatch after about 25 hours.

For further details, see p. 279. 1909/+.

Barbus stigma *Cuvier* and *Valenciennes* 1844 (Fig. 366)
India, Bengal, Burma; to 15 cm., remaining appreciably smaller in the domestic aquarium and becoming mature at 7–8 cm.

D 3/8–9; A 3/5; P 17; V 9; LL 23–26 (27). Shape typical of the genus. Barbels absent. Lateral line complete. Beautiful silver overall. Back grey-green to brownish; flanks with a somewhat bluish lustre; underside white. A deep black round blotch at the root of the tail; a similar one on the central part of the dorsal fin or also on the part of the body adjacent to the dorsal fin.

♀ at least in mature fishes, more robust; all the fins colourless.
♂ in mature fishes with brick-red anal and ventral fins; at spawning time with a delicate reddish longitudinal band from the gill-cover to the root of the tail.

Care and breeding, as given on p. 279. A very plentiful shoaling fish which can be wintered at 15–18 °C. Likes to grub about the bottom. 1927/−.

Barbus stoliczkanus *Day* 1871 (Fig. 312) Stoliczka's Barb
Basin of the lower R. Irrawaddy in Burma; to 6 cm.

D 2–3/8; A 2/5; P 14; V 9; LL 23–25. Shape typical of the genus. Barbels absent. Lateral line complete. Back olive- to moss-green. The large silver scales on the flanks are dark edged and glitter bluish or greenish according to the direction of the light. Belly white. Behind the gill-cover, at the level of the eye, a drop-shaped dark blotch which is bordered by a golden area posteriorly. A large, round, deep black blotch with a golden edge at the root of the tail. Pectoral fins colourless. Caudal fin with a yellowish base. Ventral and anal fins reddish. Iris golden, blood-red above.

♀ dorsal fin delicate reddish; all other fins almost colourless.
♂ dorsal fin brilliantly coloured: first fin-ray deep black; the reddish base merges into a brilliant blood-red which is interrupted in the middle by a dark crescent-shaped blotch or separate spots; margin deep black.

A favourite and very beautiful Barb. Care and breeding, as given on p.279. Breeding temperature 24–26°C. The young hatch after 24–30 hours. 1925/+.

Barbus terio (*Hamilton-Buchanan* 1822) (Fig. 365) One-spot Barb
Bengal, common; to 9 cm.

D 3/8; A 2/5; LL 22–23, 3–4 pierced. Shape typical of the genus. Lateral line incomplete, very short. Barbels absent. Upperside metallic green; flanks delicate green-silver; underside whitish, with a quite weak reddish or violet lustre. A large, round, golden-edged black blotch over the anal fin, from which a fine dark line runs back to the root of the tail. A transverse oval blotch at the root of the tail is not always obvious. Fins colourless, glass-clear or delicate yellowish. Dorsal fin occasionally with numerous dark streaks and spots, often united into a longitudinal band.

♀ distinctly more robust when mature.
♂ with a reddish tinge at spawning time.

Care and breeding, as given on p.279. Winter at 18–20°C. 1923/−.

Barbus ticto (*Hamilton-Buchanan* 1822) (Fig. 346) Two-spot Barb,
Tic-Tac-Toe Barb
Ceylon and the whole of India, common almost everywhere; to 10 cm.

D 3/8; A 2/5; LL 23–26, 6–8 pierced. Shape typical of the genus; older fishes are often high-backed. Barbels absent. Lateral line incomplete. Back grey- to grass-green; flanks brilliant shining silver; belly whitish. A long, transverse black blotch above the pectoral fins; another, similar but golden-edged, on the caudal peduncle over the end of the anal fin. All fins delicate greenish outside the breeding season.

♀ more robust when mature; dorsal fin only rarely dark-tipped; ventral and anal fins reddish at spawning time.
♂ lower part of the body a beautiful fawn tint at spawning time; eye blood-red above; dorsal fin usually black-tipped towards the edge.

Care and breeding, as given on p.279. Very undemanding, easily bred and does not dig up the bottom. Winter at 14–16°C. 1903/+.

Barbus tetrarupagus (*M'Clelland* 1831) (Fig. 385)
Burma, Assam, Bengal; to 12 cm.

D 2–3/8; A 2/5; P 17; V 9; LL 24–26. Body elongate, compressed. Caudal peduncle deep. Lower profile substantially less convex than the upper. One pair of

299

maxillary barbs at the corners of the mouth. Lateral line complete. Upperside brilliant olive- to brown-green; flanks pale brown to grey-yellow, with a strong silver gleam; underside pale. A black blotch behind the gill-cover; another on the caudal peduncle midway between the end of the anal and the root of the caudal. Scales dark-edged, especially on the caudal peduncle. Dorsal and anal fins with dark tips, the former often also with the whole outer part of the fin black and with a dark longitudinal band across the middle (with a black blotch, according to Arnold?). Anal and ventral fins delicate orange.

Sex-distinctions not yet described, but probably the ♀♀ are more robust.

Care, as given on p. 279. Very resistant to low temperatures; winter at 12–16°C. Probably not yet bred in captivity. 1922/–.

Barbus titteya (*Deraniyagala* 1929) (Fig. 321)   Cherry Barb
Ceylon, in shady streams; to 5 cm.

D 3/7; A 3/6; V 2/7; LL 19, 3 pierced. Body elongate, only moderately compressed. Back fairly high anterior to the dorsal fin. Caudal peduncle slim. One pair of maxillary barbels at the corners of the mouth. Lateral line very short. Back fawn with a greenish lustre; flanks and belly shining silver, more or less reddish. A brown-black to deep blue-black longitudinal band, running from the corner of the mouth, over the eye to the middle of the caudal fin, becomes broad under the dorsal fin and tapers again posteriorly. This dark band is bordered above by an equally broad band which is golden anteriorly and iridescent blue-green to sea-green posteriorly; under suitably favourable conditions this pale band displays a red lower edge. Lower part of the caudal peduncle shining gold. Gill-cover reddish. Fins, especially the anal, poppy-red to blackish-red with fine dark edges.

♀ darker, self-coloured; fins yellowish.
♂ coloration as above; brilliant red at spawning time.

Figs. 410–414

Fig. 410. *Barbus viviparus*; somewhat reduced. (See also Fig. 390)
Fig. 411. *Barbus gambiensis*; somewhat reduced.
Fig. 412. *Barbus lineomaculatus* (Seven-spot Barb); natural size.
Fig. 413. Below, right: *Tanichthys albonubes* (White Cloud Mountain Minnow); slightly enlarged.
Fig. 414. Below, left: *Aphyocypris pooni* (Venus Fish, Red-finned Wonder Fish); slightly enlarged.

Somewhat timid and retiring, likes shade. ♂♂ jealous of one another. One of the most beautiful Barbs. A brilliant red variety has been imported several times in recent years.

Care: a large tank, richly planted. Temperature 24–26°C. Omnivorous.

Breeding: temperature 25–26°C. Feed with Enchytraeids during spawning. The young hatch after about 24 hours. A successful spawning can produce about 250 offspring. For further details, see p. 279. 1936/+.

Barbus vittatus (*Day* 1865) (Fig. 383)
The whole of India and Ceylon, common everywhere; to 6 cm.

D 2/8; A 2/5; P 12; V 9; LL 20–22, 5–7 pierced. Shape typical of the genus. Barbels absent. Lateral line incomplete. Back yellowish-green to olive-green; flanks greenish-silver, each scale with a dark base and a silvery edge; belly silvery-white. A round, gold-bordered, dark blotch at the root of the caudal. Pectoral fins colourless; all other fins pale yellow to brownish yellow. Base of dorsal golden-yellow; above it an oblique, black, orange-edged band.

♀ more robust when mature, larger.
♂ slimmer.

Care and breeding, as given on p. 279. 1904/−.

African Barbus species

Barbus callipterus *Boulenger* 1907 (Fig. 386)
Niger to Cameroons, Lagos, in flowing waters; to 9 cm.

D 3/8; A 3/5; LL 23–27; TR 3/3. Body elongate, slim, compressed; upper and lower profiles almost equally convex. Caudal fin deeply forked. Two pairs of barbels of nearly equal length. Lateral line complete. Upperside dark clay-yellow to brownish; flanks silvery with a yellow, often even golden, lustre; underside yellowish to pure silver. Scales dark-edged, especially on the upper half of the body. Lateral line scales with a large dark blotch at the base. Fins yellowish at the base, in mature fishes also reddish (especially the dorsal and caudal), the outer parts transparent. Dorsal with a large dark triangular blotch.

Sex-distinctions not yet known (♀ more robust ?).

Care, as given on p. 279. Temperature 22–26°C. Probably not yet bred in captivity. 1913/+.

Barbus camptacanthus (*Bleeker* 1863) (Fig. 387)   African Red-finned Barb
Tropical West Africa, widely distributed in standing waters; to 16 cm., remaining smaller in captivity but sexually ripe at about 7 cm.

D 3/8; A 3/5; LL 21–25; TR 3–4/4. Body elongate, compressed; lower profile less convex than the upper. Back high in front of the dorsal fin. Two pairs of barbels of equal length. Lateral line complete. Upperside olive-green; flanks yellowish- to reddish-silver; underside silver-white. A very broad, brown, often very dark, longitudinal band along the middle of the side which is especially prominent beneath the pectoral fins and on the caudal peduncle; three further dark stripes above this band. Scales dark-edged, especially towards the back. All fins brilliant red.

♀ more robust; fins orange to yellowish.

♂ slimmer; coloration as described above. Develops white nodules on the sides of the head at spawning time (nuptial tubercles).

Care, as given on p. 279. Temperature 24–26 °C. Probably not yet bred in captivity. 1910/ −.

Barbus fasciolatus *Günther* 1868 (Fig. 348)   African Banded Barb
Angola, in standing or slow-flowing waters; to 7 cm.

D 3/8; A 3/5; LL 25; TR 3/3. Shape typical of the genus; lower profile, especially the throat region, more strongly convex. Snout very blunt. Two pairs of barbels. Lateral line complete, bowed down. Upperside grey-olive. Flanks silvery with a lovely blue-green lustre and 12 thin, short, black transverse bars, of which the second is always the most prominent. Fins colourless; vertical fins with a delicate brownish base.

♀ not difficult to recognise by the more robust form of the body.

Care, as given on p. 279. Temperature 22–25 °C., not less! Somewhat predatory and snappish. Probably not yet bred in captivity. 1911/ +.

Barbus gambiensis *Svensson* 1933 (Fig. 411)
West Africa, Gambia R.; to 10 cm.

D 3/8; A 3/5; LL 26–27. Shape typical of the genus. Lateral line complete. Ground-colour yellowish-silver. A brown longitudinal band from the tip of the snout to the root of the caudal. Fins, especially the dorsal, delicate yellowish, the latter also with a dark leading-edge and tip.

♀ dorsal fin yellowish.

♂ dorsal fin reddish; whole body with a reddish tinge at spawning time.

According to Pinter care presents no difficulty. Peaceful, contented and lively fishes, which do not dig up the bottom. Temperature 24–26°C., but withstands considerable cooling. Omnivorous. Soft water for breeding. The very transparent eggs are, as in almost all Barbs, shed among water plants and are slightly adhesive. According to Pinter, again, the partners do not press against one another during the actual spawning. The young fishes hatch after about 18 hours and swim freely after 4 days. 1950.

Barbus holotaenia *Boulenger* 1904 (Fig. 388)
Tributaries of the Congo in the central Congo Basin, northwards to the Cameroons; to 12 cm.

D 3/8–(9); A 3/5; LL 22–26; TR 4/4. Shape typical of the genus. Two pairs of barbels. Lateral line complete. Upperside olive-brown or olive-grey; flanks yellowish-silver; belly silvery-white. A prominent black band extends from the tip of the snout, over the eye onto the middle caudal rays. Scales above and below this longitudinal band with brown half-moon-shaped markings. Fins, with the exception of the pectorals, brilliant red, often with white borders. Dorsal fin with a black tip. Eye yellow-silver.

Reliable sex-distinctions not known.

Care, as given on p. 279. Temperature 25–27°C. Not yet bred in captivity. 1913/+.

Barbus hulstaerti *Poll* 1945 (Fig. 415)
Lower Congo; to 3·5 cm.

D 3/7; A 3/5; LL 22–23; 1–2 on the base of the caudal. Shape graceful but typical of the genus. One pair of short maxillary barbels. Coloration very pleasing and peculiarly contrasted. Upperside brown; flanks delicate yellow-brown to fawn or even coppery; underside pale, usually yellowish. Three dark to lacquer-black blotches on the flanks are especially striking (see Fig. 415). Fins brilliant yellow to delicate brownish; the dorsal, anal and ventral fins with lacquer-black edges and the middle rays of the caudal also black. Eye golden-yellow with a dark periphery.

♀ somewhat more robust; anterior lateral blotch rather ill-defined and round.
♂ slimmer; anterior lateral blotch crescentic.

This very beautiful species is very undemanding, like most of the African Barbs. Its lively, somewhat volatile, behaviour is, however, only fully displayed when it is

304

kept in a shoal. In the company of larger species, on the other hand, *B. hulstaerti* often becomes timid and inactive. Breeding not yet studied. As regards care, see also p. 279. 1956.

Fig. 415
Barbus hulstaerti; adults, somewhat enlarged. (After Meinken)

Barbus lineomaculatus *Boulenger* 1903 (Fig. 412) Seven-spot Barb
East Africa; to the west of Lake Nyasa (Zambesi?); to 7 cm.

D 3/8; A 3/5; LL 30–32; TR 4/4. Shape typical of the genus. Two pairs of barbels. Lateral line complete. Very unpretentiously coloured. Upperside olive-green to brown. Flanks grey-green with a light silver sheen and a row of dark spots whose number varies in different individuals and even between either side of the same specimen (usually 6). Underside white-grey. A broad dark blotch over the origin of the anal fin, especially in young fishes.

Sex-distinctions in coloration not known; ♀ probably more robust when mature.

Care, as given on p. 279. Not yet bred in captivity. 1925/–.

Barbus nigeriensis *Boulenger* 1902 (Fig. 389)
West Africa, in the region of the Niger delta; maximum size unknown.

D 3/8; A 3/5; LL 25–29; TR 3–4/3. Shape similar to that of *B. camptacanthus* (see p. 303), but with a shorter gape and larger eye. Two pairs of barbels. Lateral line complete. Overall silvery. Upperside brownish. A dark longitudinal band along the middle of the side is usually indistinct.

Sex-distinctions not known.

Care, as given on p. 279. Temperature 24–26 °C. Probably not yet bred in captivity. ?/–.

305

Barbus paludinosus *Peters* 1852 (Fig. 391)
Throughout South Africa, widely distributed; to 11 cm., usually smaller.

D 3/7; A 3/5–7; LL 32–39; TR 6–7/5–6. Body elongate, slim, strongly compressed. Two pairs of barbels. Lateral line complete. Shining silver. Upperside very dark grey-olive; flanks with a light bluish lustre by reflected light; underside whitish. A narrow, dark longitudinal band from the gill-cover to the root of the tail becomes increasingly prominent posteriorly. Fins reddish to brilliant red; pectorals colourless. Iris yellowish-silver.

♀ more robust; fins reddish.
♂ slimmer; fins usually brilliant red. The whole hinder part of the body becomes delicate red to deep ink-red at spawning time.

Care, as given on p. 279. A very peaceful, active shoaling fish. Not sensitive to temperature; winter at 16–20°C. Probably not yet bred in captivity. 1912/–.

Barbus setivimensis *Cuvier* and *Valenciennes* 1842 (Fig. 397)   Algerian Barb
Morocco, Algeria, Tunisia, widely distributed; to 30 cm.

D 4/7–8; A 3/5; LL 40–45; TR 7–8/7–9. Body elongate, compressed. Caudal peduncle relatively deep. Two pairs of barbels. Lateral line complete. Upperside olive or reddish-brown, with a brassy gleam by reflected light. Flanks blue-grey-silver with irregular cloudy blotches, especially on the upper half of the body and on the caudal peduncle. Fins slightly milky. In fine specimens only, the outer edges of the caudal lobes and the hinder part of the anal fin are delicate reddish. Older fishes self-coloured.

Sex-distinctions unknown; according to Meinken the ♂♂ probably have a more pointed dorsal fin.

Care not very easy, since according to Rachow these fishes are choosy about food and will not accept Enchytraeids or ever take dried food. They dig up the bottom, but are otherwise very peaceful. Very resistant to temperature changes; withstand cooling to nearly 1°C. Only young fishes are suitable for the domestic aquarium. 1924/–.

Barbus trispilos (*Bleeker* 1863) (Fig. 398)   African Three-spot Barb
Tropical West Africa, in quiet waters; to 8 cm.

D 3/8; A 3/5; LL 25–28; TR 4/4. Shape typical of the genus. Two pairs of barbels. Lateral line complete. Upperside olive-green to olive-brown. Flanks shining silver with three deep black blotches, whose arrangement is best indicated by reference to Fig. 398. Underside yellowish to delicate reddish. Fins delicate golden yellow, rarely reddish.

♀ robust; fins yellow.

♂ slimmer; fins reddish. The lower half of the body is brilliant red at spawning time.

Care, as given on p. 279; undemanding. Temperature 18–22°C. Not yet successfully reared in captivity. 1912/−.

Barbus unitaeniatus *Günther* 1866 (Fig. 399)   Slender Barb, Red-finned Barb
South Africa, from Angola to Natal; to 8 cm.

D 3/8; A 3/5; LL 30–33; TR 4–5/4–5. Shape typical of the genus. Two pairs of barbels. Lateral line complete. Upperside olive-brown to dark brown. Flanks yellowish, with a beautiful blue lustre by reflected light. Underside whitish-silvery. A dark longitudinal band extends from the gill-cover to the root of the tail; this band often includes dark blotches and is especially broad over the anal fin. Fins colourless or delicate yellowish.

♀ more robust, according to Meinken.

Care, as given on p. 279. Undemanding and temperature-tolerant. Not yet bred in captivity. 1926/−.

Barbus usarambarae *Lönnberg* 1907 (Fig. 400)
Tanga, (Zambesi?); to 8 cm.

D 3/7; A 3/5; LL 30; TR 5/5. Shape typical of the genus, slim. Two pairs of barbels. Lateral line complete. Very unpretentiously coloured. Pale brown to yellowish-grey; upperside darker; belly yellowish to dingy white. A dark band from the gill-cover to a round blotch at the root of the tail. Over the origin of the anal fin a dark blotch which may be posteriorly extended into a streak and in young fishes often runs along the lower edge of the anal fin. Pectoral fins colourless; all other fins delicate brownish with pale edges.

The ♀♀ may probably be recognised by their greater girth.

Care, as given on p. 279. Active and prefers the upper water layers. Very easily satisfied. Winter at 12–15°C. or a little above. Omnivorous. Not yet bred in captivity. 1925/−.

Barbus viviparus *Weber* 1897 (Figs. 390, 410)
Natal (South-east Africa); to 6·5 cm.

D 3/8; A 2/5; LL 29–31; TR 4/4. Shape typical of the genus. Colouring rather unpretentious.. Silvery; upperside olive with two black longitudinal stripes. A prominent dark blotch at the base of the anal fin.

Sex-distinctions unknown.

Care, as given on p. 278. No study of the reproduction in captivity is yet known to have been undertaken. Weber (*Zool. Jahrbuch*, Syst. X, 152), the first describer of this species, called it *viviparus* (= live-bearing) because he thought he had established this by dissection, as follows:–'From this self-same ovary I took out veritable young ones, moreover with large yolk-sacs 8 mm. in length. Accordingly this species is viviparous. As far as I know, this is new to the Cyprinids.' Weber's observation has never been confirmed.

Barbus werneri *Boulenger* 1905   Werner's Barb
East Africa, from Egypt to the Lake Victoria region; Sudan; to 10 cm.

D 3/(7)–8; A 3/5; LL 24–26; TR 4/3–4. Shape typical of the genus. Two pairs of barbels. Lateral line complete. Upperside delicate clay-yellow to brownish. Flanks brilliant shining silver with a bluish lustre, especially by reflected light, and with a row of dark spots and blotches. Underside whitish. Fins colourless, often slightly milky.

♀ larger and more robust when mature.

Care, as given on p. 279. Easily satisfied, lively. Omnivorous; also algae, dried food and even household scraps. A planarian-exterminator. Very resistant to lowering of temperature; winter at 12–15°C. Breeding very easy. 1902/–.

Barbus wöhlerti *Trewavas* 1938
East Africa (Mozambique?); to 3 cm.

D 3/8; A 3/5; LL 32. Shape typical of the genus, slim. Barbels and lateral line absent. Very delicate, translucent. Ground colour brownish; back with a greenish lustre, belly yellowish. A red-violet band from the hinder edge of the gill-cover to the root of the caudal. Caudal peduncle blackish below. Fins colourless. Dorsal and anal fins with dark leading-edges.

Plate 75

Fig.416. *Rasbora hengeli;* adults, slightly enlarged. (Original)
Fig.417. *Rasbora trilineata* (Scissors-tail, Three-line Rasbora); ripe fishes, natural size. (Original)
Fig.418. *Garra* sp.; 8 cm. specimen of an apparently unknown species, imported from the Congo. (Photo Dr. Foersch)

Plate 75

Plate 76

Plate 76

Fig.419. *Rasbora dorsiocellata macrophthalma;* adults, somewhat enlarged; left ♂, right ♀. (Original)

Fig.420. *Rasbora urophthalma;* adults, enlarged; above ♀, below ♂. (Original)

Fig.421. *Rasbora pauciperforata* (Red-striped Rasbora); ripe young, natural size; left ♀, right ♂. (Original)

♀ anal fin truncate.
♂ anal fin produced, sickle-shaped.

Care and breeding, as given on p. 279. Breeding temperature 25–26 °C. 1934/ – .

Genus Rasbora: Care and Breeding

The small, dainty and elegant members of the genus *Rasbora* are distributed through East Africa, South and East Asia as far as Canton, and the Indo-Australian Archipelago to Celebes and the Philippines. Most of them are shoaling-fishes which live in great schools in the upper layers of flowing and standing waters, and in some cases also undertake mass-spawning in schools. Some species, such as *Rasbora heteromorpha* and *R. maculata*, occur only in soft, slightly acid, often peaty, waters.

The majority of the *Rasbora* spp. are very slim and low-bodied; a few, like *R.heteromorpha* and *R.vaterifloris*, are relatively short and deep. Mouth terminal, upwardly directed, with a projecting lower jaw (mandibular symphysis with a knob-like process). The lateral line turns downwards at the beginning, runs then in an arch as far as the caudal peduncle and there remains in the lower half. Some species have an incomplete lateral line (*R. heteromorpha, R.pauciperforata, R.vaterifloris, R.hengeli*, etc.).

Although many species have already been imported, only a few have found a wide commercial distribution. Strangely enough, there is scarcely an amateur who has specialised in this group. As well as such very colourful species as *R.heteromorpha, R.vaterifloris, R.maculata*, etc., the genus also includes several quite inconspicuous members.

Care is, in general, not difficult. These active fishes require free swimming-space as well as clumps of plants and should be provided with soft, peat-filtered water if possible, at a temperature around 24–25°C. All *Rasbora* spp. are peaceful and may therefore be kept in the company of other peaceful fishes. Living food of all kinds, especially small crustacea and midge-larvae, is generally very willingly taken. Many species, such as *R. trilineata*, *R. dorsi-ocellata*, *R. urophthalma*, *R. elegans*, *R. daniconius*, *R. meinkeni*, are easily bred in soft, neutral to slightly acid, well-matured, fresh water. The eggs are laid among tufts of *Myriophyllum* or *Nitella*, or on such synthetic substrates as Perlon.

R. heteromorpha, *R. maculata*, *R. vaterifloris*, *R. pauciperforata*, etc., require considerably more attention. As well as the water quality, the choice of the breeding pair plays a particularly important role. The water used should, in these cases, be very soft, slightly acid (pH 5·3–5·7) and in some instances quickly filtered through peat. The best results up till now have been achieved with water taken from woodland springs. Pairs which will not spawn should be re-mated with other partners. Often these fishes spawn only some days after they have been put together (e.g. *R. maculata*). The eggs are laid after vigorous driving, and after a few false spawnings, on leaves or on finely-feathered tufts of plants to which they adhere firmly. The young hatch after 24–30 hours, hang at first on the water plants, and swim freely after 3–5 days. The parents are, as a rule, spawn-robbers and should be removed immediately after spawning. Growth of the young is rapid provided they are fed with live food; Rotifers and Nauplii at first, then larger Nauplii, and later small *Cyclops*.

Rasbora argyrotaenia (*Bleeker* 1850) (Fig. 428) Silver Rasbora
Widely distributed through Japan, China, Thailand, Malay Archipelago; to 17 cm., remaining somewhat smaller in captivity.

D 2/7; A 3/5; P 1/12–13; V 1/7–8; LL 28–32; TR 6–7 between D and V. A narrow, cream-coloured longitudinal band from the hind end of the gill-cover to the root of the tail is only vaguely differentiated from the brilliant silver of the flanks and belly; this band is accompanied below by a very narrow deep black line which becomes blue-green on the caudal peduncle. Vertical fins delicate yellowish. Caudal fin with a dark border. Eye pale yellow.

♀ profile of belly more strongly convex; all fins almost colourless.
♂ slimmer.

Care, as given on p. 310. Breeding apparently not yet achieved. 1913/—.

Rasbora borapetensis *H. M. Smith* (Fig. 429)
Thailand (Bung Borat); to about 5 cm.
D 2/7; A 3/5; LL 30; 10–14 pierced. Body elongate. Lateral line incomplete. Origin of the dorsal fin somewhat behind the insertion of the ventrals. Delicate yellowish to greenish with a broad black longitudinal band which extends from the hind end of the gill-cover to the root of the caudal and is accompanied above by a green-golden line. A black stripe along the mid-dorsal line; a broader one along the base of the anal fin. Lower lobe of the caudal reddish; all other fins colourless. (Partly after H. M. Smith)
Sex-distinctions unknown, but certainly the ♀ must be more robust as in other species.
Care, as given on p. 310. Nothing is yet known about successful spawning. 1954.

Rasbora chrysotaenia *E. Ahl* 1937 (Fig. 430)   Gold-striped Rasbora
Malay Peninsula, East Indies; to 10 cm.
D 2/7; A 3/5; LL 26–27; TR 8 between D and V. Back pale olive to greenish-brown; flanks paler; belly bluish-silver. A longitudinal band, green-golden to shining gold-red according to the light, extends from the upper jaw over the eye to the root of the tail; it is accompanied below by a blue band which commences on the lower jaw and which, especially at spawning time, is less prominent. A dark line along the edge of the belly from the vent to the beginning of the caudal fin. Fins colourless.

♀ more robust; in the full-grown state the belly is broader and more deeply convex.
♂ slim, narrow.

Care and breeding, as given on p. 310. This species is not very prolific. The young hatch after approximately 36 hours (at 25°C.), lie on the bottom during the first 2–3 days, and swim freely after 5–6 days. 1934/—.

Rasbora daniconius (*Hamilton-Buchanan* 1822) (Figs. 349, 354)   Slender Rasbora
South-east India, Ceylon, Ganges Basin, Burma, Thailand, Greater Sunda Islands;
to 20 cm.; in captivity only to 9 cm.

D 2/7; A 3/5; LL 31–34; 14 scales between head and D (see *R. einthoveni*).
Ground-colour silver, with an intense pearly lustre on the flanks. Back olive-brown
with a bronze lustre. Belly silvery. A brilliant deep-blue longitudinal band from
the tip of the snout to the root of the caudal, edged with a golden line on either
side. (The dark band may be broken up into isolated blotches.) Fins colourless to
delicate yellow. The vertical fins are pale orange in fine specimens. Eye golden.

♀ with ventral profile more strongly convex; all fins colourless.
♂ coloration as above.

Care and breeding, as given on p. 310. 1910/−.

Rasbora dorsiocellata dorsiocellata *Duncker* 1904   Eye-spot Rasbora
Malay Peninsula; Sumatra; to 6·5 cm.

D 2/7; A 3/5; LL 28–30; 12 scales between head and D. Ground-colour yellowish-silver with a bluish to violet lustre on the flanks. Back brownish, often
brown-olive. Belly silvery-white. Two narrow, often very indistinct, deep black
lines from the hind end of the gill-cover to the root of the tail; these diverge more
strongly under the dorsal fin. The lower dark line is often broken up into streaks.
Vertical fins delicate yellow. The dorsal fin is especially characteristic and exhibits
a large black spot with a white rim. Eye yellowish.

♀ with ventral profile more strongly convex. Caudal fin yellowish.
♂ caudal fin reddish.

Care and breeding, as given on p. 310. Very prolific. 1935/+.

Rasbora dorsiocellata macrophthalma *Meinken* 1951 (Fig. 419)
Malay Archipelago; to 3·5 cm.

Eyes larger. Head shorter. Scale-count in middle longitudinal series lower than

Plate 77

Fig. 422. *Rasbora tornieri;* adult ♂, natural size, in the Hellabrunn Aquarium, Munich.
(Original)
Fig. 423. *Rasbora lateristriata lateristriata;* ripe fishes, natural size; above ♀, below ♂, in
the Hellabrunn Aquarium, Munich. (Original)
Fig. 424. *Rasbora lateristriata elegans* (Elegant Rasbora, Yellow Rasbora); ripe ♀♀, na-
tural size, in the Hellabrunn Aquarium, Munich. (Original)

Plate 77

Plate 78

Plate 78

Fig. 425. *Rasborichthys altior;* adult, natural size, in the Hellabrunn Aquarium, Munich. (Original)

Fig. 426. *Rasbora rasbora* (Rasbora); ♀, natural size. (Original)

Fig. 427. *Rasbora vaterifloris* (Pearly Rasbora); ripe fishes, natural size; left ♀, right and above ♂♂. (Original)

in the typical subspecies (according to Meinken). Ground-colour delicate olive-green with a strong grass-green gleam when the sun shines on it. Back delicate brown-olive. Belly silvery, tinged with green. Dorsal fin milky greenish with a large black blotch. Lower half of the eye with a vivid blue-green iridescence.

Care and breeding, as given on p. 310.

Rasbora einthoveni (*Bleeker* 1851) (Fig. 431)   Brilliant Rasbora, Einthoven's Rasbora

Malacca, Singapore, Thailand, isolated islands of the Malay Archipelago; to 9 cm.

D 2/7; A 3/5–6; LL 29–32; in contrast to *R. daniconius* 12–13 scales between head and D. Very similar to the species *R. taeniata* and *R. daniconius*, from which, however, it may be distinguished by the somewhat stockier body and the more greenish yellow-brown to yellow-olive colour of the back (according to Meinken). The flanks show a bluish lustre by reflected light. A deep black to shining brilliant green longitudinal band extends from the tip of the snout to the root of the caudal and is edged above by a rust-red to golden line; both lines are slightly down-bowed. Belly delicate yellowish to silver. Fins colourless. The anterior rays of the dorsal fin are occasionally dark-coloured.

♀ ventral profile more strongly convex.

Care and breeding, as given on p. 310. 1909/+.

Rasbora gerlachi (*E. Ahl* 1928) (Fig. 434)

Locality unknown; ? cm.

D 2/7; A 3/4–5; LL 24–26. Lateral line deeply bowed down towards the belly. Coloration (according to Ahl): ground-colour yellow. Back brownish-yellow to yellow-olive. Flanks lemon-yellow with a narrow, slightly down-bowed, deep-blue longitudinal band edged with a gleaming yellow line above. Belly yellowish to white. Vertical fins delicate brownish at their bases, distally transparent.

Sex-distinctions unknown.

Care, as given on p. 310. Not yet bred in captivity. Only a few specimens have been imported, in 1928, and these very soon died.

Rasbora hengeli *Meinken* 1956 (Fig. 416)
Near Djambi, Sumatra; to 3 cm.

D 2/7; A 2/6; V 7; LL 23, of which 4–5 pierced; TR 8 between D and V. Similar to the better-known Harlequin Fish *(R. heteromorpha)* in shape and colouring, but altogether appreciably slimmer, more delicate and more translucent. The colouring is very pleasing but does not attain the brilliance that it does in the Harlequin. Here the substantially narrower wedge does not stand out so prominently blue-black, the red-violet is weaker, frequently merely indicated. Lateral line incomplete.

♀ more robust and usually paler.

Care and breeding, as given on p. 310. This species will breed under the same conditions as the Harlequin, that is to say, in soft, slightly acid fresh water, best of all, spring water, which has been allowed to stand for 2–4 weeks, and if necessary quickly filtered through peat. Not very prolific, otherwise very hardy and easily contented. 1955.

Rasbora heteromorpha *Duncker* 1904 (Fig. 378)   Harlequin Fish, (Red) Rasbora
Malay Peninsula (Malacca), Thailand, Eastern Sumatra; to 4·5 cm.

D 2–3/7; A 3/5; LL 26–27. Lateral line incomplete. One of the greatest favourites among aquarium fishes. A pronounced shoaling-fish, best kept in company with *R. vaterifloris*. Body silver-grey with a dull poppy-red to violet sheen. Belly paler. The hinder part of the body exhibits a wedge-shaped blue-black blotch. The part anterior to this blotch has a golden lustre. Vertical fins deep, dark carmine at the base, merging into yellowish on the outer parts.

Figs. 428–433

Fig. 428. *Rasbora argyrotaenia* (Silver Rasbora); adult, reduced.
Fig. 429. *Rasbora borapetensis;* maximum size.
Fig. 430. *Rasbora chrysotaenia* (Gold-striped Rasbora); adult.
Fig. 431. *Rasbora einthoveni* (Brilliant Rasbora, Einthoven's Rasbora).
Fig. 432. *Rasbora lateristriata lateristriata;* adult, somewhat reduced.
Fig. 433. *Rasbora lateristriata elegans* (Elegant Rasbora, Yellow Rasbora); adult, somewhat reduced.

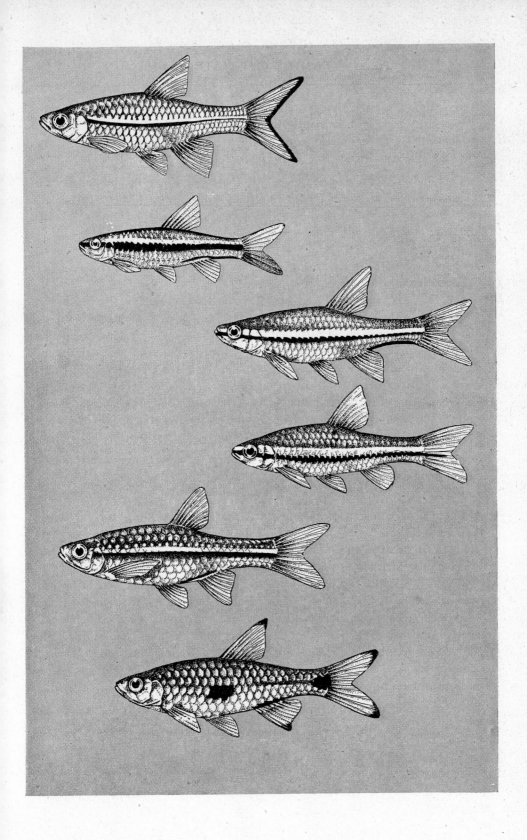

♀ ventral profile more strongly convex. The lower anterior corner of the wedge lies over the ventral fin-base and is often somewhat indistinct.

♂ slimmer. The lower anterior corner of the wedge is produced and often reaches to the mid-ventral line.

Care and breeding, as given on p. 310. Prefers to spawn on the underside of *Cryptocoryne* or *Hygrophila* leaves. Breeding temperature 24–28 °C. Particularly slim, elongate ♂♂ should be chosen. The young hatch after 24–28 hours. Breeding today no longer difficult. 1906/+.

Rasbora jacobsoni *Weber* and *de Beaufort* 1916 (Fig. 435)　　Jacobson's Rasbora
Western Sumatra; to 7 cm.

D 2/7; A 3/5; P 1/13; V 2/8; LL 25–27. Ground-colour fawn to red-brown. Flanks brownish-white. Belly yellowish-white. The scales on the flanks and those in front of the dorsal fin, in particular, have dark edges. A very dark longitudinal band runs from the lower jaw, over the eye, to the root of the tail; beneath the dorsal fin this band becomes especially broad and is edged above with a fine golden band which is especially brilliant on the caudal peduncle. A second, less distinct dark band runs from the pectoral fin-base to the hinder end of the anal fin. Dorsal and anal fins yellow-brown at the base, distally fawn with a triangular blotch which has blurred edges. Caudal fin delicate brownish.

♀ plumper when full-grown, ventral profile more strongly convex. Very stout at spawning time.

♂ slimmer.

Care and breeding, as given on p. 310. 1932/−.

Rasbora lateristriata lateristriata (*Bleeker* 1854) (Figs. 423, 432)
Thailand, Greater and Lesser Sunda Islands; to 12 cm.

D 2/7; A 3/5; P 1/14; V 1/6–7; LL 26–30. Back brown-olive with a brilliant green lustre by reflected light. Flanks delicate brownish with a golden lustre. Underside greenish-white. A brilliant rust-red longitudinal band from the gill-cover to the root of the tail, edged by a dark bluish or violet zone below. Scales dark-edged, decorated with silver spots, especially over the lateral band. A narrower dark stripe parallel to the anal fin-base. Dorsal and caudal fins rust-red to brownish, anal fin reddish.

♀ ventral profile more strongly convex; considerably plumper at spawning time.

♂ slimmer.

316

Care and breeding, as given on p. 310; also tolerates temperatures around 18 –20°C. 1930/+.

Rasbora lateristriata elegans (*Volz* 1903) (Figs. 424, 433)   Yellow Rasbora, Elegant Rasbora

Malay Peninsula and Archipelago; to 13 cm.

Distinguished from the typical subspecies by the lower lateral line count: 24–29. Back olive-brown. Flanks bright fawn above with a brilliant rust-red to greenish sheen by reflected light; towards the belly delicate brownish to clay-yellow. Underside silvery. Scales adjacent to the back distinctly black-edged. A large deep black blotch at the level of the dorsal fin is often linked with a similar black blotch at the root of the tail by a narrow, dark or shining blue, line. A less dark longitudinal stripe runs parallel to the anal fin-base. Vertical fins delicate yellowish, especially at their bases. Caudal fin often with dark tips.

♀ ventral profile more strongly convex; often not so brilliantly coloured.
♂ smaller; coloration as given above.

Care and breeding, as given on p. 310. Very prolific. 1911/+.

Rasbora leptosoma (*Bleeker* 1855) (Fig. 436)
Sumatra, chiefly in streams and rivers; to 8 cm.

D 2/7; A 3/5; P 1/13; V 2/7; LL 31–32. Back dark brown to brilliant brown; flanks yellow-brown to yellowish; belly whitish. A reddish, above golden, band runs from the tip of the snout over the eye to the root of the tail, and is accompanied ventrally by a dark band which broadens posteriorly. A fine dark line parallel to the anal fin-base. Fins transparent; dorsal and caudal fins occasionally light reddish.

♀ ventral profile more strongly convex.
♂ slimmer.

Care and breeding, as given on p. 310. 1910/+.

Rasbora maculata *Duncker* 1904 (Fig. 379)   Spotted Rasbora, Pigmy Rasbora
Southern Malay Peninsula and Singapore, Sumatra; in ponds and ditches; to 2·5 cm.

D 2/6; A 2–3/5; LL 30–31. A very decorative species. On an olive ground the back is brick-red, the flanks yellowish-red and the belly yellow. A large, round, blue-grey to black blotch on the side at the level of the pectoral origin. Similar smaller blotches appear on the anal fin-base, the caudal peduncle and the root of

317

the tail. Fins red-yellow. Dorsal fin with a black leading-edge and black tip. Anal fin with a black blotch on the leading-edge.

♀ more yellowish; ventral profile rounded.
♂ cherry-red, slimmer; ventral profile straight.

Care and breeding, as given on p. 310. Does especially well with a dark bottom-soil (peat). Use soft, peaty water for breeding. The sexes should be separated at first and well fed. Up to 200 eggs at a spawning. The young hatch after 24 hours and after 4–5 days should be fed with the finest Nauplii. 1905/+.

Rasbora meinkeni *de Beaufort* 1931 (Fig. 437)   Meinken's Rasbora
Sumatra; to 7 cm.

D 2/7; A 3/5; P 1/12; V 1/6; LL 25–26. Ground-colour shining brass-colour. Back brownish-olive; flanks and belly brass-colour. A deep black longitudinal band from the hind end of the gill-cover to the middle rays of the caudal fin is accompanied above by an equally wide golden band. Above and below this double band is a row of faintly iridescent bluish scales. A black stripe along the anal fin-base is characteristic of this species. Scales on the belly dark-edged.

♀ larger and more robust when full-grown; shapelessly stout at spawning time.
♂ slim, narrow.

Care and breeding, as given on p. 310. 1928/−.

Rasbora pauciperforata *Weber* and *de Beaufort* 1916 (Fig. 421)   Red-striped
Rasbora
Sumatra; to 7 cm.

D 2/7; A 3/5; P 1/11–12; V 2/7; LL 32–33; TR 8 between D and V. Lateral line incomplete. One of the loveliest *Rasbora* spp. Head and nape yellow-olive. Back almost glassy, yellowish to brownish, scales dark-edged. Flanks silvery with a

Figs. 434–440

Fig. 434. *Rasbora gerlachi;* natural size.
Fig. 435. *Rasbora jacobsoni* (Jacobson's Rasbora); natural size.
Fig. 436. *Rasbora leptosoma;* adult ♀.
Fig. 437. *Rasbora meinkeni* (Meinken's Rasbora); maximum size.
Fig. 438. *Rasbora paucisquamis* (Large-scaled Rasbora); adult.
Fig. 439. *Rasbora philippinica* (Philippine Rasbora); natural size.
Fig. 440. *Rasbora rasbora* (Rasbora); somewhat reduced.

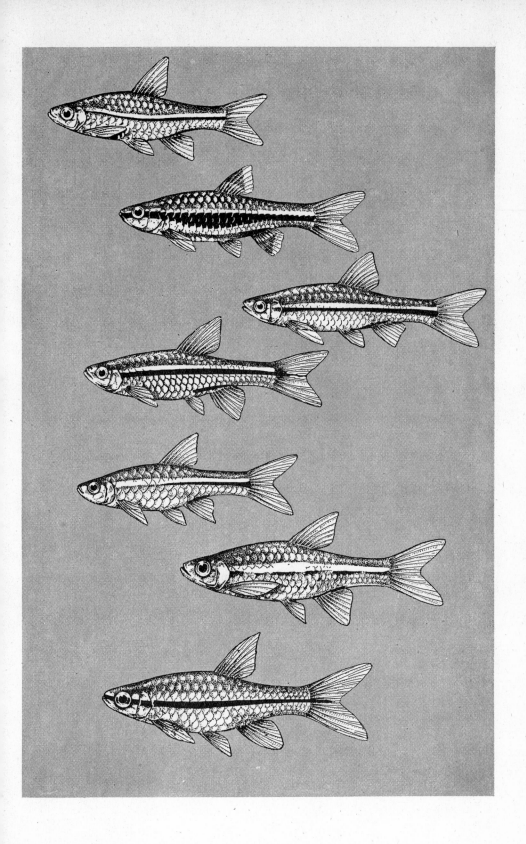

grass-green to patina-like lustre. Belly silvery-white. A shining poppy- to copper-red longitudinal band from the tip of the snout to the root of the tail is bordered below by a blue-black longitudinal band. Lower edge of caudal peduncle dark- to copper-coloured. Eye poppy-red above, golden yellow below. Fins transparent, light yellowish.

♀ plumper when full-grown; ventral profile strongly curved.
♂ slim, narrow.

Care and breeding, as given on p. 310. 1928/+.

Rasbora paucisquamis *E. Ahl* (Fig. 438)　　　　　　　Large-scaled Rasbora
Malay Archipelago; to 6 cm.

D 2/7; A 3/5; LL 22. Scales very large. Ground-colour delicate olive-green. Back olive-brown; flanks, especially towards the belly, with a bluish lustre; belly silvery-white. From the gill-cover to the root of the tail there extends a golden to brassy-yellow band which, from the level of the dorsal fin onwards, is bordered below by an increasingly broad dark band. A second, though seldom distinct, band over the anal fin-base. Vertical fins delicate yellowish.

♀ ventral profile more strongly convex, very convex at spawning time.
♂ slimmer, somewhat smaller.

Care and breeding, as given on p. 310. 1934/−.

Rasbora philippinica *Günther* 1880 (Fig. 439)　　　　　　Philippine Rasbora
Mindanao (Philippine Is.); to 7 cm.

D 2/7; A 3/8; LL 28–30. Ground-colour pale olive-green. Scales partly dark-edged. Back darker; belly silvery-white. A brass-coloured longitudinal band extends from the shining golden gill-cover to the root of the tail and is accompanied below by an irregular, often frequently interrupted, dark band. A fine dark stripe along the base of the anal fin. Vertical fins delicate yellowish.

Care and breeding, as given on p. 310. Breeds only in shallow water. 1909/−.

Plate 79

Fig. 441. *Noemacheilus barbatulus* (Stone Loach); fine specimen, natural size. (Original)
Fig. 442. *Cobitis taenia* (Spined Loach); 9 cm. ♀. (Original)
Fig. 443. *Misgurnus fossilis* (Weather-fish); 25 cm. specimen. (Original)

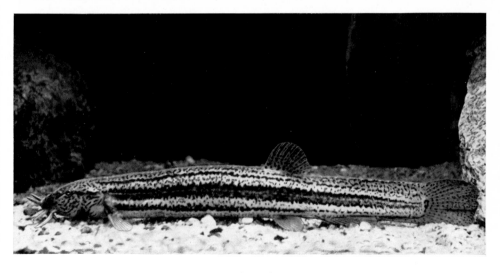

Plate 79

Plate 80

Fig. 444. *Noemacheilus barbatulus* (Stone Loach); head, twice natural size. (Original)
Fig. 445. *Cobitis taenia* (Spined Loach); head, more than twice natural size. (Original)
Fig. 446. *Misgurnus fossilis* (Weather-fish); head, about twice natural size. (Original)

Rasbora rasbora (*Hamilton-Buchanan* 1822) (Figs. 426, 440)   Rasbora
Burma, Thailand, Malay Peninsula; to 10 cm.

D 9; A 8; P 13; V 9; LL 25–26. Description, according to E. Ahl: ground-colour brownish-yellow, the back darker, the flanks paler. Gleaming gold by reflected light. Belly yellowish. A black-blue iridescent longitudinal band from the tip of the snout to the root of the tail, sometimes even onto the anterior part of the caudal fin. Fins yellowish.

♀ ventral profile more strongly convex.
♂ slimmer.

Care and breeding, as given on p. 310. 1913/ –.

Rasbora steineri *Nichols* and *Pope* 1927 (Fig. 447)   Steiner's Rasbora
Hainan (China); to 7·5 cm.

D 2/7; A 2–3/5; LL 27–29. Brownish to delicate red-brown, the underside with a silvery gleam. A black longitudinal stripe from the gill-cover to the root of the tail, edged above by a reddish to red-gold line. Fins delicate yellowish. Base of caudal fin muddy red to brilliant brick-red.

♀ more robust; dorsal fin yellowish.
♂ dorsal fin with a reddish base.

Care, as given on p. 310. No report of successful breeding so far. 1955.

Rasbora taeniata (*E. Ahl* 1922) (Fig. 448)   Black-striped Rasbora
Sumatra; to 8 cm.

D 2/7; A 3/5; LL 30–31; TR 8 between D and V. Back olive-green, grass-green in sunlight; flanks paler; belly silvery with a reddish tinge. A deep blue, almost black, longitudinal band from the hind end of the gill-cover to the root of the tail, edged above by a fine, gleaming red-golden stripe. The root of the tail and the caudal fin are separated by a fine dark line.

♀ more robust, plumper. Caudal fin dull orange.
♂ caudal fin reddish.

1913/ –.

321

Rasbora tornieri *E. Ahl* 1922 (Figs. 422, 449)

Sumatra; to 10 cm.

D 2/7; A 3/5–6; LL 29–31; TR 4/3. Fawn to delicate violet, scales dark-edged. Three more or less distinct grey to deep black longitudinal bands from the gill-cover to the root of the tail. While the uppermost of these bands is often cut short behind the dorsal fin, the middle one often extends onto the caudal. The lowermost band runs obliquely from the anterior end of the anal fin and runs along the lower edge of the caudal peduncle. The stripe between the upper pair of bands has a brilliant golden to red-gold gleam, while that between the lower pair has a more brassy colour. Belly silvery. Dorsal and anal fins yellow-brown at the base, yellow distally. Caudal fin delicate yellow with a heavy black edge. A very beautiful species.

♀ ventral profile more strongly convex; coloration as intense as in the slimmer ♂.

Care, as given on p. 310. Not yet bred in captivity. 1929/–.

Rasbora trilineata *Steindachner* 1870 (Fig. 417)   Three-line Rasbora, Scissors-tail

Malay Peninsula and Greater Sunda Islands; to 15 cm.

D 2/7; A 3/5; P 1/15; V 1/7; LL 29–33, including the scales on the base of the caudal. Young fishes, especially, are as transparent as glass.

Back dark olive-yellow to green with a blackish median ridge. Flanks silvery, sometimes with a rainbow sheen. Belly whitish. A fine dark longitudinal band begins at the level of the ventral fins and extends to the middle part of the anal. Pectoral fins colourless. Dorsal, anal and ventral fins light brownish-yellow. The very characteristically whitish caudal fin has a deep black transverse bar on each lobe.

Sexes distinguished only by the greater girth of the ♀.

Care and breeding, as given on p. 310. 1932/–.

Figs. 447–451

Fig. 447. *Rasbora steineri* (Steiner's Rasbora); natural size.
Fig. 448. *Rasbora taeniata* (Black-striped Rasbora); natural size.
Fig. 449. *Rasbora tornieri;* natural size.
Fig. 450. *Rasborichthys altior;* adult.
Fig. 451. *Varicorhinus damascinus;* adult, natural size.

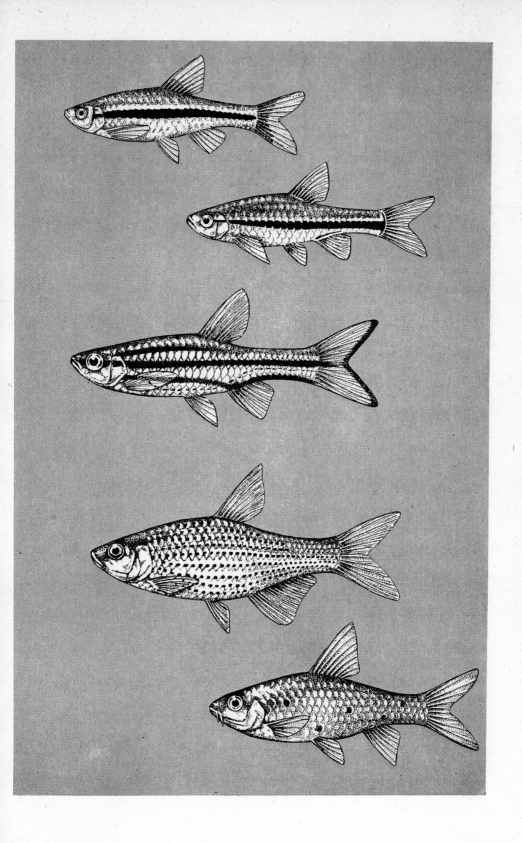

Rasbora urophthalma *E. Ahl* 1922. (Fig. 420)
Sumatra; to 2·5 cm.

D 2/7; A 3/5; LL 25. Nape and back red-brown; flanks paler red-brown to yellowish-white; belly silver-white. A steel-blue longitudinal band begins at the hinder end of the gill-cover, broadens out beneath the dorsal fin and then becomes very fine until it terminates in a round, gold-yellow-edged blotch. A fine gold-red band borders the upper edge of the dark one. Pectoral fins colourless; all other fins delicate brownish. The leading-edges of the dorsal and anal fins, as well as the upper and lower edges of the caudal, are blackish. Iris of eye green-golden.

♀ dorsal fin without whitish blotch and without blackish oblique bar.
♂ dorsal fin with a whitish blotch at the base, and an oblique blackish bar above this. Considerably slimmer.

Care and breeding of this very small species, as given on p. 310. Quite small vessels are adequate for breeding. The eggs are laid on the undersides of the leaves of small-leaved water plants, or upon algae. The fishes spawn on further succeeding days. Temperature 26–28 °C. 1913/+.

Rasbora vaterifloris *Deraniyagala* 1930 (Fig. 427)   Pearly Rasbora
Ceylon, in mountain streams; to 4 cm.

D 2–3/7–8; A 3/5; LL 25. *R. vaterifloris* is less elongate than almost all other *Rasbora* species; in this respect its shape approaches more to that of the Harlequin. Lateral line incomplete.

Back olive-green; flanks grey-green; belly whitish. A lovely pearly sheen by reflected light. Sides of belly often tinged with orange. Dorsal, anal and basal part of caudal fin orange-yellow to red. The anal fin edge is very strongly indented.

♀ fins yellowish.
♂ fins orange to reddish; usually smaller.

Care and breeding, as given on p. 310. 1936/+.

A closely related, more coppery or geranium red form from Ceylon was described as *Rasbora nigromarginata* by Meinken in 1957. This fish differs from *R*

Plate 81
Fig. 452. *Botia horae;* natural size. (Original)
Fig. 453. *Botia lecontei;* half-grown fish, enlarged. (Original)
Fig. 454. *Botia berdmorei;* half-grown fish, natural size. (Original)

Plate 81

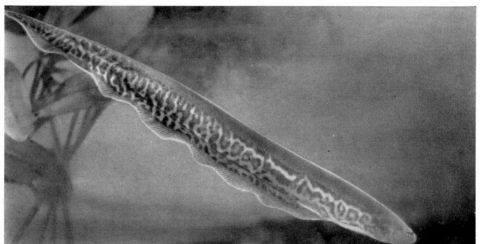

Plate 82

Plate 82

Fig. 455. *Lepidocephalus thermalis;* half-grown, somewhat enlarged. (Original)
Fig. 456. *Gymnotus carapo* (Banded Knife-fish); young, natural size. (Original)
Fig. 457. *Silurus glanis* (European Catfish, Wels, Waller); 25 cm. young. (Original)

vaterifloris in fin-formula and body-proportions as well as in coloration, and is known in Germany as the 'Rote Rasbora' (= Red Rasbora).

Rasborichthys altior *Regan* 1913 (Figs. 425, 450)
Singapore; to 9 cm.

D 2/7; A 1/17; LL 36–38. Form of body *Barbus*-like, deep, strongly compressed, but, of course, without barbels. Belly keeled between the ventral and anal fins. Lateral line complete, not bowed down (!). Upperside grey-green. Flanks silver with a greenish lustre, shining very strongly by reflected light. Numerous disorderly longitudinal rows of dark spots (each scale with a dark blotch at the base). Fins colourless.

♀ more robust, ventral profile more strongly convex.
♂ slimmer.

Care of these peaceful shoaling-fishes, as given for *Barbus* spp. (see p. 279). Temperature 22–24°C., not less than 10°C. in winter. Omnivorous. 1911/+.

Varicorhinus damascinus (*Cuvier* and *Valenciennes* 1840) (Fig. 451)
Asia Minor and northern Arabia, especially Jordan, Israel, Syria, common everywhere; to 7 cm.

D 11; A 8; LL 70–78; TR 14–17/16. Bleak-like. Mouth somewhat ventral. One pair of barbels. Scales very small. Coloration, according to Arnold: a strong silver gleam, which passes into steel-blue by reflected light. Many small round black spots irregularly strewn over the sides of the body.

♀ considerably more robust when mature.

Care and breeding easy. A very suitable species for the unheated domestic aquarium, very undemanding and breeding very readily. However, it must be admitted that the European Moderlieschen and Bitterling are more interesting to keep and also more attractively coloured. 1904/−.

North American Cyprinidae

The North American *Cyprinidae* have similar requirements in captivity to those of the European species (see p. 233). Their areas of distribution, however, are in some cases so large that local forms of one species may have very different temperature-tolerances. Fishes from the southern U.S.A., for example, need greater warmth than those from the basin of the Great Lakes. For this reason, when buying North American Cyprinids, one should always ascertain the locality of origin.

In the interests of the European cold-water enthusiasts an increased importation of these often quite beautiful species is greatly to be desired.

Chrosomus erythrogaster *Rafinesque* 1820 (Fig. 471)   Redbelly Dace
Southern Canada, northern and central U.S.A.; to 7 cm.

D 7; A 7–8; LL about 85; TR 16/10. Body elongate, slim, strongly compressed. Mouth directed forwards. Scales quite small. Lateral line incomplete. Coloratior not unlike that of the European Minnow *(Phoxinus)*. Back dark brown to brown olive, the occasional fish with cloudy dark blotches. From the mouth to the root of the tail extend two dark bands, of which the upper is narrower and extends from the upper lip across the upper border of the eye. The lower band runs from the lower jaw across the lower part of the eye, is slightly bowed downwards to the root of the tail and is broadest under the dorsal fin. The two longitudinal bands are united on the root of the tail by a small dark spot which throws a grey shadow onto the middle rays of the caudal fin. The space between the bands is gleaming gold. Belly silver-white. Fins dull yellow to brownish. At spawning time the golden band is redder, the dark bands are deep black, and the belly and throat gleaming carmine, while the fins are then deep red at the base and golden yellow outside.

♀ with plumper body and less intense coloration.
♂ coloured as described above. At spawning time white tubercles (nuptial tubercles) appear on the gill-cover.

Care, as for the European *Cyprinidae* (see p. 233); large tank, well-oxygenated water and plenty of swimming space. Summer temperature 15–23 °C.; cool wintering at 12–15 °C. Omnivorous. Spawns, after a cool wintering, in spring at a temperature of 20–24 °C. Pairing occurs among plants; rules for breeding in general

326

like those for *Danio* spp. (see p. 265). A good community fish with other cold-water spp. 1912/−.

Erimyzon sucetta (*Lacépède* 1803) (Fig. 458)   Lake Chubsucker
Basin of the Great Lakes, Mississippi basin, locally in Virginia and Texas; to 25 cm.

D (11)–12; A 7; V 9; LL about 35. Body elongate, compressed, the upper profile more strongly convex. Mouth directed slightly downwards; upper lip protrusible. Lateral line absent. Caudal fin only slightly emarginate. Arrangement of scales often quite irregular. The coloration changes very much with the age of the fish. Young *Erimyzon* exhibit a broad dark longitudinal band (especially prominent in specimens from clear, flowing waters) accompanied above by a pale stripe; in older fishes this band breaks up into individual blotches which occasionally may even take on the shape of broad transverse bands. Old specimens are uniformly brown with a somewhat darker upperside and paler underside, occasionally with a coppery sheen. Fins dark or smoke-grey, often with a reddish tinge.

♀ considerably more robust when sexually ripe.
♂ at spawning time with three large tubercles on each side of the snout. Anal fin more or less convex.

Care, in cold-water aquaria, much as given for the European *Cyprinidae* (see p. 233). Omnivorous, with a preference for worms. Rather delicate. Only the young are suitable for domestic aquaria. 1896/−.

Clinostomus vandoisilus (*Cuvier* and *Valenciennes* 1844) (Fig. 473)
U.S.A., eastward from the Alleghanies in Georgia and westward of these mountains in tributaries of the Tennessee and Cumberland; to 13 cm.

D 9; A 8; LL 47–50. Shape, like the Bleak *(Alburnus)*. Mouth large, directed forwards. Lateral line complete, bowed down. Young almost uniformly grey-green. Sexually ripe adults show a strong pearly lustre by reflected light. Upperside bluish-green with some darker blotches. Flanks paler, with a dark longitudinal band accompanied above by a pale stripe. Lower half of caudal peduncle dark. Belly pale whitish. Fins colourless; according to Arnold the anterior part of the dorsal fin is yellowish.

♀ more robust when sexually ripe.
♂ slimmer. At spawning time the regions behind the head and above the pectoral fin are reddish; parts of the belly and the anal fin are likewise reddish.

327

Care of this lively, shoaling fish in cold-water tanks, as for the European *Cyprinidae* (see p. 233). Omnivorous. Cold wintering. Acclimatisation difficult. 1912/ –.

Notropis hypselopterus (*Günther* 1868) (Fig. 475)
The numerous species (about 100) of the genus *Notropis* are the characteristic inhabitants of the flowing waters of North America east of the Rockies. All the species are small, slim and more or less compressed. Mouth usually directed forwards. No barbels. Scales large. Lateral line complete. In many ways reminiscent of the European *Alburnus* and *Leuciscus* spp. Colouring usually silvery, but often gayer at spawning time.

Notropis hypselopterus is native to the states of Alabama, Georgia and Florida, U.S.A.; to 6 cm.

D 8; A 11; LL 35; TR 8. Shape typical of the genus. A very handsome decorative fish which does best at room-temperature and is very beautifully coloured even outside the breeding season. Ground-colour brown to dark brown; back olive-brown, grass-green by reflected light; belly yellowish to whitish. From the tip of the snout to the root of the tail extends a blue-black longitudinal band which is accompanied above by a very striking fiery-red stripe. Dorsal, caudal and anal fins brick-red at the base, outside this reddish to yellowish. Ventral fins yellowish-green with bluish tips. Pectorals colourless.

♀ dorsal fin without black tip; 'fiery-red' stripe only yellowish-red.
♂ dorsal fin with black tip.

Care and breeding, as for *Chrosomus erythrogaster*. Winter at 16–18 °C. The commercial distribution of this very beautiful species is much to be desired. 1900/ –.

Notropis lutrensis (*Baird* and *Girard* 1853) (Fig. 476)
U.S.A., southern Illinois to South Dakota; to 8 cm.

D 9; A 8–10; LL 34–38; TR 6–8/4. Shape typical of the genus (see previous species). Coloration outside the breeding season: upperside grey-blue to greenish; flanks and belly silvery, tinged a delicate reddish. About the level of the anal fin there begins a dark longitudinal stripe which extends to the root of the tail. A wedge-shaped, gleaming violet transverse band behind the gill-cover, particularly conspicuous in the ♂. Dorsal fin colourless; all other fins yellowish to faint reddish.

Coloration during the breeding season: flanks and belly handsome carmine to violet, more rarely greenish.

328

♀ more robust and also at the breeding season less brightly coloured.

♂ coloration as described above. Nuptial tubercles present during the breeding season.

Care, as given for *Chrosomus erythrogaster*. Temperature in winter not lower than 14–16°C. 1935/ –.

Phoxinus neogaeus *Cope* 1866 (Fig. 472)   American Minnow
Mississippi-Missouri basin, tributaries of the White River, Wisconsin, Arkansas, etc., not common; to 8 cm.

D 3/6–7; A 2/7; LL about 80; TR 18/10. Closely related to the European Minnow. Body elongate, little compressed up to the caudal peduncle. Mouth small, forwardly directed. Lateral line incomplete, short, not reaching as far as the level of the ventral fins. Scales very small. Coloration dark overall. Back dark olive to blackish. Flanks with a broad black longitudinal band which extends from the snout to the root of the tail and is bordered above by a pale stripe. Underside whitish. Fins colourless to brownish.

♀ more robust; belly yellowish at spawning time.

♂ with carmine belly, pectoral, ventral and anal fins.

This delicate species should be cared for in much the same way as the European Minnow (see p. 246). 1896/ –.

Rhinichthys atratulus atratulus (*Hermann* 1804) (Fig. 474)   Blacknose Dace
South-east Canada, basin of the Great Lakes and thence southwards to Ohio; to 12 cm.

D 7/8; A 7; LL 62–71; TR 9–11/8–10. The North American genus *Rhinichthys* comprises elongate, slim, only slightly compressed fishes inhabiting chiefly clear-water brooks. These fishes are further characterised by a sub-terminal mouth; a dorsal fin which is inserted behind the ventral fins; small barbels and very small scales. Lateral line complete. The individual species are difficult to distinguish.

Adult *Rhinichthys atratulus atratulus* are strikingly coloured from spring to autumn. Upperside dark olive-green to blackish, often with dark blotches. Flanks with a broad black band from the snout to the root of the tail, bordered by a golden stripe above and a yellowish one below. Underside silver-white. Fins delicate yellowish. Ventral and anal fins with a reddish base. At spawning time (April to July) the coloured longitudinal band becomes lacquer-black or black-red and the lower half of the body brilliant red. The fins are likewise more or less red. The lower half of the body becomes orange during the autumn. The young exhibit a quite unpretentious colouring.

♀ easily recognised by her less intense coloration.

The elegant *Rhinichthys* spp. are easily cared for in cold-water tanks and require clear, frequently renewed water, good aeration and plenty of room to move about. Winter as cold as possible, 4–8 °C.; in summer, not much above 20 °C. Not choosy about their food. The fishes spawn in shallow water in much the same fashion as *Gobio* sp.; it is therefore necessary to allow the bottom to rise at one side to the surface of the water. According to Meinken the fishes press in pairs against the beach; here the ♂ embraces the ♀ with his caudal peduncle and she thereupon emits an egg. The process is many times repeated and the fishes spawn almost daily for several weeks. Put in several pairs at the same time. The young hatch after 3–5 days. Open-air basins, such as garden ponds, are particularly favourable for a rational breeding. Re-importation is greatly to be desired. 1896/ –.

Rhinichthys atratulus obtusus (*Agassiz* 1854)
This subspecies, chiefly from the states of Ohio and Virginia, U.S.A., is not quite so slim, overall more brownish to yellow-brown, and not so red at spawning time. The characteristic longitudinal band is at most only grey-brown. A dark blotch at the base of the dorsal fin (according to Arnold).

Other details as for the previous subspecies.

Semotilus corporalis (*Mitshill* 1817) (Fig. 459)   Fallfish
Eastern U.S.A., from the St. Lawrence River to the eastern side of the Alleghanies, in clear flowing waters; to 40 cm., by far the largest Cyprinid in the eastern U.S.A.

D 8; A 8; LL about 45; TR 8/4. Body elongate, robust. Head large. Mouth forwardly directed, upper jaw protrusible. One pair of small barbels (absent in juveniles). Lateral line complete. Very attractively coloured: upperside steel-blue, flanks and belly bright silver. Paired fins and anal fin pink or carmine. Dorsal fin

Figs. 458–461

Fig. 458. *Erimyzon sucetta* (Lake Chubsucker); adult, reduced.
Fig. 459. *Semotilus corporalis* (Fallfish); greatly reduced.
Fig. 460. *Labeo forskali;* adult, greatly reduced.
Fig. 461. *Luciosoma spilopleura;* young, natural size.

colourless with a dark blotch at the base. Young fishes are almost uniformly silver. The sexes are difficult to distinguish.

♀ more robust at spawning time.
♂ with nuptial tubercles on the snout at spawning time.

Care, in cold-water aquaria, much the same as for the European Barbel (see p. 238). Large specimens are fine showpieces for public aquaria. Unfortunately this is a delicate species and only seldom imported. 1885/—.

Family Gyrinocheilidae

This south-east Asian family, extremely interesting to the biologist, contains only the genus *Gyrinocheilus* with three species.

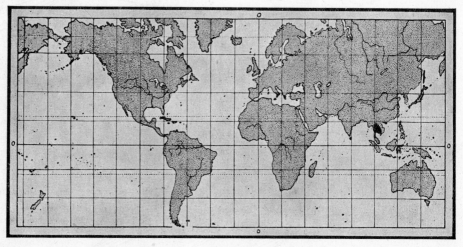

Fig. 462
Distribution of the *Gyrinocheilidae;* note S.E. Asia.

Plate 83

Fig. 463. *Doras (Amblydoras) hancocki;* half-grown, somewhat enlarged. (Original)
Fig. 464. *Mystus tengera;* young, natural size. (Original)
Fig. 465. *Parauchenoglanis macrostoma;* 22 cm. specimen, in the Hellabrunn Aquarium, Munich. (Original)

Plate 83

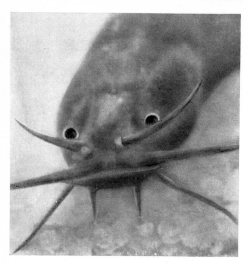
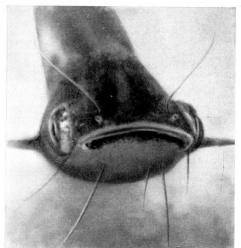

Plate 84

Plate 84

Fig. 466. *Parailia longifilis;* half-grown fish in the natural swimming-position, enlarged. (Photo Dr. Foersch)

Fig. 467. *Bunocephalus* sp.; somewhat enlarged, in the Hellabrunn Aquarium, Munich. (Photo Dr. Foersch)

Fig. 468. (Lower left) *Channalabes apus;* head, three times natural size, showing the disposition of the barbels. (Photo Dr. Foersch)

Fig. 469. (Lower right) *Schilbe marmoratus;* head of a young specimen, twice natural size. (Photo Dr. Foersch)

Gyrinocheilus aymonieri (*Tirant* 1883) (Fig. 403)

Thailand, widely distributed; to about 25 cm., usually remaining substantially smaller.

The species of the genus *Gyrinocheilus* possess an interesting specialisation. Above the usual gill-opening there is an additional aperture which acts as an inhalant opening admitting respiratory water to the gill-chamber. The mouth is ventral and surrounded by well-developed lips which together form a sucking organ and are provided with rasp-like folds. Pharyngeal teeth absent. *Gyrinocheilus* spp. are chiefly stream-dwellers and feed exclusively on algae which they graze with the rasp-like ridges of the suctorial mouth. Normal respiration, that is to say, by the admission of water through the mouth, is here completely suppressed. This peculiar situation becomes comprehensible only when it is considered as an adaptation to a specialised habit of life. Sucking animals cannot take in water through the mouth and thus carry on normal respiration without breaking off their other activity. This disability has evidently led to the evolution of an independent inhalent opening to the gill-chamber. A very similar situation has already been noted in the Lampreys.

Body elongate, only slightly compressed. Dorsal fin large (9 soft rays). Coloration uniform grey-brown with dark blotches on the back. A vague dark lateral band, usually broken up into blotches. Underside pale.

♀ more robust when sexually mature (more than 10 cm.). Fewer tubercles on the snout than in the ♂.

Gyrinocheilus is one of the best alga-destroyers for the aquarium and leaves higher plants quite undamaged; in fact its performance as a cleaner is better than that of *Otocinclus* and *Plecostomus* spp. It requires either good aeration or thick planting. Feed with algae or with withered lettuce leaves; dried food is also taken. Nothing is known about the reproduction of these fishes. The young are very undemanding and peaceful but the adults become quarrelsome and pugnacious. 1955.

30 Sterba

333

Family Cobitidae (Loaches and Spiny Loaches)

The Loaches are typical representatives of the fish-fauna of the Old World, whose distribution extends from Spain across the whole of Eurasia to the Pacific coast and, with few exceptions, includes the northern regions of both

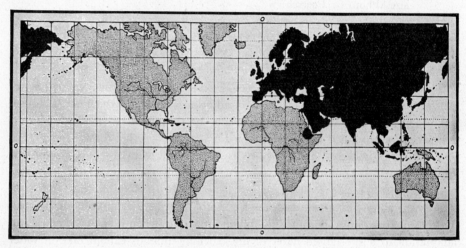

Fig. 470
Distribution of the *Cobitidae*. The European distribution also extends across to Morocco.

continents. To the south their distribution extends locally into Africa (Morocco, Ethiopia). The family attains its greatest diversity in southern Asia and the Malay Archipelago. The majority of the species are relatively small; only some members of the genera *Misgurnus* and *Botia* attain a length of

Figs. 471–476

Fig. 471. *Chrosomus erythrogaster* (Redbelly Dace); natural size.
Fig. 472. *Phoxinus neogaeus* (American Minnow); natural size.
Fig. 473. *Clinostomus vandoisilus;* adult, reduced.
Fig. 474. *Rhinichthys atratulus atratulus* (Blacknose Dace); natural size.
Fig. 475. *Notropis hypselopterus;* natural size.
Fig. 476. *Notropis lutrensis;* natural size.

334

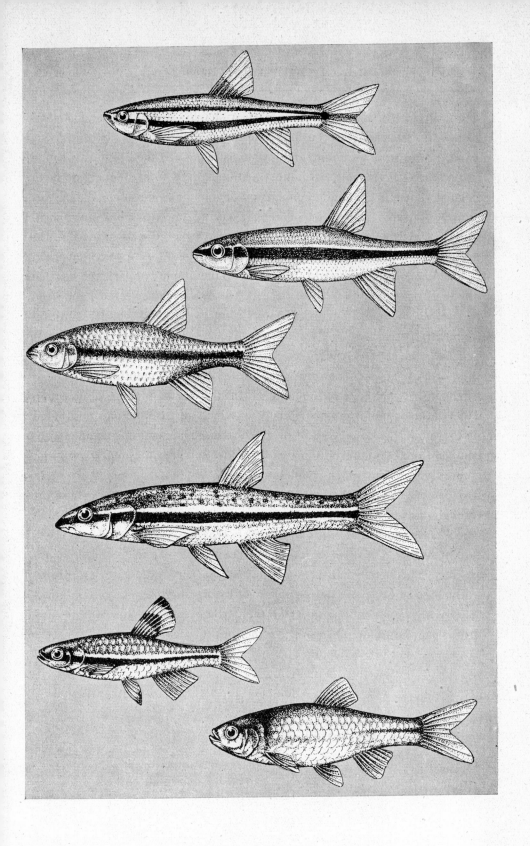

about 30 cm. All Loaches betray by their shape – worm-like or, if *Barbus*-like, with a flattened lower surface – their clear adaptation to a bottom-living habit. Forms from mountain and lowland streams are likewise mostly round or flattened *(Noemacheilus)* in cross-section. Forms from standing or slow-flowing waters are laterally compressed (*Botia, Acanthophthalmus, Misgurnus*, etc.). Many Loaches *(Misgurnus, Cobitis*, some *Botia* and *Acanthophthalmus* spp., *Lepidocephalus)* at times burrow into the sand or mud on the bottom and in this way protect themselves from predators or pass the winter.

The popular name Spined Loach refers to the simple or bifid spine situated obliquely below and in front of the eye. This spine may be erected and fixed and so become fatal to many predators; larger fishes and even birds not infrequently perish through swallowing loaches whose spines stick in their gullets. In the genus *Noemacheilus* the spine is quite tiny and concealed in the skin, or quite absent. The somewhat ventral, toothless mouth is surrounded by the lips (upper edge of the mouth formed from the premaxillaries only). Three, four or more pairs of barbels, of which at least one pair is situated on the snout. Scales very small or much reduced. Lateral line complete, incomplete, or absent. Certain species are able to carry on intestinal respiration, an accomplishment which enables many Loaches to live in muddy, oxygen-poor waters. These fishes rise to the surface and take in atmospheric air through the mouth; this is passed into the intestine where the intestinal mucosa (especially that of the hind-gut) absorbs the oxygen and releases waste carbon dioxide. The spent air is then expelled through the vent. Some Loaches are very dependent on air-pressure and become very restless when this falls.

The food of Loaches consists chiefly of worms and insect-larvae, obtained by very sagacious hunting in which the barbels render good service. A few species eat plant material, mainly in the form of algal films.

Plate 85

Fig. 477. *Labeo erythrura;* adults, reduced. (Original)
Fig. 478. *Labeo frenatus;* adult, enlarged. (Original)

Plate 85

Plate 86

Plate 86
Fig.479. *Kryptopterus bicirrhis* (Indian Glass Catfish). (Original)
Fig.480. *Electrophorus electricus* (Electric Eel); heads of two specimens in the Hellabrunn
Aquarium, Munich; reduced. (Original)

Little is known concerning the reproduction of the tropical species. According to Simanowski *Acanthophthalmus* spp. spawn at the surface in very shallow water where the ♂ and ♀ press close against one another.

Some of the genera are very sharply distinguished. The genus *Noemacheilus* has no spine under the eye. The tropical genera with spines under the eyes may be recognised by the following characters (partly according to Smith):–

Botia: The eyes are not covered with skin; the spine is bifid; the origin of the dorsal fin is over or anterior to the insertion of the ventrals; 3 pairs of barbels (2 pairs of rostral, 1 pair of maxillary barbels).

Lepidocephalus: Elongate, low-bodied; eyes covered with transparent skin; head partly scaled; 4 pairs of barbels (2 pairs of rostral, 1 pair of maxillary, 1 pair of mandibular barbels).

Acanthopsis: Elongate, low-bodied; eyes covered with transparent skin; head quite scaleless; 3 pairs of barbels (1 pair of rostral, 2 pairs of maxillary barbels); lateral line complete.

Acanthophthalmus: Elongate, worm-like; eyes covered with transparent skin; head quite scaleless; the origin of the dorsal fin is well behind the insertion of the ventrals; 4 pairs of barbels (1 pair of rostral, 2 pairs of maxillary, 1 pair of mandibular barbels); lateral line absent.

Two species are native to Britain: the Stone Loach *(Noemacheilus barbatulus)*, which is widely distributed, and the Spined Loach *(Cobitis taenia)*, which has a more restricted and sporadic distribution, mainly in southern England. In continental Europe these species are joined by a third, *Misgurnus fossilis*. For the care of these see under the individual descriptions.

In the care of the tropical Loaches the first consideration must be for their shy and retiring nature. The well-being of these fishes depends very largely on the lighting conditions and on the provision of suitable hiding-places. The tank should be kept dark and placed at eye-level, so that the fishes are not constantly disturbed by passers-by, and should be provided with a soft, sandy bottom-soil and inverted coconut-shells, pieces of flower-pot and other concealed hiding-places. Although it is possible to keep single specimens in company with *Barbus* spp. or small Catfishes, one should really aspire to keeping a small group of Loaches together. The fishes display a different pattern of behaviour in the company of their own kind to that which they show as isolated individuals. Planting can be quite sparse. Soft to medium-hard water, partly replaced from time to time, will meet the needs of larger specimens. Many tropical Loaches require a great deal of oxygen and aeration is therefore generally recommended. Feeding is easy; as well as our familiar food-animals (small crustacea, *Tubifex*, Enchytraeids, midge-larvae), kitchen scraps and dried foods may also be included. Plant material in the form of algae or softened rolled oats is vitally necessary to many species. Temperature in general around 24°C. In capturing Loaches only coarse-mesh nets should be used, so that the spines are only lightly entangled. It is inevitable that the hands will be pricked occasionally when handling these fishes, but the punctures are not poisonous. So far the breeding of tropical Loaches in captivity has hardly been a success; only *Acanthophthalmus* spp. have spawned in aquaria. Strange to say, reports on breeding behaviour

Figs. 481–487

Fig. 481. *Acanthophthalmus kuhlii kuhlii* (Coolie Loach, Leopard Eel, Prickly Eye, Striped Loach); adult, enlarged.
Fig. 482. *Acanthophthalmus kuhlii sumatranus;* adult, enlarged.
Fig. 483. *Acanthophthalmus myersi;* adult, enlarged.
Fig. 484. *Acanthophthalmus semicinctus* (Half-banded Coolie Loach); adult, enlarged.
Fig. 485. *Acanthophthalmus shelfordi;* adult, enlarged.
Fig. 486. *Acanthophthalmus cuneovirgatus;* about twice natural size.
Fig. 487. *Acanthophthalmus robiginosus;* about twice natural size.

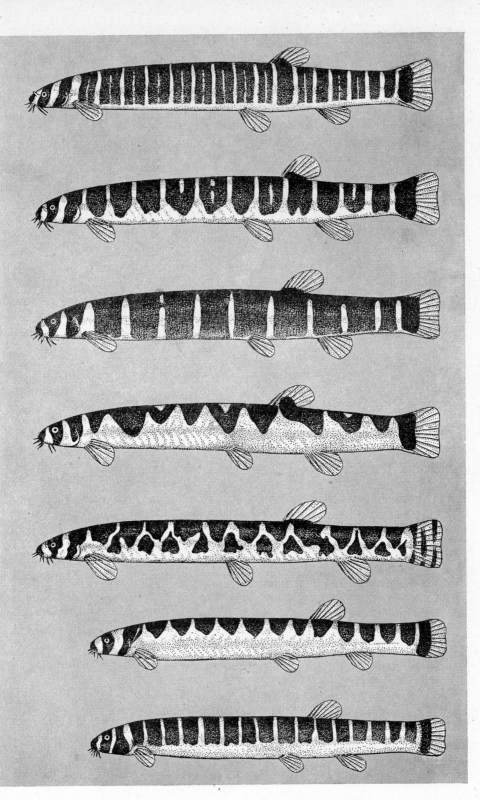

are quite contradictory; even the construction of a bubble-nest has been described!

Exact observations on breeding could provide valuable contributions to the biology of Loaches.

Acanthophthalmus cuneovirgatus *Raut* 1957 (Fig. 486)
Farther India (Johore); to 5·5 cm.

D 2/6; A 2/5. Greatest depth of body about 8 times in the body-length (without caudal). Origin of anal fin close behind the hinder end of the dorsal. 3 pairs of barbels. Anterior nostril produced, tubular; an unpigmented lobe-like projection from the hinder side of the prolongation. Bright yellow, somewhat paler on the flanks. Belly whitish, with a pearly gleam in ripe ♀♀. About 14 wedge-shaped, intense black bars which at the most reach to the middle of the side; the 3 bars on the head and the ones posterior to the anal fin are somewhat longer than the others.

♀ pectoral fins smaller; second fin-ray not thickened.
♂ second ray of pectoral fin thickened. (Description according to Raut.)

Care, as given on p. 338. 1954.

Acanthophthalmus kuhlii kuhlii (*Cuvier* and *Valenciennes* 1846) (Fig. 481)
Coolie Loach, Leopard Eel, Prickly Eye, Striped Loach
Sumatra, Java; to 8 cm.

D 2/6–7; A 1–2/5–6; P 1/8; V 1/5, inserted behind the middle of the body. The anal fin commences somewhat behind the dorsal. 3 pairs of barbels. Yellowish to delicate salmon-pink, with about 15–20 dark brown to deep black transverse bars (the first 3 on the head), which may be split up the middle by a pale streak and which reach nearly to the underside. Intervals narrower than the transverse bands. Underside paler.

Sex-distinctions are not certainly known.
Care and breeding, as given on p. 338. 1910/+.

Figs. 488–491

Fig. 488. *Acanthopsis choiorhynchus;* reduced.
Fig. 489. *Botia beauforti;* adult, reduced.
Fig. 490. *Botia modesta;* adult, somewhat reduced.
Fig. 491. *Botia lecontei;* maximum size.

Acanthophthalmus kuhlii sumatranus *Fraser-Brunner* 1940 (Fig. 482)
Sumatra; to 8 cm.

Distinguished only by the coloration and markings from the typical subspecies *A. kuhlii kuhlii*, *A. k. sumatranus* displays 12–15 transverse bars (the first 3 on the head) which are usually wedge-shaped and do not quite extend to the belly but do reach broadly below the middle of the side. Inner margins of the bars often pale. Intervals between the bars red-golden above, delicate salmon-pink on the flanks, pale yellowish below. Belly white in the ♀.

Acanthophthalmus myersi *Harry* 1949 (Fig. 483)
Thailand (Kao Sabap); to 8 cm.

D 2/8; A 2/6–7; P 1/9; V /15. Altogether very similar to *A. kuhlii kuhlii* in coloration; according to Klausewitz possibly only a subspecies of *A. kuhlii*. Ground-colour bright yellow to salmon-red, with (10–)11(–14) broad, dark brown transverse bars which reach to the pale belly or even fuse with the opposite bands to form complete rings. The bars are always uniformly coloured; there is never a pale inner zone.

Sex-distinctions and care, as given on p. 338. 1955.

Acanthophthalmus robiginosus *Raut* 1957 (Fig. 487)
West Java, near Rangkas-Betong; to 5 cm.

D 2/6; A 2/5. Greatest depth of body contained about 7 times in the body-length (without caudal). The anal fin commences immediately under the end of the dorsal. 3 pairs of barbels. Anterior nostril as in *A. cuneovirgatus* (tubular with a lobe on the hinder edge). Muddy yellow-brown to bright rust-red; belly somewhat paler but never white. The flanks have a steel-blue lustre by reflected light. About 21 narrow, dark brown, transverse bands, without pale inner zones, which reach somewhat below the middle of the side.

In the ♂ all the fins are larger and the second ray of the pectoral is thickened. (Description according to Raut.)

Care, as given on p. 338. 1953.

Figs. 492–493

Fig. 492. *Botia lucas bahi;* natural size. (Top figure only)
Fig. 493. *Botia lohachata;* natural size. Below two sketches are given showing the commonest patterns of markings in this species. (After Klausewitz)

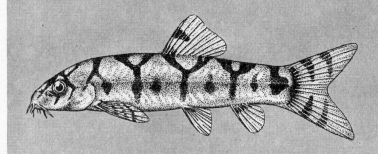

Acanthophthalmus semicinctus *Fraser-Brunner* 1940 (Figs. 392, 484)

East Indies; to 8 cm.   Half-banded Coolie Loach

D 2/6–7; A 2/5. This is the easiest species to recognise among those so far imported. Ventral fins inserted about the middle of the body. The anal fin begins about the level of the hinder end of the dorsal. 12–16 dark brown to black transverse bars which (with the exception of the 3 on the head and the one at the root of the tail) do not extend below the middle of the side. Bars broadly wedge-shaped, often with a pale inner space. Intervals between the bars beautiful golden-red, more salmon-pink towards the belly; underside white.

♀ fins smaller.

♂ with second pectoral ray thickened.

Care, as given on p. 338. Import data not certainly known.

Acanthophthalmus shelfordi *Popta* 1901 (Fig. 485)

Borneo; to 8 cm.

D 2/5–6; A 2/4–5; V 1/5, inserted in the middle of the body-length (without caudal). The anal fin origin is about a dorsal fin-base behind the dorsal. Two alternating rows of bars leaving at the most only narrow stripes of delicate pink to salmon-pink between them. Occasionally the bars are reduced to irregular black blotches so that the fishes appear to be mottled. Underside whitish.

Sex-distinctions not known.

Care, as given on p. 338. 1911, 1913?/ –.

Acanthopsis choiorhynchus (*Bleeker* 1894) (Fig. 488)

South-east Asia, Greater Sunda Islands; to 18 cm.

D 2/10–11; A 2/5–7. Scales very small. Body elongate, slim, compressed. Upper profile more strongly convex than the lower. Head large, drawn out to a point. Mouth ventral, small. Lower lip fringed. 3 pairs of short barbels. Preorbital spine bifid. Coloration and markings very variable, depending on age and locality of

Plate 87

Fig. 494. *Auchenoglanis occidentalis;* 40 cm. specimen in the Hellabrunn Aquarium, Munich. (Original)

Fig. 495. *Malapterurus electricus* (Electric Catfish); 30 cm. specimen in the Hellabrunn Aquarium, Munich. (Original)

Fig. 496. *Leiocassis poecilopterus;* young, somewhat enlarged. (Original)

Plate 87

Plate 88

Plate 88
Fig. 497. *Synodontis angelicus;* 3 cm. young. (Original)
Fig. 498. *Corydoras hastatus* (Dwarf or Pigmy Corydoras); natural size. (Photo Dr. Foersch)

origin. As well as uniformly ochre-coloured fishes there are varieties which bear a dark longitudinal band, or at least a row of blotches, along the flanks. Upon this fundamental pattern there may be superimposed narrow transverse bars, wavy lines, spots or other markings in pale to dark brown tints. Fins colourless or yellowish. Dorsal and caudal fins often with brown spots or lines.

Sex-distinctions not known.

Care, much the same as for other tropical Loaches. According to Holly these fishes like to burrow into the bottom, which should therefore be soft and fine-grained. Various small worms, *Daphnia* (especially dead) and midge-larvae may be given as food. Temperature 25–28 °C.; see also p. 338. 1929/–.

Botia beauforti *Smith* 1931 (Fig. 489)
Thailand; to about 20 cm.

D 3/9; A 2–3/4–6. Body elongate, strongly compressed, of almost uniform depth. Insertion of dorsal fin somewhat anterior to the ventrals. Delicate grey to grey-green with four rows of spots on the flanks, each spot with a pale border. Several dark longitudinal stripes behind the eye, continued as rows of spots on the body and passing into the base of the dorsal fin. Dorsal and caudal fins bright orange with rows of spots; anal fin yellowish with several spots near the base.

Sex-distinctions unknown. Import doubtful.

Botia berdmorei (*Blyth* 1860) (Fig. 454)
Burma and Thailand; to 25 cm., usually remaining smaller.

D 2/9; A 2–3/4–6. Body elongate, similar to that of the previous species, but the caudal peduncle appreciably less than the greatest depth of the body. In this case, too, the origin of the dorsal fin is well behind the ventrals. Cream to delicate ochre with 10–11 broad, not very bright though quite distinct, transverse bars. Rostral barbels black, joined to the eyes by narrow black bands. Two prominent intense black bands behind the eye, continued along the flanks as rows of blotches. Dorsal fin yellowish with transverse bars. Caudal fin with 2 to 3 strong transverse bars at the base.

Sex-distinctions not certainly known. ♂ with a reddish dorsal fin (?).
Care, as given on p. 338. 1953.

Botia hymenophysa (*Bleeker* 1852) (Fig. 394)
Thailand, Malay Peninsula, Singapore, Greater Sunda Islands; to 21 cm.

D 1/12–13; A 2/6; P 1/11; V 1/7. 3 pairs of barbels. Somewhat slimmer than the better-known Clown Loach. Upperside brownish to brown-yellow. Flanks grey-yellow to delicate grey-green with about 11 narrow transverse bars which are somewhat backwardly inclined and which may have dark blue-grey or even brown or dark edges. Intervals between the bars always narrower than the bars themselves. Underside yellowish. Fins delicate yellow to greenish; dorsal and caudal fins with dark lines or rows of spots.

Sex-distinctions unknown.

Care, as given on p. 338. A very lively but shy species. 1936/+.

Botia horae *Smith* 1931 (Fig. 452)
Thailand, widely distributed; to about 10 cm., usually remaining smaller.

Apart from the coloration, the principal distinguishing character of this species is the dorsal fin, which consists of only 8 soft rays and is inserted directly opposite the ventrals. Overall green-yellowish with a dull metallic gleam, upperside more grey, underside pale. An intense black stripe extends along the ridge of the back from the tip of the snout nearly to the caudal fin and merges with a broad transverse bar at the root of the tail. Four narrow short transverse bars on the flanks, not always clearly apparent. Fins delicate grey-green or colourless; caudal yellowish, often with rows of dark spots.

Sex-distinctions unknown.

Care, as given on p. 338. 1953.

Botia lecontei *Fowler* 1937 (Figs. 453, 491)
Thailand; to 7 cm.

D 3/7–8; A 3/4–5. Shape similar to *B. hymenophysa*, that is, very slim. Profile of belly (according to Klausewitz) almost straight. Overall greenish to delicate blue-grey with a dull silky sheen; underside pale. A large round blotch at the root of the tail with a quite ill-defined border; the blotch itself is often quite indistinct. According to Klausewitz fine transverse stripes are occasionally visible on the back. Fins yellowish to light reddish.

Care, as given on p. 338. 1954 (?).

346

Botia lohachata *Chaudhuri* 1912 (Fig. 493)

Pakistan; to 10 cm. in aquaria.

D 1/9–10; A 1/5–6; P 14; V 8. This species belongs to the elongate *Botia* group. 4 pairs of barbels. The origin of the dorsal fin is exactly midway between the tip of the snout and the root of the tail. Caudal fin moderately notched. Ground-colour silver-grey, often with a dull golden gleam, with very variable transverse and oblique bars whose arrangement is best indicated by reference to Fig. 493. Fins colourless to delicate grey, partly with dark blotches and bars.

Sex-distinctions unknown.

This species is said to be sociable, as well as less timid and pugnacious than other *Botia* spp. According to Bader clear, well-oxygenated water and temperatures between 25 and 28 °C. are preferred. Omnivorous. A peculiar habit of these fishes which may be mentioned is that of creeping along the bottom on one side and resting in that position without any evident reason; burrowing, however, has not been observed.

Care, as given on p. 338. 1956.

Botia lucas bahi *Fowler* 1937 (Fig. 492)

Thailand (Tachin River); to about 8 cm.

This species has a similarity to *B. hymenophysa* and is not quite certainly distinct from it. Smith (1945) and Wahlert (1956) have indeed emphasised the possibility that it is merely a subspecies. Its characteristic feature is that the dorsal fin is wholly or partly black, or at the very least black-edged. Importation doubtful.

Botia macracanthus (*Bleeker* 1852) (Fig. 393)   Clown Loach, Tiger Botia

Sumatra, Borneo; to 30 cm., usually remaining smaller.

D 1/10; A 2/6; P 1/13; A 1/8. Body elongate, compressed. Profile of belly almost straight. Insertion of the dorsal fin anterior to the ventrals, as in almost all *Botia* spp. 4 pairs of barbels. A very beautiful species, whose coloration compares with that of the coral-reef fishes. The brilliant orange-red ground-colour is interrupted by 3 velvet-black wedge-shaped transverse bars on the flanks. All fins, including the pectorals, blood-red.

Sex-distinctions unknown.

Care, as given on p. 338. Breeding has not yet been very successful, despite many attempts; apparently the fishes do not become sexually mature until after several years. When kept in a shoal with their own kind, or even in company with similarly-coloured *Barbus* spp. (Banded Barbs), they swim very actively. Peaceful among themselves and toward other species. 1936/+.

Botia modesta (*Bleeker* 1865) (Figs. 395, 490)
Malay Peninsula, Indo-China, Thailand; to 10 cm.
Description partly according to Klausewitz (1957). D 2/8–9; A 3/5–6. Shape similar to *B. macracanthus*, moderately stocky. Insertion of dorsal fin anterior to ventrals. Uniformly grey, with a faint, silky greenish lustre. No transverse bars or any distinct blotch at the root of the tail. Fins yellow-grey, caudal brilliant yellow. Klausewitz (1957) describes *B. modesta* as having a somewhat convex ventral profile. The stocky shape clearly distinguishes this species from *B. lecontei*.
Sex-distinctions unknown.
Care, as given on p. 338. 1952.

Cobitis taenia (*Linnaeus* 1758) (Figs. 442, 445)   Spined Loach
Throughout Europe (including Great Britain) and large areas of Asia and North Africa, in clear lakes and running waters; to 11 cm. (Numerous subspecies have been described, but the Spined Loaches of Britain and Europe are all *Cobitis taenia taenia*.)
D 2–3/6–7; A 2–3/5–6; P 1/6–8; V 1/5. Body elongate, compressed, almost band-like. Mouth ventral, provided with swollen lips. 2 pairs of short maxillary barbels, 1 further pair at the corners of the mouth, all of equal length. Scales round, very small. Coloration changeable. Back grey-yellowish, flanks delicate grey to dull yellow, belly whitish. Back and sides very finely spotted with brown. A band of large brown blotches along the mid-line of the back from the head to the root of the tail, with a row of intense dark spots on either side of it. A longitudinal row of large, pale-edged brown blotches under the middle of the side. A vertical black stripe at the root of the tail. Fins tinted light grey, occasionally with rows of dark spots on the dorsal and caudal.

♀ pectoral fin-rays of equal thickness.
♂ second pectoral fin-ray thickened; a strikingly large scale at its base (Canestrini).

This very interesting species should be kept in a large tank in a dark situation. Its most important need is a fine, sandy bottom-soil; never, on any account, coarse gravel. The correct temperature is also important; for acclimatised fishes an upper limit of 18°C. should never be exceeded, while fresh-caught specimens must be kept still cooler. These fishes like to dig themselves into the sand until only their heads are exposed. The German name 'Steinbeisser' ('Stone-biter') is given in allusion to the peculiar manner of feeding; the fishes take up mouthfuls of sand, chew this through, and expel the residue through the gill-openings in a series of jerks. They continually search the bottom-soil for food-animals, chiefly worms, in this way. Breeding season April to June; in the aquarium a successful spawning is only attained after a cold wintering. The eggs are shed indiscriminately over the sand or among submerged roots. At a temperature of 15°C. the young hatch after 6–10 days. Rearing easy, since the young obtain most of their food from the mulm on the bottom.

Lepidocephalus guntae (*Hamilton-Buchanan* 1822) (Fig. 501)
Practically throughout India; to 15 cm.

D 2/6–7; A 2/5; P 1/7; V 1/6–7; LL about 115. Shape similar to that of the previous species. Delicate yellowish to grey, with a dully-gleaming pale stripe which extends from the snout to a small, round, deep black blotch at the root of the tail. Above and below this stripe there are irregular or even regularly arranged dark blotches. Underside pale. Dorsal and caudal fins with rows of dark spots.

Sex-distinctions uncertain.

Care, as given for the following species and on p. 338. 1920/−.

Lepidocephalus thermalis (*Cuvier* and *Valenciennes* 1846) (Fig. 455)
India, especially the coastal districts of Malabar, Ceylon; to 8 cm.

D 2/6; A 2/5; P 1/6; V 1/6. Not unlike the European Spined Loach *Cobitis*. Body elongate, low, slightly compressed anteriorly, strongly posteriorly. 4 pairs of barbels (2 pairs rostral, 1 pair maxillary, 1 pair mandibular). Dorsal fin inserted somewhat anteriorly to the ventrals. Caudal fin almost squarely truncated. Scales very small. Grey to delicate grey-green, with somewhat dark and very irregular blotches. Back usually marbled with pale and dark. Dorsal and anal fins with rows of spots.

Sex-distinctions uncertain.

Lepidocephalus spp. inhabit flowing or even clear standing waters, preferably parts which are not too deep and have a soft bottom. Like many other Spined Loaches the members of this genus have the habit of suddenly burrowing into the mud. Their food consists chiefly of worms and insect-larvae obtained from the bottom-soil. Nothing is known about their reproductive behaviour.

Care, as given on p. 338. 1954.

Noemacheilus barbatulus (*Linnaeus* 1758) (Figs. 441, 444)　　　　Stone Loach
Throughout Europe, with the exceptions of northern Scotland, northern Scandinavia, southern Spain, southern Italy and Greece. Present also in Siberia and Korea. In clear, rapid streams with a pebbly bottom, occasionally also in the inshore parts of clear lakes. To 12 cm. (occasionally to 18 cm.). Numerous subspecies, but the European form is the typical *Noemacheilus barbatulus barbatulus*.

D 2–4/7–8; A 2–4/5–6; P 1/12; V 1/7. Body elongate, anteriorly cylindrical, posteriorly slightly compressed. Mouth ventral. 3 pairs of barbels, of which 2 pairs are rostral and 1 pair, often somewhat longer, maxillary and situated in the corners of the mouth. Scales tiny. Skin very slimy. Coloration very variable, in relation to the wide geographic distribution (local forms). In Central Europe usually delicate yellow-brown, the upperside somewhat dark with an olive-green lustre, the flanks and underside paler, yellowish to yellow-greenish. Whole body covered with large and small dark blotches, usually irregularly scattered and more or less close together. Occasionally the large blotches on the flanks may be arranged in one or two longitudinal rows. Fins colourless to yellowish (especially the anal). Dorsal and caudal often with dark spots (possibly even rows of spots).

Sexes difficult to distinguish. The ♂♂ are more vigorously coloured, slimmer and smaller. Pectoral fins of ♂♂ larger (second fin-ray conspicuously thickened), with horny papillae on the inner margins. Pectoral fins of ♀♀ rounded (second fin-ray not obviously thickened), and without horny papillae on the inner margins.

The Stone Loach should be kept in a large, moderately planted tank standing in a cool position and provided with a pebbly bottom and large stones. Rather tedious, since the fishes often do not stir throughout the day, although in dull weather they do come to the surface from time to time to swallow air and then sink sluggishly to the bottom again. They eat vast quantities of worms and other prey and their vigorous burrowing periodically transforms the whole landscape of the tank.

The Stone Loach spawns, indiscriminately on stones and pebbles or among water plants, in the months of April and May. Exact observations show that the

Figs. 499–503

Fig. 499. *Noemacheilus fasciatus;* natural size.
Fig. 500. *Noemacheilus botia;* ripe fish, natural size.
Fig. 501. *Lepidocephalus guntae;* somewhat reduced.
Fig. 502. *Misgurnus anguillicaudatus* (Japanese Weather-fish); reduced.
Fig. 503. *Rhamphichthys rostratus;* adult, greatly reduced.

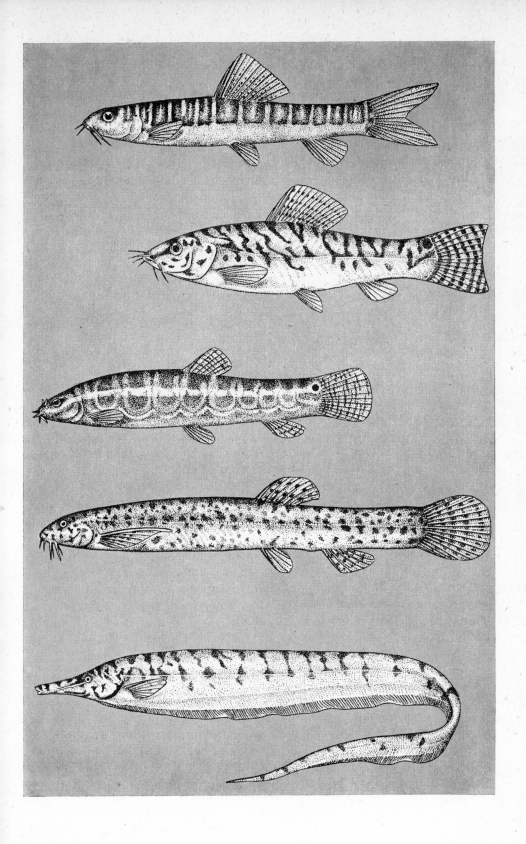

actual emission only takes place at night. At the beginning of the breeding season the ♀ is easily recognised by her greater girth. K. Spranger reports one spawning of freshly-caught fishes on the inside of an aquarium lid, after the manner of *Copeina*. The eggs are numerous, very adhesive and relatively large (about 1 mm. diameter). The young emerge after 8–11 days at 16°C., lie at first on the bottom, and commence to feed after about 8–10 days.

Growth is very rapid; as well as various small animals, algal films on stones and the sides of the tank are also eaten. The fishes are sexually ripe after only one year in captivity! It is also interesting that young Stone Loaches will grow up without aeration at about 30°C., although, indeed, with thick planting.

Noemacheilus botia (*Hamilton-Buchanan* 1822) (Fig. 500)
North-western India to Assam, absent from the Malabar coast and Ceylon; to 12 cm.

D 2/10–12; A 2/5; P 1/10; V 1/8. Body elongate, cylindrical, posteriorly compressed; not quite as slim as the European Stone Loach. Edge of caudal fin entire or slightly notched. 3 pairs of relatively long barbels. Grey-green to grey-brown with irregular dark blotches, underside whitish. Fins pale, dorsal and caudal fins with rows of spots.

Sex-distinctions in coloration not described. Dorsal fin of ♂♂ yellow (?).

A very undemanding species, which accepts any kind of food and feeds on algal films as well. The bottom-soil should be partly sandy, partly stony. 1903/–.

Noemacheilus fasciatus (*Cuvier* and *Valenciennes* 1846) (Fig. 499)
Greater Sunda Islands; to 9 cm.

D 3/9; A 3/5; P 2/9; V 1/7. Body elongate, low, strongly compressed posteriorly. 3 pairs of barbels. Caudal fin notched. Dorsal fin inserted about over the ventrals. Upperside olive to brownish, flanks clay-yellow to brimstone yellow (♂?), underside whitish or yellowish. Numerous brown wedge-shaped or band-like transverse bars. Fins colourless to delicate yellowish, partly with rows of dark spots.

Plate 89

Fig. 504. *Clarias platycephalus;* young, somewhat reduced. (Original)
Fig. 505. *Channalabes apus;* young, natural size. (Original)
Fig. 506. *Heterobranchus longifilis;* 70 cm. specimen in the Hellabrunn Aquarium, Munich. (Original)

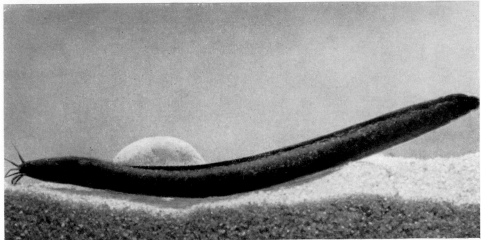

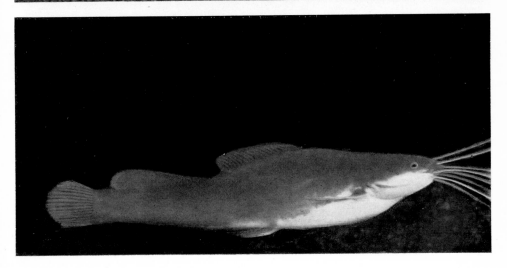

Plate 89

Plate 90

Plate 90

Fig. 507. *Ameiurus nebulosus marmoratus* (Marbled Bullhead); 30 cm. specimen in the Erfurt Aquarium. (Original)

Fig. 508. *Etropiella debauwi;* young, natural size. (Original)

Fig. 509. *Schilbe mystus;* young, natural size. (Photo Dr. Foersch)

Sex-distinctions not certainly known.

Care, as given on p. 338; hardy and undemanding. Omnivorous. 1914/−.

Misgurnus anguillicaudatus (*Cantor* 1842) (Fig. 502)   Japanese Weather-fish
North-eastern Asia southwards to central China; to 22 cm., but sexually mature at 10 cm.

D 2–4/5–7; A 2–5/5–6; P 1/9–10; V 1/5–8. Yellow-brown to olive-grey-brown marbling, underside pale, bright silvery. The appearance and way of life of this species correspond completely to those of the European Weather-fish (see below). Like the latter *M. anguillicaudatus* prefers a muddy bottom in which it likes to burrow until only the head protrudes. Omnivorous. Very hardy in unheated domestic aquaria. 1913/−.

Misgurnus fossilis fossilis (*Linnaeus* 1758) (Figs. 443, 446)   Weather-fish
Central and Eastern Europe, in standing or slow-flowing waters with a muddy bottom; to 30 cm.

D 2–4/5–7; A 2–5/5; P 1/10; V 1/5–6. Body elongate, cylindrical, strongly compressed posteriorly. Mouth small, ventral, with swollen lips. 5 pairs of barbels, (3 pairs maxillary, 2 pairs mandibular). Skin slimy. Scales very small. Head naked. Caudal fin rounded. Body clay-yellow to yellow-grey; upperside considerably darker, often dark brown; underside orange to muddy yellow. Numerous black-brown, very distinct, longitudinal bands, of which the one along the middle of the side is especially broad and prominent. Between these dark bands there are often very fine dark spots. Dorsal and caudal fins somewhat dark, usually spotted with brown; remaining fins pale. Occasionally all the fins are tinged with delicate orange.

♀ more robust. Pectoral fins round, second fin-ray not obviously thickened.

♂ pectoral fins larger, almost square-cut, the second fin-ray considerably thickened. A longitudinal swelling on the middle of the side, about the level of the hinder end of the dorsal fin.

Care, as given for the Spined Loach *(Cobitis)*, but less exacting. Aeration redundant. A thick layer of mulm is a vital requirement. Intestinal respiration is commonly made use of; the fishes come to the surface, swallow air and force this into the richly-vascular hind-gut. At almost regular intervals the exhausted air then escapes in large bubbles from the vent. Omnivorous, with a preference for worms and insect-larvae. This species becomes very tame. It spawns, after a cold wintering, in the months of April to June, on water plants or, according to other reports, in the surface mud between plant roots. A spawning can produce 150,000 eggs. The Weather-fish gets its name through the belief that it can, by its restless behaviour 24 hours previously, give warning of an impending thunderstorm. This assertion can hardly be said to have been substantiated. Packed in damp moss *Misgurnus* can be sent over long distances. Watzka *in litt.* has briefly communicated some very interesting observations. Weather-fishes are very gentle and friendly towards one another. There is an elegant courtship-behaviour; the ♂ lies along the back or belly of the ♀ so that she often becomes embraced by his body, while at other times the fishes rest on the bottom with their mouths pressed together. These fishes are also very peaceful with other species. Out of the water they can produce sounds very like the wails of an infant. The young, indeed, do like to creep out of the water.

Family Electrophoridae (Electric Eels)

Eel-like fishes with electric organs, living in South America. Dorsal and ventral fins absent. Anal fin very long, united with the caudal to form a single fin which does not extend onto the dorsal surface of the body.

Electrophorus electricus (*Linnaeus* 1766) (Fig. 480)   Electric Eel
North-eastern South America, middle and lower Amazon basin; to 230 cm.

Eel-like, body cylindrical but becoming somewhat laterally compressed in the region of the anal fin. Scales absent. The very large electric organ occupies about $\frac{4}{5}$ of the side of the body and is composed of several thousand individual elements, 'Electroblasts', arranged like cells in a dry-battery. An Electric Eel resting motionless in the water is usually electrically inert as well, but when it begins to move it emits small direction-finding impulses at a frequency of about 50 per second. The full shock can attain to a strength of 1 Ampère and the work done can exceed

354

100 Watts (about 0·5 Amp. at 200–300 Volts). Fishes and amphibians, also large mammals (such as horses) which come into contact with the Electric Eel are generally stunned; Man can withstand the shock for a short time. Fishes killed in the neighbourhood of the Eel are subsequently eaten.

Coloration uniform olive-brown, younger specimens marbled with light and dark. Young fishes with ochre-coloured pale lines and bands. Underside of head

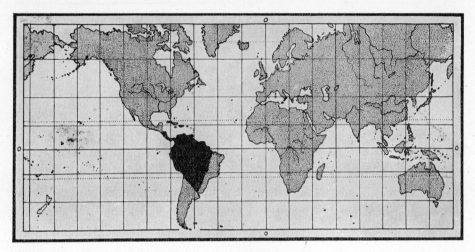

Fig. 510
Distribution of the *Gymnotidae* and *Electrophoridae*

and throat of adult brilliant orange. Edge of anal fin often pale. Eyes shining emerald green.

Sex-distinctions unknown.

Electric Eels should be kept in large and not too strongly lighted aquaria. Large specimens behave quite well together, but young ones are very snappy. Temperature 23–28 °C. Large Electric Eels prefer to eat fishes; young ones take worms and insect larvae. As bottom-soil not too coarse gravel should be provided. The potency of the electrical organ increases with the size of the fish. Since continual irritation, such as may be the lot of exhibits in public aquaria, is detrimental to these fishes, suitable hiding-places should be provided in which they can conceal themselves from time to time. For locomotion, see p. 356.

355

Families Gymnotidae, Rhamphichthyidae, Sternarchidae

The old family *Gymnotidae* has now been up-graded to a super-family, the *Gymnotiformes*, within which four families are now recognised. The *Electrophoridae*, represented by the Electric Eel, have already been dealt with; the three families remaining differ in that, although their members do produce electrical fields with which they navigate themselves and locate their prey, they cannot produce large lethal charges as can the *Electrophoridae*. The *Sternarchidae* are Gymnotiform fishes in which the dorsal fin is still present, though much reduced, and there is a small caudal fin. In the two remaining families the tail tapers to a point and there is no caudal fin; the *Gymnotidae* as now understood, have well-toothed jaws, while the *Rhamphichthyidae* have the teeth absent or only very feebly developed. For the purposes of aquarium practice it is politic to consider these last three families collectively.

The peculiar shape of these fishes has been effected by a strong forward displacement of the body-cavity, a remarkable elongation of the caudal portion and, further, by a strong lateral compression. As a result of this displacement the vent comes to lie on the underside of the head; meantime the ventral fins disappear, the anal fin becomes a long, marginal fringe which takes over the whole function of locomotion, and the dorsal and caudal fins become much reduced or absent. Ribs well developed. Swim-bladder present.

The locomotion of the *Gymnotiformes* is of special biological interest. The body is driven forwards by wave-like movements of the anal fin, and can just as easily glide backwards by a reversal of this undulation. Young fishes, especially, exhibit this unusual movement (also characteristic of the *Noto-*

Figs. 511–515

Fig. 511. *Eigenmannia virescens;* adult, much reduced.
Fig. 512. *Steatogenes elegans;* adult, reduced.
Fig. 513. *Hypopomus artedi;* somewhat reduced.
Fig. 514. *Sternarchus albifrons;* adult, much reduced.
Fig. 515. *Sternarchella schotti;* adult, reduced.

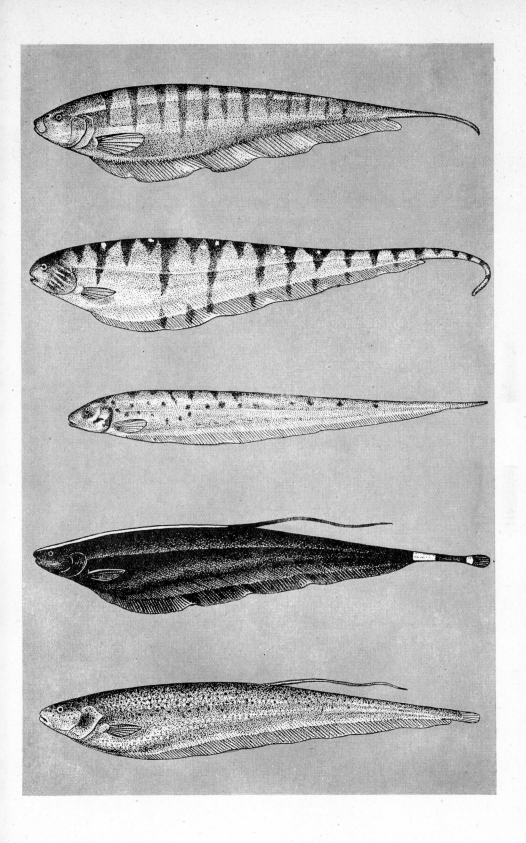

pteridae) which, in its totality, produces a worm-like effect. In this way the fishes can creep up on their prey without any revealing movement of the body, while the young can just as easily retreat before their own enemies. Something of the same kind also occurs in the *Mormyridae;* indeed, it is very interesting to see how these several unrelated families have, under the common necessities of life in dark, muddy waters and in widely separated continents, evolved common patterns of body-form, locomotion and navigation through the creation of electric fields.

The care of these highly interesting and often quite hardy fishes is generally not difficult. They should be kept in aquaria as dark as possible and provided with numerous hiding-places, particularly hollow tree-roots. Under such conditions they often belie their reputation for shyness and become quite tame. All the species greedily accept quite large food-materials; as well as live food of all kinds, pieces of meat, chopped earthworms and even rolled oats. Temperature around 23–28°C. Larger, peacefully-disposed fishes are quite suitable companions, but members of the same species are usually quite extraordinarily snappish among themselves. All Gymnotiform species are sensitive to cold.

Sex-distinctions and reproductive biology are largely unknown.

Unfortunately most of this group are too large for the domestic aquarium and therefore confined to public aquaria. In their native countries they inhabit quiet waters, weedy lagoons and shallow lakes.

Family Gymnotidae

Gymnotus carapo *Linnaeus* 1758 (Fig.456)　　　　　　Banded Knife-fish
From Guatemala southwards to La Plata, westwards to the Andes; to 60 cm.

A 200–260; P 1/14–15. Body eel-like, anteriorly almost cylindrical, posteriorly drawn out to a point and somewhat compressed. Mouth broad, oblique. Jaws each with a single row of conical teeth. Anal opening very far forward (under the head). Dorsal, caudal and ventral fins absent. The uniform anal fin serves as the only means of propulsion (see p.356). Scales numerous and very small. Electric organs small. The young of *G. carapo* have a resemblance to those of the Electric Eel. Flesh-coloured to light grey-yellow, with more or less numerous broad, dark transverse bands which, especially on the back, tend to coalesce. As well as uniformly flesh-coloured varieties there are also those with brown or brown-grey transverse bars.

Sex-distinctions have not yet been described.

Undemanding, but extraordinarily snappish with one another. *Gymnotus* is a crepuscular fish which leaves its hiding-place and goes in search of food chiefly by night. However, by providing dark conditions in the aquarium one can completely accustom the fishes to feeding by day. My specimens have not only got used to a fixed feeding-time but also take food from my hand. The diet should include small fishes, midge-larvae, worms, small pieces of meat, etc. Even very large pieces of food are greedily accepted. Large fish of other species are not generally molested. Temperature 23–28°C.

Breeding biology unknown. 1910/+.

Family Rhamphichthyidae

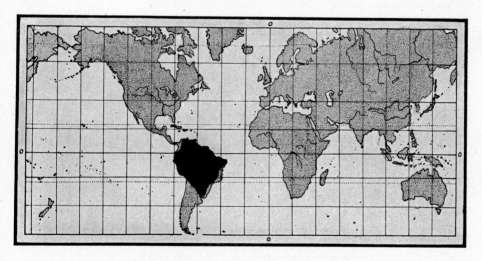

Fig. 516
Distribution of the *Rhamphichthyidae*

Eigenmannia virescens (*Valenciennes* 1849) (Fig. 511)   Green Knife-fish
Throughout northern South America, southwards to La Plata, north-westwards
to the R. Magdalena; to 45 cm.

A 215–255; P 1/17–21. Body elongate, strongly compressed, posteriorly produced
into a long whip-like tail. Teeth in a single row in each jaw. Anal opening on the
underside of the head. Dorsal, caudal and ventral fins absent. Scales numerous.
Delicate flesh-colour, the head and breast more yellowish to yellow-red (♂?).
Delicate, iridescent bluish to grey longitudinal stripes, as well as irregular transverse stripes (in young fishes), may be well-defined or absent. Zones with a dull
greenish reflexion are often apparent by direct light. According to Holly the anal
fin has a dark border.

Sex-distinctions in coloration not yet described.

Care, as given on p. 358. 1909/+.

Hypopomus artedi *Kaup* 1856 (Fig. 513)   Mottled Knife-fish, Speckled Knife-fish
Eastern Guiana (to the Paraná?); to 18 cm.

A 204–238. Body very elongate, strongly compressed. Jaws toothless. Dorsal,
caudal and ventral fins absent; anal very long. Anal opening on the underside of
the head. Delicate yellowish-green to brownish with isolated dark blotches. Anal
fin transparent. Eyes small and covered over by skin.

Sex-distinctions unknown. Care, as given on p. 358. 1927/−.

Steatogenes elegans (*Steindachner* 1880) (Fig. 512)
North-eastern South America, lower Amazon River and northern tributaries of the
middle Amazon; to 20 cm.

A 160–176; P 1/13–14. Body elongate, rather deep anteriorly; hinder part long,
drawn out into a filament, strongly compressed. Jaws toothless. Anal opening on
the underside of the head. Dorsal, caudal and ventral fins absent; anal very long.
Coloration, according to Holly: ground-colour yellow-brown, golden-brown or
ochre, becoming darker towards the back which is dark brown. Underside yellowish-white to whitish. 12–20 irregular deep brown to black-brown transverse

Plate 91

Fig. 517. *Heteropneustes fossilis;* young, 7 cm. long. (Original)
Fig. 518. *Schilbe marmoratus;* half-grown, natural size. (Original)
Fig. 519. *Synodontis alberti;* young, enlarged. (Photo Dr. Foersch)

Plate 91

Plate 92

Plate 92

Fig. 520. *Chrysichthys ornatus;* half-grown, natural size. (Photo Dr. Foersch)
Fig. 521. *Chrysichthys brevibarbis;* young, somewhat reduced. (Original)
Fig. 522. *Gephyroglanis longipinnis;* half-grown, enlarged. (Photo Dr. Foersch)

stripes, commencing on the back, extending over the flanks and narrowing ventrally. More or less distinct scattered gold-brown spots may be observed on the ridge of the back; these sometimes blend with the dark transverse stripes. The top and sides of the head are black with numerous pale yellow stripes; the cheeks are lighter. Pectoral fins with black spots. Anal fin yellowish, with blackish or dark brown blotches.

Sex-distinctions not described. Care, as given on p. 358.

There was also imported in 1951 a specimen nearly 50 cm. in length of *Rhamphichthys rostratus* (Linnaeus 1758), a species distinguished by a long drawn-out, almost proboscis-like mouth (Fig. 503).

Family Sternarchidae

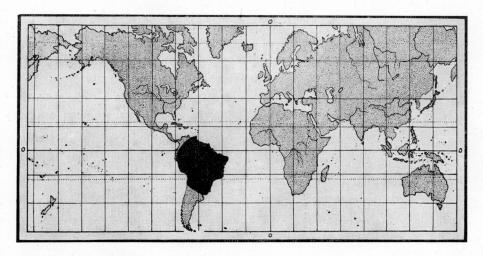

Fig. 523
Distribution of the *Sternarchidae*

361

Sternarchella schotti (*Steindachner* 1868) (Fig. 515)

Central Brazil; to 22 cm.

A 170–178. This species is immediately distinguished from the other Gymnotiform fishes by the very long filamentous dorsal fin which can be depressed into a groove along the middle of the back, and by the caudal fin, which is here neither absent nor united with the anal as in the other genera. Ventral fins absent. Anal opening very far forward, often as far as the anterior edge of the eye. Scales small. Delicate clay-colour to brownish, with numerous black dots which tend to aggregate on the upperside especially and to be separated towards the belly; the spots on the flanks are usually the largest. Fins transparent, partly sprinkled with fine dots. Fin-rays dark.

Care, as given on p. 358. Year of import unknown/+.

Sternarchus albifrons (*Linnaeus* 1758) (Fig. 514)

Amazon River and Surinam; to 50 cm.

A 140–162. Similar in shape to *Sternarchella schotti* and likewise provided with a small caudal fin and a filamentous dorsal. Fins and body uniform velvet-black. A milk-white band along the back from the tip of the snout to about the middle of the body. Two ivory-coloured transverse bars on the caudal peduncle.

Sex-distinctions and care as given on p. 358. 1934/−.

Family Doradidae (Thorny Catfishes)

The Thorny Catfishes are an exclusively South American group and usually of a thick-set, often tadpole-like, shape. The skull is generally broad and strongly ossified and is produced posteriorly as a flat, bony plate which extends as far as the base of the dorsal fin. The bones of the skull often have a granular surface and the sutures between them are quite distinct, even in the living fishes. The shoulder-girdle is strongly toothed. Jaws usually toothed. 1 pair of maxillary, 2 pairs of mandibular barbels. Dorsal fin inserted well forwards. Dorsal and pectoral fins with very strong, almost always conspicuously toothed, spines. Adipose fin usually present, small. Caudal fin rounded or squarely truncated. Flanks and upperside of body either covered with strong, spiny scutes or naked. Supplementary intestinal respiration widespread. Numerous genera.

The species so far imported are, without exception, crepuscular creatures which are often very sluggish during the daytime. They are undemanding and very hardy fishes whose needs are best met by a dark aquarium with a soft bottom-soil and a tangle of roots or pieces of bark and branches. Many species like to grub about the bottom. They will eat scraps and artificial foods as well as worms and insect-larvae. Temperature 20–26°C. Resistant to temporary chilling. Many species can, with lightning rapidity,

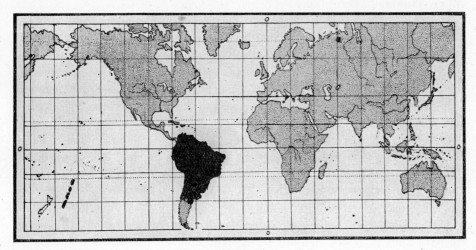

Fig. 524
Distribution of the *Doradidae*

dig themselves so deep into the bottom that only their eyes protrude; some, again, are able to emit an audible growling sound.

Little is known about the breeding behaviour; some species are said to build nests.

Doras (Astrodoras) asterifrons *Heckel* 1855 (Fig. 525)
Middle Amazon basin; to 11 cm.
D I/6; A 1/10–11; P I/7; V 1/6. Dorsal fin-spine straight, with two prominent lateral ridges and a row of tiny simple teeth on the anterior edge. Flanks covered with strongly spinous scutes. 3 pairs of barbels. Body yellow-brown to blackish.

363

Underside delicate pale brown or white. Dark, usually indistinct, transverse bars on the caudal peduncle. Vertical fins dark with white blotches, often united to form transverse bars. Maxillary barbels (1 pair) long, ringed with white. Mandibular barbels (2 pairs) shorter, brown.

Sex-distinctions unknown. Care, as given in the family description. Omnivorous and greedy. Not yet bred in captivity. 1914/—.

Doras (Amblydoras) hancocki *Cuvier* and *Valenciennes* 1840 (Figs. 463, 526)
Amazon lowlands, Peru, Bolivia, Guiana; to 15 cm.

D I/6; A 1/11; P I/6; V 1/5. Dorsal fin-spine curved, smooth, with a black anterior edge. Flanks covered with strongly spinous scutes. 3 pairs of barbels. Ground-colour brown with irregular violet-black blotches on the flank. Numerous silvery spots over a broad, pale lateral band running along the white spines of the scutes. Underside uniformly dirty white in the ♀, with pale brown spots in the ♂. Fins colourless, opaque. Barbels ringed with white and brown. Eyes opalescent blue.

Care, as given in the family description. According to the original discoverers the eggs are laid in a nest of leaves constructed by the parents. 1950.

Doras (Agamyxis) pectinifrons (*Cope* 1870) (Fig. 528)
Eastern Ecuador; to 16 cm.

D I/5; A 1/11; P I/5. Dorsal fin-spine toothed on both anterior and posterior surfaces. Spinous scutes confined to the posterior half of the body. 3 pairs of barbels. Coloration dark brown to blue-black, with numerous pale blotches on the head and body. Underside somewhat paler, similarly blotched. Fins dark, with pale stripes and spots which may run together to form transverse bars. Old individuals are almost uniformly dark brown with white blotches on the belly.

Sex-distinctions unknown. Care, as given in the family description. Not yet bred in captivity. 1933/—.

Figs. 525–528

Fig. 525. *Doras (Astrodoras) asterifrons;* adult, reduced, and dorsal view of head.
Fig. 526. *Doras (Amblydoras) hancocki;* adult, somewhat reduced.
Fig. 527. *Doras (Acanthodoras) spinosissimus* (Spiny Catfish); adult, reduced.
Fig. 528. *Doras (Agamyxis) pectinifrons;* adult, reduced.

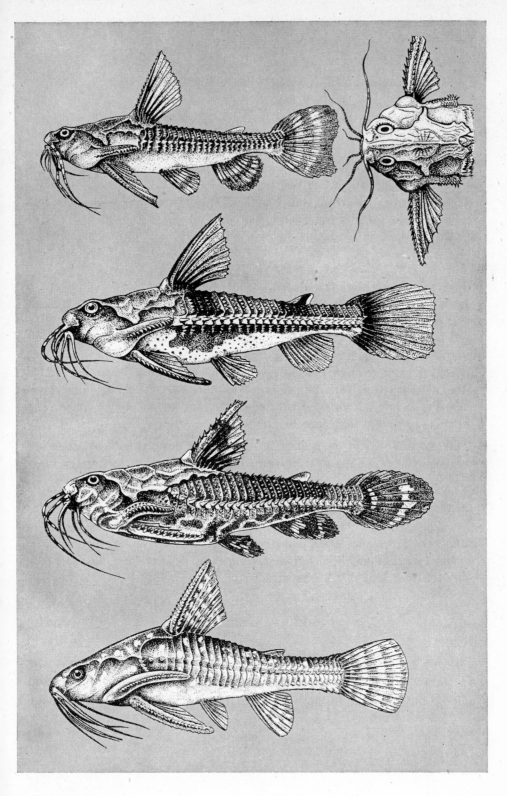

Doras (Acanthodoras) spinosissimus *Eigenmann* and *Eigenmann* 1888 (Fig. 527)

Spiny Catfish, Talking Catfish

Middle Amazon; to 15 cm.

D I/5; A 1/11; P I/6; V 1/5. Dorsal fin-spine almost straight, with rows of tiny teeth on the anterior and lateral surfaces. Flanks with strongly spinous scutes. 3 pairs of barbels. Coffee-brown, with a white band through the white spines of the lateral scutes, and white blotches on the back. Belly in the ♀ uniformly brownish; in the ♂ marbled with white and brown (according to Stettler). Fins irregularly marbled with white and brown. Anal fin with a white margin.

Care, as given in the family description. Probably not yet bred in captivity. 1921/+.

Trachycorystes striatulus (*Steindachner* 1878) (Fig. 538)

South America; south-east Brazil, Rio Parahyba, Rio Doce and Rio Mucury; to 25 cm.

D I/4–5; A 2/22–24; P I/6–7; V 1/5. Body plumper and more robust than in the previous species. Dorsal fin small. Dorsal fin-spine with one or two rows of tiny pointed teeth anteriorly. Anal fin-base long. Flanks naked. 3 pairs of barbels. Coloration very variable: yellowish-brown to yellowish-grey, the back darker and the underside grey. Numerous dark brown blotches on this ground-colour. This species practises accessory intestinal respiration.

♀. the anterior rays of the anal fin are slender and flexible; lower edge convex.
♂ the anterior rays of the anal fin are thickened, stiff, and lie close together; lower edge of anal fin wavy. (Description partly according to Rachow.)

Care, as given in the family description. 1909/–.

A further *Trachycorystes* sp. – **T. glaber** (Steindachner 1878) – has, according to Arnold (1935), been imported. More detailed particulars have not been published. (Original description in the *Sitzungsberichten der Akademie der Wissenschaften Wien* (1), 74, p. 655. 1878.)

Family Auchenipteridae

Catfishes with naked flanks, distributed from the east coast of South America, around Rio de Janeiro, to the Rio Magdalena and Peru. Dorsal fin and adipose fin short, the former with a stout and occasionally elongate spine.

3 pairs of barbels. Gill-covers united with the isthmus. The swim-bladder lies free in the body-cavity. Numerous genera. The family shows a close natural relationship with the *Doradidae*.

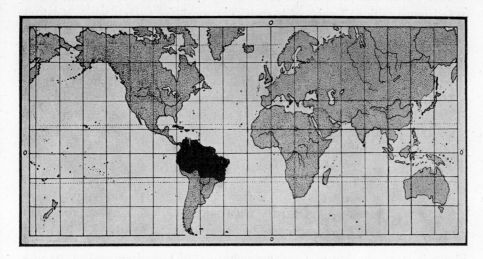

Fig. 529
Distribution of the *Auchenipteridae*

Centromochlus aulopygius *Kner* 1858 (Fig. 539)
Eastern South America, northwards from the Amazon; to 8 cm.

D I/4–5; A 8–10; P I/4; V 6. Body stocky, varying little in depth from front to back, the hinder part compressed. Dorsal fin inserted far forwards, short, with a stout spine. Adipose fin small. Caudal fin forked. Anal fin-base short. 1 pair of maxillary barbels, reaching to the pectoral fins when laid back; 2 pairs of short, very fine, mandibular barbels. Body dark brown to black with pale blotches, or pale brown with dark blotches. Middle of the underside delicate pale brown to white. The dorsal, adipose and caudal fins display the same coloration and markings as the body. The remaining fins are translucent, pale or light brownish.

According to Kner the caudal fin is more deeply forked in ♂♂ and its upper lobe may be somewhat produced.

Care, as given for *Pimelodus clarias* (p. 417). Temperature 22–25 °C. Not yet bred in captivity. 1935/–.

367

Centromochlus heckeli *Filippi* 1853 (Fig. 540)
Amazon and northern tributaries of the Paraná; to 11 cm.

D I/5; A 7; P I/6. Body slimmer and more torpedo-shaped than in the previous species. Dorsal and pectoral fins large, flag-like, with long spines which can be locked into position. 3 pairs of barbels. The maxillary barbels when laid back reach to the tips of the pectoral fins. Eyes very large. Coloration plain. The brown-grey to grey-green of the back pales to olive-green on the flanks and gradually changes to a delicate yellowish-white or white tone towards the belly. Fins greenish.

Sex-distinctions in coloration not yet described.

Since it is said by Arnold to be very lively by day it should do well in a well-planted and not too dark aquarium. Temperature 24–28 °C. Omnivorous, especially live food. Not yet bred in captivity. 1934/ –.

Family Plotosidae

Elongate, torpedo-shaped Catfishes whose skin is entirely naked. Mouth broad. Jaws with conical to blunt teeth. 1–2 pairs of maxillary barbels, 2

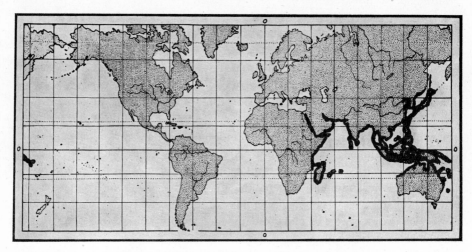

Fig. 530
Distribution of the *Plotosidae*

368

pairs of mandibular barbels. Dorsal fin short with a stout spine, inserted well forwards. Anal and caudal united into a single fin, commencing just behind the vent and extending around the tip of the tail to immediately behind the dorsal. Numerous species on the coasts of East Africa and South and East Asia, also around Japan, the Philippines, the Malay Archipelago and northern Australia. A few species in absolutely fresh water.

Plotosus lineatus (*Thunberg* 1791) (Fig. 541)
A marine fish which, however, penetrates into brackish and fresh waters; coasts of south and east Asia; to 30 cm.

D I/4–5; combined fin 80–100/ ~10/70–80; P I/10–11; V 11–12. Body elongate, torpedo-shaped, compressed. Head large. The second dorsal combines with the caudal and anal to form a uniform fringing fin. 4 pairs of short barbels. Upperside dark brown to blackish, becoming fawn towards the belly which itself is delicate brown to yellowish. Young fishes with 2(–3) striking pale, yellowish to bluish-white, longitudinal stripes. Fins brown, the combined fin often dark-edged.

Sex-distinctions in coloration not known.

Care: this species is best kept in sea- or brackish water and can only be slowly conditioned to fresh water with added sea-salt (1–2 teaspoons to 10 litres of water). Hiding-places should be provided. Temperature 22–26 °C. Live food in large quantities. Not yet bred in captivity. ?/ −.

P. anguillaris (Bloch 1793) is a synonym of this species.

Family Siluridae

Old World Catfishes, with an entirely naked skin. Body elongate, more or less compressed. Head conical or depressed, with a broad mouth. 2(–3) pairs of barbels; 1 pair maxillary (often very long) and 1–2 pairs mandibular. Jaws and palate provided with fine teeth. Dorsal fin short or reduced, not infrequently absent, and lacking a spine. Adipose fin absent. The very long-based anal fin ends shortly before the caudal or may even be united with the latter. Caudal fin rounded or forked. Ventral fins small or absent.

Pectoral fins with a strong spine. Eyes usually covered over by skin. Numerous genera.

For care, see under individual species.

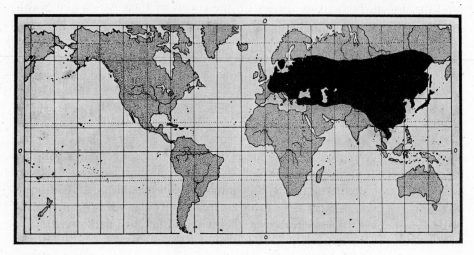

Fig. 531
Distribution of the *Siluridae*

Kryptopterus bicirrhis (*Cuvier* and *Valenciennes* 1839) (Fig. 479)   Glass Catfish
Further India, Greater Sunda Islands; to 10 cm.

D 1; A 53–70; V 1/5–6. Body strongly compressed. Dorsal fin greatly reduced (only 1 fin-ray). The very long-based anal fin is not united with the caudal. The lower lobe of the deeply forked caudal is often somewhat the larger. 1 pair of long maxillary barbels. Colour yellowish, transparent as glass. The upper surface of the head, the back, the pectoral fins and the edges of the anal and caudal fins are delicate blackish. A violet blotch over the base of the pectoral. Exhibiting a rainbow iridescence by reflected light.

Sex-distinctions unknown.

The species of *Kryptopterus* and the similarly shaped *Schilbeidae* (p. 389) are among the few Catfishes which live in mid-water. When resting they often stand obliquely, with the tail bent downwards so that the lower lobe is vertical and the upper continues the body-axis, as shown in Fig. 479.

These lively and diurnal fishes should be kept in spacious aquaria with plants and tangles of roots. The water should not be too deep. Temperature 20–25 °C.

Not sensitive to hard water. Glass Catfish should always be kept in small shoals; solitary individuals languish. They should not be kept in company with very lively species. Live food, Enchytraeids, *Daphnia*, *Tubifex*, midge-larvae, etc. Not yet bred in captivity. 1934/+.

Kryptopterus macrocephalus (*Bleeker* 1858) (Fig. 543)
East Indies; to 11 cm.
D 1–2; A over 50; V 1/5. Body strongly compressed. Dorsal fin greatly reduced (usually only 1 fin-ray). The very long-based anal fin is united with the caudal behind it by a delicate membrane. The upper lobe of the deeply forked caudal is the larger. 1 pair of long maxillary barbels. Distinguished from *K. bicirrhis* by the coloration. Translucent, delicate yellowish to greenish with a bluish lustre by reflected light, especially on the lower half of the flanks. Belly silvery-white. Numerous dark blotches on the upperside. Two parallel brownish, often blackish, longitudinal bands extend from the gill-cover to the root of the tail where they merge with a large dark blotch. A third, usually indistinct, longitudinal band over the anal fin-base. Fins pale. Caudal fin with transverse rows of dark spots. Anal fin with longitudinal rows of dark spots or streaks (partly depending on the pigmentation of the fin-rays).
Sex-distinctions unknown.
Care and further particulars, as given for *K. bicirrhis* above. 1950.

Ompok bimaculatus (*Bloch* 1794) (Fig. 544)
From Ceylon through India, Thailand, Burma to Java and Sumatra; to 45 cm.
D 4; A 57–62; P I/12–14; V 7–8. Body strongly compressed. Dorsal fin small. The very long-based anal fin ends shortly in front of the caudal and is not united with it. Upper lobe of the deeply forked caudal somewhat the larger. 2 pairs of barbels; the maxillary pair are long and, when laid back, reach nearly to the insertion of the ventral fins, while the mandibular pair are inserted well behind the lower lip and are very short. Young fishes are as transparent as glass. Older specimens dark grey-green to brownish with a bluish lustre on the flanks (by reflected light?). Underside paler. Between the dorsal and pectoral fins there is a large, black, pale-bordered blotch from which a row of dark spots or a continuous stripe extends to the root of the tail. Body and anal fin sprinkled with tiny black spots. Often a dark transverse bar across the root of the caudal fin.
Sex-distinctions not described.

371

Care, as given for *Kryptopterus bicirrhis*. Lively and diurnal. This species should always be kept in small shoals; solitary individuals languish. Only young specimens are suitable for domestic aquaria. 1934/—.

Ompok pabda (*Hamilton-Buchanan* 1822) (Fig. 545)
Northern India and Further India; to 140 cm. A food-fish.

D 4–5; A 54–60; P I/11–13; V 8; Body similar to that of the previous species, but somewhat broader anteriorly. Fins likewise similar. The maxillary barbels are somewhat shorter than in *O. bimaculatus* and, when laid back, only reach as far as the middle, or at most to the ends, of the pectoral fins. Coloration of young (according to Arnold): brown to blackish with dark to black marbling on the upper half of the body and black blotches on the lower half. Fins brownish, anal fin-base with dark spots.

Sex-distinctions not yet described.

Only young specimens are suitable for aquaria; they should be treated like *Clarias* spp. (see p. 397). 1935/—.

Silurichthys phaiosoma (*Bleeker* 1851) (Fig. 546)
Malay Peninsula, Sumatra, Borneo; to 12 cm.

D 4; A 53–58; P I/8–9; V 7. Body elongate, strongly compressed. Dorsal fin very small, standing well forward. The caudal fin is unequally lobed (superficially shark-like) and continuous with the very long-based anal. 2 pairs of very long barbels; the maxillary pair, when laid back, reach to the middle of the anal fin. Uniformly brown. Fins brown, with fine black dots; tips of caudal, anal and pectorals often black. Barbels ringed with brown.

Sex-distinctions in coloration not known.

Care, as given for *Kryptopterus bicirrhis*, with which *S. phaiosoma* may well be kept. Not yet bred in captivity. 1938/+.

Plate 93

Fig. 532. *Synodontis nummifer;* half-grown, natural size. (Original)
Fig. 533. *Synodontis* sp.; natural size. (Photo Dr. Foersch)
Fig. 534. *Synodontis angelicus;* young, about twice natural size. (Photo Dr. Foersch)

Plate 93

Plate 94

Silurodes hypophthalmus (*Bleeker* 1847) (Fig. 547)
Greater Sunda Islands, Thailand; to 35 cm.

D 3–4; A 76–82; P I/12–14; V 7–8. Body elongate, compressed. Dorsal fin very short, flag-like. Adipose fin absent. Lower lobe of caudal somewhat the longer and often angular. Anal fin-base very long. Mouth narrow. 1 pair of very long maxillary barbels which, when laid back, reach to the middle of the anal fin. 1 pair of short mandibular barbels. Delicate olive-green to yellowish, the back dark brown, the underside brownish to white. The flanks have a light bluish sheen by reflected light. A dark blotch behind the gill-cover, from which a fine longitudinal band may occasionally extend as far as a black, sharp-edged spot at the root of the tail.

Sex-distinctions not so far described.

Care, as given for *Kryptopterus bicirrhis* above. Temperature 22–25°C. Only young specimens are suitable for domestic aquaria. Not yet bred in captivity. 1936/–.

Silurus glanis *Linnaeus* 1758 (Fig. 457)   European Catfish, Wels, Waller
Central and Eastern Europe, Western Asia; has also been successfully introduced into some private waters in Southern England during the last century. In rivers and lakes, also in the mildly brackish estuaries of the Baltic; common in the Caspian Sea; to 3 m., usually only to about 1 m.

D 1/4; A 90–92; P I/14–17; V 11–13. Body elongate, cylindrical anteriorly, compressed posteriorly. Head large and depressed. Gape very wide. 3 pairs of barbels; the maxillary pair are especially long and, when laid back, reach to beyond the pectorals. The dorsal fin is very small and inserted well forward. Adipose fin absent. Anal fin-base very long. Coloration extremely variable; usually fairly dark, the upperside dark olive-green to blue-black and the flanks paler, occasionally with a red-brownish sheen. Underside, especially the belly, pale. Upon this ground-colour are imposed cloudy or spotty marblings. Entirely black-blue and quite pale individuals also occur. Fins dark, red-brownish to brown-violet.

S. glanis is the only Catfish which is truly native to Europe. These predatory and very voracious animals are entirely nocturnal in habit and spend the day resting well hidden in holes under banks, under tree-stumps and in other hiding-places. The young Catfishes eat a variety of small animals; the larger ones subsist mainly on fish, also on waterfowl and, exceptionally, perhaps, on small swimming mammals. At its maximum length of 3 m. the Catfish is one of the largest European freshwater fishes and on this account, especially in the Danube area, a legendary beast. At the breeding season (May to June) the fishes frequent shallow, weedy banks. The eggs are laid upon leaves and are said to be guarded by the ♂ (100,000 at a spawning). The entirely black, tadpole-like young grow very rapidly to sexual maturity.

Small Catfishes do very well in the unheated aquarium. They are hardy, not choosy over their food and grow very well in captivity. Large specimens are worthwhile exhibition subjects but by no means as hardy as the young ones. At all events, solitary confinement is necessary for these. Special attention must be paid to cleanliness in the aquarium. Fish provide the best food.

Family Bagridae

Naked Catfishes, of thick-set to elongate form, distributed through Africa, Asia Minor, southern and eastern Asia, Japan and the Malay Archipelago. The mouth is usually somewhat ventral, transverse or half-moon-shaped. The jaws are always toothed, and sometimes the palate also. 3 to 4 pairs of barbels (1 pair rostral; 1 pair maxillary, occasionally very long; 1 pair mandibular and 1 pair mental (on the chin)). Dorsal fin with a stout spine, inserted

Figs. 538–541

Fig. 538. *Trachycorystes striatulus;* adult, reduced.
Fig. 539. *Centromochlus aulopygius;* half-grown, natural size.
Fig. 540. *Centromochlus heckeli;* adult, reduced.
Fig. 541. *Plotosus lineatus;* adult, much reduced. Below, a sketch of the peculiar protruding arborescent structure between the vent and the anal fin.

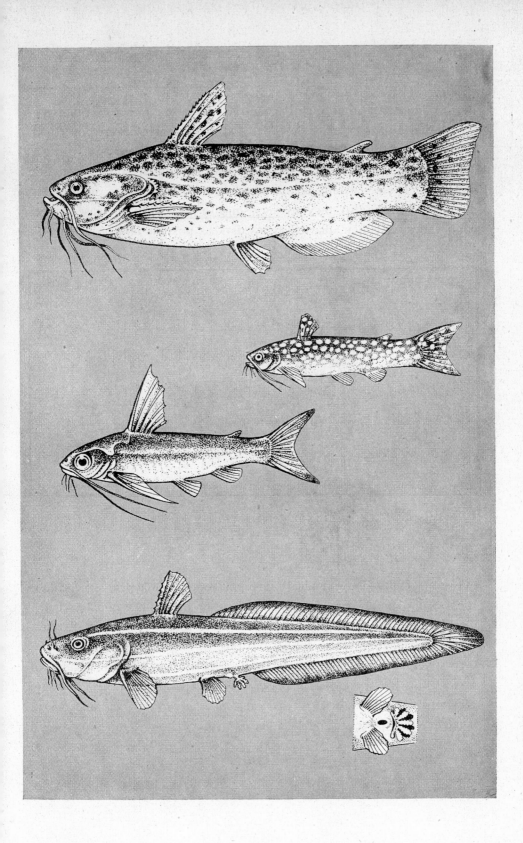

over or somewhat anterior to the ventrals. Adipose fin present, often very large. Anal fin-base usually short. Eyes in many genera covered over with skin. Numerous genera; some species grow to a very large size.

Only small species, or young specimens, are suitable for the domestic aquarium. These generally nocturnal fishes are in some cases very timid in aquaria; in some, also, they are very sluggish as well. In any case it is recommended that their quarters be as dark as possible and provided with

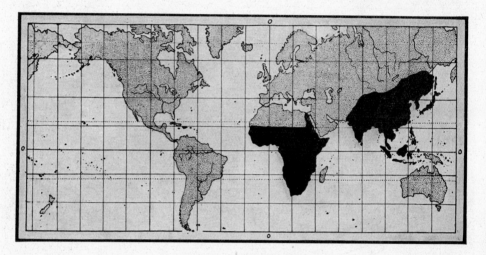

Fig. 542
Distribution of the *Bagridae*

numerous hiding-places under tangles of roots, flower-pots or coconut-shells. Some species rest in an inverted position in their hiding-places, belly-up. Feeding these voracious fishes is easy; give them live food of all kinds. Larger specimens will also eat earthworms, slugs, maggots, etc., meat and even softened rolled oats. Temperature 20–26° C., according to locality of origin. Not one species has yet been bred in captivity. Some *Bagridae* are very predatory. The species of *Auchenoglanis*, *Parauchenoglanis* and *Bagrus* make fine showpieces for public aquaria.

Auchenoglanis occidentalis (*Cuvier* and *Valenciennes* 1840) (Fig. 494)
Widely distributed through Africa, lower Nile, Senegal, Congo, Lake Chad, etc.; to 50 cm.

D I/7; A 4–5/6–7; P I/8–9; V 1/5. Body moderately thick-set, entirely naked. Snout pointed. Dorsal and pectoral fins with stout spines which can be locked into position. Adipose fin large. 3 pairs of barbels, of which the external mandibular pair are the longest and, when laid back, reach to the edge of the gill-cover. Coloration very variable: uniform dark brown to pale brown or with a lattice of pale lines delineating a honeycomb-like pattern. Underside yellowish to white. Fins brown to delicate violet, likewise with a honeycomb pattern of pale lines. Fig. 494 shows a particularly fine specimen of this species in the Hellabrunn Aquarium.

Sex-distinctions are not known.

Only young specimens are suitable for domestic aquaria. A sandy bottom, suitable hiding-places and a dim top-light suit them best. Voracious predators which must be kept in isolation. Live food of all kinds. Temperature 24–28 °C. See also family description. 1909/+.

Bagrus docmac (*Forskål* 1775) (Fig. 567)
Nile basin, Lake Victoria, Lake Stefani, widely distributed; to 60 cm.

D I/8–10; A 12–14, 8–9 branched. The *Bagrus* spp. are distinguished from the often very similar *Chrysichthys* spp. by the very large adipose fin and the number of soft rays in the dorsal. Body elongate. Head strongly depressed. Mouth broad. 4 pairs of barbels (1 pair rostral; 1 pair maxillary, very long; 2 pairs mandibular). Upper lobe of caudal produced to a point. Dark smoke-grey to olive-brown, underside pale, occasionally shining gold. Fins yellowish to dark, occasionally with brown spots (especially on the adipose fin).

Sex-distinctions unknown.

Care, as given in the family description. 1936/–.

Chrysichthys brevibarbis (*Boulenger* 1899) (Fig. 521)
Congo (Stanley Pool, etc.); to 44 cm.

D I/6; A 12, 9 branched. Distinguished from other *Chrysichthys* spp. (see following sp.) by the very elongate shape, the somewhat asymmetrical caudal fin (upper lobe slightly sickle-shaped), the position of the dorsal fin, and the very large eyes in the young. Uniform dark brown.

Sex-distinctions unknown.

Care, as given in family description. The young are very active but somewhat unsteady and clumsy swimmers. 1955.

Chrysichthys ornatus *Boulenger* 1902 (Fig. 520)

Middle and Upper Congo, Ubangi; to 19 cm.

D I/6; A 11–13, 6–8 branched. The African genus *Chrysichthys* is distinguished from other Catfishes by the following characters:–body elongate, anteriorly hardly compressed, posteriorly strongly so. Dorsal and anal fins short. Dorsal and pectoral fins with stout spines. Ventral fins inserted behind the dorsal. Adipose fin present. 4 pairs of barbels (1 pair rostral, 1 maxillary, 2 mandibular). Jaws with teeth arranged in bands. Palate toothed. *C. ornatus* is easily distinguished from the other species by its colouring: an alternation of large, irregular, dark brown to black blotches and pale, yellowish to brownish blotches, with further small dark spots among them. Belly dirty white. Fins pale with irregular dark spots; each lobe of the caudal with a blurred dark longitudinal band. This coloration is reminiscent of *Microglanis parahyba*.

Sex-distinctions not known.

This species is lively and timid, especially when young, and should be kept in a darkened tank like most other *Bagridae*. No information on special peculiarities available. 1955.

Gephyroglanis longipinnis (*Boulenger* 1899) (Fig. 522)

Congo, Stanley Pool; to 14 cm.

D I/6; A 13–14, 8–9 branched. The genus *Gephyroglanis* is distinguished from *Chrysichthys* by little more than the toothless palate. In life the members of the two genera are so similar that it is hardly possible to tell them apart. *G. longipinnis* is especially characterised by the long maxillary barbels and the large eyes. Upperside dark brown, underside paler, usually clay-brown to whitish. A vague-edged dark blotch behind the gill-cover. Fins dark, tips and edges black.

Sex-distinctions unknown.

Care, as given in the family description. Worm-foods, such as *Tubifex* and Enchytraeids. 1955.

Figs. 543–547

Fig. 543. *Kryptopterus macrocephalus;* adult, natural size.
Fig. 544. *Ompok bimaculatus;* young, natural size.
Fig. 545. *Ompok pabda;* half-grown, reduced.
Fig. 546. *Silurichthys phaiosoma;* somewhat reduced.
Fig. 547. *Silurodes hypophthalmus;* half-grown, reduced.

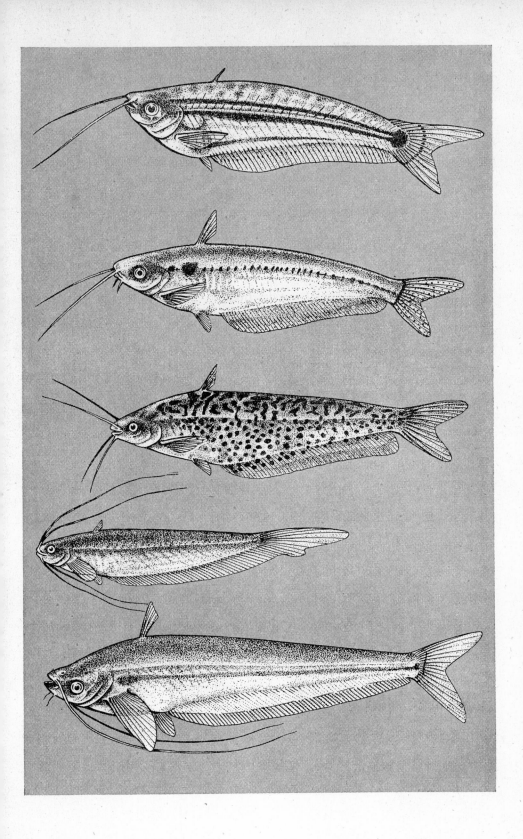

Leiocassis siamensis *Regan* 1913 (Fig. 570)
Thailand; to 17 cm. (?)

D I/7; A 16–17; P I/7. Body naked, torpedo-shaped, slightly compressed. Dorsal and pectoral fins with slender spines. Caudal fin forked. 4 pairs of relatively short barbels, the longest (maxillary barbels) when laid back reaching about to the middle of the pectoral fins. Dark coffee-brown, blue-black or grey-blue. Belly pale to yellowish. 4 irregular, pale yellow to grey-yellow or whitish, transverse bars on the flanks. Fins colourless to delicate yellowish with extensive brown blotches. The deep black of the caudal fin-base passes abruptly into the glass-clear fin proper. A brown transverse bar in each lobe. Pectoral and ventral fins almost entirely brown.

Sex-distinctions in coloration not described.

Care similar to that recommended for the *Pygidiidae* (p. 424). Temperature 22–25 °C. Live food of all kinds. 1953.

Leiocassis poecilopterus (*Cuvier* and *Valenciennes* 1839) (Fig. 496)
Java, Sumatra, Thailand, in streams; to 18 cm.

D I/7; A 15–16; P I/7–8. Shape similar to that of the previous species, from which, however, it differs markedly in coloration and markings. Especially characteristic of *L. poecilopterus* is a whitish or pale yellow blotch immediately in front of the dorsal and a similar blotch in front of the adipose fin; in full-grown individuals these blotches and the pale bars on the body are said to be brownish. Bars and fin-markings very variable. Otherwise similar to the previous species. 1955.

Mystus tengera (*Hamilton-Buchanan* 1822) (Figs. 464, 568)
North India, in flowing and standing waters; to 18 cm.

D I/7; A 2–3/9–10; V 1/5. Body elongate, somewhat compressed. Head drawn out to a rounded point. All fins rather small. Caudal fin forked. 4 pairs of barbels. The rostral (1 pair) and mandibular barbels (2 pairs) are about equal in length and, when laid back, reach to the hinder edge of the gill-cover. The maxillary barbels

Plate 95

Fig. 548. *Synodontis nigriventris* (Upside-down Catfish); natural size. (Original)
Fig. 549. *Otocinclus maculipinnis* (?); adult, enlarged. (Photo Dr. Foersch)
Fig. 550. *Pimelodella gracilis* (?); specimen 14 cm. long, in the Hellabrunn Aquarium, Munich. (Original)

Plate 95

Plate 96

Plate 96

Fig. 551. *Corydoras paleatus* (Peppered Corydoras); adults, natural size. (Original)
Fig. 552. *Corydoras melanistius* (Black-spotted Corydoras); adults, natural size. (Original)
Fig. 553. *Corydoras schultzei;* young, sexually-ripe specimens, natural size. (Original)

(1 pair) are substantially longer. Delicate greenish or bright yellow. Back only slightly darker, usually pale brown. Underside porcelain-white. On the flanks 4–5 wavy dark brown to green-black longitudinal bands which taper remarkably posteriorly and eventually disappear entirely. A dark blotch over the pectoral, not always distinct. Fins delicate bluish, transparent.

Sex-distinctions in coloration not so far described.

Care, as given in the family description. The young are quite peaceful. Not yet bred in captivity. 1903/+.

Mystus vittatus (*Bloch* 1794) (Fig. 569)
India, Burma, Thailand, in standing and flowing waters; to 21 cm.

D I/7; A 2–3/7–9; V 1/5. Body and finnage very similar to that of the previous species, from which it differs in the unequal caudal lobes, the longer maxillary barbels (which, when laid back, reach beyond the ventral fins) and the colouring. Coloration very variable; delicate grey-silver to shining golden. On this ground appear several lovely pale blue or dark brown to deep black longitudinal bands. The number of these longitudinal bands differs from one locality to another and also varies according to the state of health. There does constantly appear, either a single broad longitudinal band or two parallel more slender bands along the middle of the side, which originate in a dark blotch over the pectoral and run to the root of the tail. Underside shining white. Fins glassy, often with dark tips.

Sex-distinctions not known.

Other particulars as given for the previous species. 1903/−.

Parauchenoglanis macrostoma (*Pellegrin* 1909) (Fig. 465)
Tropical West Africa, R. Ogowe and Congo; to 24 cm.

D I/7; A 12, 9 branched. The genus *Parauchenoglanis* is very closely related to *Auchenoglanis*. Body elongate, compressed, of fairly uniform depth. Caudal fin not forked. 3 pairs of long barbels. Beautifully coloured: upperside brownish, flanks yellow-brown, underside yellowish. Especially striking are 5 transverse stripes, composed of large, dark blotches which may more or less run together. A few rows

381

of prominent spots between the bolder rows of blotches. Fins yellowish to reddish-brown. Dorsal and caudal fins with rows of dark spots.

Sex-distinctions not known.

Care, as given in the family description. 1934/+.

Family Ameiuridae

The headquarters of these Catfishes are mainly in North and Middle America. The *Ameiuridae* are more or less tadpole-shaped, with a large, broad head and a strongly compressed tail-region. Body naked. Mouth large. 4

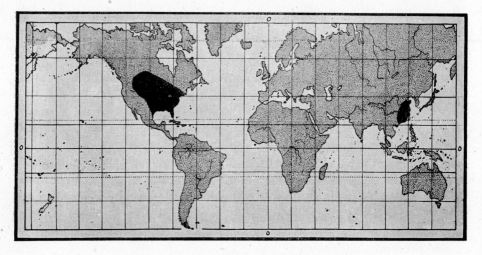

Fig. 554

Natural distribution of the *Ameiuridae;* note North America and East Asia. Some species have been introduced into Europe and have become widespread.

pairs of moderately long to long barbels. Dorsal fin short and high, with a powerful erectile spine. Anal fin long-based. Caudal fin often rounded. Adipose fin present. Lateral line conspicuous, in some species incomplete. Most of the species are quite large and are therefore only suitable for domestic

382

aquaria when young; larger ones make interesting exhibits for public aquaria. The North American species *Ameiurus melas* was introduced into European waters at the turn of the century and, being well suited, has spread very quickly.

Small *Ameiuridae* are very interesting aquarium-dwellers which make scarcely any special demands. For these large tanks are suitable, with a soft, sandy, but also here and there gravelly, bottom. Planting is not absolutely essential if there is moderate aeration and the possibility of hiding among roots and stones. Room temperature; most species tolerate considerable cooling. All the species are predators which, in their natural habitats, feed mostly on small animals; occasionally, however, also on fish-spawn and young fishes. In captivity these fishes accept only living food, such as earthworms, slugs, large insect-larvae, etc. Exceptionally they will accept bits of meat, particularly horseflesh, and, very seldom, rolled oats.

Breeding in aquaria has apparently not yet been achieved, but out-of-doors most species spawn in shallow depressions. The very numerous tadpole-like young are led by the parents. Smaller specimens may be kept quite well in the company of other fishes from temperate climates.

Ameiurus melas (*Rafinesque* 1820)   Black Bullhead
Northern New York to Kansas and Texas, including the Great Lakes region, in slow-flowing and standing waters. Introduced into Europe; to 42 cm., usually only to 30 cm.

D I/6; A (16–)17–21(–22); P I/8; V 8. Hind edge of pectoral spine not toothed. Caudal fin slightly emarginate. Coloration variable: upperside greenish, yellowish, brownish or slaty-olive, sides lighter, underside bright yellow, yellow or milk-white. Fins normally conspicuously darker than the adjacent parts of the body. Anal base pale, distal two-thirds between the rays black; in young fishes less than 10 cm. in length the entire fin may be black.

Even in their native North America the Bullheads have been confused. Specimens introduced into European aquaria and waters have been called *A. nebulosus*, but all those examined in the British Museum have proved to be *A. melas*. The two species hybridise in forced association (where shallow water precludes segregation with depth) and the possibility of wild hybrids must be taken into account.

383

Care and breeding, as given in the family description. According to Hubbs and Lagler the ♀ guards and convoys the young. Highly tolerant of turbid and polluted waters.

Ameiurus natalis (*Le Sueur* 1819) (Fig. 577)   Yellow Bullhead
Great Lakes region and Mississippi Basin; to 35 cm.

D I/7; A 1/(23–)25–26(–28); P I/8; V 8. Hind edge of pectoral spine toothed, serrations becoming blunter with age. Caudal fin rounded. Coloration very variable: clay-yellow to grey-green, usually with vague dark blotches, especially on the back; underside pale. Anal fin with a broad, vague dark band parallel to the margin along the central parts of the rays.

Care and breeding, as given in the family description. Avoids turbid waters. 1895/−.

Ameiurus nebulosus nebulosus (*Le Sueur* 1819) (Fig. 578)   Brown Bullhead
Eastern States of U.S.A., Great Lakes region; to 40 cm.

D I/6; A 1/(21–)22–23(–24); P I/8; V 8. Hind edge of pectoral spine toothed, serrations becoming blunter with age. Caudal fin very slightly emarginate. Adipose fin short, inserted above the hinder end of the anal. Lateral line complete. Dark brown, with a green, violet or bronze lustre by reflected light, often with cloudy blotches. Belly whitish to grey. Iris yellow. Anal fin variously marked, usually mottled or darkest on the basal third or half of fin, but never as in *A. melas*.

Sex-distinctions in coloration not yet described.

A. nebulosus usually occupies deeper waters than the two previous species and prefers the clearer parts of lakes; introductions into rivers have not been success-

Plate 97

Fig. 555. *Brochis coeruleus;* adult male, natural size. (Original)
Fig. 556. *Corydoras pestai;* full-grown, natural size. ♀ above, ♂ below. (Original)
Fig. 557. *Corydoras julii* (Leopard Corydoras); adults, natural size. ♀ left, ♂ right. (Original)

Plate 98 (overleaf)

Fig. 558. *Corydoras reticulatus;* adults, very slightly reduced, ♀ left, ♂ right. (Photo Gfeller and Stettler)
Fig. 559. *Corydoras reticulatus;* young, somewhat enlarged. (Original)
Fig. 560. *Corydoras agassizi;* full-grown, natural size. (Original)

Plate 97

Plate 98 (see page 384)

Plate 99 (see page 385)

Plate 100

Plate 99 (overleaf)

Fig. 561. *Corydoras arcuatus;* ripe adults, natural size; left, ♂, right ♀. (Original)
Fig. 562. *Corydoras myersi;* ripe adults, natural size; left, ♂, right ♀. (Original)
Fig. 563. *Farlowella* sp.; half-grown, natural size. (Photo P. Unger)

Plate 100

Fig. 564. *Otocinclus maculicauda* (?); half-grown, enlarged. (Original)
Fig. 565. *Otocinclus flexilis;* 5 cm. long. (Original)
Fig. 566. *Otocinclus affinis;* adults, enlarged; left, ♂, right ♀. (Original)

ful. It may hybridise with *A. melas*, as noted above. There exists much confusion between the two species, and the remarks which follow must therefore be accepted as of rather uncertain application. Apart from the differing anal counts the most reliable distinguishing character is the pectoral spine, which is strongly serrated on the hinder edge in *A. nebulosus*, smooth or only slightly roughened in *A. melas*.

This Catfish has been a great favourite in aquaria since the end of the last century. It has greatly multiplied in breeding tanks and has been planted out in European waters where it has become almost endemic. Scientific researches have shown that it can definitely appreciate sounds; it responds to loud whistling, bells, flute notes, etc.

Care, as given on p. 383.

A definitely crepuscular fish which sets forth in search of food in the evening. The breeding season in Europe, as in North America, is from March to May. A shallow depression is made by the ♂ and ♀ in some shallow place warmed by the spring sun, or under an overhanging bank. The eggs are laid in balls and adhere firmly to the bottom. The black young hatch after about 8 days and are cared for by the ♀. Economically valueless to us. Flesh orange-coloured.

Ameiurus nebulosus marmoratus (*Holbrook* 1855) (Figs. 507, 579) Marbled Bullhead U.S.A., replacing *A. n. nebulosus* further south from Indiana and Carolina to Florida; to 45 cm.

Olive-green, back brown-green, underside yellowish to white. Numerous irregular brown, greenish or whitish blotches on the head, back and flanks make a marbled pattern upon the ground-colour. Fins greenish, in part with dark blotches.

Care and breeding, as given in the family description. 1890/+.

385

Ictalurus punctatus (*Rafinesque* 1818) (Fig. 580)   Spotted Cat, Channel Catfish
South and south-western U.S.A., in lakes and slow-flowing waters (Food-fish); to 110 cm., usually only to 70 cm.

D I/6; A 1/25–30; P I/9; V 8. The genus *Ictalurus* is distinguished from *Ameiurus* by the deeply forked caudal fin. Mouth not quite so wide as in other *Ameiuridae*. Jaws equal. Coloration variable: pale brown to grey-green, back darker, underside yellowish to clear white with a silver gleam. Sparsely sprinkled dark spots on the flanks. Fins colourless, occasionally with dark edges.

Care and breeding, as given in the family description. The adults migrate to smaller streams for spawning. 1888/ – .

Schilbeodes gyrinus (*Mitchill* 1818) (Fig. 581)   Tadpole Madtom
North-eastern States of U.S.A., widely distributed; to 18 cm.

D I/7; A 1/14–15. Adipose fin long and low. Pectoral spine not toothed, but with a groove posteriorly with which a venom-gland is associated. Ground-colour clay-yellow to grey-olive, occasionally very dark. Back usually olive-green. Underside lemon-yellow to delicate pale yellow. A narrow, dark longitudinal band along the flanks, from the hinder edge of the gill-cover to the root of the tail, occasionally with a further 1–2 lines above.

Care and breeding, as given in the family description. 1895/ – .

Family Chacidae

This small family contains only the following species: –

Chaca chaca (*Hamilton-Buchanan* 1822) (Fig. 582)
India, Burma, Sumatra, Borneo, Banka; to 20 cm.

D I/3–4; A 7–10; P I/4–5; V 6. Body tadpole-like, anteriorly broad and strongly depressed, posteriorly strongly compressed, without lateral scutes but covered

Figs. 567–570
Fig. 567. *Bagrus docmac;* adult, much reduced.
Fig. 568. *Mystus tengera;* adult, somewhat reduced.
Fig. 569. *Mystus vittatus;* adult, reduced.
Fig. 570. *Leiocassis siamensis;* adult, reduced.

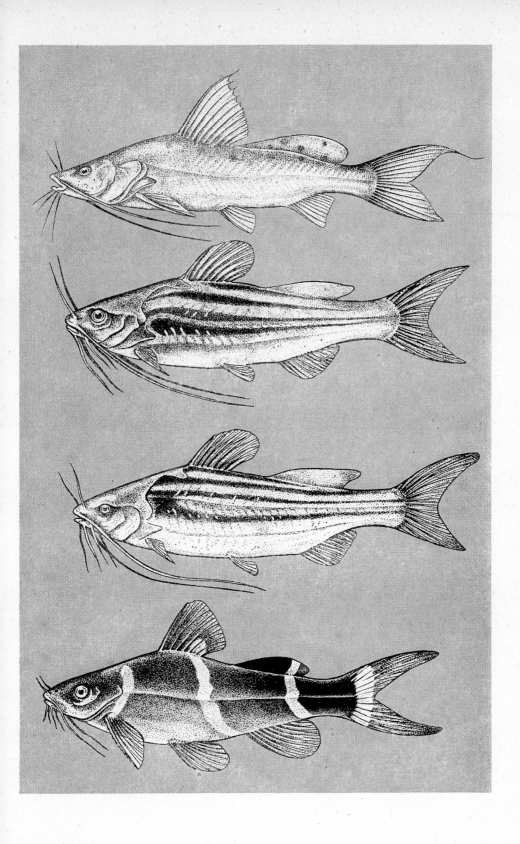

with a thick, horny skin. Mouth very broad. Dorsal fin small. The rounded caudal
fin extends far forwards on both dorsal and ventral surfaces. 1 pair of very short,
often merely peg-like, barbels at the corners of the mouth. Older specimens have
small, arborescent appendages on the head. Coloration, according to Meinken:
black-brown with numerous black and pale spots and blotches, the head somewhat

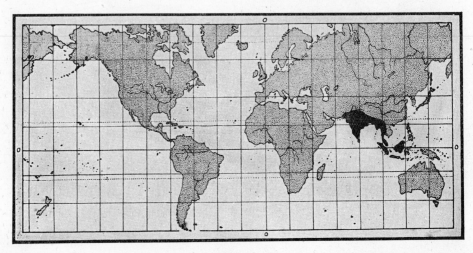

Fig. 571
Distribution of the *Chacidae*

paler and the belly white with closely-approximated dark blotches. Fins dark
brown with black blotches and whitish to fawn edges.

Reliable sex-distinctions have not yet been described.

Care, as given for *Pimelodus clarias* (see p. 417). A very sluggish nocturnal fish
which, even when touched, does not abandon its cryptic behaviour and so often
passes for a piece of moving wood. Omnivorous. According to Meinken the great
mouth appears to serve as a weir-basket-like trap. Temperature 22–24 °C. 1938/ –.

Plate 101

Fig. 572. Above, left and right: young stages of a *Loricaria* sp., twice natural size. (Photo
Dr. Foersch)

Fig. 573. *Loricaria* sp. – ♂ resting on the spawn; the embryos may be seen through the
egg-membranes. (Photo Dr. Foersch)

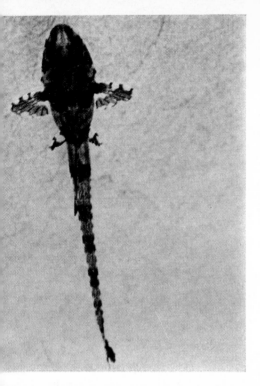

Plate 101

Plate 102

Plate 102

Fig. 574. *Aphyosemion sjoestedti* (Golden Pheasant, Red Aphyosemion); young ♂, enlarged. (Photo Dr. Foersch)

Fig. 575. *Micropanchax myersi;* about twice natural size. This figure has been retouched. (Photo Dr. Foersch)

Family Schilbeidae

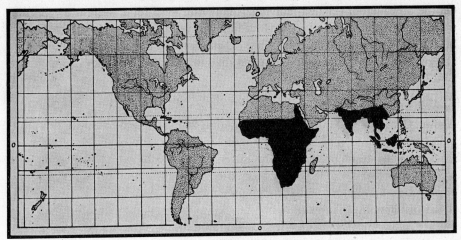

Fig. 576
Distribution of the *Schilbeidae*

Catfishes of Asia and Africa which, to some extent, show a considerable resemblance to many *Siluridae*. Body elongate and as a rule compressed. Head tapering, conical or slightly depressed. 2 to 4 pairs of barbels. Jaws and palatine bones toothed. Dorsal fin short with a stout spine. Adipose fin present or absent. Anal fin very long-based. Caudal fin usually forked. Pectoral fins with stout spines. Numerous genera.

For care, see under individual species.

Etropiella debauwi (*Boulenger* 1901) (Fig. 508)
Congo (Stanley Pool, among other localities); to 8 cm.

D I/5; A 3–4/35–43. Body elongate, caudal peduncle strongly depressed. Head rounded anteriorly. 3 pairs of short barbels. The small dorsal fin is inserted very

389

far forward. Adipose fin present. Caudal fin forked. Anal fin long-based. Very translucent, with a silvery-white throat and belly. 3 sharp-edged steel- to black-blue longitudinal stripes on the flanks become increasingly prominent with age.

The ♀♀ show paler stripes and become distinctly more robust.

E. debauwi is an extremely lively shoaling-fish. Like the Indian Glass Catfish it swims somewhat obliquely, fanning continuously with its tail and with the caudal fin suspended in the water. In contrast to the Indian Glass Catfish, however, *E. debauwi* is constantly on the move, restlessly exploring every corner of the aquarium. On the other hand, isolated individuals languish. Live food, such as small crustacea, Enchytraeids, *Tubifex*, etc. Breeding not yet achieved in captivity. Not to be kept with appreciably larger fishes. When captured they erect their dorsal fins and remain lightly suspended in the net, like many other Catfishes. Temperature 24–27°C. 1954.

Eutropius grenfelli (*Boulenger* 1900)
Ogowe, Chari, Congo (among other localities, Stanley Pool); to 28 cm.

D I/6; A 4/48–49. This species is only a little different from the next and when alive is hardly distinguishable. Grey-silver, upperside brownish, underside pale grey. A large dark blotch with a blurred edge over the pectoral fin. The young display a dark longitudinal band along the flanks.

Sex-distinctions unknown.

Care, as for *Schilbe mystus* (see p. 394). 1956.

Eutropius niloticus (*Rüppel* 1829) (Fig. 583)
Widely distributed: Nile, Senegal, Ogowe and tributaries; to 40 cm.

D I/5–6; A 3–4/50–65. Body strongly compressed. Dorsal fin short, inserted somewhat anterior to the ventrals. Anal fin long-based. Adipose fin present. 4 pairs of relatively short barbels (1 pair rostral, 1 pair maxillary, 2 pairs mandibular). Back dark olive to blackish. Flanks delicate fawn to faded salmon-pink with an attractive bronze or silver gleam. Belly pale pink or whitish. A large dark blotch

Figs. 577–580

Fig. 577. *Ameiurus natalis* (Yellow Bullhead); adult, much reduced.
Fig. 578. *Ameiurus nebulosus nebulosus* (Brown Bullhead); adult, much reduced.
Fig. 579. *Ameiurus nebulosus marmoratus* (Marbled Bullhead); adult, greatly reduced.
Fig. 580. *Ictalurus punctatus* (Spotted Cat, Channel Catfish); adult, much reduced.

The barbels are often shown as wavy in these drawings, but in life they are carried stiffly and splayed out.

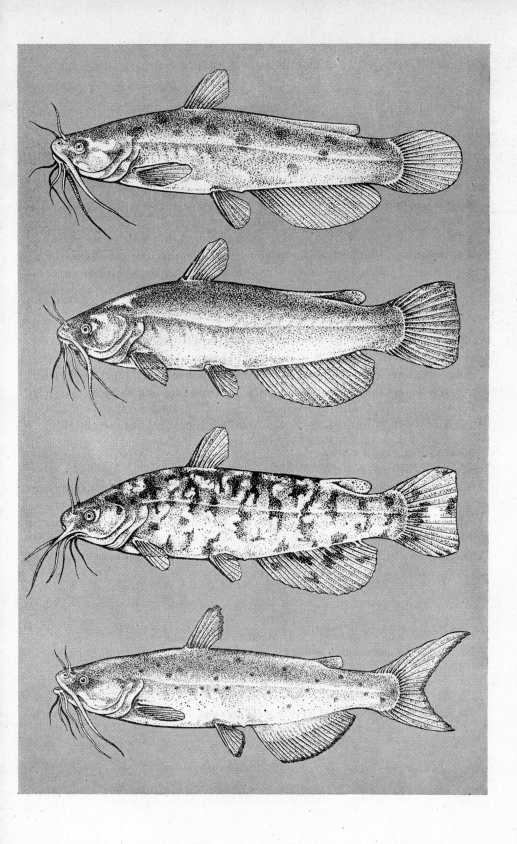

with a shining light green edge over the pectoral fin. Fins dark to clay-coloured. Dorsal fin with a dark base, caudal lobes with dark tips. The young are translucent.

Sex-distinctions not known.

Care, as given for *Schilbe mystus* (see p. 394). Not yet bred in captivity. 1901/−.

Parailia longifilis *Boulenger* 1902 (Fig. 466)
Congo (Stanley Pool among other localities); to 10 cm.

D −; A 80–90. This species is reminiscent of the better-known one following, from which it is clearly distinguishable by the coloration and the absence of an adipose fin. Transparent pale to yellowish with numerous somewhat regularly disposed pigment spots. The fins, likewise, have numerous dark but appreciably smaller spots. Upper caudal lobe with a narrow, dark, longitudinal stripe.

Sex-distinctions unknown.

Parailia is a crepuscular fish which during the daytime adopts a very peculiar attitude. In strong light, or in the absence of hiding-places under roots or among stones, the fishes lie on the bottom and appear as though dead. In the evening,when it begins to get dark, they abandon this rigid posture and swim as shown in Fig. 466. Live food, such as crustacea (*Daphnia, Cyclops*), Enchytraeids, midge-larvae, etc. Temperature 25–28 °C.; sensitive. Best kept in a darkened tank. 1955.

Physailia pellucida *Boulenger* 1901 (Fig. 584)   African Glass Catfish
Upper Nile; to 10 cm.

A 65–74; V 1/5. Body strongly compressed. Dorsal fin absent. Adipose fin present. Anal fin long-based. 4 pairs of barbels of approximately equal length. Almost entirely colourless, transparent as glass. The vertebral column, swim-bladder and other organs may be clearly distinguished. Some black pigment-spots along the middle of the back and in the anal fin region. All fins colourless. The whole body shows a weak bluish iridescence by reflected light.

Figs. 581–585

Fig. 581. *Schilbeodes gyrinus* (Tadpole Madtom); adult, reduced.
Fig. 582. *Chaca chaca;* adult, reduced.
Fig. 583. *Eutropius niloticus;* half-grown, reduced.
Fig. 584. *Physailia pellucida* (African Glass Catfish); natural size.
Fig. 585. *Schilbe mystus;* adult, much reduced.

The barbels are often shown as wavy in these drawings, but in life they are carried stiffly and splayed out.

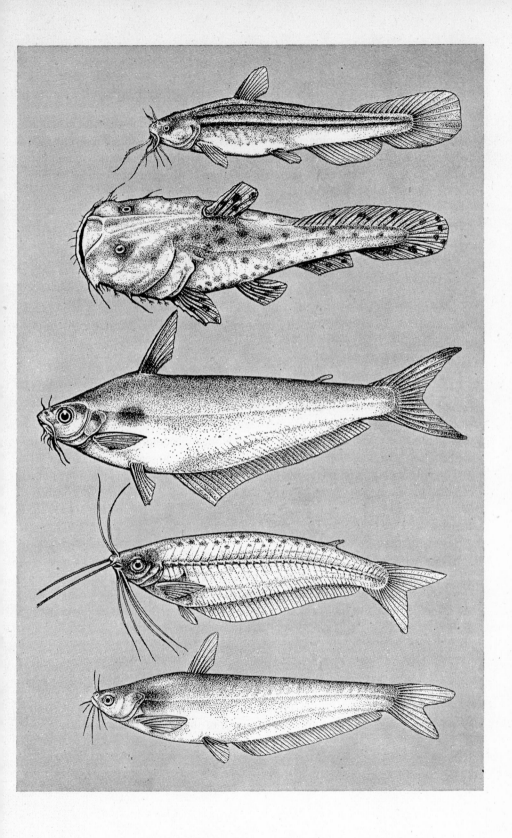

Sex-distinctions unknown.

This very active and interesting species rests and swims somewhat obliquely, as though the tail were drooping in the water. A very peaceful shoaling-fish, which does not prosper very well in isolation. Large, thickly-planted aquaria, standing in a rather shady position. Temperature not less than 25°C. Live food only, especially Enchytraeids, *Tubifex*, midge-larvae. Breeding unknown. 1927/+.

Schilbe marmoratus *Boulenger* 1911 (Figs. 469, 518)
Congo and tributaries; to 16 cm.

D I/5; A 52–54. Similarly shaped to the following species, from which it is distinguished by its coloration and by the anal fin which reaches to the caudal. Clay-coloured or pale grey, sprinkled with brown. A large round blotch over the pectoral fin, occasionally some broader, cloudier blotches along the middle of the side as well. Fins brownish, partly dark-tipped. Base of caudal dark, the outer parts yellowish.

Sex-distinctions unknown.

Care, as given for the following species. 1956.

Schilbe mystus (*Linnaeus* 1762) (Figs. 509, 585)
Nile Basin; to 35 cm.

D I/6; A 3–4/55–56; P I/11; V 6. Body elongate, compressed. Characteristic of the whole genus *Schilbe* are the low dorsal fin, the absence of an adipose fin (the only difference from the genus *Eutropius*), the deeply-forked caudal, the long-based anal fin which extends nearly to the caudal, and the 4 pairs of short barbels. Almost uniformly silver with a darker upperside. A large black blotch astride the lateral line behind the gill-cover. Fins opaque grey.

Sex-distinctions not described.

A very active and gregarious species whose main needs are sufficient swimming-space, a dark bottom-soil and the provision of possible hiding-places among branches and roots. Temperature 22–26°C. Freshly-imported specimens, and those kept in too much light, are often very timid and lie motionless on the bottom. 1934/+.

Pangasius micronemus *Bleeker* 1847 (Fig. 593)
Greater Sunda Islands, Malay Peninsula, Thailand; to 55 cm.

D II/7; A 28–34; P I/11–14; V 6. Body elongate, compressed. Dorsal fin short, inserted well forward. Adipose fin very small. Mouth narrow. 1 pair of short maxillary barbels (shorter than half the length of the head); 1 pair of still shorter

394

mandibular barbels. Yellowish to delicate yellowish-brown, upperside cinnamon-brown to dark brown, underside silvery. Fins yellowish. Dorsal fin, caudal, and occasionally the pectorals, blackish. The young are translucent.

Sex-distinctions not yet described.

Care, as given for *Kryptopterus bicirrhis* (see p. 370). Not yet bred in captivity. Only young specimens suitable for domestic aquaria. 1934/—.

Family Clariidae

Elongate, sometimes eel-shaped, Catfishes with a broad, flat head and transverse mouth. 4 pairs of often very long barbels (2 nasal, 2 maxillary, 4 mandibular). Teeth small, arranged in bands on the jaws and vomer. Swim-bladder

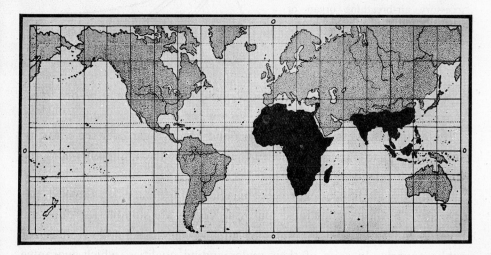

Fig. 586
Distribution of the *Clariidae*

very small. Skin quite naked. Especially characteristic of the whole family are the accessory air-breathing organs. These may be developed either as paired tubular blind sacs which extend backwards from the gill-chamber on

395

either side of the vertebral column, or as cauliflower-like processes projecting into an extension of the gill-chamber.

These accessory air-breathing organs not only enable the *Clariidae* to live in very oxygen-poor waters but also permit them to exist for hours at a time out of the water. Thus these Catfishes not infrequently come ashore at night

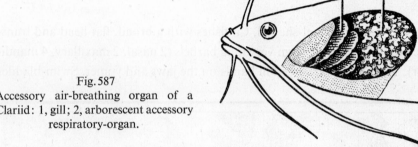

Fig. 587
Accessory air-breathing organ of a Clariid: 1, gill; 2, arborescent accessory respiratory-organ.

in search of food. Even more extensive land excursions may be observed. During the dry season many species burrow for days in the mud.

The distribution extends from Africa and Madagascar over the whole of southern Asia to east Asia and further includes the Philippines and the Malay Archipelago.

In captivity all the species are very tenacious of life and easily satisfied, but they are, above all, voracious. Only the young are suitable for domestic aquaria, but full-grown examples of large species make fine exhibits for public aquaria. In spite of their undemanding qualities, which guarantee

Plate 103

Fig. 588. *Aphyosemion multicolor* (Many-coloured Lyretail/Aphyosemion); left, ♂; right, ♀; enlarged. (Photo Dr. Foersch)
Fig. 589. *Aphyosemion gulare coeruleum* (Blue Gularis); adult ♂, slightly reduced. (Photo Dr. Foersch)

Plate 103

Plate 104

Plate 104

Fig. 590. *Aphyosemion bivittatum bivittatum.* (Red Lyretail/Aphyosemion) The ♂ illustrated here departs somewhat in coloration from the normal type. About twice natural size. (Photo Dr. Foersch)

Fig. 591. *Aphyosemion cognatum;* ♂, much enlarged. (Photo Dr. Foersch)

Fig. 592. *Aphyosemion australe australe* (Cape Lopez Lyretail/Aphyosemion); ♂, about twice natural size. (Photo Dr. Foersch)

success under almost any circumstances, the *Clariidae* should still receive special treatment. Soft, sandy, better still slightly muddy, bottom-soil, some cavities among stones or tangled roots, strong and sparse plants. Temperature 20–25°C. Feeding easy: live food of all kinds, worms, mussel-, fish- and mammal-flesh. Many species will also accept potato and softened rolled oats. Very often these fishes eat so much that their bellies become positively spherical. All the species are very predatory, especially in confined quarters, and can only be kept in company with robust fishes.

Sex-distinctions are only known in some cases. Breeding in aquaria has only been achieved in the case of *Heteropneustes fossilis (q.v.).*

The imported genera may be distinguished as follows:–

Clarias: In side-view torpedo-shaped. Dorsal and anal fins long-based. Pectoral and ventral fins well-developed. No adipose fin.

Heteropneustes: In side-view torpedo-shaped. Dorsal fin short-, anal long-based. Pectoral and ventral fins well-developed. No adipose fin.

Gymnallabes: In side-view low, worm-shaped. Dorsal, caudal and anal fins together forming a uniform long fringing fin. Pectoral and ventral fins small. Head, in dorsal view, with projecting cheeks.

Channallabes: In side-view low, worm-shaped. Dorsal, caudal and anal fins together forming a uniform long fringing fin. Pectoral fins greatly reduced. Ventral fins absent. Head, in dorsal view, without cheeks.

Heterobranchus: In side-view torpedo-shaped. Dorsal fin long-based. Adipose fin present.

Channallabes apus (*Günther* 1873) (Figs. 468, 505)
Congo Basin, Angola; to 31 cm.

D 140–150; A 125–130. Eel-like. Pectoral fins, in contrast to the similar genus *Gymnallabes*, greatly reduced. No ventrals. Uniform dark brown.

Sex-distinctions unknown.

Care, as given in family description. 1956.

Clarias angolensis (*Steindachner* 1866) (Fig. 594)
Tropical West and Central Africa, in a variety of waters including brackish ones; to 35 cm.

D 70–82; A 55–63. Coffee-brown to blackish with a bronze lustre on the back and sporadic to numerous pale blotches and spots on the flanks. Belly pale brown, yellowish or white. Fins thick, opaque, greenish. Caudal fin with a dark edge.

Sex-distinctions unknown.

Care, as given in the family description. 1910/ – .

Clarias anguillaris (*Linnaeus* 1762) (Fig. 595)
North-east Africa, Nile, Lake Victoria, Lake Chad; to 75 cm.

D 65–76; A 53–62. Coffee-brown with a greenish lustre on the back. Flanks sometimes indistinctly marbled. Belly pale brown to white. Head frequently with a vague dark longitudinal band under the eye. Fins edged with brown-yellow to bright orange. Occasionally spotted with black.

Sex-distinctions unknown.

Care, as given in the family description. 1906/ – .

Clarias batrachus (*Linnaeus* 1758) (Fig. 596)
Widely distributed, from Ceylon through eastern India to the Malay Archipelago; to 55 cm.

D 62–76; A 45–58. Brownish to green-blue, the back darker with a greenish

Figs. 593–596

Fig. 593. *Pangasius micronemus;* adult, much reduced.
Fig. 594. *Clarias angolensis;* adult, much reduced.
Fig. 595. *Clarias anguillaris;* adult, very much reduced.
Fig. 596. *Clarias batrachus;* adult, much reduced.

The barbels are often shown as wavy in these drawings, but in life they are carried stiffly and splayed out

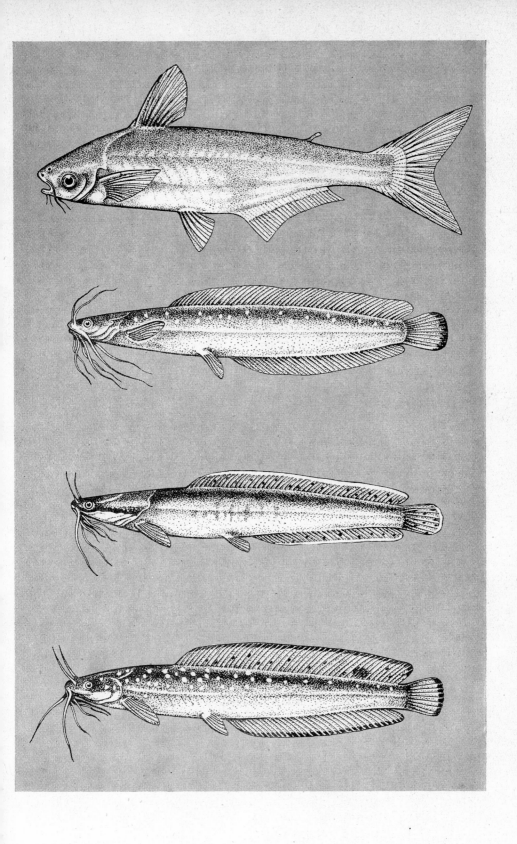

lustre. Underside pale brown to delicate reddish, occasionally blue-white. Numerous striking pale to pure white spots on the flanks. Fins grey-green. Dorsal fin more yellow-green, vertical fins with red borders.

♀ coloration less strongly contrasted; dorsal fin without dark markings.
♂ dorsal fin with black spots and a dark blotch on the hinder portion.

Care, as given in the family description. 1899/−.

Clarias dumerili *Steindachner* 1866 (Fig. 602)
Angola and Old Calabar; to 16 cm.
D 66–72; A 49–55. Uniform dark chocolate-brown with a greenish lustre on the back. Belly pale brown to white. Fins brown.
Sex-distinctions unknown.
Care, as given in the family description. Probably about 1910/−.

Clarias lazera *Cuvier* and *Valenciennes* 1840 (Fig. 603)
Syria, Nile, Senegal to Niger; to 120 cm.
D 62–82; A 50–65. Anal fin long-based. Coloration very variable, in relation to the wide distribution. Uniformly grey-brown to olive-brown or vaguely marbled. Upperside usually very dark, underside whitish. Vertical fins grey-olive, often bordered with yellow-olive to pale yellow. Caudal occasionally with black spots. Young with a dark longitudinal band.
Sex-distinctions unknown.
Care, as given in the family description. 1915/+.

Clarias mossambicus *Peters* 1852 (Fig. 604)
Throughout East Africa; to 70 cm.
D 62–78; A 50–62. Head, back and flanks olive-brown to dark coffee-brown marbled with pale brown to whitish. Belly pale grey to white. Vertical fins dark brown, often with dark edges. Dorsal fin with pale marbling.

Plate 105

Fig. 597. *Plecostomus punctatus;* half-grown, natural size. (Original)
Fig. 598. *Loricaria filamentosa;* ♂, lateral view, natural size. (Original)
Fig. 599. *Loricaria filamentosa;* dorsal views of, above, ♀, below, ♂. (Original)

Plate 105

Plate 106

Plate 106

Fig. 600. Pairs of various *Aphanius* spp. (♀ above, ♂ below in each case)

Aphanius fasciatus
Aphanius dispar richardsoni
Aphanius chantrei; population from Samsun.
Aphanius burduricus iconii; population from Konya.

All species somewhat enlarged. The figures were made by arrangement with the Zoologisches Staatsinstitut, Hamburg. (Photo Dr. Villwock)

♀ without a produced anal papilla.
♂ with a long, conical anal papilla.

Care, as given in the family description. Probably around 1925/ – .

Clarias platycephalus *Boulenger* 1902 (Fig. 504)
Southern Cameroons, Upper and Middle Congo; to 35 cm.

D 65–70; A 56–62. Coloration dusky grey-brown, marbled light and dark, especially on the upper part of the flanks. Underside pale brown. Fins opaque grey-brown. Caudal fin with dark transverse bars. Anal fin with a pale border.

Sex-distinctions unknown.

Care, as given in the family description.

Heterobranchus longifilus (*Cuvier* and *Valenciennes* 1840) (Fig. 506)
Very widely distributed through Africa, Nile, Niger, Congo, Zambesi; to 72 cm.

D 29–34; A 44–54. Members of the genus *Heterobranchus* are easily recognised by their long dorsal and long adipose fins. Body elongate, anteriorly cylindrical, posteriorly slightly compressed. 4 pairs of barbels, of which those on the maxillary are the longest and reach practically to the ventrals when laid back. Anal fin long-based, pectoral and ventral fins small. Upperside dark olive to blue-grey, the flanks being only slightly paler. Belly white, sharply contrasted with the flanks. Dorsal and anal fins grey-green with dark edges, occasionally partly bordered with red. Adipose fin dark with a black hinder end. Caudal fin yellowish to orange at the base, the outer part with a broad, black transverse bar.

Sex-distinctions not known.

This very hardy, but also exceedingly sluggish, species is hardly to be recommended for the domestic aquarium. The fishes lie motionless on the bottom and only show signs of life when food is offered to them. All kinds of food are eaten greedily and in very large quantities. The adults do very well on meat and rolled oats. 1955.

Heteropneustes fossilis (*Bloch* 1792) (Figs. 517, 605)

Ceylon, Eastern India, Burma, South Viet-Nam; to 70 cm.

D 6–7; A 60–79. Dorsal fin small and short. Uniform grey-brown to olive-brown, sometimes dark brown to black. Two narrow, pale to yellowish, longitudinal bands and numerous black spots on the flanks. Fins often fawn. Anal fin occasionally with dark marbling. Eye yellow.

♀ more robust.

♂ slimmer.

Care, as given in the family description. Has been bred in captivity. According to Fränkel the ♀ sucks the ♂ sex-aperture. The eggs are about the size of millet-seed, yellowish in colour and laid in balls in depressions fanned out and guarded by the adults. The adults likewise tend the young for a very long time. 1891/+.

Gymnallabes typus (*Günther* 1867) (Fig. 606)

Tropical West Africa, lower Niger and Old Calabar; to 25 cm.

D 98–110; A 82–88; V 1/5. Body elongate, eel-like. The dorsal, caudal and anal are united into one fringing fin. Dark brown with a greenish lustre on the back and shining violet to reddish or rust-red zones on the flanks (by reflected light). Underside fawn to pale. Fins dark brown to pale brown.

Sex-distinctions unknown.

Care, as given in family description. 1912/–.

Family Mochokidae

Entirely naked Catfishes, distributed through the whole of Africa with the exception of the region north of the Sahara. Body usually somewhat thick-set, slightly compressed, the lower profile weakly, the upper strongly, convex. Dorsal and pectoral fins with stout, often serrated, spines. Adipose fin present, occasionally very large. Anal fin-base short. 3 pairs of barbels, those on the maxillary being the longest and only exceptionally feathered; mandibular and mental barbels feathered or plain.

The *Mochokidae* are crepuscular fishes which gather in large shoals and inhabit slow-flowing waters and lagoons. During the day they hide in suitably protected places and then especially like to rest upright against a stake or bank or under overhanging roots. Some species swim on their backs, a habit which may or may not be accompanied by a reversal of the normal light-dark pigmentation.

Sex-distinctions and breeding biology are unknown in almost all the species. The ♀ is, as a rule, decidedly more robust.

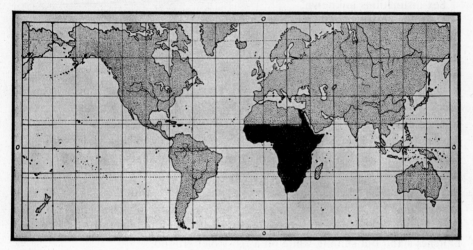

Fig. 601
Distribution of the *Mochokidae*

Members of this family do very well in captivity. Although properly regarded as typical crepuscular fishes they frequently display their lively and inquisitive behaviour during the day, incessantly exploring every corner of the tank or swimming along the glass sides. Their needs are best met by large aquaria with dim light and a dark, soft bottom-soil. In any case they should be provided with a vertical stake against which they can rest. Temperature 22–26°C. Small live food, also plant material (algae, lettuce). The species of *Synodontis* are very peaceful indeed, though they often tend to disturb other animals with the barbels with which they incessantly investigate their surroundings. A very interesting group of fishes.

403

Synodontis alberti *Schilthuis* 1891 (Fig. 519)
Congo (Stanley Pool, etc.); to 16 cm.

D I/7; A 3–4/8–9. The very long, unfeathered, maxillary barbels when laid back often reach to the caudal fin. Dorsal fin-spine not serrate on the anterior edge. Very uniformly blue-grey to olive-brown, the underside somewhat paler. Back and upper part of the flanks often with large dark blotches. Dorsal and caudal fins with rows of dark spots.

Sex-distinctions unknown.

Care, as given in family description. 1954.

Synodontis angelicus (*Schilthuis* 1891) (Figs. 497, 534)
Tropical West Africa, Congo, River Ja; to 20 cm.

D I/7; A 4/7–8. Maxillary barbels not feathered, somewhat longer than the head. Shoulder-process longer than broad, pointed. Pectoral fin-spines strongly toothed on both sides. Lobes of caudal drawn out to points, the upper usually the longer. Coloration of larger specimens (9–20 cm.): grey to dark violet with numerous reddish-yellow to dark brown-red, uniformly distributed, sharp-edged, large round blotches on the head, flanks, adipose fin and, partly running together, on the belly. The blotches on the flanks are usually edged with dark violet. Dorsal, caudal, anal and ventral fins dark violet with brownish blotches and transverse bars. Young fishes (4–9 cm.) are extraordinarily beautifully coloured: the round blotches stand out shining white on a red-violet ground.

Sex-distinctions not yet described.

Care, as given in the family description. 1954.

Synodontis batensoda (*Rüppel* 1832) (Fig. 607)
Nile Basin, Chad tributaries, Senegal, Gambia River, Congo (?); to 24 cm.

Figs. 602–606

Fig. 602. *Clarias dumerili;* adult, much reduced.
Fig. 603. *Clarias lazera;* adult, very much reduced.
Fig. 604. *Clarias mossambicus;* much reduced.
Fig. 605. *Heteropneustes fossilis;* much reduced.
Fig. 606. *Gymnallabes typus;* adult, much reduced; on the right, above, dorsal view of head.

The barbels are often shown as wavy in these drawings, but in life they are carried stiffly and splayed out.

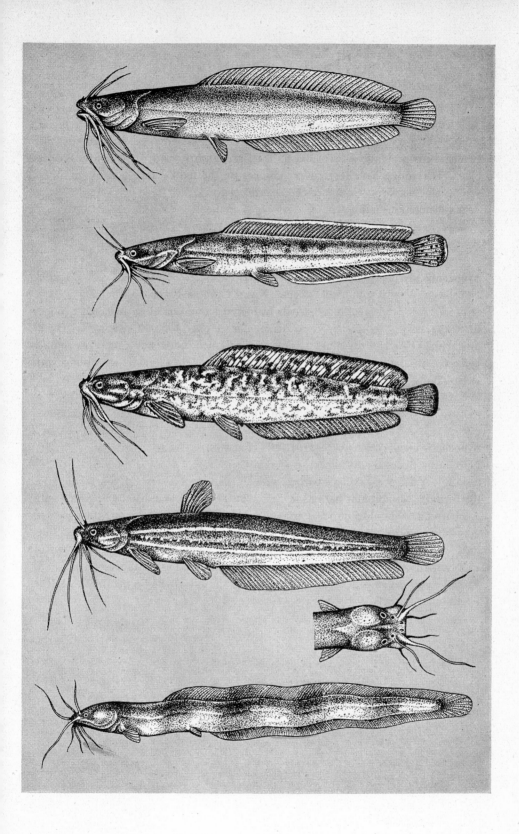

D I/7; A 5/7–9. Maxillary barbels with a broad posterior membrane throughout their length; mandibular barbels without membrane. Shoulder-process rectangular. Adipose fin very large. Adults are silver-green to blue-grey, occasionally delicate reddish-brown. Underside blackish. Fins grey, partly with dark spots. Barbels black. The young have large dark blotches on the flanks, separated by an intervening pale network. Compare *S. membranaceus*.

Sex-distinctions unknown.

Care, as given in family description. Also eats mud (Daget, 1954). This species swims on its back like *S. nigriventris*, hence the dark belly. 1955.

Synodontis clarias (*Linnaeus* 1762) (Fig. 609)
Nile Basin, Chad tributaries, Senegal, Niger, Gambia River; to 27 cm.

D I/7; A 5/7–9. Maxillary barbels feathered along one edge, somewhat longer than the head. Shoulder-process triangular. Upper lobe of caudal somewhat longer than lower. Grey-blue, upperside olive-green, underside pale. Fins smoke-grey, the caudal (according to Boulenger) often with a red tinge. Young with large, almost black blotches on the body.

Sex-distinctions unknown.

Care, as given in family description. 1908/ –.

Synodontis membranaceus *Geoffroy* 1809 (Fig. 608)
Nile Basin, Senegal and Niger; to 45 cm.

D I/7; A 5/8–9. Maxillary barbels with a broad posterior membrane throughout their length. Mandibular barbels feathered at their base and distally provided with a membrane. Shoulder-process triangular. Adipose fin very large. Blue-grey to grey-silver, underside dark to black. Barbels pale, barbel-membranes black. Fins grey, without markings. Young with large dark spots on the flanks and rows of spots on the fins. This species is mainly distinguished from the very similar *S. batensoda* by peculiarities of dentition and by the presence of a membrane on the mandibular barbels.

Figs. 607–610

Fig. 607. *Synodontis batensoda;* adult, reduced.
Fig. 608. *Synodontis membranaceus;* adult, much reduced.
Fig. 609. *Synodontis clarias;* adult, much reduced.
Fig. 610. *Synodontis melanostictus;* adult, much reduced.

Sex-distinctions unknown.

Care, as given in family description. Also eats mud (Daget, 1954). Swims on its back. Import date unknown.

Synodontis melanostictus *Boulenger* 1906 (Fig. 610)

Zambesi, Lake Tanganyika, Lake Bangweulu, Lake Mweru; to 32 cm.

D I/7; A 4/7. The maxillary barbels are not feathered and reach to about the middle of the pectorals when laid back. Narrow membranes at the bases of the barbels. Shoulder-process triangular, pointed. Upper lobe of caudal usually some-what larger than lower. Altogether dingy, pale to dark brown with numerous coarsely-scattered black spots. Underside paler.

Sex-distinctions unknown.

Care, as given in family description. 1954.

Synodontis nigrita (*Cuvier* and *Valenciennes* 1840) (Fig. 615)

White Nile, Senegal, Niger, Gambia River, widely distributed; to 17 cm.

D I/7; A 4/8–9. The maxillary barbels are not feathered, but have a broad membrane along the basal third of their length; they are usually distinctly longer than the head. Dorsal fin-spine not serrate on anterior edge. Caudal fin crescentically emarginate, the upper lobe somewhat longer than the lower. The young are coffee-brown with numerous black spots which are occasionally arranged in transverse rows. Underside pale brown with dark blotches. Especially characteristic of this species are 2–3 irregular transverse bars on the caudal peduncle and a pale, dark-bordered band from the eye onto the snout. Adults are quite uniformly brown, often with a delicate greenish lustre and numerous black spots. Fins dark; caudal with black transverse bars.

Plate 107

Fig. 611. Pairs of various species of Tooth-Carps from Asia Minor (♀ above, ♂ below in each case)

Anatolichthys transgrediens; from Akpinar on the Aeigol.
Anatolichthys burdurensis; from Burdur.
Anatolichthys splendens
Kosswigichthys asquamatus

All species somewhat enlarged. The figures were made by arrangement with the Zoologisches Staatsinstitut, Hamburg. (Photo Dr. Villwock)

Plate 107

Plate 108

Plate 108

Fig. 612. *Aphanius iberus;* ♂ above, ♀ below; both specimens somewhat enlarged. (Photo Dr. Foersch)

Fig. 613. *Aphanius iberus;* ♂, greatly enlarged. (Photo Dr. Foersch)

Fig. 614. *Aphanius mento;* ♂ above, ♀ below, in breeding dress, somewhat enlarged. (Photo Dr. Foersch)

Sex-distinctions unknown.

Care, as given in family description. 1951.

Synodontis nigriventris *David* 1936 (Fig. 548)   Upside-down Catfish

Streams of central Congo; to 6 cm.

D I/7; A 4/4–9. Body form and finnage as given for *S. schall*. Characteristic of this species are (according to Trewavas) the smooth anterior face of the dorsal spine, the narrow separation of the eyes, the large size of the eyes and the uniformly black belly. Pale grey to cream-coloured with dark brown to black blotches which may run together to form irregular broad transverse bars. Belly uniformly black *(nigriventris)*. The fins are often darkly spotted on a colourless ground.

The sexes are easily distinguished by the greater plumpness of the ♀♀.

This species should be kept in small tanks with thick planting and a dark bottom-soil. Temperature 23–27 °C. Live food, scraps and algae. An undemanding and hardy fish with a particularly interesting habit of swimming usually belly-up close to the surface of the water. The reversal of the usual pattern of obliterative shading (dorsally dark, ventrally light) is undoubtedly related to this unusual habit, and is repeated again in *S. batensoda* which also swims on its back (see p. 406). In contrast to other Catfishes even feeding is accomplished in the same position. Algal food appears to be indispensable to the well-being of *S. nigriventris* and it has a special preference for grazing on the undersides of leaves of water plants. Breeding has already been achieved in captivity; the fishes spawned in a flowerpot but further details are not available. 1950.

Synodontis notatus *Vaillant* 1893 (Fig. 536)

Congo (Stanley Pool, etc.); to 22 cm.

D I/7; A 4/7–8. Maxillary barbels not feathered, somewhat longer than the head. Shoulder-process very broad and rounded. Adipose fin short. Grey to silver-grey, upperside substantially darker, underside whitish. A large, round, deep black blotch on the flank over the ventrals; occasionally a few smaller blotches appear behind the large one.

Sex-distinctions unknown.

Care, as given in family description. 1952.

Synodontis nummifer *Boulenger* 1899 (Fig. 532)
Congo (Stanley Pool, etc.); to 18 cm.

D I/7; A 2/7–8. This species is very similar to *S. notatus* in coloration and markings. Living specimens are easily distinguished by the length of the maxillary barbels, which in *S. nummifer* are no longer than the head; by the adipose fin (short in *S. notatus*, long in *S. nummifer*), and, finally, by the eyes, which are round in *S. notatus* and rather oval in *S. nummifer*.

Further details as given for *S. notatus*.

Synodontis resupinatus *Boulenger* 1904 (Fig. 616)
Upper Niger, Congo?; to 26 cm.

D I/7; A 4/8. Maxillary barbels somewhat longer than the head, with a broad membrane on the inner side at the base. Mandibular barbels with short branches, some of which are merely knob-like projections. Shoulder-process large, sugar-loaf shaped. Adipose fin very large. This species is easily recognised, when mature, by the great depth of the body, the very long dorsal fin-spine, the long and pointed caudal fin-lobes, and the black underside. Upperside brownish, flanks grey, more yellowish in the young. Barbels white.

Sex-distinctions unknown.

Care, as given in family description. Swims on its back? Import data unknown.

Synodontis robbianus *Smith* 1873 (Fig. 617)
Old Calabar, lower Niger; to 12 cm.

D I/7; A 2–4/8–9. Maxillary barbels not feathered, not much longer than the head. Anterior edge of dorsal spine not serrate; outer edge of pectoral spine toothed. Adipose fin very long. Clay-colour to nut-brown, more or less darkly spotted;

Figs. 615–618

Fig. 615. *Synodontis nigrita;* half-grown, somewhat reduced.
Fig. 616. *Synodontis resupinatus;* adult, much reduced.
Fig. 617. *Synodontis robbianus;* somewhat reduced.
Fig. 618. *Synodontis schall;* half-grown, somewhat reduced.

underside paler. Ventral fins very dark. Dorsal, adipose and caudal fins rather pale, irregularly spotted. Young fishes with a pale band from the eye onto the snout and often with regular band-like markings on the fins.

Sex-distinctions unknown.

Care, as given in family description. 1908/+.

Synodontis schall (*Bloch* and *Schneider* 1801) (Figs. 537, 618)
Africa, widely distributed: Nile, Senegal, Lake Chad, etc.; to 40 cm.

D I/7; A 4/8–9. Maxillary barbels not feathered and reaching to the middle of the pectoral fins when laid back. Outer mandibular barbels feathered along one edge. Mental barbels with nodular branches. Shoulder-process long and pointed. Adipose fin long. Caudal deeply forked. Old fishes are almost uniformly dark grey to brown, the underside pale to white. Paired fins and anal often blackish. Half-grown specimens exhibit numerous dark brown to black spots on a dark ground. The young are marbled with dark brown on a pale brown to olive-brown ground and have well-contrasted wavy yellow bands on the snout.

Sex-distinctions in coloration not so far described.

Care, as given in family description; only young specimens are suitable for domestic aquaria. 1935/+.

Brief mention may be made of two further species which were imported into Europe during 1955–1957.

Synodontis flavitaeniatus *Boulenger* 1919 (Fig. 535).
Chocolate-brown, with lovely and very variable yellow to orange longitudinal bands.

Synodontis brichardi *Poll* 1959
Deep black, with five brilliant yellow transverse bars and fins banded with black and yellow.

Figs. 619–623

Fig. 619. *Acentroichthys leptos;* somewhat reduced.
Fig. 620. *Heptapterus mustelinus;* reduced.
Fig. 621. *Heptapterus ornaticeps;* reduced.
Fig. 622. *Microglanis ater;* adult, somewhat reduced.
Fig. 623. *Microglanis parahybae;* about natural size.

The barbels are often shown as wavy in these drawings, but in life they are carried stiffly and splayed out.

412

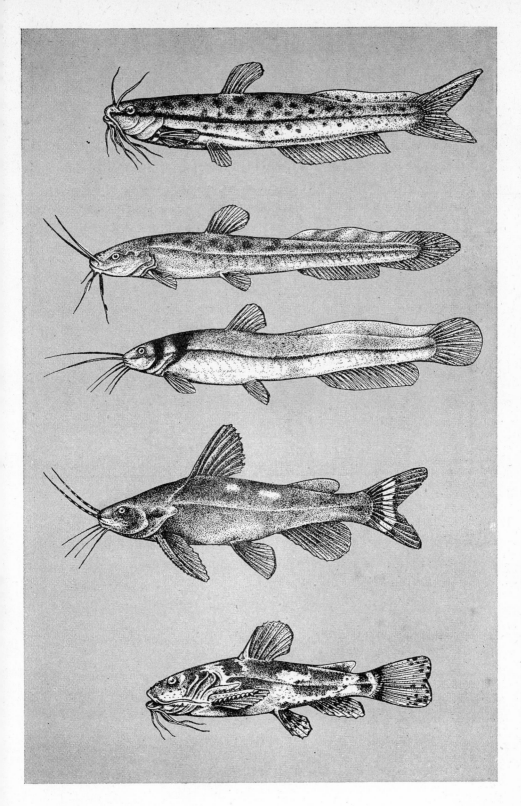

Family Pimelodidae

This very large family is distributed from southern Mexico over the whole of Central and South America, with the exception of the southernmost part (south of the 40th parallel). The *Pimelodidae* are elongate to very elongate Catfishes, entirely devoid of scales and bony plates and usually provided with long barbels (3 pairs). Dorsal fin inserted well forwards, almost always

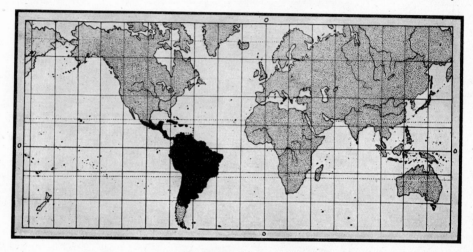

Fig. 624
Distribution of the *Pimelodidae*

with a stout spine. Adipose fin present. Caudal fin usually forked. Anal fin-base short. Mouth not very wide. Jaws toothed. The family is nearly related to the *Bagridae* of the Old World.

Care and breeding are dealt with under the individual species.

Acentronichthys leptos *R. S. Eigenmann* and *C. H. Eigenmann* 1889 (Fig. 619)
Eastern and south-eastern Brazil; to 11 cm.

D 7; A 19–23; V 6. Body cylindrical, elongate, caudal peduncle only slightly compressed. Adipose fin long and low, posteriorly united with the deeply forked caudal. 3 pairs of moderately long barbels. Back dark brown, flanks paler, underside delicate brownish to yellowish white. A narrow black longitudinal band runs from the tip of the snout over the lower edge of the eye to the caudal peduncle, where it gradually disappears. Further, less distinct, bands are distributed as follows: along the middle of the back; from the gill-cover to the anal fin and thence along the fin-base; from about the gill-cover to the insertion of the ventral fin. Dark blotches are strewn over the entire body. Fins colourless. Anal fin with brownish spots.

Sex-distinctions in coloration not yet described.

Care, as given for *Pimelodus clarias* (see p. 417). Temperature 22–25°C. Not yet bred in captivity. 1926/ – .

Heptapterus mustelinus (*Cuvier* and *Valenciennes* 1840) (Fig. 620)
Rio Grande do Sul, La Plata; to 15 cm.

D I/6; A 3/16; P I/7; V 1/5. Body elongate, anteriorly somewhat broader than deep, posteriorly compressed. The dorsal fin commences quite a little before the ventrals; its first ray is articulated, soft and unbranched. The adipose fin is very long and continuous with the caudal; the latter is very strongly rounded and ventrally reaches nearly to the long, low anal fin. 3 pairs of moderately long barbels; the maxillary pair reach to the pectoral fins when laid back. Coloration grey to blue-grey, back brown-grey, belly dirty white. Sparse black blotches are sometimes apparent on the upper parts of the flanks. Fins delicate blue-grey, occasionally with dark spots.

Sex-distinctions in coloration not yet described.

Care, as given for *Pimelodus clarias* (see p. 417). Not yet bred in captivity. 1909/ – .

Heptapterus ornaticeps *E. Ahl* 1936 (Fig. 621)
Southern Brazil, La Plata State; to 20 cm. (according to Arnold).

D I/6; A 3/16–20; P I/7; V 1/5. Description according to Ahl: body not quite so slim as in the previous species, from which *H. ornaticeps* is also distinguished by the more posterior insertion of the ventrals and the coloration. Olive-grey to yellow. A fine, dark longitudinal band extends from the snout to the root of the tail and is interrupted in the region of the gill-cover by two, broad wedge-shaped transverse bars. Fins grey to yellowish.

Sex-distinctions not known.

Care, as given for *Pimelodus clarias* (see p. 417). Not yet bred in captivity. 1935/ – .

415

Microglanis ater *E. Ahl* 1936 (Fig. 622)

Central and southern Brazil; to 10 cm.

D I/6; A 14. Description according to Arnold and Ahl: body-form and finnage similar to those of the following species, from which it differs chiefly in the somewhat greater elongation of the body, the higher number of anal rays, and the coloration. Young fishes more yellow-brown; adults, including the fins, dark violet-brown. A pale, oval blotch under the hinder end of the dorsal fin; another under the origin of the adipose fin. Caudal fin with a broad, irregular, pale transverse bar.

Sex-distinctions not known.

Care, as given for *Pimelodus clarias* (see p. 417). Not yet bred in captivity. 1935/−.

Microglanis parahybae (*Steindachner* 1880) (Fig. 623)

Rio Parahyba, Rio Doce; to 7 cm.

D I/6; A 10–14. Body thick-set, torpedo-shaped, compressed behind the pectoral fins. Dorsal and pectoral fins with stout, serrate spines. Shoulder-process long, thorn-like. 1 pair of maxillary barbels which usually reach to the pectoral origin when laid back. 2 pairs of only slightly shorter mandibular barbels. Coloration very variable, usually yellow-brown to chocolate-brown. Upperside of head black with numerous pale blotches; back dark brown; underside dark with pale blotches or entirely pale. 3 very irregular broad dark transverse bars on the flanks, together with numerous black spots. Fins pale, translucent, with dark bands, rows of blotches or spots.

Sex-distinctions in coloration have not been described.

Care of this very undemanding and peaceful species, as given for *Pimelodus clarias* (see p. 417). Exclusively crepuscular and nocturnal fish. Not yet bred in captivity. 1926/+.

Pimelodus clarias (*Bloch* 1795) (Fig. 632)

Widely distributed, from Central America and the West Indies over the whole of northern and central South America (excluding the Andes) to the Argentine; to 30 cm.

D I/6; A 4/7–8; P I/9; V 1/5. Body torpedo-shaped, compressed. Dorsal and pectoral fins with strong, erectile spines, armed with teeth (a wound from one of these spines can lead to blood-poisoning). Shoulder-girdle with a broad, smooth shoulder-process. Adipose fin large. Caudal deeply forked, the upper lobe the larger. 1 pair of very long maxillary barbels, 2 pairs of appreciably shorter mandibular barbels. Coloration of the young very variable, in relation to the wide distribution. Back dark grey to olive; flanks grey to steel-blue with large dark blotches arranged in rows (also dark fishes with light blotches). Fins grey with dark spotting. Adults uniformly grey.

Sex-distinctions in coloration have not been described.

Like all *Pimelodidae* this species is exclusively a crepuscular and nocturnal animal, which stays hidden during the day and begins to get lively and set forth in search of food at nightfall. Its welfare in captivity depends on due consideration being paid to this pattern of behaviour. A large, shaded or darkened aquarium, with a dark, soft bottom-soil, thick tangles of roots, pieces of hollow wood, overhanging stones, or thickets of plants, provides ideal living-conditions for *P. clarias* as for the *Pimelodidae* in general. Although most species are not exacting with regard to water-conditions, absolutely fresh, hard water should be avoided. Temperature for almost any species 20–26 °C. Omnivorous, with a special predilection for worms; large specimens prefer earthworms, insect-larvae, *Tubifex*, minced meat and scraps of all kinds. Very voracious and rapid-growing when well cared for. Most species are only suitable for domestic aquaria when young and should later be transferred to large exhibition tanks. Small specimens may be kept in company with surface-living fishes of other species. Large specimens are often very quarrelsome and are therefore best kept in isolation. All *Pimelodidae* have a very acute sense of smell.

Breeding of *P. clarias* in captivity has not yet been achieved. Due respect should be paid to the spines when capturing these fishes. 1895/+.

Pimelodella gracilis (*Cuvier* and *Valenciennes* 1840) (Figs. 550, 633)
Orinoco and Amazon to La Plata; to 17 cm.

D I/6; A 2/9–11. Body torpedo-shaped, compressed. Anal fin rounded. Caudal, deeply forked, the upper lobe somewhat the larger. Pectoral fins with stout, toothed spines. Shoulder-girdle with a projecting thorn-like process. 1 pair of very long maxillary barbels; 2 pairs of shorter mandibular barbels. White-green to blue-grey, the upperside darker, the underside white. From the gill-cover to the root of the tail there extends a black longitudinal band which broadens posteriorly; this becomes less conspicuous with age. Fins transparent. Tips of vertical fins occasionally with a rusty tinge.

Sex-distinctions in coloration not known.

Care, as given for *Pimelodus clarias*, above. A thoroughly peaceful species which

417

may also be kept in dark community-tanks, in which it then acts as a very useful scavenger of food-scraps. Temperature 20–23 °C. Not yet bred in captivity. 1895/+.

Pimelodella lateristriga (*Müller* and *Troschel* 1849) (Fig. 634)
Eastern Brazil, in rivers flowing into the Atlantic north of the Rio Parahyba; to 18 cm.

D I/6; A 2/10–12. Body-form and finnage similar to those of the previous species. Back olive-yellow to olive-green; flanks more grey-green, but also sometimes brown-yellow; underside dirty white. From the snout through the eye to the root of the tail there extends a usually deep black longitudinal band which, just behind the gill-cover, may be expanded into a black shoulder-blotch with a blurred edge. Fins colourless to delicate greenish, their tips usually with dark spots. Adipose fin with a narrow black margin.

Sex-distinctions in coloration not known.

Care, as given for the previous species. Temperature 20–23 °C. Not yet bred in captivity. 1908/+.

Pimelodella vittata (*Kröyer* 1874) (Fig. 635)
South-eastern Brazil, in the region between the Rio San Francisco and Porto Alegre; to 9 cm.

D I/6; A 2/9–10. Body-form and finnage similar to those of *Pimelodella gracilis*, but more elongate. Upper lobe of caudal greatly produced. Brown-olive to grey-brown with a weak brassy sheen, especially in the lower part of the flanks; back only slightly darker; underside pure white. A narrow black band runs from the snout to the root of the tail; from the edge of the gill-cover onwards this band is accompanied above by a further bluish-silver band which becomes violet-silver posteriorly. Fins yellowish, the dorsal with a blackish bar (according to Meinken).

Sex-distinctions in coloration not known.

Care, as given for *Pimelodella gracilis*, above. Not yet bred in captivity. 1939/–.

Pseudopimelodus acanthochira *R. S. Eigenmann* and *C. H. Eigenmann* 1888 (Fig. 637)
Amazon delta, Rio Gurupa, Rio Tajapura; to 15 cm.

D I/6; A 10. Body moderately elongate, slightly compressed from the pectorals onwards. Head flattened dorsally. Shoulder-process triangular. Dorsal and pectoral fins with stout, serrate spines. Caudal fin rounded. The maxillary barbels (1 pair) reach to about the tips of the pectoral fins when laid back. Mandibular barbels (2 pairs) short. Eyes covered over with skin. Almost uniformly dark brown, the underside somewhat paler. An irregular pale band runs along the hind edge of the gill-cover and across the nape. Dorsal fin brown with a short translucent bar across its posterior part. Caudal fin brown at the base and towards the edge, with a transparent central field which is spotted with brown. Anal fin brown with a broad white edge. Pectoral and ventral fins brown. According to Arnold (1936) the belly is dark grey with blackish spots.

Sex-distinctions in coloration or form not known.

Care, as given for *Pimelodus clarias* (see p. 417). A little sea-salt (2 teaspoons to 10 litres of water) is recommended. Peaceful and easily satisfied. 1934/ — .

Pseudopimelodus raninus (*Cuvier* and *Valenciennes* 1840) (Fig. 638)
Matto Grosso region, Rio Huallaga, Rio Janeiro de Essequibo, to 25 cm.

D I/7; A 11; P I/7; V 6. Shape similar to that of the previous species, but rather slimmer. Caudal only slightly notched, the lobes rounded. The maxillary barbels (1 pair) reach almost to the tips of the pectoral fins when laid back; the outer mandibular barbels to about the base of the pectorals. Yellow-brown, with dark marbling; underside paler. Dorsal fin dark, often with a violet sheen and a narrow yellowish longitudinal band over the fin-base. Caudal fin translucent yellowish with dark spots and the hinder third dark. Anal fin dark, with pale specks towards the margin.

Sex-distinctions not yet described.

Care, as given for *Pimelodus clarias* (see p. 417). Very peaceful and easily satisfied. Omnivorous. 1894/ — .

Rhamdia queleni (*Quoy* and *Gaimard* 1834) (Fig. 639)
Southern Brazil, La Plata region; to 35 cm.

D I/6; A 2/10–11; P I/8. Body-form and finnage similar to those of *R. sapo*. The long adipose fin begins immediately behind the dorsal. The coloration varies between yellow-grey and olive-grey, depending on the state of health; back somewhat darker; underside grey to whitish. The whole body, including the fins, is lightly marbled with dark brown. Occasionally a conspicuous large black blotch appears behind the gill-cover. Fins delicate grey-brown or glassy.

Sex-distinctions unknown.

Care, as given for *Pimelodus clarias* (see p. 417). Temperature 20–25 °C. Only young fishes suitable for the domestic aquarium. Not yet bred in captivity. 1934/ — .

Rhamdia sapo (*Cuvier* and *Valenciennes* 1840) (Fig. 640)
Southern Brazil, La Plata region; to 40 cm.

D I/7; A 2/9–10. Body elongate, anteriorly moderately compressed, posteriorly more strongly so. Upper surface of head flat. Pectoral fins with stout spines, serrate on their outer edges. Adipose fin long and low. A pair of long maxillary barbels which, when laid back, reach at the very least to the ventral fins. 2 pairs of shorter mandibular barbels. Eyes small, oval. Uniform brown to black-brown, paling towards the underside. Belly delicate brownish to white. According to Arnold there is a round, black blotch on the hinder part of the adipose fin.

Sex-distinctions not yet described.

Care, as given for *Pimelodus clarias* (see p. 417). Temperature 18–25°C. Only young fishes suitable for the domestic aquarium. Not yet bred in captivity. 1895/ –.

Rhamdia sebae (*Cuvier* and *Valenciennes* 1840) (Fig. 649)
Throughout northern and central South America east of the Andes; to 30 cm.

D I/6; A 2/10; P I/8; V 6. Body-form and finnage similar to those of *R. sapo*. The long adipose fin commences immediately behind the dorsal. The very long maxillary barbels when laid back reach to the caudal fin. Coloration very attractive: upperside fawn to cinnamon-brown; flanks ochre to greenish with a slight brassy sheen; belly yellowish to white. Upon this ground-colour, over the whole body and the lower part of the anal fin, are strewn very dark to black spots. A dark longitudinal band runs from the tip of the snout to the root of the tail and is often continued onto the middle rays of the caudal fin. Dorsal fin with a row of dark blotches. Caudal fin with dark tips to the lobes.

Sex-distinctions not yet described.

Care of this very robust species, as given for *Pimelodus clarias* (see p.417). Only young fishes suitable for the domestic aquarium. Not yet bred in captivity. 1912/ +.

Plate 109

Fig. 625. *Aphanius mento*, imported in 1955; left ♀, right ♂; somewhat enlarged. (Photo Dr. Foersch)
Fig. 626. *Aphanius mento;* ♂, much enlarged. (Photo Dr. Foersch)
Fig. 627. *Cyprinodon variegatus* (Sheepshead Minnow); left ♀, right ♂; natural size. (Original)

Plate 109

Plate 110

Plate 110

Fig. 628. *Aplocheilus blocki* (Dwarf or Green Panchax); adults, somewhat enlarged; left ♂, right ♀. (Photo Dr. Foersch)

Fig. 629. *Aplocheilus dayi* (Ceylon Killifish); adults, enlarged; above, ♂, below, ♀. (Photo Dr. Foersch)

Fig. 630. *Oryzias javanicus* (Java Medaka); adults, enlarged; above, ♂, below, ♀. (Photo Dr. Foersch)

Sorubim lima (*Bloch* and *Schneider* 1806) (Fig. 650)

Amazon river, Rio de la Plata, Rio Magdalena and tributaries; to 60 cm.

D I/7; A 3/18; P I/8; V 1/5. Body elongate, anteriorly cylindrical, posteriorly compressed. Head strongly depressed. Snout spatulate, overhanging the mouth. Fins short. Caudal fin deeply forked, superficially shark-like, the upper lobe produced to a point, the lower rounded. 3 pairs of barbels. Practically uniform silver-grey, to some extent with a brassy sheen. Underside pure white. Vague-edged dark longitudinal bands along the ridge of the back and along the flanks. Fins colourless, the caudal with a dark centre.

Sex-distinctions in coloration not known.

Care, as given for *Pimelodus clarias* (see p.417). Not yet bred in captivity. 1929/−.

Family Pygidiidae (= Trichomycteridae)

Loach-like and worm-like Catfishes from South America. Dorsal and anal fin-bases short. Adipose fin absent. Skin naked, thickened over the head. The swim-bladder is much reduced and enclosed in a bony capsule formed from lateral processes of the vertebrae.

Some *Pygidiidae* have become very well known for their peculiar and partly parasitic habits. Thus *Stegophilus insidiosus* is a true parasite which lives in the gill-chamber of the larger Mailed Catfishes. Various diminutive *Vandellia* spp. penetrate the urinogenital openings of swimming mammals and also of Man (probably mistaking the flow of urine for the exhalant stream from the gill-chamber of a fish) and, since they become wedged by their fin-spines, can cause severe inflammation and haemorrhage.

For the care of these interesting fishes, see under *Pygidium itatiayae*.

421

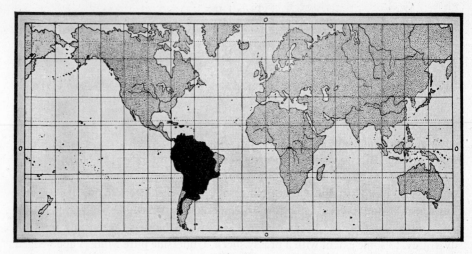

Fig. 631
Distribution of the *Pygidiidae*

Homodiaetus maculatus (*Steindachner* 1879) (Fig. 652)
La Plata basin; to 10 cm.

D II/7; A 2/5; P I/5. Body elongate, compressed. Head broad, depressed. Adipose fin absent. 2 pairs of very short barbels. Opercular and pre-opercular (bones of gill-cover) with prickly spines. Clay-yellow to pale brown, back olive-brown, underside delicate yellowish to brownish or white. Several longitudinal rows of dark blotches on the upper half of the body. Fins transparent as glass. Bases of dorsal and anal fins often with dark spots. Caudal base with a black transverse bar.

Sex-distinctions in coloration not yet described.

Care, as given for *Pygidium itatiayae* (below). Needs a great deal of oxygen (aeration). Not yet bred in captivity. 1923/—.

Figs. 632–635

Fig. 632. *Pimelodus clarias;* half-grown, somewhat reduced.
Fig. 633. *Pimelodella gracilis;* young, natural size.
Fig. 634. *Pimelodella lateristriga;* young, natural size.
Fig. 635. *Pimelodella vittata;* natural size.

422

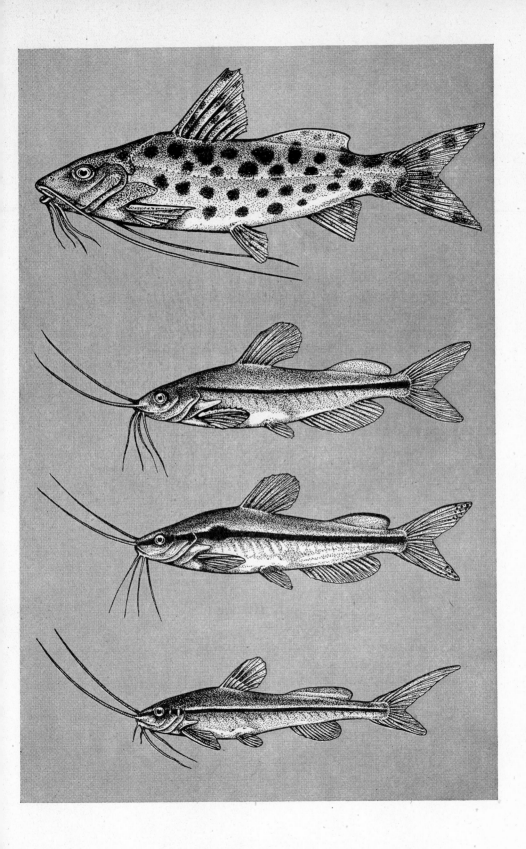

Pygidium itatiayae *Miranda Ribeiro* 1906 (Fig. 651)

Eastern Brazil, neighbourhood of Rio de Janeiro (according to Arnold), upper course of the Paraná; to 15 cm.

D II/6–7; A 2/5. Body elongate, cylindrical, similar to that of the European Loaches. Dorsal fin inserted well back. Adipose fin absent. Caudal rounded. Anal fin-base short. 3 pairs of short barbels. Accessory intestinal respiration. Alternately pale brown to olive-coloured on a pale ground-colour of clay-yellow; back somewhat darker. Underside yellowish to white. Numerous dark blotches, arranged in longitudinal rows on the gill-cover and flanks, which may be united into an irregular longitudinal band along the middle of the side. Fins colourless to delicate greenish.

Sex-distinctions in coloration not known. The ♀♀ are more robust.

Since the *Pygidiidae* are typically bottom-fishes and also such as like to burrow in the mulm, their welfare depends very largely upon the nature of the bottom-soil which should therefore be as dark and soft as possible. Tangles of roots and hollow pieces of wood will provide them with good hiding-places. Crepuscular animals which are, however, also quite lively in the aquarium during the daytime. Peaceful. Temperature 20–25°C. Omnivorous, with a preference for small worms. Not yet bred in captivity. 1931/+.

Vandellia cirrhosa (*Cuvier* and *Valenciennes* 1846) (Fig. 653)

South America, Hyavary; to 2·5 cm.

D 9; A 10; P 8; V 6. Body elongate, compressed, very translucent. Mouth ventral. Teeth confined to the premaxillaries. Dorsal fin small, inserted behind the level of the ventrals. Caudal fin rounded. Opercular and pre-opercular spiny. Uniform delicate yellowish. Eyes very large and dark.

Sex-distinctions not known.

Care, as given for *Pygidium itatiayae*, above. A very delicate species. 1939/−.

Family Helogenidae

This family contains only the following species:–

Helogenes marmoratus *Günther* 1863

Eastern Amazon basin and Guiana; to 10 cm.

D 5; A 42; P 8; V 6. Body moderately elongate, compressed, especially in the region of the caudal peduncle, without bony plates. Dorsal fin small, without spines, inserted well back. Adipose fin very small. The lower lobe of the deeply forked caudal is somewhat the longer. Anal fin-base very long. 3 pairs of moderately long barbels. Eyes small, covered over with skin, shine in the dark. Upper half of body dark brown, with a quite delicate reddish tinge, and marbled with numerous pale brown blotches. Lower half of body pale brown to ochre, thickly strewn with dark spots and streaks. Fins fawn, the vertical fins with dark blotches. Caudal lobes with very dark tips. According to Arnold the caudal and anal fins in older fishes have transparent margins.

Sex-distinctions have not yet been described.

H. marmoratus is a nocturnal creature which remains hidden during the daytime. It should be kept in a darkened aquarium with thick tangles of roots, pieces of hollow wood, etc. Planting not necessary. Temperature 23–28°C. Omnivorous: worms, larvae, also scraps. Not yet bred in captivity. 1913/−.

Family Bunocephalidae

Very peculiar Catfishes from the western Amazon basin. Body depressed, in appearance rather like a paper kite, with a very attenuate, compressed caudal peduncle. No adipose fin. Skin naked, but beset with large tubercles.

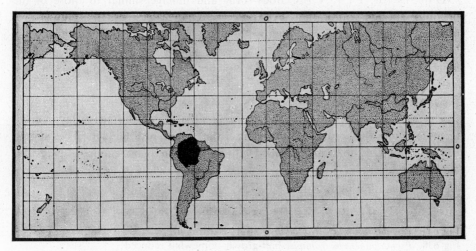

Fig. 636
Distribution of the *Bunocephalidae*

425

Besides the following species others have no doubt been imported, although not recognised as such.

Bunocephalus bicolor *Steindachner* 1882 (Figs. 660, 661)
Western Amazon basin to Ecuador, Paraná; to 15 cm.

D I/4; A 1/6–7; P I/5; V 1/5. Head and anterior part of body very strongly depressed and broad, tapering posteriorly. Caudal peduncle very long and compressed. Pectoral fin-spines very stout and toothed. No adipose fin. 3 pairs of barbels, of which those on the maxillary are the longest and reach to the pectoral fin when laid back. Skin naked; flanks with rows of tubercles. Coloration, depending on health, uniform dark brown to pale brown with dark bands and blotches. The whole body is strewn with small pale spots. Underside paler, often with brown blotches. Fins translucent brownish with pale brown to black blotches; caudal with a dark edge.

Sex-distinctions unknown.

Care, as given for *B. kneri*, below. Unfortunately the breeding of this species has not yet been achieved in captivity. 1907/ – .

Bunocephalus kneri (*Steindachner* 1882) (Fig. 662)
Western Amazon basin to Ecuador; to 12 cm.

D I/4; A 1/6; P I/4; V 1/5. Body-form and finnage similar to those of the previous species. Coloration likewise very changeable: usually grey-brown, marbled pale and dark, or with rows of dark blotches; distinct irregular dark longitudinal bands may also appear. Underside pale brown to whitish, usually with numerous closely-approximated brown blotches. Fins brownish with rows of dark spots and blotches.

Sex-distinctions unknown.

The *Bunocephalidae* are typically crepuscular fishes which, during the daytime, dig themselves into the bottom-soil rather after the fashion of Flounders. They should be kept in a large aquarium, provided with a soft bottom-soil, clumps of twigs and

Figs. 637–640
Fig. 637. *Pseudopimelodus acanthodira;* adult, natural size.
Fig. 638. *Pseudopimelodus raninus;* half-grown, somewhat reduced.
Fig. 639. *Rhamdia queleni;* half-grown, reduced.
Fig. 640. *Rhamdia sapo;* adult, much reduced.

stones. Planting is not necessary. Omnivorous. Preferred temperature between 20–25°C. Nothing is known about their breeding behaviour. 1921/–.

Family Malapteruridae (Electric Catfishes)

This family contains only the following species:–

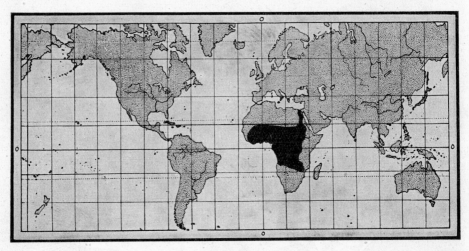

Fig. 641
Distribution of the *Malapteruridae*

Malapterurus electricus (*Gmelin* 1789) (Fig. 495) Electric Catfish
Africa, with the exception of Lake Victoria and the rivers of East Africa north of the Zambesi; to 65 cm.

Plate 111

Fig. 642. *Oryzias latipes* (Japanese Ricefish); adults, enlarged; above, ♂, below, ♀. (Original)

Fig. 643. *Aphyosemion arnoldi* (Arnold's Lyretail); adults, enlarged; left, ♀, right, ♂. (Photo Dr. Foersch)

Fig. 644. *Aphyosemion cognatum* (Red Lyretail); enlarged; left, ♂, right, ♀. (Photo Dr. Foersch)

428

Plate 111

Plate 112

Plate 112

Fig. 645. *Aphyosemion arnoldi* (Arnold's Lyretail/Aphyosemion); ♂, greatly enlarged. (Photo Dr. Foersch)

Fig. 646. *Aphyosemion schoutedeni;* ♂, greatly enlarged. Photo from a block provided by courtesy of Dr. Max Poll, Musée Royal d'Afrique Centrale.

Fig. 647. *Aphyosemion gardneri* (Steel-blue Aphyosemion); adults, enlarged; left, ♀, right, ♂. (Photo Dr. Foersch)

A 3/6–10. Body oblong, plump. Head thick. Eyes small, phosphorescent in the dark. No dorsal fin. Adipose fin inserted far back. Pectoral fins without spines. 3 pairs of barbels. Lips fleshy. Especially interesting for the possession of a pair of electric organs embedded in the thick skin on either side of the body so as to envelop the whole trunk. The electrical discharge is under voluntary control. Back grey-brown, flanks flesh-coloured to grey, belly reddish to yellowish-white. Numerous dark blotches are strewn over the head and flanks. Pectoral and ventral fins reddish; caudal fin with a dark base and a broad grey to orange-coloured or red margin. The young have a pale band around the caudal peduncle.

Sex-distinctions unknown.

A very quarrelsome and voracious fish which remains hidden during the day and becomes active at nightfall. Only young specimens are suitable for the domestic aquarium.

Care, as for other Catfishes. Live food, especially earthworms, and meat. Growth very rapid, even in captivity. Temperature 23–30°C. Solitary confinement essential. Breeding unknown (probably a mouth-brooder?). The ♀♀ spawn in depressions. This species figures in ancient Egyptian tomb-paintings of about 6000 years ago. 1904/+.

Family Callichthyidae (Mailed Catfishes)

Small, heavily armoured Catfishes, widely distributed in the inland waters of South America and Trinidad. Characteristic of the whole family are the bony plates on the flanks, arranged in two series overlapping like the tiles on a roof. The head and the ridge of the back may also be armoured. The adipose fin has a strong movable spine. Dorsal fin large, with a powerful spine and

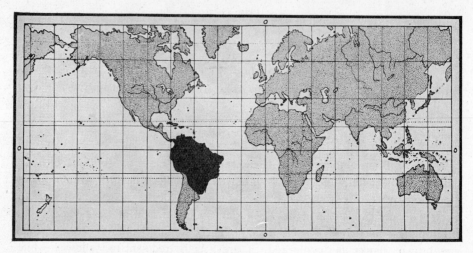

Fig. 648
Distribution of the *Callichthyidae*

7–8 soft rays. Ventral fins (1/5) usually inserted under the last third of the dorsal fin. The terminal mouth is small and the jaws may be toothed or toothless. 1–2 pairs of maxillary barbels; no mandibular barbels. Swim-bladder in two parts, encased in bone. Eyes movable.

Mailed Catfishes inhabit slowly-flowing, rarely standing, waters. Gathered in small troops they search for anything eatable in shallow water and also on occasions investigate mud and sandbanks. The powerful pectoral fin-spines are used when the fishes are moving about on land and are also employed as

Figs. 649–653

Fig. 649. *Rhamdia sebae;* half-grown, reduced.
Fig. 650. *Sorubim lima;* half-grown, reduced. Below is shown a dorsal view of the head of the same species.
Fig. 651. *Pygidium itatiayae;* adult, somewhat reduced.
Fig. 652. *Homodiaetus maculatus;* natural size.
Fig. 653. *Vandellia cirrhosa;* twice maximum natural size.

The barbels are often shown as wavy in these drawings, but in life they are carried stiffly and splayed out.

stilts. The respiration of these animals, also, is often well-adapted to an amphibious way of life. During a spell ashore, or in foul waters which are poor in oxygen, the hindgut may be brought into service as an air-breathing organ. In such cases, as with the Loaches, air is taken in through the mouth, passed through the intestine and utilised by the vascular respiratory endothelium of the hindgut. Many species can wander for considerable distances when the air is sufficiently humid.

Almost all the Mailed Catfishes prove to be quite hardy and contented in captivity. Their individual, often inquisitive and tame, behaviour constantly wins new friends for this group of fishes. Frequently they even prove to be quite useful members of the aquarium community, since they often clear up food-remains of all kinds which are of no further interest to the other inhabitants and constantly chew through the mulm on the bottom, behaviour which, among German aquarists, has earned them the title of 'Gesundheits-polizei' (= 'sanitary squad'). If food is scarce, however, or if there is no mulm-layer, or if they are continually disturbed or in poor condition, the Mailed Catfishes may cause considerable annoyance by their violent digging in the soil; in any case an efficient filtration-system is strongly recommended. Large troops should certainly be given a tank to themselves and attempts at breeding should likewise be carried out in a special tank. Feeding is a very simple matter; as well as live foods of all kinds, especially wormfoods, dried food is also accepted. Temperature 18–26°C.; considerable tolerance of cooling. The quality of the water plays, as a rule, no very large role; water which has been biologically well worked through is to be preferred, with, occasionally, the addition of fresh water which has been allowed to stand for a while. Mailed Catfishes should not be kept in water which is too acid.

Plate 113

Fig. 654. *Aphyosemion petersi* (Peters' Round-tailed Aphyosemion); adults, enlarged; left, ♀, right, ♂. (Photo Dr. Foersch)
Fig. 655. *Micropanchax macrophthalmus* (Lamp-eyed Panchax); about twice natural size; above, ♀, below, ♂. (Original)
Fig. 656. *Fundulus chrysotus* (Golden Ear); adults, natural size; above, ♂, below, ♀.

Plate 113

Plate 114

Plate 114

Figs. 657–659. Spawning behaviour of *Cynolebias belotti* (Argentine Pearlfish) on a hard, compact bottom. (Photos Dr. Foersch) For the continuation of this sequence, see Plate 115.

Figs. 657–658. The ♂ commences, grubbing up the bottom while the ♀ remains close beside him.

Fig. 659. Since the sandy bottom is too compact the attempt is abortive; the fishes therefore spawn on the bottom. The ♀ for this purpose curves her anal fin to one side, forming a conical pouch with which she partly embraces the anal fin of the ♂. In this position the eggs and sperm are shed.

The breeding of these fishes in captivity is unfortunately not easy; at least it has not so far proved possible to provoke the reproductive drive in many species. The following species, among others, have been bred: – *Callichthys callichthys, Corydoras paleatus, aeneus, hastatus, julii, melanistius, myersi, pestai, rabauti, reticulatus, schultzei* and *undulatus*. The sexes are not hard to distinguish when sexually ripe; the ♀♀ are invariably larger, more robust and bulkier in the belly and, furthermore, the dorsal fin is often rounded in the ♀ and pointed in the ♂. As a rule no particular preparations are necessary for breeding; indeed, one indefatigable breeder, *Corydoras paleatus*, will even spawn in a community tank. In the single-species tank, which should provide soft and not too pale bottom-soil, isolated clumps of plants and hiding-places under stones or broken flowerpots, spawning may be stimulated by the addition of fresh water and periodic fluctuations of temperature between 17° and 25°C. One ripe ♀ should be mated with two or three ♂♂. At the beginning of the interesting courtship the ♂♂ nudge and caress the increasingly restless ♀ which eventually begins to swim continuously about the tank attended by the dancing ♂♂. During brief pauses in this performance stones, plants and the sides of the tank are cleaned in various places. The actual pairing has been variously described. According to Knaack the ♂ is said to grip the barbels of the ♀ with his pectoral fins and to press her against his ventral side. Other very exact observers record a sucking by the ♀ of the genital papilla of the ♂, a process which the ♂ assists by presenting a broad flank. In the former case the sperm would be brushed onto the eggs by

433

movements of the fins and gill-cover without actually passing into the mouth. In the latter case the sperm would be taken up in the mouth and conveyed to the eggs in the respiratory stream by strong movements of the gill-cover. The eggs are extruded during the sucking action (usually 3–5 at a time) and cradled in a pouch formed by the ventral fins.

It should be stated that the second report seems more likely in comparison with other Catfishes and is also supported from the scientific side. The ♀ now swims to a place already cleaned, cleans it a second time, and attaches the eggs. The total number of eggs laid at a spawning may be up to about 250; at the end of a spawning-period, which in well-fed fishes may comprise up to 15 spawnings at intervals of 4–7 days, fewer. Several spawning-periods may occur in one year. During a single spawning-session the fishes often have a meal-interval and should then be fed; if food is lacking the eggs which have been laid are destroyed. On this account, too, the parents should be removed from the tank after spawning. The eggs, which are nearly 2 mm. in diameter, are originally pale but become darker during development. At 20–23 °C. the young hatch, on average, after 5–8 days and are best transferred to an all-glass tank without soil, although they often thrive also in the breeding tank after a partial change of water. With good feeding – micro-foods, small Enchytraeids, nauplii, and later *Tubifex*, larger Enchytraeids and *Daphnia* – growth is rapid. Young Mailed Catfishes are among the drollest of fish-children. Some species build foam-nests (see *Callichthys callichthys*, below).

Callichthys callichthys (*Linnaeus* 1758) (Fig. 663)
Eastern Brazil, to La Plata; to 18 cm.
D I/6; A 1/5–6; 26–29 bony scutes in the upper lateral series, 25–28 in the lower. Body elongate, of almost uniform depth, tapering in breadth posteriorly. Head broad, flattened dorsally. Two rows of bony scutes on the flanks, arranged like tiles

Figs. 660–663
Fig. 660. *Bunocephalus bicolor;* adult, somewhat reduced.
Fig. 661. *Bunocephalus bicolor;* dorsal view.
Fig. 662. *Bunocephalus kneri;* somewhat reduced.
Fig. 663. *Callichthys callichthys;* adult, reduced.

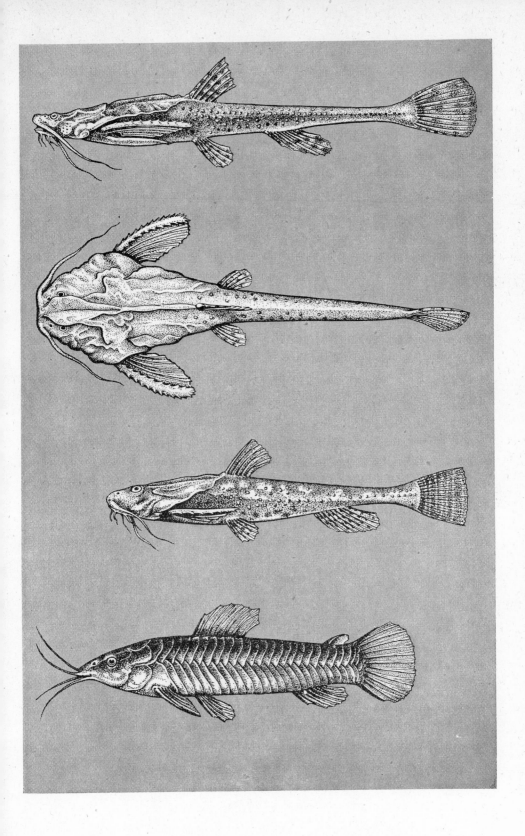

on a roof. Caudal fin rounded. 2 pairs of maxillary barbels, which reach to the pectoral fins when laid back. Eyes small. Dark olive-green to dark grey with a delicate blue or violet sheen on the flanks. Underside blue-grey to brownish. Fins grey with dark spots, the margins pale or, in fine specimens, orange to reddish.

The ♂♂ are distinguished from the ♀♀ by their brighter colouring and stouter pectoral spines.

C. callichthys is a crepuscular fish which goes in search of prey chiefly at night. Aquarium arrangements as given in the family description. The breeding behaviour of this species shows several peculiarities. The eggs (about 120 at a spawning) are laid in a bubble-nest built under broad floating leaves or under *Riccia*. The care of the nest is taken over by the ♂ which now and then during this period emits loud grunts. The young hatch after 4–5 days and should be treated in much the same way as young *Corydoras* spp. 1897/+.

Brochis coeruleus (*Cope* 1872) (Figs. 555, 693)
Upper Amazon near Iquitos; to 7 cm.

D I/10–11; A 1/6–7; P I/7–9; V 1/5; 21–22 bony scutes in the upper lateral series, 20–21 in the lower. More strongly compressed than the *Corydoras* spp., from which the genus *Brochis* is further distinguished by the longer-based dorsal fin and the armoured snout. Coloration, according to Schultze (1938): upper part of head over the eyes brown with a dirty green tinge; lower part of the head and the greater part of the flanks a lovely shining emerald green; underside and a narrow edging along the lower row of scutes a beautiful ochre-yellow. Dorsal, adipose and caudal fins transparent brownish; remaining fins yellowish. A very beautiful species.

Further particulars as given in the family description. 1938/+.

Corydoras aeneus (*Gill* 1858) (Fig. 664)   Bronze Corydoras
Venezuela, Trinidad, southwards to the La Plata streams; to 7 cm.

D I/7; A 1/6–7; 21–23 bony scutes in the upper lateral series, 19–21 in the lower.

Figs. 664–670

Fig. 664. *Corydoras aeneus* (Bronze Corydoras); natural size.
Fig. 665. *Corydoras schultzei;* natural size.
Fig. 666. *Corydoras pestai;* natural size.
Fig. 667. *Corydoras nattereri* (Blue Corydoras); natural size.
Fig. 668. *Corydoras trilineatus;* natural size.
Fig. 669. (Below, left) – *Corydoras griseus;* natural size.
Fig. 670. (Below, right) – *Corydoras hastatus* (Dwarf Corydoras); somewhat enlarged.

Coloration uniform yellow-brown to delicate reddish-brown with a strong metallic glint on the sides of the head and body, sometimes shining green, sometimes coppery or, in sunlight, golden. The coloration along the middle of the flanks is substantially darker.

For further particulars, see family description. 1933/+.

Corydoras agassizi *Steindachner* 1877 (Figs. 560, 677)   Agassiz's Corydoras
Western Brazil, widely distributed; to 6·5 cm.

D I/7; A 1/6–7; P I/6; V 1/5; 23 bony scutes in the upper lateral series, 21 in the lower. Upperside pale brown to clay-colour, paling considerably on the flanks to a delicate yellowish to silver. Underside white. Along the middle of the flank, from the gill-cover to the root of the tail, there extends a very pale, broad band which encloses three longitudinal rows of dark blotches. Further blotches, mainly of elongate-oval shape, may be present, loosely distributed over the whole body. Fins translucent grey, vertical fins with regular rows of brown spots. Anterior part of the dorsal fin, involving the first three rays, black.

For further particulars, see family description. 1936/+.

Corydoras arcuatus *Elwin* 1939 (Figs. 561, 692)   Arched Corydoras
Amazon Basin near the town of Teffé; to 5 cm.

D I/7; A 1/6; 22–24 bony scutes in the upper lateral series, 20–22 in the lower. Grey-yellowish to delicate grey-green; underside pure white. A broad, dark longitudinal band commences at the corner of the mouth and passes across the eye into an arched course following the profile of the back to the root of the tail where it turns abruptly downwards and, becoming narrower, continues along the lower edge of the caudal fin. No other markings. Fins colourless; caudal with fine dark spots and a blackish upper edge.

For further particulars, see family description. 1938/+.

Corydoras barbatus (*Quoy* and *Gaimard* 1840) (Fig. 695)   Banded Corydoras
From Santos to Rio de Janeiro; to 10 cm.

D I/7–8; A 1/6–7; 24–27 bony scutes in the upper lateral series, 22–23 in the lower. Body, in contrast to other species, greatly elongated. Brilliant yellow-brown, the lower flanks golden. Underside delicate yellowish to white. Blackish to lovely yellow-brown markings on the flanks, leaving clear two large golden blotches on the upper side of the caudal peduncle. Large, gleaming brassy spots on the upper surface of the head and on the cheeks. Vertical fins with rows of brownish spots.

438

♂ snout bristly; dorsal and pectoral fins more strongly produced than in the ♀.

For further particulars, see family description. 1934/ –.

Corydoras cochui *Myers* and *Weitzmann* 1953 (Fig. 682)
Central Brazil, Santa Maria Nova, Rio Uruguay; to 2·5 cm.

D I/7; A 1/6; 22 bony scutes in the upper lateral series, 20 in the lower. Shares with *C. hastatus* the distinction of being the smallest Mailed Catfish. Grey-brown to silver-grey with a yellowish to golden sheen on the flanks. Irregular, often almost rectangular, dark blotches on the upper half of the body, somewhat resembling a chessboard pattern in their arrangement. Underside uniform white-grey. Fins colourless. The first rays of the pectoral and dorsal fins are dark. Dorsal and caudal fins with rows of fine dark spots.

For further particulars, see family description. 1954.

Corydoras elegans *Steindachner* 1877 (Fig. 679)
Middle Amazon River; to 6 cm.

D I/7; A 1/6–7; 21–22 bony scutes in the upper lateral series, 20 in the lower. Coloration of freshly-preserved specimens (according to Rachow): ground-colour yellowish. Upperside somewhat darker, approaching to pale ochre. Underside paler, white apart from the lateral scutes. Upper surface of head marbled with grey-brown. A dark, vague-edged, wedge-shaped band extends from the hinder part of the head to the root of the tail, its anterior portion passing through several blotches. Below this band is accompanied along the flanks by a pale stripe which, in turn, has a row of dark spots along its lower edge. This row of spots commences at the upper edge of the gill-cover and curves down towards a dark stripe along the upper edges of the lateral scutes with which it eventually unites. In the triangular area contained between the row of spots and the dark lateral stripe there are three further dark spots. Beneath the dark stripe along the scutes there is a pale band, bounded below by yet another row of dark spots. A black, wedge-shaped blotch on each of the anterior scutes of the lateral series. Gill-cover brilliant pale blue. Fins grey, the dorsal often with dark blotches.

For further particulars, see family description. 1938/ –.

Corydoras grafi *Holly* 1940
Brazil, district around Manaos; to 6·5 cm.

D I/7; A 1/6; P I/7; V 1/5; 23 bony scutes in the upper lateral series, 20 in the lower. Silver-grey to yellowish grey, thinly strewn with brown-black spots on the head and flanks. A conspicuous wedge-shaped band across the eye. Dorsal fin with large, dark blotches, which to some extent overlap the back. Caudal fin with pronounced dark transverse bands. Adipose fin with a black blotch.

For further particulars, see family description. 1938/+.

Corydoras griseus (*Holly* 1940) (Fig. 669)
The smaller and smallest tributaries of the Amazon; to 5 cm.

D I/7; A 1/6; P I/7; V 1/5; 23 bony scutes in the upper lateral series, 20 in the lower. Coloration (according to O. Schultze): uniform yellowish-grey. A 3 mm. broad dark band from the crown of the head running somewhat obliquely downwards and forwards across the eye. A narrow black stripe along the bony scutes where these overlap on the flanks. A dark hind edge to each bony scute. All fins colourless.

For further particulars, see family description. 1938/+.

Corydoras hastatus *R. S. Eigenmann* and *C. H. Eigenmann* 1888 (Figs. 498, 670)
Dwarf or Pigmy Corydoras
Amazon Basin, near Villa Bella; to 3 cm.

D I/7–8; A 2/5–6; 22 bony scutes in the upper lateral series, 20 in the lower. Ground colour grey-green to golden yellow. Back green-olive, flanks yellowish, belly whitish. Head, body and fins sprinkled with small dark spots. A black longitudinal band runs from behind the gill-cover to a lozenge-shaped blotch at the root of the tail; the latter blotch has a yellowish margin above and below. A second, broader streak runs along the lower edge of the caudal peduncle. Fins dull grey, the base of the caudal blackish.

For further particulars, see family description.

A dainty, very often free-swimming, species which is quite happy in the smallest aquarium and likes to live in shoals. 1912/+.

Plate 115

Figs. 671–673. Spawning behaviour of *Cynolebias belotti* (Argentine Pearlfish), sequence continued from Plate 114.
Fig. 671. The ♀ separates herself vigorously from the ♂ and thrusts herself against the bottom.
Fig. 672. The anal fin of the ♀ is pushed, like a shovel, into the sand
Fig. 673. which is whirled high as she swims away, so covering over the eggs which have been laid.

Plate 115

Plate 116

Plate 116

Fig. 674. *Epiplatys duboisi;* ripe adults, about twice natural size; above, ♀, below, ♂. (Photo Dr. Foersch)

Fig. 675. *Epiplatys multifasciatus;* a species imported from the Congo Basin in 1956, enlarged; above, ♂, below, ♀. (Photo Dr. Foersch)

Fig. 676. *Epiplatys chaperi* (Fire-mouth Panchax); young pair, enlarged; above, ♂, below, ♀. (Original)

Corydoras julii *Steindachner* 1906 (Figs. 557, 688)   Leopard Corydoras
(= *Corydoras leopardus* Myers 1933)
Smallest tributaries of the lower Amazon; to 6 cm.

D I/7; A 2/6; P I/9; V 1/6; 22 bony scutes in the upper lateral series, 21 in the lower. Silver-grey, sprinkled with numerous small black spots which, on the gill-cover and the upper surface of the head, coalesce into worm-like lines. Between the upper and lower rows of lateral scutes there is a dark longitudinal band which is edged by grey-silvery bands above and below. The whole body has a delicate greenish metallic lustre by reflected light. Fins silver-grey, the tip of the dorsal black and the anal fin spotted with black. Caudal with curved vertical rows of spots.

The form described as *C. leopardus* is at most only a subspecies of the above. For further particulars, see family description. 1933/ +.

Corydoras macropterus *Regan* 1913 (Fig. 694)
Southern Brazil; to 7 cm.

D I/8; A 1/6–7; 24–25 bony plates in the upper lateral series, 21–22 in the lower. The cheeks of this species are bristly. Grey-brown to clay-coloured, the upperside darker, the underside delicate pale brown to white. Flanks with a greenish to bluish lustre, according to the light, with dark to blackish markings whose arrangement is best indicated by reference to Fig. 694. Dorsal and anal fins with rows of dark spots. Dorsal fin-spine black.

♂ with stronger bristles on the cheeks, and the dorsal and anal fins more strongly produced.

For further particulars, see family description. Not too high a temperature, 18–21 °C. 1912/ –.

Corydoras melanistius *Regan* 1912 (Figs. 552, 681)   Black-spotted Corydoras
Northern South America: Essequibo; to 6 cm.

D I/7; A 1/6; 21–23 bony scutes in the upper lateral series, 19–20 in the lower.

441

Yellowish-white to grey with a faint reddish tinge, strewn with numerous small brown spots. A wedge-shaped black band extends from the nape across the eye and cheek to the lower edge of the latter. A similar band runs from the base of the dorsal fin to the insertion of the pectoral. Anal and caudal fins finely spotted, remaining fins colourless.

For further particulars, see family description. 1934/+.

Corydoras myersi *H. Ribeiro* 1942 (Figs. 562, 691) Myers' Corydoras
Small tributaries of the Amazon above the junction with the Rio Negro; to 6 cm.

D I/7; A 1/6; 22–23 bony scutes in the upper lateral series, 20–21 in the lower. A very brilliantly coloured species. Bright orange-red with, here and there, a slight delicate blackish tinge. Nape and throat somewhat paler to yellowish. A very broad, dark brown band, which commences in front of the dorsal fin and runs almost straight to the upper root of the tail, is characteristic of this species. The region around the eye is likewise dark brown. The gill-cover and the region immediately behind it are often iridescent greenish. Fins uniform pale grey.

For further particulars, see family description. 1948.

Corydoras nattereri *Steindachner* 1877 (Fig. 667) Blue Corydoras
Eastern Brazil; to 6·5 cm.

D I/7; A 1/5–7; 21–23 bony scutes in the upper lateral series, 20–21 in the lower. Back greenish-brown, flanks iridescent bluish-green, belly yellowish to orange or pink. A dark irregular blotch beneath the first dorsal fin-ray. A dark longitudinal band, tapering posteriorly, from the gill-cover to the root of the tail. Fins grey, the dorsal, especially, often black-tipped.

For further particulars, see family description. 1920/−.

Figs. 677–682

Fig. 677. *Corydoras agassizi* (Agassiz's Corydoras); natural size.
Fig. 678. *Corydoras treitli;* somewhat enlarged.
Fig. 679. *Corydoras elegans;* natural size.
Fig. 680. *Corydoras punctatus;* natural size.
Fig. 681. *Corydoras melanistius* (Black-spotted Corydoras); natural size.
Fig. 682. (lower right) – *Corydoras cochui;* somewhat enlarged.

Corydoras paleatus (*Jenyns* 1842) (Figs. 545, 687)   Peppered Corydoras
South-eastern Brazil and the La Plata basin; to 7 cm.

D I/7–8; A 1/6; 22–24 bony scutes in the upper lateral series, 20–22 in the lower. Back dark olive-brown to -green, flanks yellowish-green with a metallic glint, belly yellowish-white. On the back and flanks there are large, irregular blotches which may coalesce into transverse bars. Whole body strewn with numerous small, dark spots. Dorsal, caudal and anal fins grey with rows of blackish streaks and spots.

For further particulars, see family description. This species was bred by Carbonnier in Paris as long ago as 1878. 1893/+.

Corydoras pestai *Holly* 1940 (Figs. 555, 666)
Smallest tributaries of the Amazon; to 5 cm.

D I/7; A 1/6; P I/7; V 1/5; 24 bony scutes in the upper lateral series, 22 in the lower. The fins of this species are relatively short. Coloration (according to Schultze): head pale brown, marbled with dark. The gill-cover is marked with shining green blotches and the red gills show through. Back dark green up to the end of the dorsal fin; the lateral scutes at this level have dark edges. The dark dorsal region is bounded laterally by a broad, shining gold stripe which, behind the dorsal fin, spreads up onto the back itself. The lower parts of the upper row of lateral scutes are a lovely dark green. From the mid-line upwards the body is golden yellow. Each scute of the lower lateral series bears a dark, comma-shaped stripe. Fin-membranes colourless, fin-rays dark.

For further particulars, see family description. 1938/+.

Corydoras punctatus (*Bloch* 1794) (Fig. 680)
Basins of the Orinoco, Essequibo and Amazon; to 6 cm.

D I/7; A 1/6; 22–24 bony scutes in the upper lateral series, 20–21 in the lower. Delicate smoke-grey or yellowish-grey with numerous black spots which are especially thick on the back and upper parts of the flanks; those on the head are the largest. A row of dark spots along the line of overlap of the lateral scutes. Fins

Plate 117

Fig. 683. *Cynolebias belotti* (Argentine Pearlfish) during preliminaries to spawning; left, ♀, right, ♂; about natural size. (Photo Dr. Foersch)
Fig. 684. *Aplocheilus lineatus;* adults, natural size; above, ♀, below, ♂. Specimens in the Erfurt Aquarium. (Original)

Plate 117

Plate 118

Plate 118

Fig. 685. *Aphyosemion calabaricus* (Calabar Lyretail); ♂, twice natural size. (Photo Dr. Foersch)

Fig. 686. *Cynopoecilus ladigesi;* pair, somewhat enlarged; above, ♂, below, ♀. The brownish bands in this ♂ are usually dark wine-red, and the pale bands sea-green. (Original)

translucent. Outer part of dorsal fin pitch-black, caudal and anal fins with rows of dark spots, adipose fin with a dark blotch.

For further particulars, see family description. 1935/+.

Corydoras rabauti *La Monte* 1941 (Fig. 732) Dwarf or Rabaut's Corydoras
Amazon River in the neighbourhood of Manãos; to 3 cm.

D I/7; A 1/5–6; P I/9; V 1/5. Coloration (according to Axelrod and Schultz): no dark bar through the eye. A broad, dark zone begins immediately behind the gill-cover and reaches up to the dorsal fin, covering the whole body between the pectoral fins and the end of the anal.

For sex-distinctions, care and breeding, see family description. *C. myersi* is often erroneously figured as *C. rabauti*. Importation into Europe very doubtful.

Corydoras reticulatus *Fraser-Brunner* 1938 (Figs. 558, 559, 689)
Reticulated Corydoras
River Amazon, near Monte Alegre; to 7 cm.

D I/7; A 1/6; P I/9; V 1/6; 22 bony scutes in the upper lateral series, 21 in the lower. One of the most beautiful of the Mailed Catfishes. Head, back and flanks dark brown netted with black to form a trelliswork or honeycomb pattern. The spaces enclosed by the trellis are a lovely and intense shining green-red; towards the underside this brilliant colouring becomes lost and the markings less distinct. Underside pale. An ochre-coloured band extends along the ridge of the back from the dorsal fin-base. Fins transparent. Dorsal fin with a dark base and dark brown to black spots; with a large, black, white-margined blotch in the young. Caudal fin with thick rows of dark spots. Anal fin likewise with dark blotches. The coloration described above only appears in sexually ripe fishes; the young are more or less grey to reddish with an indistinct network of markings.

In the ♀♀ the honeycomb pattern is not so clear as in the ♂♂.

For further particulars, see family description. 1938/+.

Corydoras schultzei *Holly* 1940 (Figs.553, 665)
Small tributaries of the Amazon; to 6·5 cm.

D I/7; A I/6; P 1/7; V 1/5; 24 bony scutes in the upper lateral series, 21–22 in the lower. Coloration (according to Schultze): alongside the dark ridge of the back there is a broad golden zone which is prettily contrasted with the dark green to black of the mid-flank. Belly brilliant yellow, head and gill-cover dark brown. All fins transparent grey.

For further particulars, see family description. 1938/+.

Corydoras treitli *Steindachner* 1806 (Fig.678)
Eastern Brazil, also neighbourhood of Pernambuco; to 5·5 cm.

D I/8; A 1/7; 23 bony plates in the upper lateral series, 21 in the lower. Coloration (according to Arnold): upperside brownish-yellow. Flanks paler to pale yellow, with a golden glint by reflected light. An irregular dark longitudinal band along the middle of the body to the root of the tail. Upper half of body with dark spots and streaks. A dark zone extends from the dark brown dorsal fin-base to the middle of the flank. An almost black streak from the dark hinder part of the head, across the eye, to the snout. Fins grey with rows of dark spots.

For further particulars, see family description. 1933/−.

Corydoras trilineatus *Cope* 1871 (Fig.668)
Middle reaches of the Amazon, around Iquitos and Pebas; to 7 cm.

D I/7; A 1/7; 23–24 bony scutes in the upper lateral series, 20–22 in the lower. Silver-grey to olive-grey. Underside pale grey to white. Gill-cover with a greenish lustre. On the upper half of the body are three dark, irregular and repeatedly interrupted longitudinal bands, which either disappear on the caudal peduncle or break up into rows of blotches. Fins colourless, transparent. Dorsal with a large black blotch. Caudal fin with loose transverse rows of dark spots.

For further particulars, see family description. 1938/+.

Figs.687–692

Fig.687. *Corydoras paleatus* (Peppered Corydoras); natural size.
Fig.688. *Corydoras julii* (Leopard Corydoras); natural size.
Fig.689. *Corydoras reticulatus* (Reticulated Corydoras); adult, natural size.
Fig.690. *Corydoras undulatus;* maximum size.
Fig.691. *Corydoras myersi* (Myers' Corydoras); natural size.
Fig.692. *Corydoras arcuatus* (Arched Corydoras); slightly enlarged.

Corydoras undulatus (*Regan* 1912) (Fig. 690)
La Plata State and eastern Brazil; to 5·5 cm.

D 1/7; A 1/6–7; 21–23 bony scutes in the upper lateral series, 19–20 in the lower. Back yellowish to brownish-olive, flanks paler, belly ochre-coloured. Underside of head and throat yellowish-white. Head and flanks with numerous dark blotches and spots which, especially on the flanks, unite into wavy lines. Between the dark spots there are isolated shining green-gold spots which, on the gill-cover, run together into wavy lines. Fins with rows of dark spots and streaks.

In the ♂ the dorsal fin is said to have a black tip.

For further particulars, see family description. 1912/+.

In 1938 a specimen of a new species was imported which Holly (*Anz. Akad. Wien*, Vol. 77, p. 108, 1940) called *Corydoras grafi*. Details of the living fish are not available.

The fish often offered in the trade as *Corydoras auratus* is probably not a distinct species but merely a particularly fine colour-variety of *Corydoras aeneus* Gill.

Hoplosternum littorale (*Hancock* 1828) (Fig. 696)
Trinidad, Guiana, Brazil, southwards to the Paraná; to 20 cm.

The genus *Hoplosternum* is very close to the genus *Callichthys*, and both are clearly distinguished from *Corydoras* and *Brochis* by the armouring of the ridge of the back which is absent from the last two genera mentioned.

D I/8; A 2/5; 25 bony scutes in the upper lateral series, 23 in the lower. Body slightly thick-set, club-shaped, of pretty uniform depth. Caudal fin only moderately forked. Two pairs of fairly long maxillary barbels. Upperside blackish to green-black. Flanks blue-grey to dark grey, gradually paling towards the underside, which is pale grey to greenish. Fins pale grey to colourless, transparent.

Sex-distinctions in coloration not yet described.

Figs. 693–697

Fig. 693. *Brochis coeruleus;* natural size.
Fig. 694. *Corydoras macropterus*; ♂, maximum size.
Fig. 695. *Corydoras barbatus* (Banded Corydoras); somewhat reduced.
Fig. 696. *Hoplosternum littorale;* adult, reduced.
Fig. 697. *Hoplosternum thoracatum;* adult, reduced. (The caudal fin of the specimen figured appears to be considerably eroded – Ed.)

The barbels are often shown as wavy in these drawings, but in life they are carried stiffly and splayed out.

Care, as given in the family description. Omnivorous. According to Vipan, this species is said to build a bubble-nest which is strengthened with pieces of plant material; the ♂ takes care of the young. 1950 (?).

Hoplosternum thoracatum (*Cuvier* and *Valenciennes* 1840) (Fig. 697)
Amazon Basin, Guiana, Trinidad; to 20 cm.
D I/8; A 1/6–8; 25–26 bony scutes in the upper lateral series, 23–24 in the lower. Body-form and finnage similar to those of the previous species. Coloration very variable, in relation to the wide distribution. Dark olive-brown to grey brown. Upperside often blackish-olive, underside pale brown to whitish. The whole body, including the belly, is covered with large and small black blotches which may occasionally coalesce like transverse bands. Fins, especially the dorsal and caudal, with dark spots. Caudal fin with a broad, pale transverse stripe at the base.
Sex-distinctions in coloration not yet described.
Schubert has described the breeding behaviour as follows:–each ♀ is courted by several ♂♂ which build a bubble-nest at the surface. A ♂ stations himself vertically under the nest and the ♀ abstracts sperm from him by sucking with her mouth. The ♀ sinks, shooting abruptly to the bottom and then, with eggs cradled between her ventral fins, rises again to the surface bringing eggs and sperm to the bubble-nest. The ♂♂ take care of the young which hatch after about 4 days.
Further particulars as given for the previous species. 1911/+.

Family Loricariidae

The *Loricariidae* are confined to northern and central South America, where they mainly inhabit small and very small flowing waters of the type of our mountain and meadow streams. Members of the genera *Plecostomus*, *Xenocara* and *Ancistrus* only are sometimes found also towards the mouths of rivers, i.e., in slightly brackish water. Typical of the *Loricariidae* is the strong armouring of the body, which is in many ways reminiscent of the condition in the *Callichthyidae* but differs in that, whereas in the latter family there are only two series of lateral bony scutes on the flanks, in the *Loricariidae* there are generally three to four series following after the likewise armoured head. In the genera *Loricaria*, *Farlowella*, *Otocinclus*, and others, the ventral surface of the body is also armoured (ventral series of scutes); the genera *Plecostomus*, *Xenocara*, *Ancistrus*, *Stoneiella* and others are, on the contrary, naked on the lower side which is at most covered with tiny splinters of bone. The first group is further easily distinguished from the second by the absence of an adipose fin. An exception in the matter of armouring is provided by the sub-family *Argiinae* whose members are completely naked. The body is, in general, strongly flattened, particularly on the ventral side, and the head

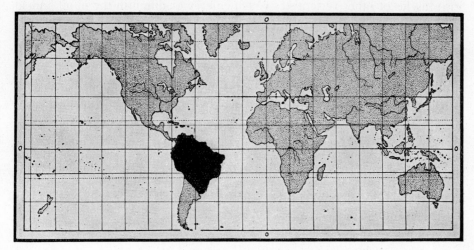

Fig. 698
Distribution of the *Loricariidae*

almost always very broad. The caudal peduncle is more or less strongly attenuated and laterally compressed. Excepting the caudal, all the fins are characterised by a powerful spine (the first fin-ray) which, in the pectoral fins often especially thickened, may serve the fishes for locomotion on land.

The mouth is ventral, surrounded by broad, lobed lips, and serves as a sucking-mouth which represents a notable adaptation to the natural environment of the fish. The *Loricariidae* are bottom-dwellers which live among stones or roots and work themselves forward by clinging to these objects against the force of the often strong current. They are able to swim in mid-water only for a short time. Their food consists mainly of algae which are grazed from stones or plants. The *Loricariidae* are unique among fishes in that they possess an iris-lobe, i.e., a small peg-shaped process of the upper iris which projects down into the pupil. In light the iris-lobe expands and covers almost the entire pupil; in darkness it contracts leaving the pupil completely unobscured. The iris-lobe discharges the same function as the iris-muscles of other vertebrates which enlarge or diminish the pupil and so control the amount of light entering the eye. In many species the sexes are easily distinguished, since the ♂♂ carry a peculiar head-decoration in the form of antenna-like outgrowths and may also have bristly cheeks, whereas in the ♀♀ these structures are always more weakly developed and less conspicuous.

Almost all *Loricariidae* can be kept in richly-planted, not too dark aquaria, once they have been slowly accustomed to the poor oxygen supply. Many species, like the members of the genera *Otocinclus* and *Plecostomus*, prove to

Plate 119

Fig. 699. A group of various favourite Live-bearing Tooth-carps
(Individual figures after Innes)
Left-hand series:–
Xiphophorus variatus ♂ (Variegated Platy); example of a variety with a yellowish ground-colour to the body.
Xiphophorus variatus ♂ and ♀; examples of a variety with a delicate blue to greenish ground-colour to the body.
Xiphophorus maculatus, var. – Red Platy.
Xiphophorus maculatus, var. – Wagtail Platy.
Xiphophorus maculatus, var. – Golden Platy.
Xiphophorus maculatus, var. – Green Tuxedo Platy.
Xiphophorus maculatus, var. – Red Tuxedo Platy.

Right-hand series:–
Mollienesia sphenops, var. – Orange-tail Molly.
Mollienesia velifera × *Mollienesia latipinna*, var. – Perma-black Molly.
Mollienesia sphenops ♂, normal wild form.
Xiphophorus maculatus, var. – Salt-and-pepper Platy.
Xiphophorus maculatus, var. – Blue Platy.
Xiphophorus helleri, var. – Red Wagtail Swordtail.

Plate 119

Plate 120

Plate 120

Fig. 700. (above): Normal Swordtail ♂ (*Xiphophorus helleri*). Beneath this are shown stages in the gradual transformation of a ♀ into a functional ♂ (Sex-reversal). (After J. W. Harms)

Fig. 701. (below): *Periophthalmodon schlosseri* (Mudskipper); 20 cm. (After B. Eggert)

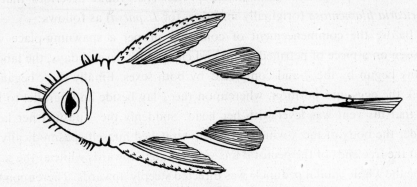

Fig. 702

Xenocara dolichoptera (Blue-chin Xenocara), ventral view, showing the broad, flat expanse of the ventral surface which is considerably augmented by those of the paired fins. The mouth is provided with broad, rough lips with the aid of which the fish is able to scrape off algal films.

be extraordinarily useful, since they keep down algal growth and graze plants, stones and aquarium sides clean in the shortest possible time, with the added advantage that this process is generally accomplished without damage to the plants. Almost all the species are quite accommodating in the matter of temperature (21–25°C.) and, indeed, temporary cooling even seems to do them good. The larger species of *Plecostomus, Xenocara* and *Ancistrus* should obviously be kept only in large tanks. Since all the species are crepuscular and like to hide throughout the day, keeping them singly is not exactly to be recommended. Even the largest species are quite harmless to different, smaller species. They prosper better in soft to medium-hard water than in hard. The main food should be algae, supplemented by lettuce leaves, scraps, worms and also dried food; it must be emphasised that vegetable food is vitally necessary to these fishes. Many species dig themselves in like Flounders into the soil, which should therefore be fine-grained and soft.

The following species have been reared in captivity: *Loricaria filamentosa*, *Loricaria parva*, *Otocinclus flexilis* and *Xenocara dolichoptera*. The spawning-behaviour is probably similar in all species. H.J.Franke describes that of *Loricaria filamentosa* (originally mistaken for *L. parva*) as follows:–

'Before the commencement of courtship proper a spawning-place was chosen on a piece of petrified wood and cleaned for several days, the labour being begun by the ♂ and completed by both sexes. Finally the ♀ began to stick the eggs into position, whereupon the ♂ lay beside and parallel to her so that his vent was level with her head. Suddenly the ♀ pushed her head under the body of the ♂ which forthwith stretched himself spasmodically so that the free ends of the pectoral fins were rotated upwards while at the same time the whole caudal peduncle was directed steeply upwards. Thereupon the ♀ sucked firmly on the right ventral fin of the ♂. In this position both fishes waited several seconds; meantime the ♀, lying on the eggs and breathing heavily, made vigorous fanning movements with her ventral and anal fins, an activity interrupted by beating movements to left and right with the caudal peduncle. Probably the fertilisation of the eggs is accomplished in the following manner: during the stretching of the ♂ body the sperm is emitted which, by means of the vigorous breathing-movements of the ♀, is carried to the ventral fins and, by the beating of the fins and of the caudal peduncle, reaches the eggs. A direct sucking-up of the sperm was not in evidence since for this purpose the ♀ would have had to turn onto her back. The eggs, about 100–200 in number, are large (2 mm.), at first whitish, later yellowish and, a little before hatching, brownish.'

W.Foersch reports the following peculiarities concerning spawning and the rearing of the young (personal communication):–

'The usual spawning-time is from the end of December to June. Most spawnings were wrecked on account of lack of proper opportunities. Narrow crevices, caves, glass or porcelain tubes about 3·5 mm. in diameter, sunk in sand or between stones, or other such things, should be provided in advance.

454

The ♀♀ lay profusely as early as 9 months. The provision of a vegetable diet (lettuce, spinach) notably encourages the onset of spawning. Too many fishes in one tank only damage one another. Occasionally a ♂ completes a spawning in the same tube at intervals of a few days with several ♀♀. The spawning-places should not be too close together, otherwise they will cause bitter fights between the ♂♂. On these occasions the ♂♂ lift the upper body somewhat from the bottom and beat sideways with spread pectoral fins. These fights may last for about 1–2 hours, after which the victor frequently takes possession of the contested spawning-place.

'The young hatch at 20–30°C. after 9–12 days. If there are other fishes in the tank it is recommended to remove the brood-caring ♂ and the spawn carefully into a small private aquarium (with slight aeration, but without filtration). The ♂ frees the young from the egg-membranes by blows with the fins and by sucking up the spawn with the mouth. The rearing of the young, already 1 cm. long, is appropriately carried out during the first few weeks in a small aquarium, without soil but with filtration. Once the yolk-sac is absorbed the hungry young find food on the bottom without difficulty, even when the water-level is high, and are quite ready to hunt moving food. Geisler has established, in the young of *Loricariichthys brunens*, that the proportion of animal nourishment taken is greater than in grown fishes. 'Micro' and *Artemia salina* (which in fresh water soon inhabit the neighbourhood of the bottom) are devoured with vigorous to-and-fro movements of the body. Even large nauplii and the smallest *Cyclops* are at once eagerly snapped up, but such food is difficult to swallow and is unsuitable during the first weeks. If too much food is given at once, losses may result. Chopped small Enchytraeids and *Tubifex* should only be provided in the smallest quantities during the first weeks. The brood overeat themselves easily on a diet too rich in protein without bulk and then pack up. I give – from the first days – supplementary algae, finely-divided and sieved through an aquarium sieve. Still more of this is taken after 2 weeks. Then I go on to small pieces of tender lettuce leaves which soon become soft when weighted in water. After 3–4 weeks entire Enchytraeids of the smaller species may be given, and

455

increasing quantities of chopped *Tubifex*, while at the same time the vegetable diet continues. Only fishes reared in this way are healthy. Larger fishes also gladly take spinach which has been boiled for a short time. If fed with pure *Tubifex* even young of 4–4·5 cm. suddenly become thin and pack up, and these faults in feeding are usually noticed too late. After a few weeks *Cyclops* and small *Daphnia* are gladly taken. The young then sit on the cleanest places on the sides of the tank in thick food (i.e. in the lightest areas, where these crustacea congregate – Ed.). The brood are not specially sensitive to bacterial troubles in the water; if necessary, however, Trypaflavine may be added. Mulm or dead food must be cleared away frequently. The addition of fresh water (about $1/_3$ of the total quantity at intervals of a few days) furthers growth.'

So far, representatives of the following genera have been imported: *Loricaria, Farlowella, Otocinclus, Plecostomus, Ancistrus, Lasiancistrus* (?), *Hemiancistrus* (?), *Stoneiella.*

Ancistrus cirrhosus (*Cuvier* and *Valenciennes* 1840) (Fig. 703)
Paraguay, Amazon Basin, Guiana; to 14 cm.

D I/7; A I/4; P I/6; V I/5; 23–24 bony scutes in a lateral series; 9–13 hooked spines on the movable interopercular (see *Xenocara dolichoptera*). Dark olive-brown to black-brown, the underside pale grey-green or fawn. Numerous irregular pale blotches, in places very thickly scattered, on the head and over the whole body. Fins translucent brownish with dark round blotches which are often arranged in transverse rows. A conspicuous deep black blotch between the first two dorsal rays towards the base of the fin.

Sex-distinctions, as given for *X. dolichoptera.*

Care, as given for *Plecostomus commersoni.* Not yet reared in captivity. 1931/ – .

Figs. 703–706

Fig. 703. *Ancistrus cirrhosus;* adult, natural size.
Fig. 704. *Xenocara dolichoptera* (Blue-chin Xenocara); adult ♂, natural size.
Fig. 705. *Xenocara multispinis;* adult ♂, natural size.
Fig. 706. *Stoneiella leopardus;* adult ♂, natural size.

Farlowella acus (*Kner* 1853) (Figs. 563, 716)

The genus *Farlowella* is distinguished from the closely-related *Loricaria* by the slimmer, more elongate body; by the position of the dorsal fin which is here inserted directly above the anal, and by the elongate head which is strongly produced in front of the mouth to form a rostrum which, in the ♂, is set with fine bristles. Several species have been imported so far, of which, however, only three are known with certainty.

Farlowella acus is a native of Venezuela and southern Brazil (?); to 14·5 cm.

D I/6; A I/5; P I/5–6; V I/4–5; 33–34 bony scutes in a lateral series. On the belly the rows of lateral scutes are closely approximated. Olive-green to yellow-brown, underside yellowish. A very distinct irregular dark band, often beset with blotches, extends from the head to the root of the tail. Fins transparent, the rays with dark spots. Each caudal lobe with a dark band.

Sex-distinctions not certainly known.

Care, as given in the family description. Not yet bred in captivity. 1933/ – .

Farlowella gracilis (*Regan* 1904) (Fig. 717)

Rio Caquetá, Cauca valley, southern Colombia; to 19 cm.

D I/6; A I/5; P I/5–6; V I/4–5; 33 bony scutes in a lateral series. On the belly there is a row of ventral scutes inserted between the lateral series. Grey, with irregularly distributed and indistinct blotches over the whole body. Underside pale grey to yellowish. Fins transparent, colourless; dark spots on all the fin-rays. A conspicuous black longitudinal band on the upper lobe of the caudal.

Sex-distinctions not certainly known.

Care, as given in the family description. Not yet bred in captivity. 1934/ + .

Farlowella schreitmuelleri (*E. Ahl* 1936)

Amazon around Santarem; to 20 cm.

D I/6; A I/5; P I/6; V I/5; 32–33 bony scutes in a lateral series. On the belly there is a row of ventral scutes inserted between the lateral series. Outer rays of caudal fin produced. Coloration (according to Schreitmüller, 1936): brownish-olive, black-brown or more towards yellow-brown, depending on health; flanks paler below; belly yellowish-white. The whole body is strewn with irregular dark blotches which may unite into longitudinal bands. Fins pale, translucent. Uppermost ray of caudal fin dark brown, lower lobe blotched with brown. Pectoral and ventral fin-spines spotted with dark.

♂ distinguished from the ♀ by the fine bristles on the rostrum.

Care, as given in the family description. Not yet reared in captivity. 1935/−.

Loricaria filamentosa *Steindachner* 1878 (Figs. 598, 599, 726, 730)
R. Magdalena; to 25 cm., usually smaller.

D I/7; A I/5; P I/6; V I/5; 31–32 bony scutes in a lateral series. The pectoral fin-spines reach to the insertions of the ventrals when laid back. Uppermost ray of caudal fin strongly produced. On the hinder part of the belly there are 2–3 irregular rows of ventral scutes between the lateral ones; on the anterior part numerous small ventral scutes. Upperside grey to yellow-brown with numerous dark blotches; underside delicate yellowish to white. All fins with irregular dark blotches. Caudal with a broad dark margin.

♂♂ have the sides of the head covered with bristles when full-grown.

Care and breeding, as given in the family description. A re-examination of the species described as '*L. parva*' by H. J. Franke shows that it was actually *L. filamentosa*. 1938/+.

Loricaria lanceolata *Günther* 1868 (Figs. 727, 730)
Upper reaches of the Amazon, Xerebros and Canelos; to 13 cm.

D I/7; A I/5; P I/6; V I/5; 29–30 bony scutes in a lateral series. The pectoral fin-spines reach to the insertions of the ventrals when laid back. Uppermost and lowermost rays of caudal fin produced, thread-like. On the hinder part of the belly there are 3–4 rows of ventral scutes between the lateral ones; on the anterior part numerous small ventral scutes. Upperside grey to yellow-grey with dark blotches which are often organised into transverse bars. An irregular dark streak from the eye to the tip of the snout. Underside delicate pale yellow. Dorsal fin pale, with brown blotches which are often united into transverse rows. Caudal fin-base dark, followed by a broad pale zone and again by a dark inner margin. All other fins usually pale at the base and sprinkled with dark distally.

♂♂, when sexually mature, are distinguished by the bristles on the sides of the head and on the leading-edges of the pectoral fins.

Care, as given in the family description. Probably not yet reared in captivity. 1925/−.

Loricaria microlepidogaster *Regan* 1904 (Figs. 572 (?), 573 (?), 728, 730)
Rio Grande do Sul; to 9·5 cm.

D I/7; A I/5; P I/6; V I/5; 29 bony scutes in a lateral series. The pectoral fin-spine reaches to the second quarter of the ventral fin-spine when both are laid back. Uppermost and lowermost rays of caudal fin not produced or thread-like. On the hinder part of the belly there are 6 rows of ventral scutes between the lateral ones; on the anterior part numerous small ventral scutes. Upperside grey-brown to grey-yellow with 6 dark irregular transverse bars. Fins pale, with dark blotches on the rays. Base and outer margin of the caudal dark, centre pale.

♂ with bristles on the sides of the head when full-grown.

Care, as given in the family description. Probably not yet reared in captivity. 1928/ — .

Loricaria parva *Boulenger* 1895 (Figs. 729, 730)
Paraguay and La Plata; to 12 cm.
D I/7; A I/5; P I/5; V I/4; 29 bony scutes in a lateral series. The pectoral fin-spine reaches to the second quarter of the ventral fin-spine when both are laid back. Uppermost and lowermost rays of caudal fin produced, thread-like. On the hinder part of the belly there are 3–4 rows of ventral scutes between the lateral ones; on the anterior part numerous small scutes. Upperside olive-grey to grey-yellow with numerous dark blotches which are often united into transverse bars. Underside clay-yellow to whitish. An irregular dark line runs obliquely forward from the eye to the tip of the mouth. Fins transparent, with dark blotches or rows of blotches on the fin-rays.

♂ when full-grown with the sides of the head thickly covered with bristles.

Care, as given in the family description. Probably already bred in captivity; the species bred by H. J. Franke was not *L. parva* but *L. filamentosa*. 1908/ + .

Plate 121

Figs. 707–711. Spawning behaviour of *Cynolebias nigripinnis* on a peaty bottom; fishes slightly enlarged. (Photos Dr. Foersch)
Fig. 707. With fins widespread the ♂ swims in front of the ♀ (display behaviour) and arouses her instinct to mate.
Fig. 708. The ♀, nothing loth, follows the ♂ to the bottom.
Fig. 709. (left) – The ♀ nestles against the ♂ and follows him as he digs into the bottom.
Fig. 710. (right) – As the fishes press close together, partly clasping one another with their unpaired fins, the eggs and sperm are ejected.
Fig. 711. After 10–14 seconds the ♂ is the first to leave the bottom (at which time the fins are laid back) and then awaits the ♀ who appears some 3–5 seconds later.

Plate 121

Plate 122

Plate 122

Figs. 712–715. Spawning behaviour of *Pterolebias longipinnis* on a peaty bottom; fine specimens, natural size. (Photo Dr. Foersch) For the continuation of this sequence, see Plate 123.

Fig. 712. The courting ♂ (left) swims around the ♀.
Fig. 713. ♂ in typical display posture, with the fins and gill-cover outspread.
Fig. 714. The ♀ is willing to mate and swims to the bottom, closely followed by the ♂.
Fig. 715. With lightning speed the ♀ bores into the bottom and the ♂ follows her.

Two further species have been imported in small quantities: *Loricaria catamarcensis* (Berg 1895) and *Loricaria nudiventris* (Cuvier and Valenciennes 1840). Both of these have had little distribution. Yet others have been occasionally imported but have not been scientifically determined.

Otocinclus affinis *Steindachner* 1876 (Fig. 566)
South-eastern Brazil, region around Rio de Janeiro; to 4 cm.

D I/7; A I/5; P I/6; V I/5; 23–24 bony scutes in a lateral series. Ground colour pale grey-green to clay-yellow; back darker; underside delicate pale yellow to whitish. A dark, vague-edged longitudinal band from the gill-cover to the root of the tail. Fins delicate greenish or colourless, vertical fins without spots.

♀ usually easily recognised by her greater girth.

All *Otocinclus* spp. can be kept for years in well-planted community tanks. Since, however, they are fishes which lead a thoroughly secluded life during the daytime, one should avoid keeping them singly. Like almost all *Loricariidae* they prefer algal food and graze algal films from stones, leaves and aquarium-sides with their toothed sucking-mouths. Even delicate plants are not damaged provided there is an ample supply of algae; only when there is a shortage of food are fine needle-shaped leaves attacked. The fishes supplement their diet with waste, scraps and also small worms. Small ones have a preference for hanging vertically from leaves or from the glass sides of the tank to which they attach themselves by their sucking-mouths. Temperature not less than 20°C. Not particular about water conditions. *O. affinis* has often been successfully bred at the Frankfurt Tropicarium. The courtship behaviour is similar to that of *Corydoras* and the eggs are laid individually on parts of plants, tank-sides and other objects. The young hatch after about 2–3 days and attach themselves vertically at first, and eventually begin to search for food after a further 2–3 days. They should be kept in an aquarium with plenty of algae, and also given 'Micro', the smallest nauplii, or the most finely powdered egg-yolk.

These very interesting fishes make themselves very useful as alga-controllers in the aquarium. *O. affinis* was first imported in 1920.

Otocinclus flexilis *Cope* 1894 (Fig. 565)
Rio Grande do Sul (La Plata); to 6 cm.

D I/7; A I/5; P I/6; V I/5; 25 bony scutes in a lateral series. This species is very similar to the previous one and in life can hardly be distinguished from it except by the rows of spots on the vertical fins. Furthermore, the dark lateral line is broken up into large blotches, at least towards the hinder end.

Sex-distinctions and care, as given for the previous species.

According to Holly, *Otocinclus arnoldi* Regan 1909 is a junior synonym of this species. 1905/+.

Otocinclus maculicauda *Steindachner* 1876 (Figs. 564, 735)
South-eastern Brazil, south of the Amazon delta; to 6 cm.

D I/7; A I/5; P I/6; V I/5; 24 bony scutes in a lateral series. Grey-green to yellow-green, also grey-brown, with irregular blotches on the flanks which may unite into vague-edged longitudinal bands. Underside pale yellow to grey. A large dark blotch at the root of the tail, which may be more or less extended into the lower caudal lobe, is characteristic of this species.

Sex-distinctions and care, as given for *O. affinis*. 1938/+.

Otocinclus maculipinnis *Regan* 1912 (Fig. 549)
La Plata Basin; to 4 cm.

D I/7; A I/5; P I/6; V I/5; 22–24 bony scutes in a lateral series. Green-grey or grey-yellow to pale brown with numerous large and small dark blotches, arranged irregularly or in rows on the body and colourless fins. Underside delicate yellowish or white.

Sex-distinctions and care, as given for *O. affinis*. 1909/+.

Figs. 716–717

Fig. 716. (left) – *Farlowella acus;* maximum size. Centre, above, the anterior ventral surface.

Fig. 717. (right) – *Farlowella gracilis;* natural size. Centre, below, the anterior ventral surface.

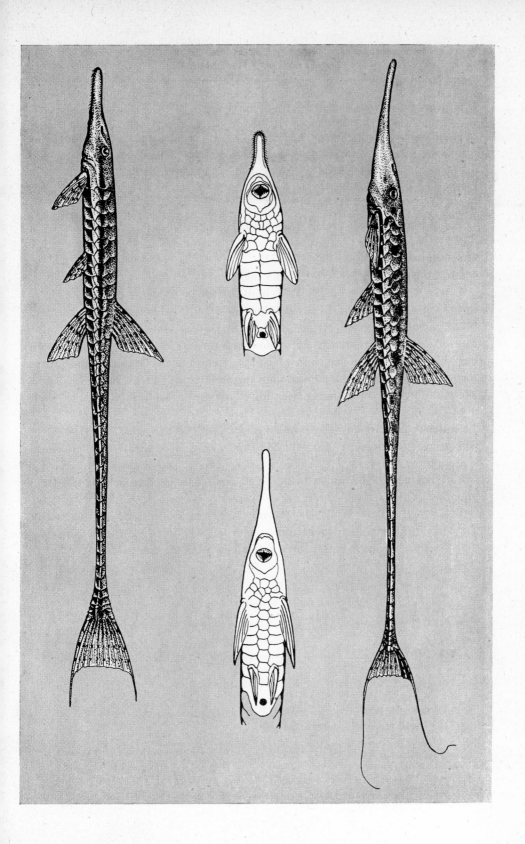

Otocinclus nigricauda *Boulenger* 1891 (Fig. 734)
Rio Grande do Sul; to 4·5 cm.

D I/5; A I/5; P I/6; V I/5; 24–26 bony scutes in a lateral series. Grey-olive to yellowish; back darker; belly usually pure white. Isolated, very indistinct blotches on the flanks, especially below the dorsal fin. Fins transparent, with rows of dark spots. Caudal fin blackish, with white spots organised into transverse bars.

Sex-distinctions and care, as given for *O. affinis.* 1906/+.

Otocinclus vittatus *Regan* 1904 (Fig. 733)
Matto Grosso, Paraguay basin; to 5·5 cm.

D I/7; A I/5; P I/5; V I/5; 21–22 bony scutes in a lateral series. Grey-olive to brownish; back darker; belly delicate yellowish to white. A not very distinct broad longitudinal band extends from the tip of the snout, across the eye, to the root of the tail. Fins transparent, colourless. Caudal fin dark at the base, with dark blotches on the outer parts which are often organised into transverse bars; the longitudinal band is continued onto the middle rays of the caudal.

Sex-distinctions and care, as given for *O. affinis.* Probably 1921/+.

Plecostomus commersoni (*Cuvier* and *Valenciennes* 1848) (Fig. 1172)
The genus *Plecostomus* is distinguished from *Loricaria* by the absence of ventral scutes on the belly.

La Plata basin, Rio Grande do Sul; to 40 cm., remaining considerably smaller in aquaria.

D I/7; A I/4; P I/6; V I/5; 28–31 bony scutes in a lateral series. The base of the dorsal fin is markedly longer than the distance between the end of the dorsal and the adipose fins. Ventral surface of adult fishes covered with tiny splinters

Plate 123

Figs. 718–721. Spawning behaviour of *Pterolebias longipinnis*, continued from Plate 122.
(Photos Dr. Foersch)

Fig. 718. (left) The fishes' bodies are violently agitated as they strive to penetrate as deeply as possible into the bottom.
Fig. 719. (right) ♂ and ♀ leave the soil simultaneously after pairing (note the depressed fins).
Fig. 720. Sometimes the ♂ is the first to reappear; he then waits for the ♀.
Fig. 721. The ♂ renews his courtship.

Plate 123

Plate 124

Plate 124

Fig. 722. *Pachypanchax homolotus;* adults, natural size. (Photo Dr. Foersch)
Fig. 723. *Pachypanchax playfairi;* young, sexually-ripe fishes, natural size; left, ♂, right, ♀. (Original)
Figs. 724–725. *Jordanella floridae* (American Flagfish); fine specimens, natural size; left, ♂, right, ♀. (Photo Dr. Schapitz)

of bone. Back and flanks grey-olive to grey-brown or dark brown, sparsely or thickly sprinkled with dark blotches. Underside pale grey-green, usually with numerous dark blotches. Fins brownish, occasionally with rows of dark spots along the blackish fin-rays.

Sex-distinctions in coloration not yet described.

Care, as given in the family description (see p. 452).

Like all *Plecostomus* spp. an enthusiastic destroyer of algae, capable of cleaning an aquarium and its coarse-leaved plants in the shortest possible time and usually without damage to the latter. Peaceful and easily satisfied. According to older accounts *Plecostomus* spp. are said to be very fond of burrowing, a statement which is hardly supported when the fishes are kept in large tanks which offer suitable hiding-places. Crepuscular in habit. Undemanding as regards temperature, 18–26 °C. Worms, dried foods and plant food (algae, lettuce). Food is taken from the bottom. Often somewhat difficult to acclimatise; the use of sea-salt (1 teaspoon to 10 litres of water) is recommended. Very interesting fishes. 1893/+.

Plecostomus punctatus (*Cuvier* and *Valenciennes* 1840) (Figs. 597, 1173)
Southern and south-eastern Brazil; to 30 cm., remaining considerably smaller in aquaria.

D I/7; A I/4; P I/6; V I/5; 28–30 bony scutes in a lateral series. The base of the dorsal fin is about the same length as the distance between the end of the dorsal and the adipose fin; otherwise very similar to the previous species. Back and flanks brown-grey to brown with dark spots and blotches; usually 5 broad dark transverse bars are conspicuously present. Nostrils united by a fine dark band. Underside delicate brownish to white. Fins brownish with distinct round blotches which are usually arranged in rows.

Sex-distinctions not yet described.

Care, as given for *P. commersoni* (see also family description). 1928/+.

Plecostomus rachowi *Regan* 1913 (Fig. 1174)
Near Rio de Janeiro; to 14 cm.

D I/7; A I/4; P I/6; V I/5; 32 bony scutes in a lateral series. Adipose fin inserted very far back. Back and flanks grey to grey-brown with numerous yellow-brown to black round blotches which are partly organised into distinct longitudinal rows. Underside whitish. Fins delicate brown with distinct rows of spots.

Sex-distinctions not known.

Care, as given for *P. commersoni* (see also family description). 1913/ —.

Stoneiella leopardus (*Fowler* 1914) (Fig. 706)
Humboldt R., Novo Rivers, Sta. Catharina; to 12 cm.

D I/8; A I/5; P I/6; V I/5; 24 bony scutes in a lateral series. Similar in shape to the members of the genus *Plecostomus*, to which *Stoneiella* is closely related. Dorsal fin large, flag-like. Head and gill-cover thickly set with spines; interopercular with 12 hooked spines which are movable like those in *Xenocara* and *Ancistrus*. Pale to dark brown with numerous irregular black blotches on the body and fins. Underside grey-yellow.

Sex-distinctions in coloration not known.

Care, as given for *Plecostomus commersoni*. Probably not yet bred in captivity. Imported into North America in 1947.

Xenocara dolichoptera (*Kner* 1854) (Figs. 702, 704)   Blue-chin Xenocara
The genera *Xenocara* and *Ancistrus* are distinguished from *Plecostomus* by the peculiar structure of their gill-cover whose lower part, the interopercular, can be turned inwards and bears spines with hooked points. The snout is almost always provided with very long, erect tentacles which are forked at their tips and which may be very differently developed in the two sexes.

Xenocara dolichoptera is native to the Amazon and Guiana; to 13 cm.

Figs. 726–730

Fig. 726. *Loricaria filamentosa;* adult, reduced.
Fig. 727. *Loricaria lanceolata;* adult, natural size.
Fig. 728. *Loricaria microlepidogaster;* adult, somewhat reduced.
Fig. 729. *Loricaria parva;* natural size.
Fig. 730. Ventral views of various *Loricaria* spp.; left to right, *L. parva*, *L. microlepidogaster*, *L. lanceolata*, *L. filamentosa*.

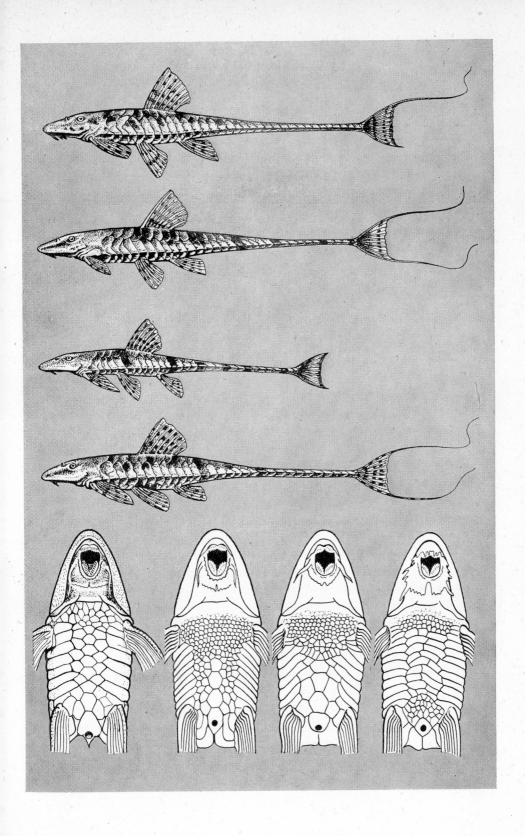

D I/8–9; A I/4; P I/5;V I/5; 23–24 bony scutes in a lateral series. 6–9 hooked spines on the movable interopercular. Colour dark brown to grey- or green-brown, to some extent with dark blotches. Healthy fishes are very dark with a blue-black sheen. Underside somewhat paler. Fins blue-black, the dorsal and anal with dirty white spots and a pale margin. In young fishes the blue tint is usually more intense and is also enlivened with numerous white spots on the body and fins. The dorsal and anal fins also have a brilliant white margin.

♀ with a single row of short, thin tentacles on the edge of the snout.
♂ with stout, long tentacles on the snout and on the forehead; altogether paler.

Care, as given in the family description (see also *Plecostomus commersoni*). According to Lehmann these fishes spawn in holes which they themselves dig under pieces of wood or stones. The ♂ practises intensive brood-care. 1911/+.

Xenocara multispinis *Regan* 1912 (Fig. 705)
Humboldt R., Novo Rivers, Sta. Catharina; to 12 cm.
D I/7; A I/4; 24 bony scutes in a lateral series. 20–25 barbed spines on the movable interopercular. Head and body dark grey to yellow-brown with numerous nearly black blotches, between which isolated pale spots are scattered. Underside paler. Dorsal and paired fins translucent brownish, similarly blotched with light and dark yellow-brown. Caudal fin with a pale border. Tentacles on snout pale.
Sex-distinctions probably as for *X. dolichoptera*. Regan describes long tentacles in the ♂♂.
Care, as given for *Plecostomus commersoni*. Not yet bred in captivity. 1934/–.

Arnold (*Wochenschrift für Aquarien- und Terrarienkunde*, Jg. 30, p. 33, 1933) reports on a specimen which, with reservations, he identifies as *Xenocara brevipinnis* for the following reasons:–'On the basis of Herr Griem's statement to me, that it came from near Santos, it must be *Xenocara brevipinnis* Regan...' The material described by Regan (1904) as *Xenocara brevipinnis*, however, came from Rio Grande do Sul, about 500 miles away from Santos in a direct line. Furthermore, Fig. 2 in the article cited can never be *Xenocara brevipinnis* (Short-finned Xenocara) (see Boulenger, *Proc. Roy. Soc. London* 1891, p. 231, Plate XXVI, Fig. 1). This species was also described by Regan (1904) as being uniformly brown.
In 1934 a specimen was imported from northern Brazil which may well have been *Lasiancistrus pictus* (Castelnau 1855).
E. Ahl (*Zool. Anz.* 1936, pp. 106–109) described a preserved specimen, 56 mm. in length, which had been imported from the neighbourhood of Rio de Janeiro, as

a new species *Hemiancistrus albocinctus* E. Ahl. This was undoubtedly only a young fish and, in view of the very marked changes in coloration and form which this group undergoes during development, we must certainly await further material before Ahl's species can be properly established.

Family Cyprinodontidae (Tooth-Carps)

This very large family is represented in every continent but Australia, but more or less confined to tropical and warm temperate climates. In Europe, for example, Tooth-Carps are found only in the southern, Mediterranean regions, and in Asia chiefly in Asia Minor, southern and south-eastern Asia. Tooth-Carps are, as a rule, small and, what is more, the family is especially rich in dwarf species. As the family-name clearly intimates, we have here a group of fishes which are indeed more or less carp-like, but divided from the true Carps (which are characterised by a toothless mouth) by the complete bordering of the bones of the jaws and pharynx with comb-like teeth. The family further exhibits the following peculiarities:–

The upper surface of the head is usually flattened. The mouth is terminal and directed slightly upwards. No barbels. The upper margin of the mouth is bounded only by the premaxillaries, which are very freely movable and therefore render the mouth eminently protrusible. Dorsal fin usually inserted well forward. No adipose fin. Caudal fin rounded or flag-like, usually depending on whether ♀ or ♂. Anal fin in the ♂♂ of live-bearing species wholly or partly modified as an intromittent organ (Gonopodium). Scales cycloid and almost always large. No lateral line.

The *Zoological Record* unites in the family *Cyprinodontidae* fishes which other authorities divide among a number of distinct and independent families:–

Cyprinodontidae, Adrianichthyidae ...   Egg-laying Tooth-Carps.
Poeciliidae, Goodeidae, Jenynsiidae, Anablepidae ... Live-bearing Tooth-Carps.

In some classifications these several families are given the status only of sub-families. The change is occasioned by the recognition of the fact that

469

certain live-bearing genera often show a closer relationship to egg-laying forms than to other live-bearing genera. Today we can admit that the live-bearing habit has originated independently in several groups. The Order *Microcyprini* of Regan accordingly contains the following families at present: *Cyprinodontidae, Goodeidae, Amblyopsidae.* (The *Goodeidae* are so sharply defined that in my opinion they cannot be included in the *Cyprinodontidae*.)

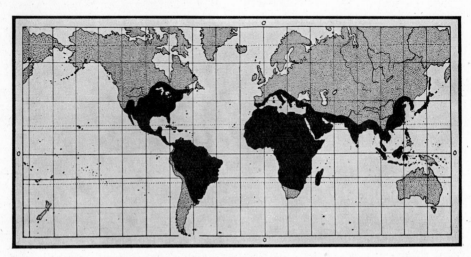

Fig. 731
Distribution of the *Cyprinodontidae*

In the interests of a clearly arranged presentation the Tooth-Carps are here dealt with in accordance with their geographical distribution by continents. Details of care and breeding are given with the individual groups.

Figs. 732–735

Fig. 732. *Corydoras rabauti;* enlarged.
Fig. 733. *Otocinclus vittatus;* adult, somewhat enlarged.
Fig. 734. *Otocinclus nigricauda;* somewhat enlarged.
Fig. 735. *Otocinclus maculicauda;* somewhat enlarged.

Tooth-Carps of Tropical and Sub-Tropical Asia

Aphanius dispar (*Rüppel* 1828) (Fig. 749)

Abyssinia, Palestine, both coasts of the Red Sea, Southern Arabia, Iraq, coastal regions of the Persian Gulf, Kutch; in fresh and brackish waters; to 8 cm.

D 8–9; A 9–10; P 16; V 7; LL 25–26. Body moderately elongate, somewhat compressed. Origin of the dorsal fin in front of the anal.

♂ brilliantly coloured, brown to dark blue, with numerous iridescent blue-silver blotches in rows on the flanks and weak brownish transverse bars on the caudal peduncle. Dorsal and anal fins with silvery blotches and dark spots. Caudal with deep blue, usually curved, transverse bars. Pectoral and ventral fins yellow.

♀ grey with a bluish-silver sheen. Numerous narrow transverse bars on the flanks. Fins colourless to light yellowish, transparent.

Aphanius dispar richardsoni (Boulenger 1907) (Fig. 600) is the name given to a population living in a spring in the neighbourhood of the Dead Sea.

The lively *Aphanius* spp. are best kept in large, shallow aquaria in brackish water of 3–6⁰/₀₀ (3–6 grammes of sea-salt per litre of water), and provided with hiding-places among stones or tufts of algae. Temperature 20–25°C. Live food of all kinds, but also supplementary plant food in the form of algae, cooked spinach or lettuce. In a tank to themselves these fishes will often breed without any special assistance. A serious breeder, however, segregates the sexes first of all and partly replaces the water. Spawning takes place preferably on the fine submerged leaves (often wrongly called roots) of *Salvinia*, or on the roots of *Eichhornia*; well-teased Perlon or other synthetic substitutes serve equally well. After spawning the parents should either be removed or the plants with the large eggs transferred to a separate rearing tank. The young hatch after 10 to 14 days and are easily raised. A well-fed pair can be several times mated. 1904/+.

Plate 125

Fig. 736. *Fundulus heteroclitus* (Zebra or Common Killie); adults, natural size; above, ♂, below, ♀. (After Axelrod and Schultz)

Fig. 737. *Rivulus* sp.; one of the species imported and often bred in recent years; sexually-ripe adults, somewhat enlarged; above, ♂, below, ♀. (Photo Dr. Foersch)

Fig. 738. *Rivulus cylindraceus* (Green or Brown Rivulus); adults, somewhat enlarged; above, ♀, below, ♂. (Original)

472

Plate 125

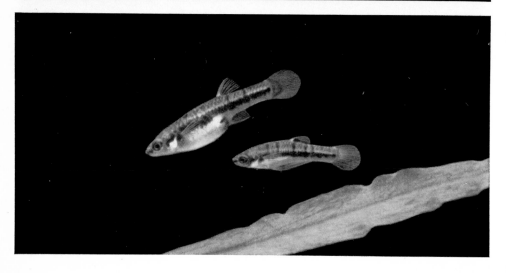

Plate 126

Plate 126

Fig. 739. *Valencia hispanica* (Spanish Tooth-Carp); adult ♂, somewhat enlarged. (Photo Dr. Foersch)

Fig. 740. *Gambusia affinis holbrooki* (Mosquito Fish); adults, somewhat enlarged; above, ♀, below, ♂. (Original)

Fig. 741. *Heterandria formosa* (Dwarf Top Minnow, Mosquito Fish); adults, enlarged; above, ♀, below, ♂. (Original)

Aphanius mento (*Heckel* 1843) (Figs. 614, 625, 626)
Persia, Syria, Asia Minor, also in brackish waters; to 5 cm.

D 11; A 10; P 13–15; V 5–6; LL 27–30. A very attractive species and well suited to life in aquaria.

♂ dark brown, during the breeding season blue-black with shining bluish-silver to whitish spots and blotches on the flanks. Occasionally there are 8–10 prominent narrow pale transverse bands. Fins black with pale spots.

♀ yellow-brown, blotched and marbled with dark on the flanks. A dark brown longitudinal band is often present.

Care and breeding, as given for *A. dispar*. 1910/+.

Aphanius cypris (Heckel 1843) is a synonym of *A. mento*. *A. sophiae* (Heckel 1846), sometimes confused with *A. mento*, is a distinct species, which has probably not yet been imported.

Aphanius fasciatus (*Valenciennes* 1811) (Fig. 600)
Mediterranean countries, in various kinds of waters including brackish; to 6 cm.

D 10–13; A 9–12; P 14–15; V 6–7; LL 25–30. Shape similar to *A. dispar*. Coloration very variable.

♂ olive-green to blue-green. Back dark. Underside pale to pure silvery. 10–15 broad, dark transverse bars. Fins yellow to orange. Dorsal fin with a dark leading-edge. Caudal fin usually with a single vague dark transverse band.

♀ grey, with very indistinct narrow transverse bands. Fins grey or colourless.

Care and breeding, as given for *A. dispar*. 1913/+.

Aphanius iberus (*Cuvier* and *Valenciennes* 1846) (Figs. 612, 613)
Spain and Algeria; to 5 cm.

D 9–10; A 9–10; LL 26–28. Shape similar to *A. dispar*. Body thick-set, moderately compressed.

473

♂ blue-green to aquamarine. Back olive. Belly whitish. About 15 narrow shining pale blue transverse bars on the body, which tend to break up into blotches towards the back. Caudal fin dark blue with transverse bands and a pale margin, sometimes spotted with white. Dorsal and anal fins dark, with pale spots, the tip of the dorsal pale blue. Ventral fins yellowish to bluish, with dark marbling.

♀ olive-green to bluish-green with brown streaks and blotches on the flanks. Fins colourless.

A. iberus should be kept in a well-planted aquarium with pure fresh water. Temperature 18–25°C. Live food, especially midge-larvae. After a lively courtship, in which the ♂ flutters around the ♀ butterfly-fashion, the fishes spawn on floating plants and other fine-leaved plants. They only attack the spawn when they are hungry. The young hatch after 6–8 days. Feeding should be delayed until the yolk-sac has been absorbed. 1911/+ .

Besides the *Aphanius* spp. mentioned above, certain others, imported from various parts of Turkey, are being scientifically studied at the Zoologisches Institut, Hamburg:–

Aphanius chantrei (Gaillard 1895) (Fig. 600)
Aphanius burduricus Aksiray 1948 (Fig. 600)

(A definitive classification of the members of the genus *Aphanius* will not be possible until more intensive studies of geographical and environmental variation in these often widely distributed fishes have been completed. Some modifications of Prof. Sterba's original account have been made in the light of unpublished researches by Dr. E. Trewavas and Dr. H. Steinitz. *Ed.*)

Some species of the nearly-related genus *Anatolichthys*, first described in 1944, have likewise been imported for scientific purposes:–

Anatolichthys splendens Kosswig and Sözer 1944 (Fig. 611)
Anatolichthys burdurensis Aksiray 1948 (Fig. 611)
Anatolichthys transgrediens Aksiray 1948 (Fig. 611)

The genus *Anatolichthys* is especially interesting scientifically because its members characteristically display a more or less strong suppression of the scales. The degree of reduction is determined by environmental conditions and so provides us with the opportunity to understand the nature of these conditions and of their bearing upon speciation. The genus *Kosswigichthys*, whose members are tooth-carps which have almost completely lost their scales, shows the ultimate condition resulting from this tendency.

Kosswigichthys asquamatus *Sözer* 1942 (Figs. 611, 750)
Anatolia, Hazer Golu; to 4 cm.

D 9–12; A 11–13; V 6–7. Body strongly elongate, low, somewhat compressed. Dorsal fin inserted somewhat before the anal. Scales reduced; among completely scaleless *Kosswigichthys* there may also be found some which retain just the merest rudiments of scales. Description (after Kosswig):–sexually-ripe ♂♂ are dark with a paler underside, or entirely black overall. 15–16 conspicuous silver transverse stripes on the flanks. Dorsal fin lacquer-black with 2 silver bands which converge anteriorly. Remaining fins pale to dark grey. Anal fin often with a dark margin.

♀ pale; belly silvery; 13–18 irregular dark blotches on the flanks.

Care of this undemanding species as given for *Aphanius* spp., see p. 472. Room temperature. Very peaceful. Live and dried food. Some sea-salt (1–2 teaspoons to 10 litres of water). The eggs are laid on fine-leaved plants and the young hatch after 14 days at 25°C. 1938/+.

Valencia hispanica (*Cuvier* and *Valenciennes* 1846) (Fig. 739) Spanish Tooth-Carp
South-eastern and eastern Spain, Greece, in standing waters; to 8 cm.

D 10–11; A 12–14; P 14; V 6; LL 29–32. The genus *Valencia* is closely related to *Aphanius*, but differs in having conical teeth whereas those of *Aphanius* are tricuspid. Body moderately elongate, somewhat compressed, pike-like.

♂ pale to dark brown with a greenish sheen. Underside yellowish to silvery-white. Scales dark-edged. A large, round, dark blotch behind the gill-cover. Several narrow dark transverse bands on the flanks. Vertical fins lemon-yellow to orange with dark spots and dark edges.

♀ very pale, without a distinct shoulder blotch. Fins colourless, all faintly dark-edged.

This very undemanding species should be kept in a large, sunny aquarium at room temperature. Living and dried food. Quarrelsome; only to be kept with fishes of similar size. The large eggs are laid on water plants after a stormy court-ship. Remove the parents after spawning, or else! The young hatch after 11–14 days at 20–22°C., and grow very rapidly. 1881/+.

Genera Aplocheilus and Oryzias: Care and Breeding

The Tooth-Carps of the genera *Aplocheilus* and *Oryzias* are chiefly distributed through southern Asia, also through eastern Asia and the Indo-Australian Archipelago. They are usually surface-living fishes inhabiting a great variety of different waters. Not infrequently the same species may be found in drainage ditches as well as in mountain and lowland streams. Some species have been locally protected because they are useful in controlling mosquito larvae.

Most species do very well in captivity. They are best kept in aquaria with a relatively large water-surface, standing in a situation which is not too bright but which does receive some occasional sunshine. The Asiatic Tooth-Carps can also be used to contribute some animation to the surface of a community tank. Temperature 20–25°C. As regards water-conditions they are not so particular as most of their African relatives, although they should not be kept in definitely hard water. Live food of all kinds, with a preference for black mosquito-larvae; also occasional dried food.

Tanks of at least 12–15 litres should be used for breeding, with fine-leaved plants, best of all floating plants like *Riccia* and *Salvinia*, peat-filtered water and sunshine. The ♂♂ often drive the ♀♀ very vigorously. The eggs are laid preferably on floating plants. In the majority of species the eggs remain for some time gathered in clusters suspended from the ♀♀, as in the African

Plate 127

Fig. 742. Above, left: Anal fin of ♀ Guppy, enlarged.
Fig. 743. Above, right: Anal fin of ♂ Guppy, modified as an intromittent organ (gonopodium).
Fig. 744. Centre, left and right, and below:

Ripe, unfertilised Guppy egg, dissected from the ovary.

Guppy embryo in the egg-membrane, dissected from the oviduct.

Guppy embryo dissected from the egg-membrane.

Fig. 745. *Gambusia affinis affinis* (Spotted Gambusia); adults, somewhat enlarged; left, ♂, right, ♀. (After Axelrod and Schultz)

476

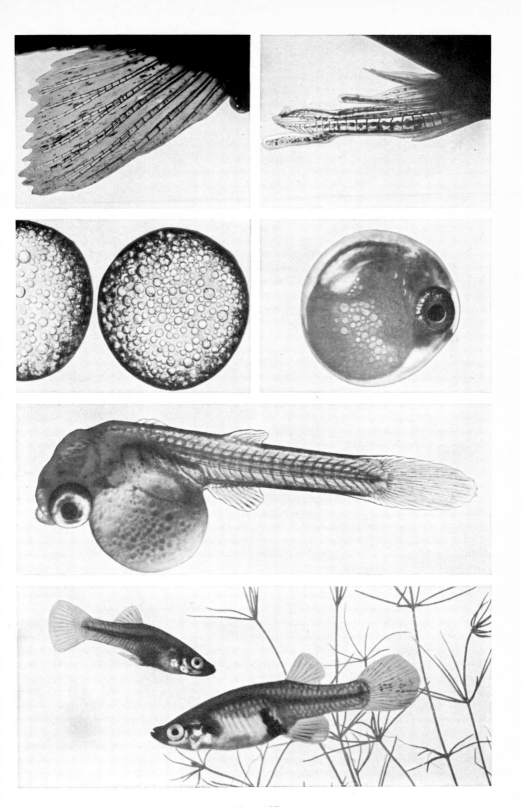

Plate 127

Plate 128

Plate 128

Fig. 746. *Limia melanogaster* (Blue Limia); ripe adults, somewhat enlarged; left ♂, right ♀. (Original)

Fig. 747. *Phalloceros . caudomaculatus reticulatus* (Caudo); adults, somewhat enlarged; above, ♀, below, ♂. (Photo Dr. Foersch)

Fig. 748. *Phallichthys amates* (Merry Widow); adults, somewhat enlarged; above, ♀, below, ♂. (Original)

Micropanchax spp., and are later stripped off on the plants. A spawning period often lasts for 1–3 weeks; the serious breeder therefore transfers the plants to rearing tanks as they become loaded with eggs. The young hatch after a few days and should be fed immediately with the finest food (nauplii, Rotifers). Rearing not difficult. Breeders sometimes adopt an alternative method and pick the hard-shelled eggs off the plants and transfer them to bowls of soft, peaty water to hatch. (See also the instructions for *Aphyosemion* spp., p. 482.)

Aplocheilus blocki (*Arnold* 1911) (Fig. 628)   Dwarf or Green Panchax
Madras, Ceylon; to 5 cm.

D 7–8; A 15–20; P 12; V 6; LL 26–30. The smallest of the Asiatic *Aplocheilus* spp. Body metallic yellowish-green with rows of brassy-yellow to red spots. Belly shining blue-green. Vertical fins lemon-yellow with red to brown spotting and striping. Ventral fins orange. Pectoral fins colourless. Eye golden.

♀ considerably paler in colour; yellow-grey to greenish with a dark longitudinal band along the flanks and a few transverse bands which are chiefly prominent on the caudal peduncle. Fins almost colourless; a black blotch at the base of the dorsal.

Care and breeding, as given above. Spacious aquaria, with thick clumps of plants and not too great a depth of water (20 cm.) provide the best conditions for this species. Warmth-loving; temperature 24–28 °C. Live food, especially worms, midge- and mosquito-larvae and small crustacea; these fishes also like plant aphides which may be sprinkled on the surface of the water. After a delightful courtship in which the ♂ circles the ♀ with a peculiar nodding and dancing behaviour, spawning takes place on fine-leaved plants or on the roots of floating plants. Breeding temperature 26–28 °C. The young hatch after 12–14 days and should be provided with the finest food. It is recommended that the parents be removed before hatching. 1909/+.

Aplocheilus dayi (*Steindachner* 1892) (Fig. 629)   Ceylon Killifish
Ceylon; to 7 cm.

D 6–7; A 15; LL 29–30. Body quite elongate.

♂ flanks shining metallic green; back golden; underside delicate bluish to violet. Scattered red spots are strewn over the whole body. Dorsal fin yellowish. Caudal fin greenish with a red band on the outer part. Anal fin greenish at the base with numerous fine red stripes running parallel to the fin-rays. Eyes large with a pale yellow to greenish iris.

♀ similar, but not so brightly coloured. 6–7 dark transverse bands on the lower half of the caudal peduncle.

Care and breeding, as given on p. 476. The fishes prefer to spawn, however, on roots or parts of plants near the bottom. About 8–10 eggs are laid each day. Soft water. Temperature 25°C. The young hatch after about 12 days. 1936/+.

Aplocheilus lineatus (*Cuvier* and *Valenciennes* 1846) (Fig. 684)
India and Ceylon; to 10 cm.

D 7–9; A 15–17; P 14–15; V 5; LL 32–34. Coloration very variable, in relation to the wide distribution.

♂ Back olive-brown, sides paler, belly yellowish. The flanks are covered with gleaming green-golden spots which are mostly united into longitudinal stripes. The breast region and the lower half of the flanks are sprinkled with brilliant red spots. 6–8 narrow dark transverse bands on the flanks and caudal peduncle. Iris emerald green; gill-cover gleaming yellow-green to blue-green. Dorsal fin red and yellow; caudal fin orange at the base, the outer part red and the edge intense red. Anal fin yellow-green to blue at the base with shining spots, the outer part red. Pectoral and ventral fins yellow, often with red tips.

♀ usually darker than the ♂. The bands on the flanks are broader and more numerous; the first lies behind the pectoral fin. Dorsal fin with a dark blotch at the base.

Figs. 749–753

Fig. 749. *Aphanius dispar;* drawing of ♂ and rough sketch of ♀ above; natural size. (The figure of the ♂ is poor, or at least atypical – Ed.)
Fig. 750. *Kosswigichthys asquamatus;* ♂ with ♀ below; maximum size.
Fig. 751. *Aplocheilus panchax* (Blue Panchax); ♂ with ♀ below; natural size.
Fig. 752. *Oryzias melastigma;* ♂ with ♀ to right; very slightly enlarged.
Fig. 753. *Oryzias celebensis* (Celebes Medaka); ♂ with ♀ to right; maximum size.

Care and breeding, as given on p. 476. This species can only be kept in company with larger fishes. In contrast to other *Aplocheilus* species *A. lineatus* is very light-ihy. 1909/+.

Aplocheilus panchax (*Hamilton-Buchanan* 1822) (Fig. 751) Blue Panchax
India, Burma, to Malaya, Ceylon and the Indo-Malay Archipelago; to 8 cm.

D 7–8; A 15–16; LL 30–33. Coloration very variable, in relation to the wide distribution. Selective breeding has led to the production of very beautiful varieties, some of which have been dignified with 'scientific' names (*lutescens*, *Mattei*, etc.).

♂ grey-yellow; back darker. Belly yellowish with a bluish iridescence by reflected light. Each scale has a bluish centre and a delicate dark edge. Dorsal fin bluish with a large black blotch at the base and a dark edge. Caudal fin with a pale yellow centre and a white border which is again edged with deep black. The long anal fin is orange at the base and reddish with dark spots on the outer parts.
♀ paler in colour; fins rounded.

Care and breeding of this rather predatory species, as given on p. 476. Undemanding and easily bred. 1899/–.

Oryzias celebensis (*M. Weber* 1894) (Fig. 753) Celebes Medaka
Celebes, in streams; to 5 cm.

D 7–9; A 17–23; P 13–14; V 6; LL 30–36. The genus *Oryzias* is distinguished from all other Tooth-Carps by the non-protrusible upper jaw. Vomer not toothed. Pectoral fins inserted high up on the sides. Anal fin-base long.

♂ grey-green, with a beautiful bluish to brassy sheen by reflected light. Underside white-silver. A narrow dark band along the side, commencing just behind the pectoral fin, bifurcates broadly at the root of the tail and continues onto the caudal fin. A second, short, band along the insertion of the anal fin. Dorsal and anal fins colourless to bluish, produced and flag-like.
♀ grey. Dorsal and anal fins rounded. Usually larger.

Care, as given on p. 476. Breeding, as given for *O. latipes*. Seldom reared in Germany. 1912/–.

Oryzias javanicus (*Bleeker* 1854) (Fig. 630) Java Medaka
Java, Singapore?, Malay Peninsula; to 4 cm.

D 7; A 21–23; P 11–12; LL 29–30. Grey-green, each individual scale with a brassy glitter by reflected light. Back darker, often with a dark stripe along the dorsal ridge. Underside silvery. A dark line along the middle of the side and a second line along the anal fin are seldom apparent. Vertical fins yellowish. Dorsal fin produced to a point.

♀ yellowish-grey. Dorsal fin short.

Care and breeding, as given on p. 476 and for the next species; simple. 1910/+.

Oryzias latipes (*Schlegel* 1850) (Fig. 642) Geisha-girl Medaka, Japanese Medaka, Ricefish

Japan; to 4 cm.

D 6; A 19; P 11; V 6; LL 29. Very similar to the previous species.

♂ dull in colour, rather transparent. Uniformly greenish-grey to bluish, with a blue to violet iridescence by reflected light. Dorsal fin produced to a point. Anal fin fringed (individual rays produced), occasionally bordered with yellow.

♀ dorsal fin rounded. Edge of anal fin entire.

Care and breeding, as given on p. 476. A delicate species. Medium-sized tanks with moderate planting, a low water-level and a dark bottom-soil. Temperature 25–30°C. The water should be slightly brackish (1 teaspoon of sea-salt to 10 litres of water). Live food. Pairing takes place among plants, at 28–30°C. The eggs are at first carried around in a mucus-sheath on the belly of the ♀ and only later stripped off among plants or roots. Plants and eggs should be transferred to a separate rearing-tank. The young hatch after 10–12 days and are very small at first and must be fed with Infusoria; after a few days they may be given powdered food, small Nauplii, etc. The young seldom grow as large as the imported wild fishes. In Japan a red variety of this species has been developed and has been imported into Europe. The imported fishes were large, robust and only slightly delicate; unfortunately these characters were lost with subsequent breeding. 1897/−.

Oryzias melastigma (*McClelland* 1839) (Fig. 752)

India, including Ceylon; to 5 cm.

D 6–7; A 20–24; P 15; V 6; LL 27.

♂ translucent, grey-blue with a bluish tinge. Underside silvery. Several dark blotches on the flanks, as well as a narrow longitudinal band which forks on the caudal peduncle as in *O. celebensis*. Fins colourless, occasionally delicate orange.

♀ grey, usually larger. Dorsal and anal fins smaller.

Care and breeding, as given on p. 476. See also *O. latipes*. 1910/−.

481

Tooth-Carps of Africa
Genus Aphyosemion: Care and Breeding

The members of the genus *Aphyosemion* are mainly natives of tropical West Africa and, through the brilliance and diversity of their colour patterns, may be regarded as the most beautiful among aquarium fishes. Their often garish and yet so harmoniously contrasted tones, their whirling courtship and the interesting mode of development of their eggs have won them many enthusiastic admirers.

The natural occurrence of this group is in many cases limited to small bodies of water, often only temporary, such as are formed in many places during the rainy season by the overflowing of rivers, irrigation ditches, etc. To these conditions of life almost all the species of *Aphyosemion* are highly adapted. Many forms can even survive the dry season as eggs embedded in the mud.

As regards their care practically all *Aphyosemion* spp. have fundamentally similar requirements. They are fishes which flourish only in an aquarium reserved for one species and which to a greater or lesser degree languish in a community aquarium. Since the ♂♂ are rather quarrelsome among themselves it is best to keep the fishes in pairs, or to give a ♂ a small harem of♀♀. This precaution is obligatory for large, unmannerly species like *A. gulare*, *A. sjoestedti* and others.

Almost all the species are light-shy and look for hiding-places when kept in tanks which are standing in the light. On this account their natural liveliness is only demonstrated in dark, richly-planted aquaria; they are especially happy in the twilight beneath a thick roof of floating plants which best simulates the shaded conditions of their natural habitats. For bottom-soil they should be given fine, not too pale sand on which a thin layer of well-boiled peat-mould or charcoal has been laid. All the species thrive in soft, slightly amber-coloured water ('black water') such as may be produced by peat-filtration. Some tolerate relatively low pH values around 4·5, but in general values will suffice which lie only a little below the neutral point (say

around pH 6·5) such as often characterise their natural waters. The temperature should not rise above 24°C., since too high a temperature shortens
their lives and may even result in sudden death. Live food of all kinds,
especially black mosquito-larvae. The welfare of these fishes is said to be
considerably enhanced by the addition of common salt or, better, sea-salt to
the water (1 heaped teaspoon to 10 litres).

For serious breeding it is best to provide small all-glass tanks (6–10 litres;
for the larger species about 15 litres). The genus may be divided into two
groups on the basis of their spawning behaviour:

(A) Species which spawn on a plant substrate ('Adhesive-Spawners'), e.g.,
    A. australe and *A. multicolor;*
(B) Species which confide their eggs to the soil ('Bottom-Spawners'), e.g.,
    A. sjoestedti, A. arnoldi, A. gulare.

It must be understood that this division is to some extent arbitrary in that the
individual species may be more or less capable of adapting their spawning
behaviour to given conditions. The degree of this capacity for adaptation is
specific and in particular cases is so wide that normally adhesive-spawners
may sometimes behave almost like bottom-spawners and vice versa. One
species, *A. calabaricus*, takes up an exactly intermediate position and,
according to opportunity, is now an adhesive- and now a bottom-spawner
(Foersch 1956).

(A) Adhesive-spawning *Aphyosemion* spp. are best installed in all-glass
tanks which are set up with fine-leaved plants or with well-teased Perlon or
other synthetic substitutes. The reflecting bottom can be covered with Willow
Moss (*Fontinalis*), algae, peat-moss or even Perlon yarn.

The water already described above is also suitable for breeding. The prospective partners, previously segregated and well fed, are put together in the
breeding tank and often spawn after only a short time. Temperature 23–24°C.
When members of a species are kept in a tank by themselves it is often
unnecessary to prepare a special breeding tank. As a rule a spawning
period lasts for several weeks and during this time the partners spawn almost

daily. For serious breeding, however, it is better to put the pairs together every 4–5 days and to feed them well in the intervals between matings. The easily visible, fairly large, and generally hard-shelled eggs are best picked or shaken off the plants and transferred to shallow bowls where, at a low water-level (3–4 cm.), they can be stored until the young fish hatch. Cover the bowls! The use of good peat-water, which can be changed several times, and the careful removal of the dead (white) eggs usually guarantees a high rate of development. As an additional precaution the development of bacteria can be checked by the use of Trypaflavine (1 gm. to 150 litres of water). The eggs of adhesive-spawning species usually take an average of 12–18 days to develop; however, a longer lying, particularly at a cooler temperature (18–20°C.), may usually be allowed without any ill effects. As Meder and Foersch have pointed out, the eggs of adhesive-spawners may even be removed to moist peat-mould and thus transported or stored for a long time. A uniform hatching of the young can often be achieved by the use of fresh water; often even a vigorous agitation or an addition of Tripaflavine is sufficient. If this method does not produce the desired result a very little dried food ('Wawil' or similar, *not* dried water-fleas) may be strewn on the surface of the water, with the result that after a few hours the water becomes turbid through the development of bacteria and almost all the eggs hatch

Plate 129

Fig. 754. *Limia nigrofasciata* (Black-barred Limia); ripe young, somewhat enlarged; left ♀, right ♂. (Original)
Fig. 755. *Mollienesia sphenops* (Molly); ripe young; above ♀, below ♂. In the Hellabrunn Aquarium, Munich. (Original)
Fig. 756. *Xiphophorus helleri*, var. (Tuxedo Swordtail); adults, natural size. (Photo H. Schmidt)

Plate 130 (overleaf)

Fig. 757. *Mollienesia velifera* (Sail-fin Molly); above ♀, below ♂. (Original)
Fig. 758. *Xiphophorus xiphidium;* a species first imported in 1955. Adults, somewhat enlarged; above ♀, below ♂. (Photo Dr. Foersch)
Fig. 759. *Xiphophorus xiphidium;* ♂, about three times natural size. (Photo Dr. Foersch)

Plate 129

Plate 130 (see page 484)

Plate 131 (see page 485)

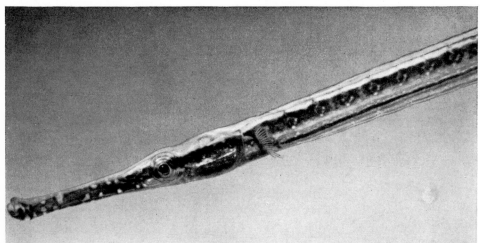

Plate 132

Plate 131 (overleaf)

Fig. 760. *Xiphophorus maculatus* (Platy: wild type). The ♀ of the colour-variety here illustrated exhibits large black blotches on the flanks; the ♂ dark edges to the scales and a dark dorsal fin-base. Somewhat enlarged. (Photo Dr. Foersch)

Fig. 761. Platy: wild type ♂, much enlarged. (Photo Dr. Foersch)

Fig. 762. *Xiphophorus montezumae* (Montezuma Swordtail); adults, somewhat enlarged; above ♀, below ♂. (Photo Dr. Foersch)

Plate 132

Fig. 763. *Dermogenys pusillus* (Halfbeak); adults, natural size; left ♀, right ♂. (Original)

Fig. 764. Head of the Large Freshwater Pipefish *(Microphis smithi)*; about twice natural size. (Photo Dr. Foersch)

Fig. 765. Head of the Lesser Freshwater Pipefish *(Syngnathus pulchellus)*; about three times natural size. (Photo Dr. Foersch)

simultaneously! This phenomenon cannot yet be explained. It may be that the bacteria attack the egg-shells and so facilitate the hatching of the young fish; it may also, however, be possible that the resulting lack of oxygen causes the uniform hatching (or the creation of osmotic pressures – *Ed.*). The contents of the bowl are now very carefully poured through a fine gauze net and the young put into appropriate water (see above). A careful transference with a spoon naturally serves the same purpose. The young grow rapidly with suitable feeding; *Cyclops*, Rotifers, Micro-worms, etc.

(B) Bottom-spawning *Aphyosemion* spp., in contrast to the adhesive-spawners, according to Foersch exhibit very far-reaching parallels with the South American bottom-spawning *Cynolebias* and *Pterolebias* spp. Like the latter, the bottom-spawning *Aphyosemion* spp. sink their eggs in the soil without directly penetrating it; rather the two partners, pressed close together side by side, nestle against the bottom and finally bury the laid eggs by a powerful blow with the caudal fin. The breeding tank for bottom-spawners should be provided with a layer of well-boiled peat-mould or, for the larger species, of fine sand.

As regards the treatment of the spawning fishes and the spawning-rhythm, reference may be made to the account of the adhesive-spawners. The spawn, on the other hand, requires somewhat different treatment. The eggs themselves are somewhat light-sensitive, develop slowly and require a resting-period. After spawning the water should be carefully decanted so that the bottom-soil is still covered and the aquarium, well covered, put away at a temperature of 18–24 °C. After about 14–20 days the whole contents can be emptied into a fine-meshed gauze and carefully crushed so that the peat disintegrates and crumbles apart. The disintegrated peat-mould, with the eggs, should now be transferred to a dish or bowl and lightly pressed down. When the surface has dried out cover the dish and put it away at 18–20 °C. for 3 to 6 weeks according to the species. A longer storage of up to double the normal period does no harm as a rule. The eggs travel very well in a moist condition; a cooling to about 15° C. usually does no harm either. At the end of the resting period the whole contents of the dish are covered with soft, lukewarm water, whereupon the young often promptly hatch. If hatching is retarded the techniques previously described (see p.484) may help. When spawning has taken place in fine sand the eggs can be sieved out and transferred to brood-dishes in the first place and later into moist peat.

This information regarding the bottom-spawning Tooth-Carps *(Aphyosemion, Cynolebias, Pterolebias)* is derived from the study by Foersch (1956), according to whom the embryonic period may be divided into the following phases:–resting egg, embryonic development, resting embryo, emergence from the egg-membrane. As a rule the first stage is elided and embryonic development commences immediately after the eggs have been spawned. Occasionally, however, it is observed that the embryonic development of many species is postponed and suddenly commences after an interval of months without any satisfactory explanation of this phenomenon yet having been found. Foersch has demonstrated, by experiments on *Cynolebias belotti*, that a postponement of the embryonic development of the eggs occurs less frequently in eggs which quickly enter on a dry period than in eggs which lie moist for a long time to begin with. This observation hardly provides an explanation, of course; its essential value lies rather in the disclosure of the various capacities for adaptation given to these fishes in order to survive the

486

dry season. The resting period for the eggs of *Cynolebias belotti* may last many months. Initiation of development may even then be produced by a fall in temperature to $+5°C$., or through other changes in the environmental conditions (fresh water, etc.). In contrast to earlier accounts Foersch has found that raising the temperature speeds up the rate of embryonic development itself. Interesting, also, is the discovery that fishes from eggs which are kept too warm are often less brilliantly coloured. In this connexion it should be noted that more intense pigmentation can be induced in many butterflies by keeping the pupae cool. These considerations apart, it must be emphasised that the resting phase as a rule follows after embryonic development and that this phase, the 'resting embryo', may likewise be of many months duration in some species. The eggs of bottom-spawners show a microscopic hair-like covering.

Very many *Aphyosemion* spp., quite irrespective of the considerations mentioned above, lose their beauty of coloration and vitality in the first generation through improper care; in any case, the fishes bred in captivity often remain smaller than the first-imported wild stock. On this account it is especially important to mitigate these deteriorations through painstaking care and careful selection of breeding partners.

Aphyosemion arnoldi (*Boulenger* 1908) (Figs. 643, 645)   Arnold's Lyretail/
                                                                Aphyosemion

Niger delta; to 6 cm.
    D 15–16; A 15–17; LL 25–27.
♂ Upper and lower caudal rays produced, forming pointed lobes. Coloration very
    variable. Back red-brown; flanks olive-green; caudal peduncle blue-green to
    indigo. Carmine-red blotches and vermiform stripes on the sides of the head and
    trunk. Lower lip edged with carmine-red. Eye brilliant blue-green. All the colours
    are more intensely iridescent by reflected light. Pectoral fins delicate carmine-red
    with orange edges. Dorsal and anal fins yellow-green with red spots at their
    bases and a broad ochre-yellow band on the upper or lower thirds respectively.
    Caudal fin with brown-red upper and lower edges, this colour being continued
    into the pointed prolongations, and with a yellow-green centre spotted with
    carmine-red. Ventral fins orange-yellow.

♀ Soberly coloured; brownish-olive to grey-brown with carmine-red spots and streaks on the flanks.

One of the loveliest and most highly esteemed of the *Aphyosemion* spp., *A. arnoldi* is divided into many local races which are mainly distinguished by differences in the ground-colour of the fins. The best known of these local races are the yellow and the blue varieties; the former has the dorsal fin delicate olive-green spotted with carmine-red and the caudal and anal predominantly orange; the latter has the fins predominantly blue.

Care and breeding, as given on p. 482. Bottom-spawner. The ♂♂ are very quarrelsome and it is therefore recommended that this species be kept in individual pairs in all-glass tanks of about 8–12 litres capacity. Very prolific. During the spawning period (4–6 weeks with good feeding) 15–25 eggs are laid almost daily. Only pairs of the same local race should be chosen for breeding as the eggs resulting from racial crosses are said to be frequently incapable of development. The eggs of the 'Blue Arnoldi' are somewhat larger than those of the yellow race. The eggs take 35–40 days to develop. 1908/+.

Aphyosemion australe australe (*Rachow* 1921) (Fig. 592)   Cape Lopez Lyretail/
Aphyosemion

Ogowe delta, near Cape Lopez, Gabon delta; to 6 cm.
    D 10–12; A 15–18; LL 31–33.

♂ Ground-colour brownish red. Gill-cover and the part immediately behind green to bluish. Body and fins sprinkled with red spots. Dorsal and anal fins enlarged and flag-like, with a dark violet inner margin and white tip. Caudal fin with upper and lower rays produced forming pointed lobes; the centre sea-green to blue spotted with red, the upper and lower edges with a red-violet band and the pointed prolongations white.
♀ Pale brown with isolated red spots. Tips of dorsal and caudal fins not prolonged.

Care and breeding, as given on p. 482. Adhesive-spawner. Hjerresen has recently developed an especially beautiful variety (*'A. australe hjerreseni'* Meinken) which is distinguished by a yellow ground-colour. 1913/+.

Aphyosemion bitaeniatum (*E. Ahl* 1924) (Fig. 766)   Striped Lyretail/Aphyosemion
Tropical West Africa; to 6 cm.
    D 9–10; A 12; LL 33–36.

♂ Similar in shape to *A. bivittatum*. The moss-green colouring of the flanks passes into dark olive-green towards the back and grey-yellow towards the belly. Gleaming brilliant green spots on the gill-cover and caudal peduncle. Characteristic of this species are two chocolate to fawn longitudinal bands. The upper band runs along the edge of the lower jaw, across the eye and the gill-cover to a point a little beyond the pectoral fin-insertion and is thence continued as a row of spots to the upper corner of the caudal peduncle. The lower band extends unbroken from the throat to the lower corner of the caudal peduncle. Dorsal fin with a dirty red to yellow-red base, the outer part greenish with dark red spots and the tip dark red-brown. Caudal fin greenish to yellow with a dark red-brown border above and below. Anal fin delicate yellow to green-yellow with a broad dark red-brown band.

♀ Yellow-brown, with weaker longitudinal bands. Caudal fin rounded.

Care and breeding, as given on p. 482. Adhesive-spawner. A little-known species. 1934/−.

Aphyosemion bivittatum bivittatum (*Lönnberg* 1895) (Fig. 590) Red Lyretail/
Aphyosemion

Cameroons and lower Niger; to 6 cm.
 D 11–13; A 13–14; LL 26–29.

♂ Fins produced to points. Ground-colour reddish-brown, paling towards the belly. Caudal peduncle brilliant pale green. Scales beneath the dorsal fin edged with brilliant violet, those on the flanks with brick-red. Several dark red vermiform blotches on the gill-cover. Under favourable living conditions two brown- to blue-black longitudinal bands are distinctly apparent, the upper one extending from the lower lip across the eye to the upper corner of the caudal peduncle, and the lower from the throat over the pectoral insertion to the lower corner of the caudal peduncle. Dorsal fin brown-red, delicately spotted with black. A bright red blotch at the base of the caudal. Centre of caudal fin greenish, upper and lower portions yellow-red, margins blackish. Anal fin yellowish with a black-red margin. Ventral fins delicate green. Pectoral fins colourless. Iris golden.

♀ Fins rounded. Quite differently coloured. Ground-colour black-brown. Belly yellow-whitish. Two dark bands on the sides like those of the ♂. Dorsal fin weak brown-red. Caudal fin with a red spot at the base and a red border. Anal and pectoral fins colourless.

489

Care and breeding, as given on p. 482. A very beautiful species and an active swimmer. An adhesive-spawner, usually spawning near to the bottom but never actually on the bottom. Eggs quite large, glass-clear at first, later yellowish. The young hatch after 15–20 days. 1908/+.

Aphyosemion bivittatum hollyi *Myers* 1933 (Fig. 767)   Blue Aphyosemion
Equatorial West Africa; to 5·5 cm.
   D 12; A 14; LL 28–29.

♂ Distinguished from the typical subspecies *A. b. bivittatum* (Lönnberg) by the more bluish ground-colour, as well as by other characters. Upperside dark olive anteriorly, yellow-olive in the region of the caudal peduncle. Flanks watery blue. Snout reddish. Upper lip edged with black. A few brown to violet-brown blotches and spots on the gill-cover and under the back. Dorsal fin brownish with a yellow leading-edge and a black hinder edge. Anal fin pale blue at the base, the outer parts green-yellow finely spotted with reddish. Caudal fin deep blue above, pale blue in the centre with a brilliant red band below.
♀ Brownish, with two distinct longitudinal bands on the flanks.

Care and breeding, as given for the typical subspecies. 1920/−.

Aphyosemion calabaricus (*E. Ahl* 1936) (Fig. 685)   Calabar Lyretail/Aphyosemion
                                                       (incorrectly Blue Cape Lopez Lyretail)
Hinterland of Calabar; to 5 cm.
   D 9–11; A 14–15; LL 30.

♂ Ground-colour sea-green to steel-blue. Body with dark red spots, fins with smaller red spots. Tips of dorsal and caudal fins less strongly produced than in

Figs. 766–770
♂♂ on the left, sketches of corresponding ♀♀ on the right

Fig. 766. *Aphyosemion bitaeniatum* (Striped Lyretail); maximum size.
Fig. 767. *Aphyosemion bivittatum hollyi* (Blue Aphyosemion); enlarged.
Fig. 768. *Aphyosemion calliurum calliurum* (Red-chinned Aphyosemion); enlarged.
Fig. 769. *Aphyosemion calliurum ahli* (Ahl's Aphyosemion); enlarged.
Fig. 770. *Aphyosemion cameronensis* (Cameroon Round-tailed Aphyosemion); maximum size.

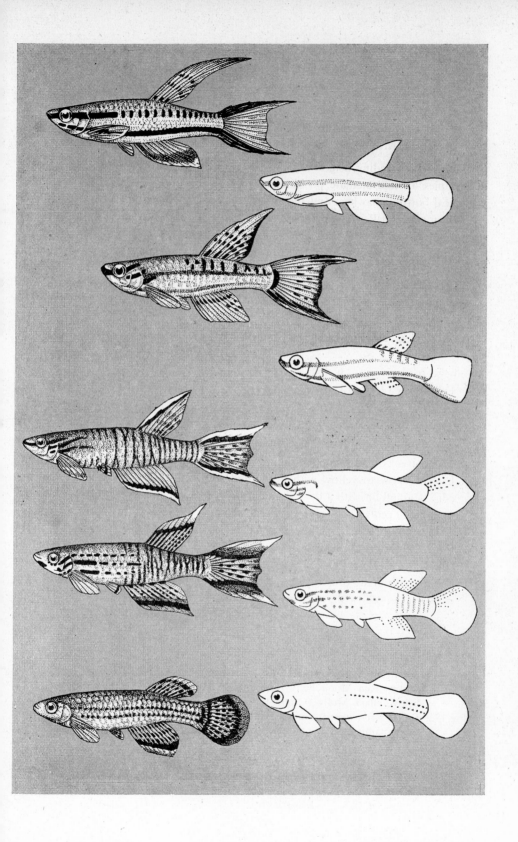

most of the previous species. Caudal fin sea-green with a red border edged with sulphur-yellow; anal and ventral fins similarly bordered.

♀ Brownish, with a dark blotch on the upper part of the caudal fin.

Care and breeding, as given on p. 482. As Foersch (1956) has shown, this species occupies an intermediate position, as regards breeding behaviour, between the typical bottom-spawners and the adhesive-spawners. When provided with a hard bottom-soil and Perlon yarn these fishes spawn on the yarn; with a soft bottom-soil and without yarn they then behave as bottom-spawners. This intermediate position is also indicated by the remarkably short ripening period of the eggs (12–14 days) which corresponds to that found in the adhesive-spawners; the eggs themselves are very soft-shelled. Unfortunately this species remains somewhat timid and delicate. 1935/+.

Aphyosemion calliurum calliurum (*Boulenger* 1911) (Fig. 768)   Red-chinned Aphyosemion

Liberia to Loanda; to 6 cm.
D 9–10; A 12–13; LL 29–30.

♂ Coloration, in relation to the wide distribution, very diverse. Upperside dark olive to grass-green. Flanks anteriorly (including the gill-cover) blue-green; behind the pectoral fins ochre-yellow or fawn. Belly yellowish. Cinnabar vermiform streaks and blotches on the sides of the head and body. Dorsal fin brown-yellow to yellow with brown-red spots and a narrow blue-grey upper edge. Caudal fin with a dark red band above and below, outwardly edged with pale blue; centre pale blue with reddish spots; produced tips porcelain-white. The greatly-produced yellow anal fin has a brilliant red band across its lower third. Pectoral and ventral fins greenish with a fine red stripe near the outer edges.

♀ Soberly coloured; brown-yellow to yellowish. Spots on the flanks merely suggested. Fins yellowish, often with red spots.

Plate 133

Fig. 771. Some cultivated varieties of Live-bearing Tooth-Carps. Above: Red Platy; centre: Red Moon Platy; centre, right: Red Wagtail Platy; centre, left and below: Black Molly. (Original)

Fig. 772. *Lebistes reticulatus* (Guppy); cultivated varieties. Centre: ♂ Flagtail Guppy; the remaining ♂♂ are Double Swordtail or Lyretail Guppies. (Original)

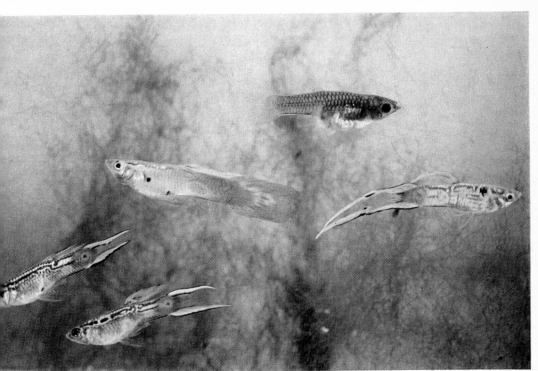

Plate 133

Plate 134

Plate 134

Fig.773. *Syngnathus pulchellus* (Lesser Freshwater Pipefish); natural size. (Photo Dr. Foersch)

Fig.774. *Gasterosteus aculeatus* (Three-spined Stickleback); ♂ in breeding-dress guarding brood. (Original)

Care and breeding, as given on p. 482. Adhesive-spawner. The ♀♀ of this species should not be permitted to breed too early. Spawning period 2–3 weeks; about 15–20 eggs per day. The young hatch after 12–20 days. 1908/+.

Aphyosemion calliurum ahli *Myers* 1933 (Fig. 769)   Ahl's Aphyosemion
Tropical West Africa; to 6 cm.
   D 9–10; A 12–13; LL 29–30.

♂ Distinguished from the typical subspecies by the stronger tint of the blue ground-colour, which is a brilliant ink-blue over the whole body. Back blackish, often with a greenish sheen. Numerous brilliant red streaks and spots on the head, gill-cover and anterior part of the body. Irregular dark red transverse bars on the caudal peduncle. Dorsal fin-base sea-green with red spots and streaks; outer part of the fin brilliant clay-yellow, tip white. Centre of caudal fin sky-blue with red spots, bounded above and below by curved dark red bands which are further succeeded by pale blue and golden-yellow bands; tips white. Anal fin sky-blue towards the body, with brilliant yellow outer parts, a dark red band and a blue edge.

♀ Yellowish to ash-grey. Belly with reddish tinge. Fins often slightly bluish.

This very beautiful form should be treated like the typical subspecies. 1933/−.

Aphyosemion cameronensis (*Boulenger* 1903) (Fig.770)   Cameroon Round-tailed
                                                                                          Aphyosemion
Southern Cameroons, Gabon, lower Congo; to 6 cm.
   D 11–12; A 14–15; LL 30–34.

♂ Coloration variable. Ground-colour brilliant sky-blue to emerald green; back darker. Two rows, to some extent very dense, of scarlet-red spots from the gill-cover to the root of the tail, each scale having a red spot. Dorsal and anal fins yellow-green with red spots and streaks, and bordered with brilliant blue or,

493

occasionally, red. Caudal fin greenish, with numerous red spots, a red band above and below and bluish to white edges. Eye brilliant green.

♀ Rows of spots only weakly defined.

This somewhat divergent species has unfortunately received little attention so far. *A. cameronensis* is a sprightly, surface-living fish, not timid and very ready to breed in captivity. Adhesive-spawner; the young hatch after 15–20 days. The ♂♂ of this species are unfortunately quarrelsome. 1913/+.

Aphyosemion cognatum *Meinken* 1915 (Figs. 591, 644)
Lower Congo; to 5 cm.
D 8–9; A 13–14; LL 30–31.

♂ Flanks clay-yellow to brown-olive, occasionally tinged with red; back dark olive; belly paler; gill-cover sea-green. The whole body is strewn with numerous red spots which may combine to form irregular transverse bars. Dorsal and anal fins lemon-yellow to clay-yellow, bounded with red and edged with sky-blue. Centre of caudal fin clay-yellow, often with a greenish lustre, spotted with red; above and below this there follow successively bands of smoke-blue, delicate yellow and, finally, a brilliant red margin.

♀ Grey to yellowish; gill-cover delicate blue.

Care and breeding, as given on p. 482. An adhesive-spawner, preferring to spawn close to the surface. Breeding season usually in spring. The young hatch after 12–16 days and are at first very dark in colour. 1950/+.

Aphyosemion fallax *E. Ahl* 1935 (Fig. 775)
Ghana; to 6 cm.
D 13–14; A 15–16; LL 34.

♂ Similar in shape to *A. gulare coeruleum*. Flanks brilliant sea-green; back dark olive-green. Three brilliant red longitudinal bands extend from the gill-cover

Figs. 775–779

♂♂ on the left, sketches of corresponding ♀♀ on the right

Fig. 775. *Aphyosemion fallax;* enlarged.
Fig. 776. *Aphyosemion filamentosum* (Plumed Lyretail); enlarged.
Fig. 777. *Aphyosemion gulare gulare* (Yellow Gularis); adults, natural size.
Fig. 778. *Aphyosemion meinkeni* (Meinken's Aphyosemion); enlarged.
Fig. 779. *Aphyosemion oeseri* (Emerald Aphyosemion); enlarged.

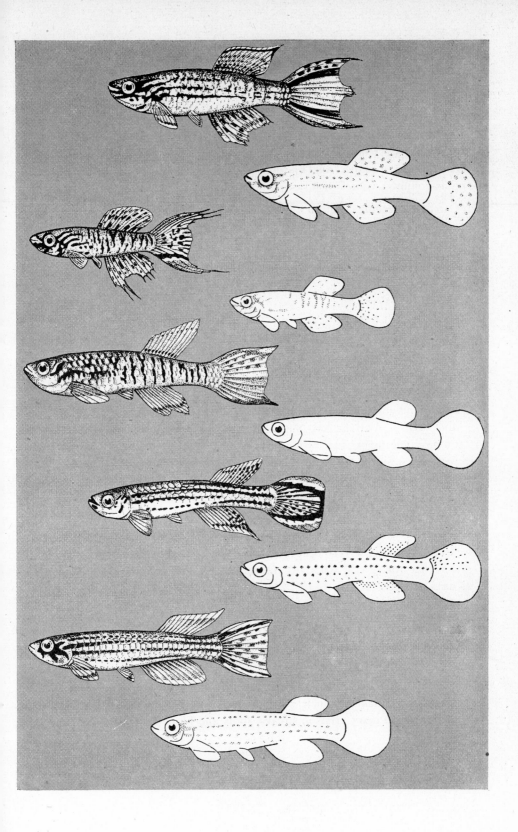

to the root of the tail, posteriorly, especially, breaking up into dots. Dorsal fin pale green to yellow-green, with numerous red spots and a narrow red border. Upper and lower tips of caudal fin produced, sickle-shaped; centre orange, bounded by a bold red band above and below; upper part of fin spotted with red, lower part yellow. Anal fin yellowish with a reddish margin. Eye blue-green.

♀ Clay-coloured to brownish, with a longitudinal band of spots.

Care and breeding, as given on p. 482. Bottom-spawner; a species seldom kept. 1930/−.

Aphyosemion filamentosum (*Meinken* 1933) (Fig. 776)   Plumed Lyretail/Aphyo-semion

Togo (?); to 4·5 cm.

D 13; A 14; LL 28.

♂ Snout and back black with a greenish tinge. Gill-cover and breast green. Upper parts of body iridescent sky- to dark blue; belly iridescent blue-violet. On the sides of the head and body are numerous, usually transverse, carmine blotches and streaks which, on the gill-cover especially, unite into three to four oblique vermiform bands extending to the nape. Dorsal fin greenish-blue with red blotches and streaks. Anal fin sky-blue with rows of copper-coloured spots. Caudal fin pale blue: upper part with several fine red longitudinal lines; centre spotted with red; lower part with a red longitudinal band edged with blue and a golden-yellow lower sector. The rays in the upper and lower points of the caudal, like the anterior and posterior rays of the anal, are produced and plume-like.

♀ Considerably duller in colour. Edges of fins entire.

Care and breeding, as given on p. 482. This species spawns on the bottom as well as on plants. A very beautiful, lively species which lives in midwater and is said to live for several years. At the earliest the young do not hatch until after 14 days. 1932/−.

Aphyosemion gardneri (*Boulenger* 1911) (Fig. 647)   Steel-blue Aphyosemion

Equatorial West Africa; to 5 cm.

D 12–13; A 14–16; LL 28–32.

♂ Ground-colour pale green to delicate violet, more velvety olive-green towards the back. Caudal peduncle pale- to steel-blue. Belly reddish. The head and flanks exhibit many crimson streaks, spots and blotches. Dorsal and anal fins very similar, with deep red spots and blotches on a pale blue ground and an outer yellow zone edged with red. Centre of caudal fin sky-blue with red spots margined with crimson above and below.

♀ a very modest brownish-olive. Fins with dark red spots.

Care and breeding, as given on p. 482. Bottom-spawner. A very lively, free-swimming and undemanding species; the ♂♂, however, are quarrelsome. The young hatch after 20 days at the earliest. 1908/+.

Aphyosemion gulare caeruleum (*Boulenger* 1915) (Fig. 589)   Blue Gularis
Niger delta, Cameroons; to 12 cm.

D 15–16; A 16–18; LL 30–34. One of the loveliest *Aphyosemion* spp. Coloration exceedingly variable.

♂ Upperside red-brown, with an olive-green lustre; flanks green-blue; belly bluish-green to pure bluish. Brilliant carmine-red dots and spots on the sides of the head and body, often uniting into vermiform streaks and blotches. Several transverse bands of spots, especially on the caudal peduncle which is often iridescent bluish. Dorsal fin serrated, blue-green to yellow-green with carmine-red spots. The upper, middle and lower rays of the caudal are produced into three long points, and the fin itself has three sharply differentiated longitudinal fields. The uppermost field is green-blue with red longitudinal stripes, the central one brilliant yellow and the lowermost field sky-blue, again with red longitudinal stripes. Anal fin blue-green, yellowish at the base, with red streaks and blotches. Ventral fins yellowish, tipped with red. Pectoral fins pale blue.

♀ Monotonously coloured, brown-red to greenish, with red spots on the sides. Fins yellow-green, rounded.

Care and breeding, as given on p. 482. Bottom-spawner. A very hardy species; ♂♂ very quarrelsome. The young hatch after 3–9 weeks. 1905/+.

Aphyosemion gulare gulare (*Boulenger* 1901) (Fig. 777)   Yellow Gularis
Liberia to the Cameroons; to 9 cm.

D 15–16; A 16–18; LL 30–34. Coloration exceedingly variable.

♂ Back olive-brown; flanks iridescent bluish-green; belly yellowish. An irregular red-brown longitudinal band, flanked by two brilliant blue lines, from the eye to the root of the tail. Lower lip edged with red. Throat carmine-red. Gill-cover with several red vermiform streaks and blotches and a red edge. Back with red

497

spots. Dorsal fin yellow-green with red spots. Caudal fin-lobes produced. Upper caudal lobe blue-green or reddish with red streaks and blotches; centre of fin often yellowish; lower third orange- to brick-red. Anal, pectoral and ventral fins yellow to green-yellow, bordered with red. Eye red-golden.

♀ Caudal fin rounded. Streaks and blotches merely indicated.

Care and breeding, as given on p. 482. Bottom-spawner. Isolation of the pairs essential since the ♂♂ are very quarrelsome. The young hatch after 3–8 weeks, usually after 5. 1907/+.

Aphyosemion loennbergi (*Boulenger* 1903) (Fig. 783)   Lönnberg's Aphyosemion
Niger to the Cameroons; to 5 cm.
D 11–12; A 12–13; LL 26–28.

♂ Ground-colour brassy-yellow to bronze-colour, with gleaming blue-green to grass-green blotches and lines; belly clay-yellow; lower jaw deep dark blue; blood-red vermiform markings on the gill-cover. The greatly produced dorsal fin is fawn at the base, pale yellow in the centre and more or less bluish at the edge, with a sulphur-yellow tip. Centre of caudal fin spotted with red, central margin bright red, upper and lower edges sky-blue, produced tips sulphur-yellow. Anal fin sulphur-yellow to ochre-yellow with a bright red border and a narrow blue edge. Eye pale yellow.

♀ Brownish with a green lustre; two dark longitudinal bands.

Care and breeding, as given on p. 482. Adhesive-spawner. A very lively species. Up to 200 eggs, according to length of spawning period (about 14 days). The young hatch after 12 days at the earliest. 1905/–.

Figs. 780–785

♂♂ on the left, sketches of corresponding ♀♀ to the right

Fig. 780. *Aphyosemion roloffi* (Roloff's Aphyosemion); enlarged.
Fig. 781. *Aphyosemion splendopleuris;* enlarged.
Fig. 782. *Aphyosemion vexillifer;* maximum size.
Fig. 783. *Aphyosemion loennbergi* (Lönnberg's Aphyosemion); maximum size.
Fig. 784. *Epiplatys fasciolatus;* natural size.
Fig. 785. *Epiplatys dorsalis;* ♂ only; natural size.

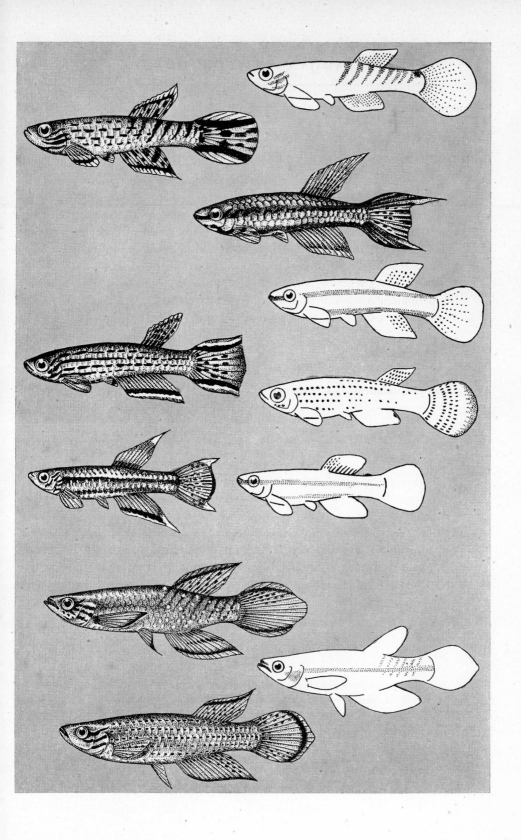

Aphyosemion meinkeni *Myers* 1933 (Fig. 778)   Meinken's (Round-tailed)
                                                     Aphyosemion

Tropical West Africa; to 5 cm.

D 12; A 14; LL 34.

♂ Body brilliant sea-green; gleaming grass-green blotches on the caudal peduncle; back darker. Scales edged with black. Blood-red spots and stripes, irregularly arranged on the head, forming dense and loose rows on the body (each scale has a red spot). Basal portion of dorsal fin yellow-green with fawn spots and streaks, upper portion golden yellow. Caudal fin rounded: centre sea-green with scarlet streaks and spots followed, above and below, by, successively, a bright red band, a sky-blue line and finally a yellow edge. Anal fin similar to dorsal but with angular rows of red spots. Eye golden yellow.

♀ Fawn to ochre-coloured, with four rows of weaker spots.

Care and breeding, as given on p. 482. Adhesive-spawner. Frequents the water-layer near the bottom. The young hatch after 12 days at the earliest. 1930/—.

Aphyosemion multicolor (*Meinken* 1929) (Fig. 588)   Many-coloured Lyretail/
                                                          Aphyosemion

Lagos, Cameroons, Nigeria; to 6 cm.

D 10; A 13; LL 26. Shape similar to that of *A. bivittatum* (Lönnberg); a very beautiful species.

♂ Back olive-green. Flanks brownish-red, with a rainbow iridescence by reflected light. Lower lip red. Some brown-red vermiform blotches on the gill-cover are continued as a similar row of spots which sometimes form a uniform band and extend to the upper part of the root of the tail. A similar dark longitudinal band extends from the insertion of the ventral fins into the lower part of the root of the tail. The dorsal fin is of various shades of brown, with a pale green leading-edge and a reddish tip. Centre of caudal fin sulphur-yellow followed, above and below, by, successively, a broad fawn band and a yellow to sea-green margin;

Plate 135

Fig. 786. *Pterolebias peruensis* (Peruvian Longfin), a species first imported into Europe in 1958. ♂, about twice natural size. (Photo Werner, Michigan)

Fig. 787. *Gynochanda filamentosa;* imported specimens, slightly enlarged; above ♂, below ♀. (Original)

Plate 135

Plate 136

Plate 136

Fig. 788. *Nannacara anomala* (Golden-eyed Dwarf Cichlid); adults, natural size, left ♀, right ♂. (Original)

Fig. 789. *Cichlasoma meeki* (Fire-mouth Cichlasoma); coloration outside the breeding season, above ♂, below ♀. (Original)

produced tips brilliant dark green. Anal fin yellow with a red margin. Eye golden yellow.

♀ More soberly coloured, with rounded, yellowish fins.

Care and breeding, as given on p. 482. Adhesive-spawner. Further details as for *A. loennbergi*. 1912/+.

Aphyosemion oeseri *E. Ahl* 1928 (Fig. 779)   Emerald Aphyosemion
Niger delta, Calabar region; to 5·5 cm.

♂ Shape not unlike that of *A. cameronensis*. Ground-colour brilliant grass-green with numerous gleaming blotches. Back darker. Belly green-yellow. Several close rows of blood-red spots (each scale with a red blotch) from the gill-cover to the root of the tail. Dorsal and anal fins grass- to sea-green, bordered with delicate violet and edged with blue-white. Caudal fin grass-green to pale green, with red spots; the central field is bounded above and below by a red line outwardly succeeded by a bluish to yellow-green tint. Eyes brilliant green.

♀ Rows of red spots much looser.

Care and breeding, as given on p. 482. Probably as for *A. cameronensis*. Hitherto seldom kept in aquaria. 1928/−.

Aphyosemion petersi (*Sauvage* 1882) (Fig. 654)   Peters' (Round-tailed) Aphyosemion

Ghana, French Equatorial Africa; to 6 cm.
D 9–10; A 14; LL 29–31.

♂ Ground-colour olive-green; behind the gill-cover a more iridescent, metallic green. Red blotches, like strings of beads, around the flanks. Especially characteristic of this species are a large, carmine-red blotch over the ventral insertion and 6–8 fine, more or less prominent narrow dark transverse bands (especially clear in the young). Dorsal fin sea-green with fine red spots. Anal fin coloured

501

likewise at the base, but with the outer part yellow and the edge red. Centre of caudal fin green with vertical rows of red spots, the upper and hinder edges smoke-grey and the lower part pale yellow.

♀ Fawn, with a similar arrangement of blotches on the flanks; a distinct shoulder blotch.

Care and breeding, as given on p. 482. Adhesive-spawner. Lively and not timid. 1951.

Aphyosemion roloffi *E. Ahl* 1936 (Fig. 780)   Roloff's (Round-tailed) Aphyosemion
Tropical West Africa; to 5 cm.
D 12–13; A 14–15; LL 28–30. Caudal fin rounded in both sexes.

♂ Ground-colour brilliant pale to dark green, becoming more yellow-green towards the caudal and with gleaming metallic green to violet blotches. Gill-cover shining green with 3 to 4 blood-red bands. On the flanks several blood-red to brownish blotches combine to form 4 to 5 loose longitudinal bands. 5–10 narrow, curved transverse bands are more sharply defined, being especially distinct on the caudal peduncle. Dorsal fin yellow-green with red spots, a blood-red border and a bluish edge. Anal fin similarly coloured. The yellow-green centre of the caudal fin is delimited by two red-brown, often arched, bands from upper and lower bright sulphur-yellow to golden fields. Pectoral and ventral fins greenish to yellowish with a red to orange border.

♀ Plainly coloured. Red-brown to grey-brown, often with a greenish sheen on the flanks. The transverse bars are only faintly indicated. Fins yellowish to greenish, faintly spotted with red.

Care and breeding, as given on p. 482. The eggs are laid indiscriminately on plants or on the bottom. The young hatch after 12 days at the earliest. A very light-shy species. 1936/ – .

Aphyosemion schoutedeni (*Boulenger* 1920) (Fig. 646)   Schouteden's Aphyosemion
Congo Basin; to 4 cm.
D 8; A 14; LL 27–28.

♂ Back greenish-blue; flanks anteriorly more sky-blue; head brilliant green-blue; caudal peduncle more or less clay-coloured. Numerous irregularly scattered spots on the flanks. Dorsal fin yellowish with red spots, a red border and a porcelain-white tip. Anal fin greenish-yellow. Caudal fin with a central pale yellow

502

area bounded by green above and below, and a red edge. Tips of fins white. Eye greenish.

♀ Uniform brownish-olive with isolated red spots.

Care and breeding, as given on p. 482. Adhesive-spawner. 1949.

Aphyosemion sjoestedti (*Lönnberg* 1895) (Fig. 574)   Golden Pheasant/Red Aphyosemion

Upper Guinea to the Cameroons; to 9 cm.

D 17–19; A 17–19; LL 33–36. A very beautiful species, but also predatory and sluggish.

♂ Upperside of head brownish-green; nape brass-coloured; back brilliant red; throat and gill-cover indigo, the last with carmine-red spots and vermiform blotches. Along the flanks a very irregular brilliant golden-yellow longitudinal band, bounded by carmine-red stripes above and below. Flanks and caudal peduncle brilliant dark blue and blue-green spotted with carmine-red. Dorsal fin blood-red at the base, externally dull reddish with a violet band and a pale edge. Caudal fin pale blue above, below often yellowish-white with dark violet blotches and streaks. Anal fin dull blue spotted with red, with a violet band and a pale edge. Pectoral and ventral fins delicate bluish, occasionally reddish with bluish edges.

♀ Considerably paler. Pale brown to grey-brown with reddish blotches on the sides. Fins rounded, yellowish.

Care and breeding, as given on p. 482. Exclusively a bottom-spawner. The ripening-period for the eggs is very long (5–6 months). It is essential to keep this species in isolated pairs. 1909/+.

Aphyosemion splendopleuris (*Meinken* 1930) (Fig. 781).

Cameroons; to 5 cm.

D 11; A 13; LL 26–27.

♂ Olive- to yellow-green with rows of shining scales on the flanks. Scales edged with red-brown, especially on the back. Caudal peduncle golden yellow. From the eye to the upper part of the root of the tail there extends a dark longitudinal band which, especially anteriorly, is made up of red-brown spots and blotches. A similar longitudinal band commences behind the pectoral fin and ends in the lower part of the root of the tail. Lower lip edged with blue-black. Gill-cover with a red blotch. Belly yellow. Breast and pectoral fins yellow to greenish. Dorsal fin anteriorly green with red spots, the central part brownish-red, the tip yellow. Caudal fin yellow-green in the centre, the outer parts chrome- to dark grey (with a red blotch on the lower part) and the produced tips yellow. Anal fin yellow-green at the base, the outer part reddish to golden yellow.

♀ Grey-brown to grey-yellow with iridescent violet flanks. Fins rounded.

Care and breeding, as given on p. 482. Adhesive-spawner. The young hatch after 12 days at the earliest. Very lively species. 1928/—.

Aphyosemion vexillifer *Meinken* 1929 (Fig. 782)
Tropical West Africa; to 6 cm.
   D 9; A 14; LL 32.

♂ Ground-colour a lovely sea-green, becoming black-green towards the back. The irregular brilliant red blotches and streaks on the head and gill-cover are continued along the body as loose longitudinal rows of spots. Dorsal fin sea-green, spotted with red. Centre of caudal fin iridescent green with red spots; above and below this is bounded by arched red lines, followed externally by blue and, finally, golden yellow bands. Anal fin yellow with a broad dark red band and a brilliant yellow tip.

♀ Ochre-yellow with rows of faint red spots.

Care and breeding, as given on p. 482. Adhesive-spawner. The young hatch after 12 days at the earliest. Very lively species. 1928/—.

Two further species which have been imported are *A. rubrostictum* (E. Ahl 1924) (1932/—) and *A. liberiensis* (Boulenger 1908) (1908/—). Since hardly anything is known about the care and breeding of either species, and since also they are not among the more colourful members of the genus, their descriptions are here omitted. The import of *A. gambiensis* is greatly to be desired.

Genus Aplocheilichthys: Care and Breeding

Although several species have lately been included in this genus, all, except *A. spilauchena*, really belong to the next genus, *Micropanchax*. Besides having structural differences in the mouth, *A. spilauchena* stands apart from the *Micropanchax* spp. by its larger size, preference for brackish water, larger eggs and probably longer life. It is a West African species, especially character-

504

istic of the antimalarial channels at Lagos where it helps to control the mosquito-larvae. *Aplocheilichthys spilauchena* requires hard, well-oxygenated water with 25% seawater. In its natural habitat it spawns on plants, but since the normal aquarium plants will not stand seawater Perlon or other synthetic yarn should be used. Eggs large. According to Meder (1953) the young hatch after 12–14 days and are sensitive to water cooling.

Aplocheilichthys spilauchena (*Dumeril* 1859) (Fig. 795)
West Africa, from Senegal to the Congo, in lagoons and fresh water; to 7 cm.

D 7–8; A 13–14; LL 25–28. A typical surface-living fish. Ground-colour yellow-green with a blue lustre by reflected light; upper half of iris red; a silver-white spot on the nape is conspicuous from above. Vertical fins lemon-yellow.

♂ Several narrow silver cross-bands on the hind half of the body; bases of dorsal and anal fins with dark red and silver-white spots.
♀ Dorsal and anal fins smaller, without spots.

(Description partly from field-notes by Dr. E. Trewavas.) Care, as given above. 1904/+.

Genus Micropanchax: Care and Breeding

The numerous species of this genus are native to the waters of the Nile and tropical Africa. Most of them are tiny, silver-blue or pale yellow-green fishes with large, shining eyes, but in the lakes there are related species which grow larger and have more colour. They inhabit bodies of water of many kinds, but probably choose shallow, reedy places wherever they are and feed on small mosquito-larvae and other insects.

Micropanchax spp. should be kept in small, moderately-planted and not too brightly-lit aquaria with a few floating plants, such as *Riccia* and *Salvinia*, and provided with a dark bottom (fine sand and boiled peat or basalt chips). Soft, slightly acid or peat-filtered water, now and again partly changed, is suitable for every species. Temperature 23–26°C. Small live food. Small Mailed Catfishes or peaceful surface-living fishes make suitable tank-mates.

Many *Micropanchax* spp. are at their liveliest only when they are kept in shoals.

The conditions recommended above also apply to breeding. The spawning period, which is characterised by delightful courtship behaviour, often lasts for several weeks. The eggs are produced singly, more rarely in little clusters, fertilised by the ♂ and then stripped off by the ♀ onto the leaves of fine-leaved water plants from which they remain hanging. The egg-shell, at first soft, hardens during the early hours. The parents do not generally molest the eggs. The young, which hatch after 12 to 18 days, are often very tiny and should at first be fed on Infusoria or the very smallest nauplii. The growth of some species is slow at first. Most of them are annual fishes, living no longer than a year.

Micropanchax flavipinnis (*Meinken* 1932) (Fig. 790)   Yellow-finned Panchax
Lagos, in sluggish waters; to 3·5 cm.

D 6–7; A 13–14; LL 30–31.

♂ Dirty yellow to grey, darker on the back. Lower parts of flanks and belly yellowish, with a lovely brassy-yellow to grass-green iridescence by reflected light. Gill-cover brilliant yellow-green. Dorsal and anal fins lemon-yellow with a bluish edge. Caudal fin lemon-yellow. Ventral fins orange-red. Iris of the large eye iridescent grass-green above, dark below.
♀ Paler; ventral fins almost colourless.

Care and breeding, as given on p. 505.

This species is very easily bred. Several pairs can be put together in the same tank. The ♀♀ lay their eggs in small clusters; the young grow very quickly. Good jumpers! 1929/ –.

Figs. 790–795

♂♂ on the left, sketches of the corresponding ♀♀ to the right

Fig. 790. *Micropanchax flavipinnis* (Yellow-finned Panchax); somewhat enlarged.
Fig. 791. *Micropanchax loati;* enlarged.
Fig. 792. *Micropanchax katangae;* somewhat enlarged.
Fig. 793. *Micropanchax macrurus;* somewhat enlarged.
Fig. 794. *Micropanchax* sp.; maximum size.
Fig. 795. *Aplocheilichthys spilauchena;* natural size.

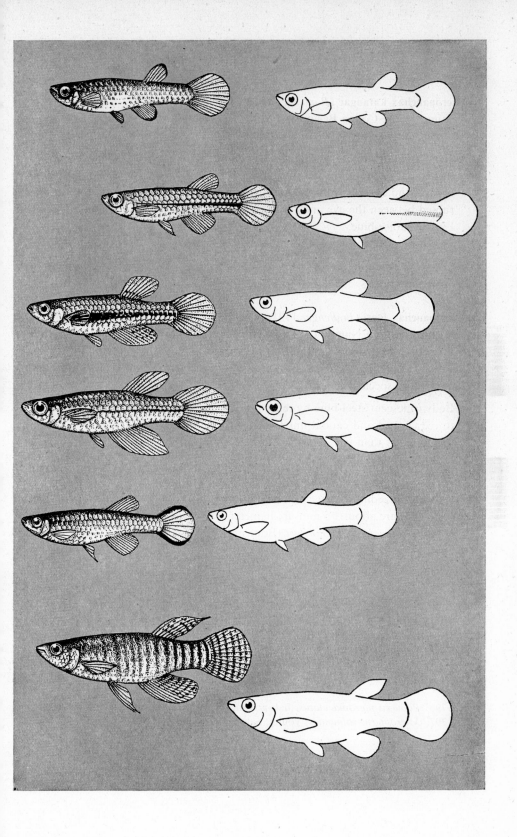

Micropanchax katangae (*Boulenger* 1912) (Fig. 792)
Katanga, in the Congo Basin; to 4·5 cm.
  D 9–10; A 14–16; LL 25–27.

♂ Head and back ochre-yellow to pale yellow. Flanks, especially the lower part of the caudal peduncle, iridescent bluish. Throat and belly white. An increasingly broad band extends from the tip of the snout to the root of the tail but is interrupted between the eye and the pectoral base. Fins yellowish to faint greenish. Eye turquoise-blue.
♀ Less brilliantly coloured; fins colourless.

Care and breeding, as given on p. 505. Eggs relatively large. The young hatch after about 3 weeks. 1937/−.

Micropanchax loati (*Boulenger* 1901) (Fig. 791)
Nile and Northern Nigeria (and Chad basin?), probably in quiet waters; to 3 cm.
  D 7–8(9); A 11–13(14); LL 25–27. Coloration according to Roloff (personal communication):–ground-colour yellowish-green; iris shining green, but fainter than in other species.

♂ Body iridescent steel-blue by reflected light. Anal and ventral fins yellowish-red to red; dorsal and caudal fins faintly red. Dorsal and anal fins not noticeably longer in ♂♂ than in ♀♀; ventrals very slightly longer. Head and anal fin sometimes bearing minute spines.
♀ Ventral fins very slightly shorter; head and anal fin never spinose.

Care and breeding, as given on p. 505. Probably not yet bred in captivity. Ripe ovarian eggs are about 1·5 mm. in diameter (Trewavas, personal communication). 1935/−. *Micropanchax schoelleri* (Boulenger 1904) is a synonym, but was for a long time not recognised as identical with *M. loati* because of errors in the original description of the latter. (Sandon, 1950)

Micropanchax macrophthalmus *Meinken* 1932 (Fig. 655)   Lamp-eyed Panchax
Lagos; to 3·5 cm.
  D 7; A 11; LL 26. Very slightly translucent.

Plate 137

Fig. 796. *Pomoxis nigromaculatus;* half-grown, somewhat reduced. (Photo P. Unger)
Fig. 797. *Micropterus salmoides;* young, natural size. (Photo P. Unger)

Plate 137

Plate 138

Plate 138

Fig. 798. *Mesogonistius chaetodon* (Black-banded Sunfish); adult pair with young. (Photo P. Unger)

♂ Back yellow-olive to yellow-grey with a brownish-red to brick-red band along the dorsal ridge. Flanks and belly pale yellowish with a strong brassy gleam. A lovely gleaming brilliant blue-green band runs from behind the gill-cover to the root of the tail, and is bordered above and below by a fine black stripe. Gill-cover iridescent. Dorsal, anal and ventral fins glass-clear, with broad pale blue to slate-grey borders. Caudal fin greenish with dark green spots, the outer parts with red spots. Pectoral fins colourless. Dorsal and anal fins produced to points.

♀ More modestly coloured; dorsal and anal fins rounded.

The eyes in both sexes are very large with a lovely green-golden iridescence; it must be emphasised that they merely reflect light and are not self-luminous.

Care and breeding not difficult if the rules given on p. 505 are observed. The species likes to live in shoals and gives very good value in an aquarium with shaded top-lighting. *Telmatherina ladigesi* is an especially suitable species to keep with it. The very small young hatch after 10–14 days and should at first be fed with the very finest food. Growth is slow during the early days but more rapid later. The serious breeder should put several pairs together in a large tank and let them spawn on bundles of plants or on Perlon yarn. The spawning-substrate together with the eggs should be removed after 2–3 days and replenished. The eggs can easily be picked off into hatching dishes; better still, the egg-laden substrate can be bodily transferred to a rearing tank. 1929/+.

Micropanchax macrurus (*Boulenger* 1904) (Fig. 793)
Angola and Calabar; to 5 cm.
D 7–8; A 12–15; LL 24–27.

♂ Somewhat translucent, glassy. Ground-colour blue-grey to grey-green, with a lovely pale blue to violet iridescence by reflected light; upperside often brassy-yellow at the same time. Numerous golden to green-golden spots on the flanks. Fins grey to smoke-grey.

♀ Without the spots.

Care and breeding, as given on p. 505. Probably not yet bred in captivity. 1910/−.

Micropanchax myersi *Poll* 1952 (Fig. 575)
Congo (Leopoldville); to 2·2 cm.
D 7; A 10–11; LL 25–26. A very beautiful, lively species.

♂ Ground-colour olive-green to brownish, a lovely shining blue-green by reflected light. Dorsal fin with produced rays, pennon-like, deep yellow at the base, more blackish on the outer parts. Caudal fin similarly coloured. Ventral and anal fins pure yellow, the latter produced, flag-like. Eye brass-coloured.
♀ Stockier; body similarly coloured, fins colourless.

Care and breeding, as given on p. 505. Young very minute. 1952.

Genus Epiplatys: Care and Breeding

The members of the genus *Epiplatys*, mainly native to tropical West Africa, are typical surface fishes and mostly inhabit sluggish or standing waters. Their elongate, spindle-shaped body is outstandingly adapted to this mode of life. Thus the line of the back and top of the head forms one plane, whereby the very broad mouth is directed upwards. The *Epiplatys* spp. are predators which, like the Pike, lurk after their prey. Their aquarium should have a large surface-area, partly covered with floating plants or plants with floating leaves. Keeping them together with shoaling fishes which swim in the middle water-layers is sometimes advantageous, since many *Epiplatys* are often very sluggish when kept alone. They are best suited by soft to medium hard, neutral to slightly acid water at temperatures of 24–28 °C. However, almost all the species seem to become unhappy if the surface is very much disturbed, as it may be with over-vigorous filtration or aeration. Live food of all kinds, especially insects and insect-larvae. Some will also take artificial foods.

The sexes are usually easily distinguished. The ♂♂ are not only larger and more robust but also more brightly coloured.

For breeding choose tanks which are not too small and provide rich floating plant cover (*Salvinia*, *Riccia*, floating *Myriophyllum* stalks). Soft to medium hard water, filtered through peat; temperature 26–28 °C. Some ♂♂

510

drive very hard. The spawning period usually lasts 2–3 weeks and several hard-shelled eggs are laid on the plants each day. The serious breeder removes the plants, with the eggs adhering to them, to a darkened rearing tank and then replenishes the breeding tank with fresh plants. The young usually hatch after 8–18 days and should be fed with the finest live food (nauplii, Rotifers, Micro-worms). It is essential to sort the young into size-classes, since the larger ones eagerly pursue their smaller brothers. Growth rapid. Many species do better if salt or sea-salt is added to the water (1 teaspoon to 10 litres). Heated open-air establishments provide the best conditions for breeding. The eggs travel quite well in moist peat-mould, a fact which probably indicates that these fishes can survive a dry season as resting eggs.

Similar care and breeding-conditions suit the *Pachypanchax* spp. of East Africa.

Epiplatys chaperi (*Sauvage* 1882) (Fig. 676)   Fire-mouth Epiplatys
Sierra Leone, Liberia; to 5·5 cm.
   D 7–8 (small); A 14–15; P 15–16; V 5; LL 25–27.

♂ Back olive-green; flanks yellow- to blue-green; belly yellowish. The scales on the back have dark red edges and those on the belly blackish. 5–7 (usually 6) narrow, dark, somewhat oblique, transverse bands on the flanks, of which two lie immediately behind the gill-cover and the others across the caudal peduncle. The final band is continued ventrally into the lower, somewhat produced, rays of the caudal fin. Lower jaw and throat brilliant cinnabar; edge of lower jaw black. Eyes green above, red below. Vertical fins grey-green, spotted and streaked with dark. Anal fin edged with black.
♀ Coloration duller, more brownish. Eyes yellow. Lower jaw and throat yellow-brown. Lower rays of caudal fin not produced.

Care and breeding, as given on p. 510. No sea-salt necessary. The spawning period lasts for several weeks; it is best to provide two ♂♂ to a ♀. The spawn-laden plants should be carefully removed to a rearing tank. The young hatch after 8–10 days at 25°C. and grow very slowly. Up to 200 young may result from a spawning period. A species very suitable for the community tank. 1908/+.

Epiplatys chevalieri (*Pellegrin* 1904)   Chevalier's Epiplatys
Congo (Stanley Pool, etc.); to 6·8 cm.

D 7–8; A 13–14; LL 27–28. This species, at first sight easily confused with
E.macrostigma or *E.sheljuzhkoi*, is distinguished by the following characters: the
separate red spots in the longitudinal rows stand so close in the lower part of the
body that they run together. Gill-cover slightly greenish with bright red vermiform lines. Vertical fins with dark edges. Dorsal fin and upper part of caudal
spotted with red.

♀ rather dull, with rows of red-brown spots.

Care as given on p. 510. Probably not yet bred in captivity. 1950.

Epiplatys dorsalis *E.Ahl* 1936 (Fig.785)   Jewelled Epiplatys
Calabar River; to 8 cm.

D 14; A 18; LL 28.

♂ Ground-colour fawn with a brassy gleam. Back olive-brown; belly yellowish.
Edges of mouth carmine-red. Gill-cover with irregular red streaks. Further very
loose rows of blood-red spots on the flanks, each scale bearing a small red
blotch. Dorsal and anal fins yellowish-green with numerous red spots and red-
brown edges. Caudal fin greenish with a red-brown inner border.
♀ Smaller, reddish strewn with red-brown spots.

Care and breeding, as given on p. 510. Further imports desirable. 1935/–.

Epiplatys duboisi *Poll* 1952 (Fig.674)   Dubois' Epiplatys
Congo (Leopoldville); to 3·5 cm.

♂ D 10; A 15–16; ♀ D 9; A 14; LL 25–26. One of the most beautiful *Epiplatys*
spp. Coloration (according to Meder, 1955):–

Figs.799–803

♂♂ on the left, sketches of corresponding ♀♀ on the right

Fig.799. *Epiplatys macrostigma* (Large-spotted Epiplatys); maximum size.
Fig.800. *Epiplatys senegalensis* (Senegal Epiplatys); enlarged.
Fig.801. *Epiplatys grahami* (Graham's Epiplatys); maximum size.
Fig.802. *Epiplatys sexfasciatus* (Six-barred Epiplatys); adult, somewhat reduced.
Fig.803. *Epiplatys nigromarginatus* (Black-edged Epiplatys); natural size.

512

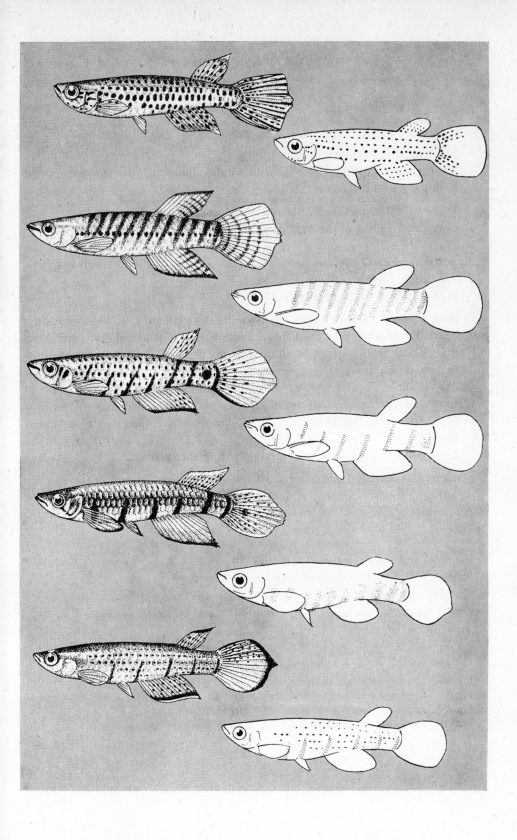

♂ Brilliant emerald green with longitudinal rows of small, brown-red spots. Vertical fins very elegant, shining greenish set with brown-red spots, those on the margin uniting to form a narrow brown-red stripe along the edge. Pectoral and ventral fins colourless.

♀ Smaller and less brilliantly coloured; ground-colour yellowish-brown, spotted as in the ♂. All fins colourless.

In the wild lives in association with *Micropanchax myersi*.
Care and breeding of this very peaceful species, as given on p. 510. 1955.

Epiplatys fasciolatus (*Günther* 1866) (Fig. 784)   Banded Epiplatys
Sierra Leone, Liberia to Nigeria; to 8 cm.
D 11–12; A 16–18; P 16–17; LL 27–29.

♂ Back blackish to brown-olive; flanks more olive-coloured, paling towards the belly. By reflected light the flanks have a bluish glint and display numerous shining pale green spots. A small carmine-red blotch at the base of each scale. 6 narrow, dark transverse bands on the flanks, beginning at the level of the ventral fins and about equally spaced. Lower lip with a blue edge. Throat with red spots and streaks. Gill-cover with 3–4 red vermiform bands. Caudal fin produced to a point, yellow-green, with red-brown longitudinal bands above and below.

♀ Fins yellowish-green, without markings. Altogether plainer.

Care and breeding, as given on p. 510. Sea-salt advised (2 teaspoons to 10 litres of water). These fishes are somewhat delicate to transfer. The young hatch after 12–14 days. Only suitable for the community tank in special circumstances. 1911/+.

Epiplatys grahami (*Boulenger* 1911) (Fig. 801)   Graham's Epiplatys
Southern Nigeria, in rivers and marshes; to 6 cm.
D 7–8 (short); A 15–16; LL 28–30. The live ♂ is distinguished from the rather similar *Epiplatys macrostigma* by the following characters:–flanks with evident

Figs. 804–807

♂♂ on the left, sketches of the corresponding ♀♀ to the right

Fig. 804. *Epiplatys longiventralis;* enlarged.
Fig. 805. *Epiplatys ornatus* (Emerald Epiplatys); natural size.
Fig. 806. *Epiplatys sheljuzhkoi;* somewhat enlarged.
Fig. 807. *Fundulus catenatus* (Chained Top Minnow); adults, somewhat reduced.

514

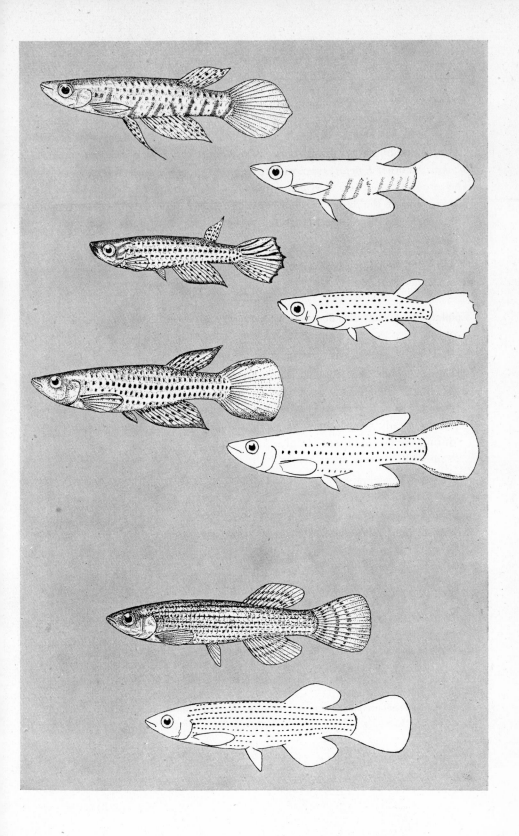

narrow and somewhat oblique dark stripes; lower jaw with a bright red bridle-band; rows of spots regular in the lower half of the body as well as in the upper. From the likewise rather similar *E. sheljuzhkoi* the living *E. grahami* is most readily distinguished by the red bridle-band on the lower jaw, which is lacking in *E. sheljuzhkoi*. All other *Epiplatys* spp. with rows of red spots are quite differently marked. The ground-colour of *E. grahami* is clay-colour to pale brown with a slight bluish sheen on the flanks. An iridescent bluish blotch on the gill-cover. Fins delicate yellow-green; vertical fins spotted with red, especially on the outer parts.

♀ darker; transverse bands always distinct.

Care and breeding, as given on p. 510. Lively and peaceful, but not very prolific. 1912/+.

Epiplatys longiventralis (*Boulenger* 1911) (Fig. 804)
Tropical West Africa, mainly in Southern Nigeria; to 5·5 cm.
D 8–9; A 15–16; LL 25–27.

♂ Similar to the previous species, but with much longer ventral fins and also lacking the blue blotch on the gill-cover. Dorsal and anal fins spotted all over, in contrast to *E. grahami* in which only the tips are spotted. Oblique transverse bands usually more numerous. Longitudinal rows of spots distinctly rust-red during the breeding season only.
♀ Yellowish; rows of spots brown.

Care and breeding, as given on p. 510. A very warmth-loving species. 1908/−.

Epiplatys macrostigma (*Boulenger* 1911) (Fig. 799)   Large-spotted Epiplatys
Mouth of the Congo and nearby tributaries; to 6 cm.
D 8–10; A 15–18; LL 27–28. Lower jaw projecting somewhat. Middle caudal rays in ♂ produced, forming a small lobe.

Plate 139

Fig. 808. *Lepomis megalotis* (Long-eared Sunfish); young, somewhat reduced.
(Photo P. Unger)
Fig. 809. *Mesogonistius chaetodon* (Black-banded Sunfish); ripe adults, natural size.
(Original)
Fig. 810. *Micropterus dolomieu;* 20 cm. long, in the Hellabrunn Aquarium, Munich.
(Original)

Plate 139

Plate 140

Plate 140

Fig. 811. *Ambloplites rupestris;* young, natural size. (Photo P. Unger)
Fig. 812. *Lepomis gibbosus* (Pumpkinseed Sunfish); young, somewhat enlarged. (Original)
Fig. 813. *Lepomis gibbosus;* adult, 18 cm. long, in the Hellabrunn Aquarium, Munich. (Original)

♂ Upperside olive-green to delicate brown-red; flanks brassy-yellow to pale greenish; underside whitish. Characteristic of this species are several longitudinal rows of large claret spots, of which those on the lower half of the side, especially in the caudal region, are irregular. Vertical fins colourless to quite pale yellow-green, irregularly spotted with rust-red and with yellow tips or borders. No dark transverse bands.

♀ Pale olive-brown with rows of faint brown spots, especially on the anterior portion of the body. Dark transverse bars occasionally appear on the lower half of the caudal peduncle.

Care and breeding, as given on p. 510. Remains somewhat timid in captivity. 1911/+.

Epiplatys nigromarginatus *E. Ahl* 1937 (Fig. 803) Black-edged Epiplatys
Tropical West Africa; to 7 cm.
  D 9; A 15–16; LL 29–30.

♂ Ground-colour blue-grey to dirty pale brown; back darker. Gleaming blue blotches on the gill-cover and caudal peduncle. Numerous rust-red spots on the flanks; alternatively 6 longitudinal rows of spots. Occasionally several narrow dark transverse bands appear. Dorsal and anal fins grey, with fine red spots and dark borders. Caudal fin yellow, outer parts pale blue and white, margin dark.

♀ blue-grey to pale grey; transverse bands usually distinct.

Care and breeding, as given on p. 510. Not very prolific. 1938/–.

Epiplatys ornatus (*E. Ahl* 1928) (Fig. 805) Emerald Epiplatys
Cameroons to Gabon; to 6 cm.
  D 9; A 16; LL 28.

♂ Back coffee-brown; flanks pale brown-green to dull blackish-green; belly delicate reddish-brown to yellowish. Each scale on the sides bears a deep red to black-red spot, the several spots forming 6–7 longitudinal rows. A few vermi-

517

form red blotches on the gill-cover and nape. The flanks are gleaming golden to gold-green by reflected light. Vertical fins yellow-green with red spots and streaks. Anal fin with a pale blue base and reddish border.

♀ More dully coloured, lacking the golden glint on the sides. Fins pale yellow throughout.

Care and breeding, as given on p. 510. The courtship is less stormy. With much quivering on the part of both parents an egg is laid in a plant thicket and sent whirling into the plants with a blow of the caudal fin, where it remains hanging by a short filament. The young hatch after 12–14 days at 26°C. and are very small; they should be fed with the finest food. Since the young prefer to keep to the cover of the plant thickets they are often very difficult to see. A spawning period can result in up to 80 offspring. The parents are sexually ripe again after 2–4 weeks. 1928/+.

Epiplatys senegalensis (*Steindachner* 1870) (Fig. 800)　　　　Senegal Epiplatys
Tropical West Africa; to 5 cm.
　D 8–9; A 15–16; LL 26–29.

♂ Ground-colour brassy-yellow; back olive-coloured; belly yellow. Flanks with 10–12 dark, very uniform and somewhat oblique transverse bands. 1–2 rows of red spots along the sides. Vertical fins bluish with rows of dark spots and black-red borders.

♀ Paler; fins edged with delicate brown at the most.

Care and breeding, as given on p. 510. Rachow states that this species is very frail. 1910/−.

Epiplatys sexfasciatus *Gill* 1862 (Fig. 802)　　　　Six-barred Epiplatys
From Liberia to the Congo; to 10 cm.
　D 10–12; A 15–17; P 16; V 5; LL 28–32.

♂ Upperside fawn to brown-olive; flanks becoming increasingly dark towards the back; throat and belly porcelain-white; scales edged with dark red. Some vermiform red bands extending from the hinder part of the head to the eye. Lips black. Eye blackish-green with a narrow gold periphery. Dorsal fin yellow-green towards the body with rows of red spots, outer parts blue-green, border pale blue. Caudal fin olive-green with red spots, outer parts grey, with a brilliant pale blue border above and below. Anal fin rectangular, green-yellow towards the body, pale yellow in the centre, and with a bright red border. Especially

518

characteristic of this species are 6 broad dark transverse bars which are confined to the lower half of the body.

♀ Coloration paler; dorsal and anal fins rounded.

Care and breeding, as given on p. 510. The young hatch after 14–16 days and
are sexually ripe themselves after 10–12 months. 1910/+.

In 1938 a subspecies was imported from Sierra Leone, *Epiplatys sexfasciatus
leonensis* E.Ahl 1938, which differs from the typical subspecies *E.s.sexfasciatus*
in having a larger number of transverse bars on the lower half of the body and in
possessing a broad dark longitudinal band from the eye to the root of the tail.
Each scale further possesses a red spot.

Epiplatys sheljuzhkoi *Poll* 1953 (Fig. 806)
West Africa, neighbourhood of Abidjan (Ivory Coast); to 6 cm.

D 11; A 16; LL 28–30. This species is very similar to *E.macrostigma*, but is
sharply distinguished by the following characters:–rows of red spots quite
regular, in the lower half of the body as in the upper. Vertical fins often slightly
bluish with reddish-brown borders and somewhat spotted at the bases.

♀ often with not very distinct dark transverse bars, especially on the lower half
of the body.

Care and breeding of this very robust species, as given on p. 510. 1953.

Epiplatys multifasciatus (Boulenger 1913) has also been imported. (Fig. 675)

Genus Nothobranchius: Care and Breeding

The beautifully coloured but short-lived species (about 12) of this genus
inhabit large to very small water-masses in East Africa and Central Africa
as far as Nigeria. Unfortunately not much is known about their biology; the
little that is known, however, suggests that parallels may be drawn with the
Aphyosemion spp. The body in *Nothobranchius* spp. is thick-set and
somewhat compressed, and the dorsal and anal fins are strongly developed.
So far as is known attempts to breed these fishes have met with scant success,
a major difficulty being that the ♀♀ of the first captive-bred generation remain
so small that further breeding from them is impossible. These accounts,

dating from well before the War, are chiefly indicative of improper care and especially of the use of unsuitable water. It is not difficult to foresee that, when *Nothobranchius* spp. are again imported, they will be successfully propagated once the instructions given for the care and breeding of the bottom-spawning *Aphyosemion* spp. are properly taken into account. (See p. 485.) The ♂♂ are appreciably larger and more brilliantly coloured. All the species kept so far have proved to be very timid.

(The predictions made above with regard to breeding have meanwhile been confirmed. Species first imported into Central Europe in 1958 have been bred with great success.)

Nothobranchius guentheri (*Pfeffer* 1893) (Fig. 814)
East Africa; to 7 cm.
   D 17–18; A 18–19; LL 27–30.

♂ Back brownish-green; flanks brilliant yellow-green to blue-green; belly greenish-yellow. Scales edged with red, those on the back further with a dark red blotch. Several vermiform carmine-red lines on the gill-cover. Dorsal fin brownish-red with carmine-red spots and a dark red border with a bluish edge. Base of caudal fin carmine-red, outer parts brownish with a dark brown border. Anal fin red-brown with rows of red spots and streaks. Pectoral and ventral fins bluish.
♀ Grey-brown, underside yellowish-white. Fins without colour or markings.

Care and breeding, as given for the genus *Aphyosemion* (see p. 482). Temperature 23–26 °C. Bottom-spawner. The young hatch after 3–6 weeks. A very beautiful, but also quarrelsome bottom-living fish which must be kept in isolated pairs. 1913/+.

In 1958 the very similar species *Nothobranchius palmquisti* (Lönnberg 1907) was imported and successfully bred. This species is distinguished from *N. guentheri* chiefly by the more yellowish ground-colour and by the absence of dark edging to the dorsal and anal fins.

Nothobranchius mayeri *E. Ahl* 1935 (Fig. 815)
East Africa, Beira; to 7 cm.
   D 16; A 17; LL 28.

♂ Ground-colour a lovely red-violet. Each scale has a deep red edge, especially those on the back and the upper flanks; the scales toward the belly have a further

520

brilliant red blotch. Similar spots and blotches on the head, especially on the gill-cover. Vertical fins pale red at the base, outer parts wine-red with cinnabar spots and streaks. Pectoral and ventral fins yellow with red borders.

♀ Smaller, more yellowish. Fins colourless, faintly spotted with red.

Care, breeding and other particulars, as given on p. 482. 1936/−.

Nothobranchius orthonotus (*Peters* 1844) (Fig. 816)
Coastal regions of East Africa, especially in Mangrove swamps; to 7 cm.
D 15–16; A 14–16; P 12–13; V 6; LL 28–30.

♂ Back grey-brown; head and flanks blue-green. The whole fish has an intense wine-red lustre and is sprinkled with numerous wine-red blotches. All fins wine-red, the vertical fins with rows of wine-red spots.
♀ Coloration duller, brown-red, sometimes with blotches. Fins delicate reddish.

Care, breeding and other particulars, as given on p. 482. This species has already been bred quite successfully. 1926/−.

Nothobranchius rachovi *E. Ahl* 1926 (Fig. 817)
Mozambique (Beira); to 5 cm.
D 15; A 15–16; LL 25–26.

♂ Back dark green. Flanks brilliant turquoise blue with blotches and streaks of red-gold, orange-yellow and red. Belly golden yellow. Vertical fins turquoise blue with carmine-red spots and streaks. Hinder border of caudal fin and lower border of anal fin golden yellow to red, edged with red-brown. Ventral fins dark red. Pectoral fins blue at the base, golden yellow in the outer parts; by reflected light shining azure blue and molten gold. Iris sparkling blue-green to sea-green.
♀ More modestly coloured, smaller.

Care, breeding and other particulars, as given on p. 482. 1925/−.

Pachypanchax homolonotus (*Dumeril* 1861) (Fig. 722)
Madagascar, in fresh and brackish waters; to 9·5 cm.
D 11; A 14; LL 28. Body elongate, robust. Origin of the dorsal fin about over the centre of the anal fin.

♂ The cinnamon-brown of the upperside, especially fine on the nape, extends down over the anterior part of the body in the form of transverse bars across the lovely emerald green flanks. Underside yellowish to pure white. Fins dark: dorsal and caudal fins with blackish upper edges; lower edge of caudal and free edge of anal a beautiful pale yellow. Eye honey-yellow.

♀ Smaller, likewise very attractively coloured but not quite so brilliant as the ♂.

Care and breeding of this lively, peaceful species is not difficult; the fishes will even spawn in a well-planted community tank. Sea-salt not absolutely necessary. Attempts at breeding should follow the rules given for the adhesive-spawning *Aphyosemion* spp. (see p. 483). This species is apparently indifferent to water quality. The eggs are relatively large and hard-shelled. The young hatch after about 12–16 days and, with good feeding, become hardly distinguishable from their parents. 1953.

Pachypanchax playfairi (*Günther* 1866) (Fig. 723)
East Africa, Seychelles, Madagascar; to 10 cm. The somewhat thick-set members of the genus *Pachypanchax* inhabit the fresh and brackish waters of Africa, occupy a systematic position intermediate between the Asiatic and African Tooth-Carps, and as regards certain characters (scaling of the caudal fin) they also approach the American *Rivulus* spp.

D 11–12; A 17–18; P 18–19; V 6; LL 29–30. Anterior body broad and thick, flat on top.

♂ Back dark brown; underside yellowish. Emerald green by reflected light. Rows of minute red spots on the sides of the head and body. Vertical fins yellow with rows of red spots and a pale yellow edge. Anal fin edged with black.

♀ Self-coloured; fins yellowish, without markings.

Care and breeding, as given for the genera *Epiplatys* or *Aphyosemion* (see p. 482). The young hatch after 10–12 days. The scales stand out somewhat in the ♂♂, especially at spawning time, a peculiarity which is often wrongly regarded as a disease. 1924/+.

Figs. 814–817

Fig. 814. *Nothobranchius guentheri;* maximum size.
Fig. 815. *Nothobranchius mayeri;* maximum size.
Fig. 816. *Nothobranchius orthonotus;* maximum size.
Fig. 817. *Nothobranchius rachovi;* enlarged.

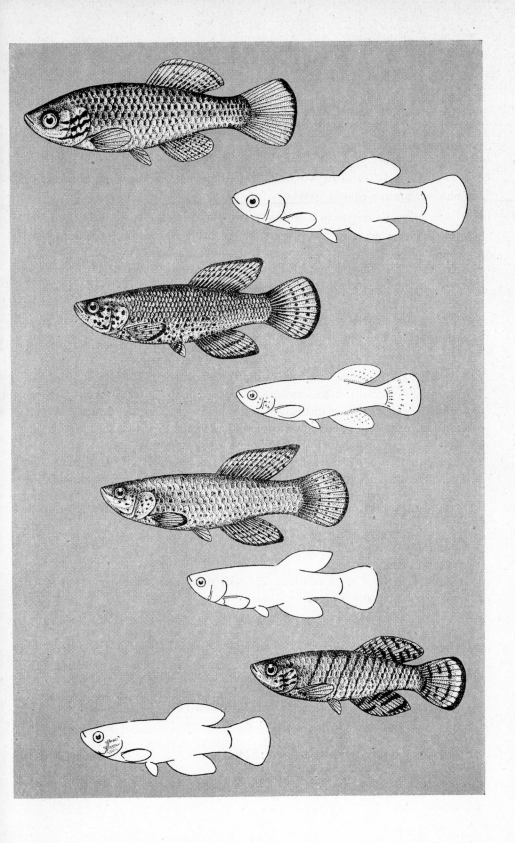

Egg-Laying Tooth-Carps of North, Central and South America

Chriopeops goodei (*Jordan* 1879) (Fig. 824)   Blue-fin Top Minnow
Florida; to 6 cm.

D 11–12; A 10–11; P 10; V 6; LL 27. Body elongate, a little compressed; upper and lower profiles equally convex.

♂ Grey-green to grey-brown, with a brassy glint, overlaid by a network formed by the pale edges of the scales; back darker; belly yellowish-white. A deep-black longitudinal band commences on the snout, crosses the eye and ends in a coppery blotch at the root of the tail. A second dark stripe begins behind the pectoral fin and extends to the hinder end of the anal fin-base. Fins yellowish. Dorsal fin with an orange base; external to this a crescentic black zone followed by a bluish-white border and a dark edge. The anal fin is similarly coloured.
♀ Blotch at caudal root whitish; dorsal fin yellowish.

Care and breeding, as given for *Fundulus* spp. (see p. 536).
A very beautiful aquarium fish. Well-planted aquarium. Temperature 19–23 °C. Live food, especially black mosquito-larvae. Spawns after vigorous driving; preferred spawning-place fine-leaved water plants close to the surface. Breeding temperature 20–24 °C. The spawning period lasts about 5 weeks, during which the ♀ lays 3–8 eggs daily which must be removed to a rearing tank at the earliest possible moment. (These fishes are arrant spawn-robbers!) Nourishing food (Enchytraeids, not *Cyclops*) must be provided during the spawning period. The breeding drive can be provoked by frequent additions of fresh water. The young hatch after 10–12 days and will take the finest food on the very first day. 1928/–.

Cubanichthys cubensis (*Eigenmann* 1902) (Fig. 825)   Cuban Killie
Western Cuba; to 8 cm.

D 11–12; A 10; P 15; V 6; LL 22–23. Body robust, a little elongate; upper and lower profiles equally convex.

Plate 141

Fig. 818. *Elassoma evergladei* (Dwarf Sunfish); left ♀, right ♂, somewhat enlarged. (Original)
Fig. 819. *Chanda wolffi* (Wolff's Glassfish); young, natural size. (Original)
Fig. 820. *Centrarchus macropterus* (Peacock-eyed Bass, Flier); young, natural size. (Photo P. Unger)

Plate 141

Plate 142

♂ Back reddish-yellow; belly yellowish-grey. Several blue-black longitudinal stripes along the flanks, separated from one another by gleaming golden bands. Fins yellowish, in part with bluish border.
♀ Paler in colour. Dorsal fin not dark-edged.

Care and breeding, as given for *Fundulus* spp. (see p. 536). Warmth-loving; temperature 22–25°C. A spawning period lasts for several weeks. As with many *Micropanchax* and *Oryzias* spp., the eggs are produced in small clusters and at first hang by a filament close to the maternal anal fin, later being stripped off onto plants. The eggs are small, glass-clear and on this account easily overlooked. Although the adults are not reputed to be spawn-robbers, it is best to transfer the egg-laden plants to rearing dishes (see p. 484). The young hatch after 10–12 days and are quite tiny. Rearing is not exactly easy, neither is the species very prolific. 1932/−.

Cyprinodon variegatus (*Lacépède* 1803) (Fig. 627)   Sheepshead Minnow
Eastern States of U.S.A. to Texas, often in brackish water; to 8 cm.

D 9–11; A 11; P 15; V 7; LL 25–27. Body short, rather plump, slightly compressed; very deep in the adults.

♂ Ground-colour brownish with a green sheen and lovely gleaming zones: the upperside, nape and flanks down to the pectoral fins are shining steel-blue, while the lower parts of the flanks are shining sea-green. Sides of head, throat and belly orange. Head and body sprinkled with numerous glittering metallic spots. Several irregular transverse bands on the flanks, usually only faintly apparent. Dorsal and anal fins greenish to blue, partly bordered with yellow to orange. Caudal fin blue-green with a dark base and black border.
♀ Paler in colour, more brownish. Fins yellowish. Dorsal fin frequently with a very distinct dark blotch.

Care and breeding, as given for *Fundulus* spp. (see p. 536). This species must not be kept too warm, 22°C. at most and preferably cooler. Sea-salt necessary (2 tablespoons to 10 litres of water). Very timid and easily frightened. Not suitable for the community tank. Very voracious. Breeding simple. Spawns on plants or on the glass sides of the tank, as well as on the bottom. The breeding pair should be removed after spawning and, when well fed, may be put together again the next day. The young hatch after 8–10 days. 1906/+.

Jordanella floridae *Goode* and *Bean* 1879 (Figs. 724, 725)   American Flagfish
Florida, in ponds and marshes; to 6 cm.

D 1/15–16; A 12–13; P 13–15; V 6; LL 25–26. Body stocky, rather deep, compressed. Coloration very variable; at its best in a well-planted aquarium shaded from direct sunshine.

♂ Ground-colour olive to brown-green, brown-olive towards the back. Each scale has a pale blotch so that, especially by reflected light, the whole body has a steel-blue to yellow-green iridescence from these rows of spots. An indistinct, faded dark blotch may be present above the insertion of the ventral fin. Dorsal and anal fins yellowish to delicate greenish with rows of spots or bands of red-brown; the hinder end of the dorsal has a dark blotch. Caudal fin orange to bluish, often with a dark border, occasionally with red spots.

♀ More yellowish and with a chess-board pattern of dark blotches on the flanks. A very distinct dark blotch over the pectoral base and another in the hinder corner of the dorsal fin.

Very accommodating in the matter of tank-size; a pair can be kept in an aquarium of only 6–8 litres, which should be well-planted, provided with a dark bottom-soil and placed in a position where it receives some occasional morning sunshine. Temperature around 20°C. Omnivorous; especially algae and soft parts of plants. After a stormy courtship spawning usually takes place in a depression on the bottom. Breeding temperature 24°C. A spawning period often lasts for several days. The daily output of eggs is small (about 25). The ♂ cares for the brood cichlid-fashion; the ♀ should be removed after the completion of spawning. Unfortunately these fishes usually remain rather easily frightened. The young hatch after 5–6 days and after another 14 days may be transferred to a tank with plenty of algae on which they thrive splendidly.

This very beautiful fish is unfortunately not often available to European aquarists. The reasons for this may be the incompatibility of the ♂♂ and the preference for plant food. 1914/+.

Leptolucania ommata (*Jordan* 1884) (Fig. 826)   Swamp Killie
South Georgia to Florida, in swamps; to 3·5 cm.

D 7; A 11; P 12–13; V 5; LL 26–30. Body elongate, spindle-shaped. Altogether rather like a *Fundulus*, from which it is mainly distinguished by the posterior insertion of the dorsal fin (behind the anal insertion) and by the absence of an anal sheath in the ♀.

♂ Colouring clay-yellow to pale brown; flanks and caudal peduncle iridescent bluish. A more or less distinct dark brown longitudinal band from the head to the root of the tail, ending in a dark blotch. Occasionally 6–8 blackish transverse bars may be present. Dorsal and anal fins yellowish to orange, partly with bluish border.

♀ Dark brown longitudinal band more obvious. Near the terminal blotch there is a second dark blotch just above the anal fin.

A very graceful and thoroughly harmless species which does very well in aquaria. Care and breeding: a well-planted aquarium at constant temperature (24°C.) and with peaty water. Smaller kinds of live food; dried food is not accepted. The eggs are laid either on plants or on the soil. The young hatch after 10–12 days and, in moderately planted aquaria which give them plenty of swimming space, are easily raised. Frequent additions of fresh water are necessary. This species can be kept together with any other harmless ornamental fishes. 1924/+.

Genera Cynolebias and Pterolebias: Care and Breeding

The genera *Cynolebias* and *Pterolebias* are confined to central and southern South America, where they inhabit small and tiny accumulations of water such as are caused by flooding or prolonged rainfall and subsequently liable to dry out. Like many of the African *Aphyosemion* spp. the members of these genera are very well adapted to such conditions and are able to survive the often long dry seasons as resting eggs embedded in the damp mud. With the onset of the rainy season the young hatch in large numbers and rapidly grow to sexual maturity; at least, a few of the stronger ones do, for all the feeble and sickly fishes fall victim to the unbounded appetites of the larger ones.

In the course of a very stormy and protracted spawning season numerous hard-shelled eggs are buried in the loose bottom-soil, so that by the beginning of the drought adequate provision has been made for the survival of a later generation. The adults, exhausted by the explosive onset and the intensity of their spawning activities, usually perish. Many species are very brilliantly coloured and may be regarded as being among the most beautiful of aquarium fishes, as well as extraordinarily interesting in their behaviour.

It is essential that each species be kept in a separate tank. The young fishes usually imported should be accommodated in large tanks, standing in not too dark a position and provided with a soft bottom-soil. Planting is not absolutely necessary but the introduction of thick clumps of plants does, however, greatly mitigate the quarrelsomeness of the growing ♂♂. Soft, slightly acid or peat-filtered water and temperatures between 22–25 °C. meet the needs of every species. Live food; very voracious. As soon as the fishes become sexually ripe the sexes should be segregated.

For breeding provide sufficient smaller tanks whose bottoms have been covered to a depth of several centimetres with well-washed and boiled peat-mould. The water already specified is equally suitable for breeding. Breeding temperature 25–26 °C. The breeding fishes are put together in pairs (a vigorous ♂ can be given two ♀♀). Courtship usually begins immediately after the association of the pair and is consummated after violent burrowing into the bottom-soil (for the several stages in spawning see Figs.707–711, 712–715 and 718–721). The spawning period usually lasts for several weeks and is substantially encouraged by diminished light. During this time the breeding pairs must be well fed, especially with midge-larvae, and transferred from time to time to new breeding tanks.

The water-level in the vacated breeding tank is now carefully reduced to a few cm. and the tank put away to cool at 20–24 °C. After 15–20 days shake out the whole contents of the tank into a fine-meshed gauze, carefully pressing out the peat-mould in which the eggs are embedded and later loosening it up, and put it into a loosely covered vessel (a finger-bowl or similar). When the surface of the peat has moderately dried out it may, if necessary, be sprinkled with a few drops of water. After a further 3 weeks (5 weeks in all) the eggs are ready to hatch. The peat-mould should then simply be shaken into soft, slightly acid water and the young fishes thereupon hatch rapidly (45–300 minutes) and can be provided with the finest food. Growth is very rapid. A longer lying of the eggs as a rule does them no harm. Fine sand is also suitable as a spawning-substrate for several species, in which case the eggs should subsequently be sieved out and transferred to peat-mould. After the 20th day of incubation the hard-shelled eggs will travel quite well if carefully packed in moist mould. A detailed description of breeding techniques will be found on p. 485.

One should make a point of only acquiring young specimens, since these are 'annual fishes' in which the life-cycle lasts only a little over 8 months. It is a peculiarity of all *Cynolebias* spp. that the sexes may be distinguished by the differing dorsal and anal fin-ray counts.

Cynolebias adloffi *E. Ahl* 1922 (Fig. 827)
South-eastern Brazil, Rio Grande do Sul, in small pools; ♂ to 5 cm., ♀ smaller.
    D ♂ 22–23, ♀ 19; A ♂ 26–27; ♀ 25; LL 28–29. Body thick-set, rather deep.

♂ Ground-colour of full-grown ♂♂ dark yellow-brown to blackish with a blue sheen and very dark, narrow transverse bands on the flanks. Fins pale blue with gleaming greenish spots. Fin-rays of vertical fins conspicuously dark.
♀ Paler, with irregular transverse bands. Two deep black blotches, one above the other at the root of the tail, are especially characteristic.

    Care and breeding, as given on p. 528. 1921/−.

Cynolebias belotti *Steindachner* 1881 (Figs. 657–659, 671–673, 683)
Argentine Pearlfish
La Plata Basin; ♂ to 7 cm., ♀ somewhat smaller.
    D ♂ 21–24, ♀ 16–19; A ♂ 26–30, ♀ 22–26; LL 28–30. Body deep, compressed.
Dorsal and anal fins opposite, almost semicircular. Ventral fins small.

♂ Coloration in healthy fish: back dark blue; flanks dark blue or grey-blue. Strongly reflecting white-blue to pale blue spots on the head, over the whole body and on the basal parts of the vertical fins. Fins brownish, greenish or

529

bluish-grey. Anal fin dark-edged. Pectoral fins pale blue. A wedge-shaped dark stripe running diagonally forwards from the nape across the eye.

♀ Clay-yellow, with dark brown or grey spots and dots.

Care and breeding, as given on p. 528. 1906/+.

For details of spawning behaviour, see legends to Figs. 657–659, 671–673.

Cynolebias elongatus *Steindachner* 1881 (Fig. 828)
La Plata Basin; ♂ to 15 cm., ♀ somewhat smaller.

D ♂ 21–23, ♀ 17; A ♂ 24, ♀ 20; LL 45–50. Body more elongate than in the other *Cynolebias* spp.

♂ Brown-yellow with a bluish sheen on the flanks; back olive-brown; belly clay-yellow. Fins yellowish to blue-grey. A prominent dark band across the eye from the nape to the throat. Eye yellow.

♀ Paler, with irregular blotches on the vertical fins.

Care and breeding, as given on p. 528. A very tough, quarrelsome species. 1906/ −.

Cynolebias nigripinnis *Regan* 1912 (Figs. 707–711)
Paraná, above Rosario de Santa Fé; to 4·5 cm.

D ♂ 26, ♀ 20–21; A ♂ 25, ♀ 18–21; LL 28.

♂ Uniform dark blue-black to velvet black, with numerous tiny, glittering, deep sea-green or green spots on the body and fins. Outside the breeding season blue-grey to grey-black.

♀ Pale, ochre to grey, with irregular blotches on the flanks forming a marbled pattern on the ground-colour.

Care and breeding, as given on p. 528. Rather delicate. A very beautiful, peaceful species which is content with quite a small tank.

For details of spawning behaviour, see legends to Figs. 707–711. 1908/ −.

Figs. 824–828

♂♂ on the left, sketches of the corresponding ♀♀ to the right.

Fig. 824. *Chriopeops goodei* (Blue-fin Top Minnow); maximum size.
Fig. 825. *Cubanichthys cubensis* (Cuban Killie); somewhat reduced.
Fig. 826. *Leptolucania ommata* (Swamp Killie); adults, reduced.
Fig. 827. *Cynolebias adloffi;* maximum size.
Fig. 828. *Cynolebias elongatus;* adults, somewhat reduced.

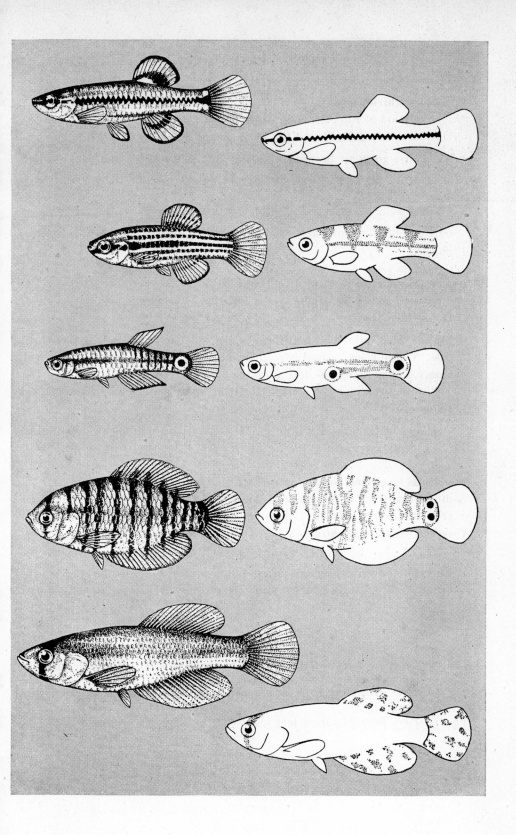

Cynolebias schreitmuelleri *E. Ahl* 1934
Neighbourhood of Rio de Janeiro; to 5 cm.
   D ♂ 18, ♀ ?; A ♂ 23–24, ♀ ?; LL 35–36. Shape similar to *C. belotti*.

♂ Back olive-green to brownish, passing into yellowish on the flanks, which are strewn with bluish and green dots. Dorsal and anal fins blue-green (according to Ahl 1934).
♀ Unknown.

Care and breeding, probably as given on p. 528. Further imports to be desired. 1934/−.

Cynolebias wolterstorffi *E. Ahl* 1924 (Fig. 835)
South-eastern Brazil, in small pools; ♂ to 10 cm., ♀ smaller.
   D ♂ 19–20, ♀ 18–20; A ♂ 25–26, ♀ 23–24; LL 40–43.

♂ Metallic blue sprinkled with delicate violet to white spots; back darker; belly pale. A deep-black vertical bar across the eye. Fins greenish to blue, set with numerous pale spots and dots as on the body.
♀ Yellowish, with numerous dark, irregular spots and blotches; vertical fins colourless.

Care and breeding, as given on p. 528. Not very warmth-loving; temperature 19–22 °C. Very aggressive. 1910/−.

Pterolebias longipinnis *Garman* 1895 (Figs. 712–715, 718–721)
South-eastern Brazil to northern Argentine; ♂ to 9 cm., ♀ considerably smaller.
   D 9–10; A 19–20; LL 31–32. Body not so strongly compressed or deep as in the *Cynolebias* spp.; more *Rivulus*-like. Anal and caudal fins in the ♂ enlarged, flag-like.

♂ Chocolate-brown, becoming more yellow-brown towards the belly; belly delicate reddish with a violet sheen. Numerous shining sea-green to brassy

Plate 143

Fig. 829. *Lucioperca lucioperca* (Pike-Perch); half-grown fish, 20 cm. long, in the Hellabrunn Aquarium, Munich. (Original)
Fig. 830. *Perca fluviatilis* (Perch); young specimen from very weedy waters, natural size. (Original)
Fig. 831. *Perca fluviatilis;* 20 cm. long specimen from a large lake. (Original)

Plate 143

Plate 144

Plate 144

Fig. 832. *Aspro asper* (Streber); adult, somewhat reduced. In the Hellabrunn Aquarium, Munich. (Original)

Fig. 833. *Acerina cernua* (Ruff or Pope); young, natural size. (Photo P. Unger)

Fig. 834. *Acerina schraetzer* (Schrätzer); half-grown, somewhat reduced. (Photo P. Unger)

yellow spots on the flanks. Over the pectoral fins are 2–3 especially striking cinnabar blotches with black margins. Fins brown to orange-brown, the bases often pure orange. Some specimens are more grey-blue with rows of fine red dots.

♀ Brown-yellow; fins appreciably smaller.

Care and breeding, as given on p. 528. For details of spawning behaviour, see legends to Figs. 712–715 and 718–721. 1930/+.

Imported specimens of these very beautiful fishes often have a very grey-blue ground-colour, but the first captive-bred generation produces a welcome improvement of colour (depending on temperature?). Partial albinos also appear sometimes (see Meder 1955).

Recently *Pterolebias peruensis* Myers 1954 (Fig. 786) has also been imported.

Cynopoecilus melanotaenia (*Regan* 1912) (Fig. 837)
South-eastern Brazil, in small pools; to 5 cm.

The genus *Cynopoecilus* shows a certain similarity to *Cynolebias*, but its discriminant sexual characters (dorsal and anal fin-counts, coloration) are much less obvious.

D 16–18; A 17–20; LL 28.

♂ Red-brown to fawn, becoming more yellow towards the belly. A broad red longitudinal stripe from the snout to the root of the tail; within this a triple row of brass-coloured spots from the eye backwards. A second red band from the pectoral insertion to the base of the anal fin. Vertical fins yellowish with carmine-red spots and blotches.

♀ Coloration similar, but without spots on the anal fin. Dorsal fin rounded.

Care, as given on p. 528.

There is little reliable information on the breeding of this species. Contrary to reports which say that it spawns on plants, we consider that *C. melanotaenia* is probably a bottom-spawner whose breeding biology is very similar to that of some *Aphyosemion* spp.

50 Sterba

533

Cynopoecilus ladigesi (*Myers* 1957) (Fig. 686)
North-west of Rio de Janeiro, in partly dried-out pools; to 3·5 cm.
Body elongate, only slightly compressed, *Rivulus*-shaped but rather stockier.

♂ Coloration overall lovely iridescent emerald-green with dark wine-red transverse
stripes. The vertical fins are similarly coloured and marked, but more intensely
so. Eye brilliant pale green.
♀ Plain grey-green to brown. Fins rather colourless.

These tiny fishes are best kept by themselves in small tanks. Breeding similar to
that of the bottom-spawning *Aphyosemion* spp. The ♀ takes up a position immediately over the bottom-soil and the pairing ♂ presses close against her side so that
his anal fin clasps her ventral surface. The eggs are laid one at a time, fall to the
bottom and are buried by a vigorous blow of the caudal fin as the partners swim
away. Microscopical examination shows that the eggs themselves, in contrast to
those of *Cynolebias* and *Pterolebias*, do not have a hair-like integument but are
covered with peg-like processes. Subsequent treatment of the eggs as given on
p. 528. During the daytime the full-grown *C. ladigesi* like to hide in dark corners
or under pieces of bark, etc. Temperature 24–26°C. Small live food. 1954.

Rachovia brevis (*Regan* 1912) (Fig. 836)
Colombia; to 6·5 cm.
D 8–9; A 12–14; LL 29–30. Closely related to the previous species, but without
the flag-like prolongation of the fins.

♂ Delicate sea-green to blue-green; back more olive-coloured; belly grey-white.
Gill-cover with brilliant red spots. The blue to violet edges of the scales give
the body a netted appearance. Dorsal and anal fins smoke-grey to green-blue,
often slightly violet, with numerous spots and streaks. Caudal fin grey-blue with
a dark hinder edge.
♀ Uniformly pale brown to flesh-coloured; fins colourless or grey.

Figs. 835–838

♂♂ on the left, sketches of corresponding ♀♀ to the right
Fig. 835. *Cynolebias wolterstorffi;* adults, reduced.
Fig. 836. *Rachovia brevis;* maximum size.
Fig. 837. *Cynopoecilus melanotaenia;* somewhat enlarged.
Fig. 838. *Jenynsia lineata* (One-sided Live-bearer); natural size.

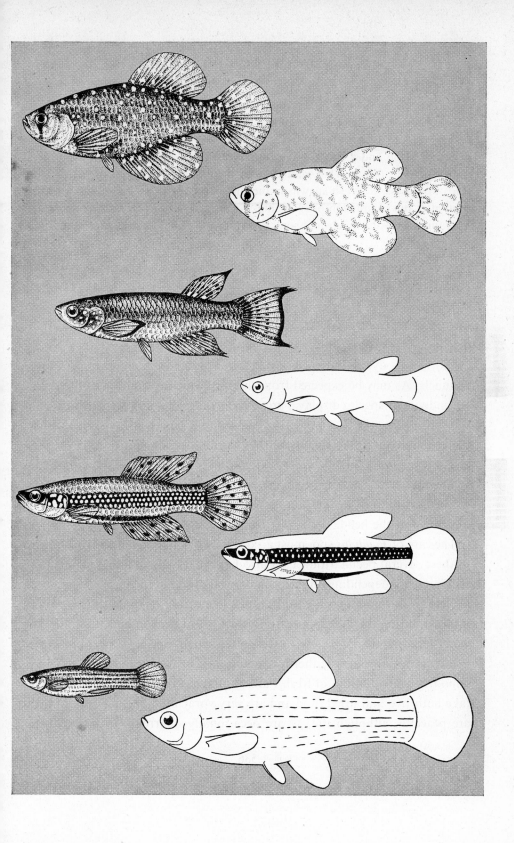

Care, as given on p.528. Breeding this short-lived species is not exactly easy, mainly because it is seldom possible to produce the right spawning-stimulus. The best procedure is as follows: place 2–3 pairs in a large, sunny aquarium with plenty of algae and a soft, sandy bottom and then slowly lower the water-level over a period of days. This simulation of the natural drying-out process usually leads to success. *R. brevis* spawns in the soil, like *Cynolebias*, and usually perishes soon after the completion of spawning. No special needs as regards temperature. Very quick-growing, lively and somewhat predatory. The young hatch after about 60 days. 1906/–.

Genus Fundulus: Care and Breeding

The genus *Fundulus* is confined to North and Middle America and to various neighbouring islands, and is very rich in species. Its representatives have a cylindrical body, a flattened head and a somewhat compressed caudal peduncle. As may be expected from the very wide distribution of the genus, the individual species display a great variety of biological peculiarities. Thus some *Fundulus* spp. are typical surface-living fishes (e. g. *F.notatus*); others prefer to remain in the vicinity of the bottom, occasionally even in the mud (e. g. *F.chrysotus*); others are to be found in brackish water and even in absolute seawater. The surface-living representatives of the genus are distinguished by the possession of a very conspicuous iridescent golden mark on the crown of the head.

The care of *Fundulus* spp. must accordingly be undertaken with due regard to these several peculiarities. They also have markedly differing temperature requirements, depending on the geographical origin of the species in question. Generally, however, they are fishes which like plenty of room to move about (at least during the breeding season), thick plant growth and sunshine. The water-level should *not* be low, as is so often stated. Special concern for water quality is not necessary, either for routine care or for breeding; on the other hand frequent additions of fresh water should not be omitted. All the species take both live and dried food and are very voracious. The majority of them are peaceful, although the ♂♂ are occasionally quarrelsome among themselves. The spawning potentialities and hardiness of the fishes are enhanced if they are kept, at least for a few weeks, at room-temperature during the winter. *Fundulus* spp. are not suitable for the community tank, since under such conditions they remain shy and show evident discomfort at the usually much higher temperature.

The sexes are easily distinguished. The ♂♂ are not only more brilliantly coloured and marked, but also altogether more robust and larger-finned. A peculiarity of the ♀♀ is the so-called sexual sac, an external prolongation of the oviduct which surrounds the sexual orifice and is supported by the first ray of the anal fin.

The breeding of many of the species is not difficult to accomplish. The small eggs are laid on plants in the course of a spawning period of several days and should, complete with plants, be transferred each day to a rearing tank (in which the water-level *should* be low), since the adults are in some cases enthusiastic spawn-robbers. Green Perlon-yarn makes an excellent spawning-substrate. The young hatch after 8–15 days and can be fed immediately. Growth is not very rapid. In America *Fundulus* spp. are commonly known as 'Killifishes'.

Fundulus catenatus (*Storer* 1846) (Fig. 807)   Chained Top Minnow
Virginia to Texas; to 20 cm., remaining smaller in aquaria.
   D 14; A 15–16; P 13; V 6; LL 48–53.

♂ Ground-colour olive to sea-green with several brilliantly reflecting blotches; back darker; belly yellow-green to grey. Numerous red spots on the flanks (each scale with a red spot) which may form longitudinal rows or necklaces. Fins yellow-green or dirty yellow, with rows of brown-red spots.
♀ Yellow-brown, with rows of indistinct brown spots.

   Care and breeding, as given on p. 536. A bottom-fish, which prefers a soft bottom-soil of sand and peat-mould. Temperature 19–22 °C. The young hatch after 10 to 14 days. 1905/−.

Fundulus chrysotus *Holbrook* 1866 (Fig. 656)   Golden Ear
South Caroline to Florida, in fresh and brackish waters; to 8 cm.
   D 8–9; A 10–11; P 13; V 63; LL 32–34.

♂ Back dark olive-green; flanks pale olive-green; belly greenish. A shining metallic blotch on the gill-cover. The flanks are strewn with wine-red to blood-red spots which shine metallic green by reflected light. Fins similarly spotted. The ventral fins and the anterior part of the anal are yellowish, the pectorals colourless. Eye golden.

♀ Coloration duller, more brownish, with dark marbling on the flanks and numerous glittering spots.

Care and breeding, as given on p. 536. The addition of common salt or sea-salt is advised (1 teaspoon to 10 litres of water). Warmth-loving (23–25°C.). Breeds readily when well cared-for. Spawning can be stimulated by the addition of fresh water and lasts for several days; temperature 24–26°C. This species has a predilection for laying its eggs in very thick clumps of plants. Since the adults lie in wait for the spawn the eggs must be carefully transferred to another tank containing identical water. Good feeding is necessary during the spawning season. The young hatch after 8–10 days and are somewhat susceptible; careful feeding. *F. chrysotus* is a gregarious species. 1904/+.

An especially beautiful black-checked variety of this species has been imported and has been widely distributed.

Fundulus cingulatus *Cuvier* and *Valenciennes* 1846 (Fig. 839)
South Carolina, Georgia, Florida, in standing waters mostly near the coast; to 7 cm.

♂ Back dark olive-green; flanks shining bluish with glittering green blotches, especially on the red-spotted gill-cover. Numerous longitudinal rows of red spots (one to each scale). Occasionally several narrow dark transverse bands on the caudal peduncle. Vertical fins yellowish to orange-red with rows of red to brown spots. Ventral and anal fins dark-edged.

♀ Grey with a greenish sheen; belly dirty white; no clear rows of spots.

Figs. 839–842

♂♂ on the left; sketches of corresponding ♀♀ to the right.

Fig. 839. *Fundulus cingulatus;* somewhat enlarged.
Fig. 840. *Fundulus diaphanus menona* (Banded Killifish); ripe adults, natural size.
Fig. 841. *Fundulus dispar dispar* (Star-head Top Minnow); somewhat enlarged.
Fig. 842. *Fundulus grandis* (Texas Killie); adult, reduced.

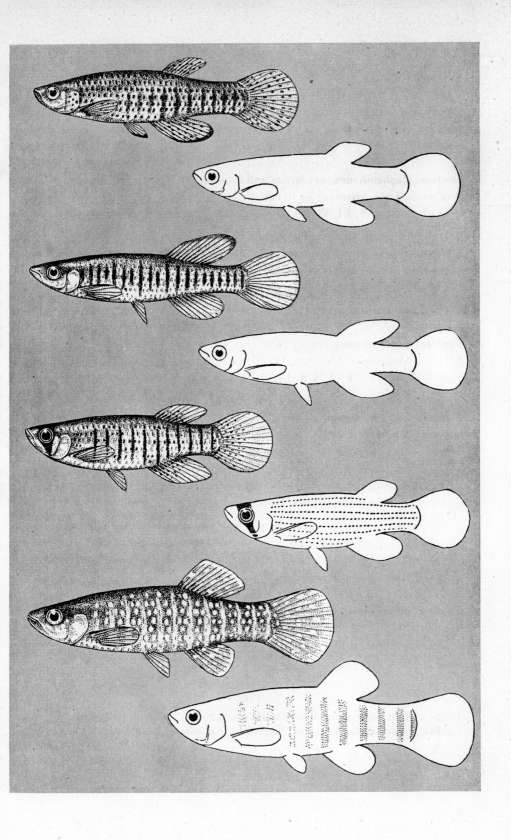

Care and breeding, as given on p. 536. Probably not yet bred in captivity. The addition of common salt or sea-salt is recommended (1 teaspoon to 10 litres of water). 1910/−.

Fundulus diaphanus menona (*Jordan* and *Copeland* 1877) (Fig. 840) Banded Killifish
Wisconsin, Lake Menona; to 10 cm.
  D 12; A 10; V 5; LL 48–50.

♂ Dull blue to blue-grey, with a strong bluish iridescence by reflected light. 15–20 irregular dark brown transverse bands on the flanks. Fins usually greenish at the base, outer parts transparent, occasionally dark-edged.
♀ Usually uniform grey.

Care and breeding, as given on p. 536. 1905/−.

Fundulus dispar dispar (*Agassiz* 1854) (Fig. 841)   Star-head Top Minnow
States of Mississippi, Missouri, Louisiana, Arkansas, Oklahoma; to 6 cm.
  D 7–10; A 9–12; P 13; V 6; LL 33–36.

♂ Ground-colour greenish. Back olive-brown to red-brown; flanks with a sea-green glint and numerous very fine, often interrupted, rows of red spots; belly paler. Vertical fins yellow-green to yellow with a delicate blackish-red tinge and dark brown spots. A broad, dark transverse band across the head is especially characteristic of this species. Narrow transverse bands on the body are only occasionally apparent. A pale blotch on the crown of the head.
♀ Rows of spots more distinct. Dorsal and anal fins not produced.

Care and breeding, as given on p. 536. Typical surface-fish. Temperature not above 21 °C., room-temperature in winter (15–18 °C.). Breeding easy; it is best to put 2 ♀♀ to a ♂. The eggs develop relatively rapidly and the young hatch after 9–12 days. 1911/−.

Fundulus dispar notti (*Agassiz* 1854)   Star-head Top Minnow
Southern States of U.S.A., in lowland streams; to 7 cm.
  D 7–8; A 8–10; P 13; V 6; LL 35–36.

Plate 145

Fig. 843. *Badis badis;* ripe adults, natural size; above ♂, below ♀. (Original)
Fig. 844. *Monodactylus argenteus* (Fingerfish); half-grown, natural size. (Original)

Plate 145

Plate 146

Plate 146

Fig. 845. *Nandus nandus* (Nandus); half-grown, natural size. (Photo Dr. Foersch)
Fig. 846. *Polycentrus schomburgki* (Schomburgk's Leaf-fish); young, natural size. (Original)
Fig. 847. *Monocirrhus polyacanthus* (South American Leaf-fish); ripe adult, natural size. (Original)

♂ Ground-colour pale grey to delicate brownish; back olive; underside silvery. Flanks with 6–7 rows of faint dark spots and 12–15 narrow deep black transverse bands. Snout red-brown to orange. A broad dark transverse bar across the eye. Fins colourless; dorsal and anal fins usually with dark spots.
♀ Without transverse bands. Rows of spots more distinct.

Care and breeding, as given for the typical subspecies. 1904/+.

Fundulus grandis *Baird* and *Girard* 1853 (Fig. 842)   Texas Killie
Texas, also in brackish waters; to 15 cm.
   D 12; A 10–11; P 18; V 6; LL 30–33.

♂ Upperside olive-brown; flanks yellowish with a bright silver gleam; underside whitish to pale pink. Flanks with 12–13 narrow transverse bands and numerous shining pearly spots. Fins delicate yellowish; vertical fins with brilliant green spots; pectorals with a yellow border.
♀ Pale brown-olive with a fine silver lustre on the flanks. Some transverse bands, usually indistinct and with larger interspaces.

Care and breeding, as given on p. 536. Very peaceful, in spite of its size. For the welfare of this species relatively very brackish, cool water is essential. The fishes spawn on algae near the bottom after vigorous driving, and the young take 10–14 days to hatch. (Description partly after Axelrod and Schultz 1955.) 1907/−. Further imports to be desired.

Fundulus heteroclitus (*Linnaeus* 1766) (Fig. 736)   Zebra or Common Killie
Canada to Mexico, Bermuda, in brackish water; to 12 cm.
Very variable in form and colouring, in relation to its wide distribution.
   D 11–13; A 10–12; P 18–19; V 6; LL 33–38.

♂ Ground-colour all shades of green mixed with brown. Numerous iridescent blue bars on the flanks which taper to points towards the belly. Vertical fins marbled or striped with blue at the bases. Dorsal fin often with a large dark blotch bordered with silver, and edged with red-brown.

51 Sterba   541

♀ Brown to ochre-coloured. Transverse bars usually not visible. Flanks often with numerous black spots.

Care and breeding, as given on p. 536. Brackish water (at least 2–3 tablespoons of sea-salt to 10 litres of water. Be careful with the plants!). Spacious tanks, best of all out-of-doors. Breeding temperature 20–22°C. The ♂ drives very hard and the ♀♀ prefer to spawn on algae (Perlon yarn may be substituted). Spawning period 6–12 days. The young hatch after 12–14 days and are easy to raise. 1906/ – .

Fundulus majalis (*Walbaum* 1792) (Fig. 848)   Striped Killifish
Canada to Florida, in rivers and streams, often in brackish water; to 15 cm.
    D 12–13; A 10–11; LL 33–36. The young have 10–18 oblong, black-brown blotches which in the ♂ become transformed into conspicuous transverse bars. In the ♀ these bars disappear and are replaced by equally conspicuous longitudinal qands. Adult coloration very variable.

♂ Full-grown fishes yellow to orange-red with dark transverse bands on the flanks. Back and top of head brass or copper-coloured. Dorsal fin dark, occasionally with a pale ocellus. Caudal fin with a dark edge. Ventrals yellowish. Anal often with dark spots and edge.
♀ Larger, with very dark longitudinal stripes and three transverse bars on the caudal peduncle. Fins pale.

Care and breeding, as given on p. 536. May be kept in unheated aquaria. Common salt or sea-salt recommended (1 teaspoon to 10 litres of water). A hardy species, so far only bred in outdoor situations. 1897/ – .

Fundulus notatus (*Rafinesque* 1820) (Fig. 849)   Starhead Top Minnow
Michigan to Texas; to 8 cm.
    D 9–10; A 11–12; P 13: V 6; LL 34.

♂ Ground-colour olive-brown to pale brown with a green lustre; back darker. A broad deep black longitudinal band from the tip of the snout, across the eye to the root of the tail. Vertical fins pale, yellowish or brownish, with dark spots and streaks. A distinct blotch on the crown of the head.
♀ Longitudinal bands paler.

Care and breeding of these very typical surface-fishes, as given on p. 536. Peaceful and very resistant to cooling. 1911/ – .

Fundulus sciadicus *Cope* 1865 (Fig. 850)
Central States of U.S.A., mainly in the Mississippi Basin; to 9 cm.
  D 7–10; A 10–12; P 13–14; V 6; LL 33–38.

♂ Ground-colour delicate bluish with a green lustre, tinged with red by reflected light. Dorsal ridge porcelain-white in front of the dorsal fin. Underside yellowish to white. Gill-cover with a strong silvery iridescence and a small dark blotch behind it. A delicate, vague-edged longitudinal band along the flanks. Vertical fins reddish, bordered with bright red. Caudal fin with faint curved transverse bars.
♀ Fins colourless, without pigmented borders.

Care and breeding, as given on p. 536. Temperature not less than 20°C. in summer, 16–18°C. in winter and 22–24°C. for breeding. The young hatch after 8–10 days. 1931/−.

Profundulus punctatus (*Günther* 1866) (Fig. 851)
In the higher-lying parts of Central America; to 10 cm.
  D 10–14; A 13–16; LL 33–34. The members of the genus *Profundulus* are rather more pike-like in shape than *Fundulus*. The dorsal and anal fins are inserted well back and often at the same level. The ♀♀ lack the 'sex-sac' which is so typical of *Fundulus* (see p. 537).
  Descriptions of specimens from western Guatemala, according to Rachow:–

♂ Younger ones olive-green to brownish on the upperside; flanks bluish; belly faint yellow to white. A shining green blotch on the gill-cover; another over the pectoral fin-insertion. A more or less distinct dark longitudinal band along the middle of the side. Fins yellowish, the dorsal and anal dark at the base. Older fishes uniformly dark. Vertical fins dark with a central colourless or white field.
♀ Dorsal and anal fins pale, sometimes with transverse bands.

Care and breeding, as given for *Fundulus* (see p. 536). Temperature not less than 20°C.; for breeding, 22–24°C. Rather unmannerly, voracious fishes and arrant spawn-robbers. The young hatch after 6–12 days and are easily reared. 1932/−.

Genus Rivulus: Care and Breeding

The very widely distributed genus *Rivulus* extends from the southern U.S.A. through Central America deep into the South American continent. The species of this genus are cylindrical in shape with an upper surface which is more or less flattened as far back as the very posteriorly-inserted dorsal fin. The caudal peduncle is somewhat compressed and the caudal fin usually rounded. Almost all *Rivulus* spp. inhabit flowing waters of the type of our meadow brooks, rich in bank vegetation, and live mainly in the lower and middle water-layers. Some of them leave the water for short periods to sun themselves lying on the floating plant-cover.

The sexes are usually similar in shape and in size, nevertheless the ♂♂ are easily recognised by their more brilliant colouring. The ♀♀ of most species show a very conspicuous round spot or ocellus on the upper part of the root of the caudal fin; in the ♂♂ this caudal spot is merely suggested or quite absent.

The care of these fishes in captivity presents no great difficulties. They are best suited by sunny, not too small, richly planted tanks with some floating vegetation. Cover the aquarium well; *Rivulus* are good leapers! Most species are completely indifferent to the composition of the water; only those native to the Amazon should be kept and allowed to spawn in water which is not too hard. Almost all the species are warmth-loving, preferring temperatures between 22–26°C., but they can also tolerate periods of cooling to 18–20°C. In suitable living-conditions they are peaceful, sprightly, active and very ready to breed.

Figs. 848–851

♂♂ to the left; sketches of corresponding ♀♀ to the right

Fig. 848. *Fundulus majalis* (Striped Killifish); adults, somewhat reduced.
Fig. 849. *Fundulus notatus* (Starhead Top Minnow); maximum size.
Fig. 850. *Fundulus sciadicus;* natural size.
Fig. 851. *Profundulus punctatus;* ripe adults, natural size.

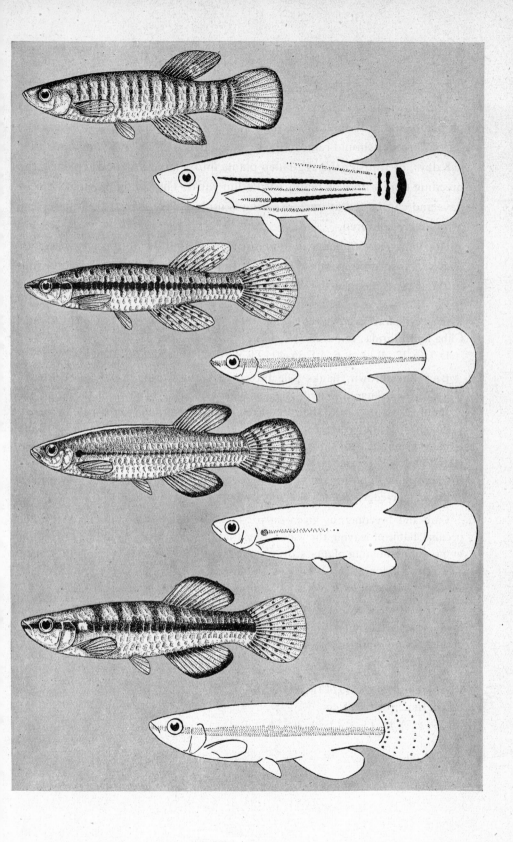

The spawning period may last for several weeks. The large eggs are placed on plants and, although the *Rivulus* spp. are not exactly spawn-robbers, the serious breeder should remove the breeding pair to a new breeding tank after 6–8 days, or transfer the egg-laden plants into a large dish and replenish the breeding tank with new plants (or Perlon yarn). The young hatch after 8–14 days and can be fed at once. Rearing is no less easy. Most species are very attractively coloured.

Hoedeman (1956) has made interesting contributions to the systematics of *Rivulus*. According to him the main groups may be distinguished according to the arrangement of the scales on the head.

Rivulus cylindraceus *Poey* 1861 (Fig. 738)   Green, Brown or Cuban Rivulus
Cuba and Florida; to 5·5 cm.
    D 9; A 12; P 13; V 6; LL 36–40; TR 9–10; 21–23 predorsal scales.

♂ Back olive-brown; flanks pale brown to green-brown; throat and belly yellowish to orange-coloured. A vaguely-defined dark band from the tip of the snout across the eye to the root of the tail. A cobalt-blue, often pale-bordered, blotch over the pectoral insertion. Several rows of red to red-brown spots and blotches on the flanks. Fins yellow to ochre-yellow; vertical fins with dark spots and blotches. Dorsal fin with a pale border.
♀ Clay-yellow to brown-red with dark spots and dots on the sides. A very distinct black, pale-edged caudal blotch on the upper root of the tail.

Care and breeding, as given on p. 544. Preferred temperature 22–28 °C. The peculiar habit of leaving the water to rest on floating leaves should be catered for by providing floating plants. Cover the tank well, as this species is a good leaper! The young hatch after 12–14 days and are easily reared. A lively species, which should not be kept with too small companions. 1929/+.

According to Hoedeman (1956) *Rivulus marmoratus* Poey 1884 is not a synonym of *R. cylindraceus* but a quite distinct species, whose importation is much to be desired. In my opinion it is very doubtful that *R. marmoratus* has so far been imported.

Rivulus dorni *Myers* 1924 (Fig. 858)   Dorn's Rivulus
Rio de Janeiro; to 5·5 cm.
    D 7–8; A 11–13; P 13–14; V 7; LL 30–31.

♂ The ground-colour alternates rapidly between reddish-brown and chocolate. Underside fawn to yellowish-white. Flanks with numerous small glittering green to yellow-green spots. 6–7 dark transverse bars on the hinder part of the body. Vertical fins greenish with brown bands and edges, the upper edge of the caudal white.

♀ Fawn to ochre with faint dark irregular blotches on the flanks. Fins pale brown, the bases spotted with greenish. This species has no caudal blotch.

Care, breeding and other particulars, as given for *R. cylindraceus*. Resistant to lowering of the temperature. 1926/−.

Rivulus harti (*Boulenger* 1890) (Fig. 859)   Hart's Rivulus
Eastern Colombia, Venezuela and adjacent islands; to 10 cm.

D 8–10; A 11–15; P 13–15; V 5–7; LL 35–42. Coloration very variable, depending on locality of origin.

♂ Back chocolate to olive-brown; flanks yellow-green with a grass-green iridescence; belly yellow-green to white; caudal peduncle more bluish-green. Several rows of red spots on the flanks (a spot on each scale), with green stripes between the rows. Dorsal and anal fins pale green with pale red spots and stripes. Centre of caudal fin blackish, hinder margin veined with black, upper and lower edges salmon-pink. Pectoral and ventral fins colourless. Older ♂♂ have no blotch at the root of the tail.

♀ More attractively coloured. Upperside red-brown; underside pale brown; rows of spots copper-coloured; dorsal and anal fins yellow to reddish. In older fishes the anal fin is bright red. Caudal fin brilliant orange-red with a black border. A dark, pale-bordered blotch at the root of the tail.

The largest species of the genus, but still quite peaceful, even with smaller fishes.

Care and breeding, as given on p. 544. A very good leaper. Warmth-loving, 23–25°C. Food-fishes in their native countries, being eaten in oil or pickled. 1929/+.

Rivulus isthmensis *Garman* 1895 (Fig. 860)
Panama and Costa Rica; to 7 cm.

D 9–10; A 11–14; LL 40–42.

♂ Upperside brownish with a green sheen; flanks shining bluish to yellow-green; throat bright red; belly yellowish; gill-cover bright silvery. Close, narrow rows of red spots on the body. Dorsal and anal fins greenish with dark areas, the anal being bordered with red. Caudal fin red, bordered with yellow-green above and orange below.

♀ Coffee-brown to ochre, irregularly marbled. A deep black, gold-rimmed caudal blotch. Rows of spots only faintly indicated.

Care and breeding, as given on p. 544. 1924/−.

Rivulus ocellatus *Hensel* 1868 (Fig. 861)   Ocellated Rivulus
Rio de Janeiro to Santos, in the coastal belt; to 7 cm.
    D 8–9; A 11–12; LL 47–50.

♂ Upperside light brownish to greenish; flanks yellow-green to yellowish; underside pure yellow. Numerous irregular dark or transverse band-like blotches on the flanks. Dorsal and anal fins bright green-yellow, with pale spots; borders pale yellow broadly edged with black. Caudal fin similarly patterned, but without the pale spots. A vague round blotch on the upper part of the caudal root.
♀ Dark; flanks marbled; caudal blotch very distinct; fins colourless.

Care and breeding, as given on p. 544. Undemanding; breeding easy. Temperature 20–24°C. Sea-salt should be added (2 teaspoons to 10 litres of water).
According to Hoedeman (1956) this species is extraordinarily difficult to distinguish from the Cuban *Rivulus marmoratus* Poey 1880, a species whose import is, in the opinion of the same author, much to be desired. 1906/−.

Rivulus roloffi *Trewavas* 1948 (Fig. 862)   Roloff's Rivulus
Haiti, San Domingo; to 4·5 cm.
    D 10–11; A 14; LL 32–33. Coloration, according to Roloff:−

♂ Back olive-brown; flanks gleaming blue, here and there changing to a green colour. An especially strongly-shining metallic blotch behind the gill-cover. Rows of brick-red spots on the flanks. Dorsal fin olive-brown with a faint

Plate 147

Fig. 852. *Aequidens pulcher* (Blue Acara); young, natural size. (Original)
Fig. 853. *Aequidens maroni* (Keyhole Cichlid); adult ♂, natural size. (Original)
Fig. 854. *Aequidens curviceps* (Flag Cichlid); adults, somewhat reduced; above ♂, below ♀. (Original)

Plate 147

Plate 148

Plate 148

Fig. 855. *Apistogramma reitzigi* (Yellow Dwarf Cichlid); natural size; above ♀, below ♂. (Original)

Fig. 856. *Apistogramma* sp.; young, natural size. A species imported from South America. (Original)

Fig. 857. *Cichlasoma biocellatum* (Jack Dempsey); ♀, showing coloration when afraid; reduced. (Original)

border. Anal and ventral fins olive-yellow with a dark border. Caudal fin yellow with colourless outer parts.

♀ Paler, with dark transverse stripes.

Care, as given on p. 544. Nothing is known of breeding in captivity. 1939/−.

Rivulus santensis (*W. Köhler* 1906) (Fig. 868) Santos Rivulus
Rio de Janeiro to Santos; to 7 cm.

D 7–8; A 12–13; P 13; V 6; LL 36–38.

♂ Ground-colour brilliant green to yellow-green; back darker; underside yellow-green to white. Numerous rows of delicate red spots along the sides. Dorsal fin dark green to blackish, with a dirty white border. Caudal fin dark, the upper edge white, the lower deep black. Anal fin dark with a deep black border.

♀ More brownish with longitudinal rows of bluish spots. Fins usually colourless.

Care and breeding, as given on p. 544. Very easily bred. 1903/−.

Rivulus strigatus *Regan* 1912 (Fig. 869) Herringbone Rivulus
Streams of Central Amazonia; to 3·5 cm.

D 8; A 12; P 13; V 6; LL 33. The loveliest and most graceful of the *Rivulus* spp.

♂ Back dark olive, marbled with brown; flanks indigo; throat and belly orange. Longitudinal rows of small red dots on the head and flanks (chiefly the anterior parts) from the ventral fins onwards become organised into several chevron-shaped carmine-red transverse bars, the angle of the V pointing towards the head in each case. Dorsal, anal and caudal fins yellow-green to yellow, with several rows of red spots. Caudal fin bordered with orange; ventral fins yellow-green, pectoral fins bluish.

♀ Coloration paler; markings hazier.

A very active species. Care and breeding, as given for *R. cylindraceus*. Put two ♀♀ to a ♂ when breeding. Temperature up to 30°C. Unfortunately this species can seldom be persuaded to breed even under the best of conditions. The number of offspring from a spawning is small, and in captivity the majority of these are ♂♂. Often very quarrelsome, despite its tiny size. 1910/−.

Rivulus urophthalmus *Günther* 1866 (Fig. 870)   Golden or Green Rivulus
North-eastern, central and eastern South America; to 7 cm.
   D 6–7; A 11–13; P 13; V 6; LL 37–42.

♂ Back dark to pale brown; flanks darker, but often with a greenish sheen; belly pale. Rows of red spots on the flanks. Dorsal, caudal and anal fins green to yellow-green with rows of red spots. Upper edge of caudal copper-red, lower black. Pectoral and ventral fins greenish. Older ♂♂ lack the caudal blotch.
♀ Brown to brown-red, occasionally with dark marbling on the flanks. A deep black blotch, with a yellowish to whitish edge, at the root of the tail.

Care and breeding, as given for *R. cylindraceus.* Breeding frequent and stormy; rearing very easy. Surface-fishes, great favourites for their lively behaviour. Very variable; may occasionally be quite green or blue in colour.

A golden-red variety of this species, to which the incorrect name *R. xanthonotus* has been applied, occurs in Nature and has been selectively bred in captivity. 1905/+.

Rivulus xanthonotus *E. Ahl* 1926 (Fig. 871)   Yellowback Rivulus
Amazon River (?); to 7 cm.
   D 6; A 11–12; P 13; V 6; LL 40.

♂ Upperside pale to reddish-yellow between the mouth and the dorsal fin; flanks dark brown with yellow-brown areas and longitudinal rows of rust-red spots; throat whitish; belly with a reddish sheen. Vertical fins yellowish to grey with rows of red spots and blotches; caudal reddish above, often bordered with black. Iris brown above, green below.
♀ Ochre-coloured. A dark, pale-bordered blotch at the root of the caudal.

Figs. 858–862

♂♂ on the left; sketches of corresponding ♀♀ to the right.
Fig. 858. *Rivulus dorni* (Dorn's Rivulus); enlarged.
Fig. 859. *Rivulus harti* (Hart's Rivulus); ripe adults.
Fig. 860. *Rivulus isthmensis;* maximum size.
Fig. 861. *Rivulus ocellatus* (Ocellated Rivulus); maximum size.
Fig. 862. *Rivulus roloffi* (Roloff's Rivulus); adults, somewhat reduced.

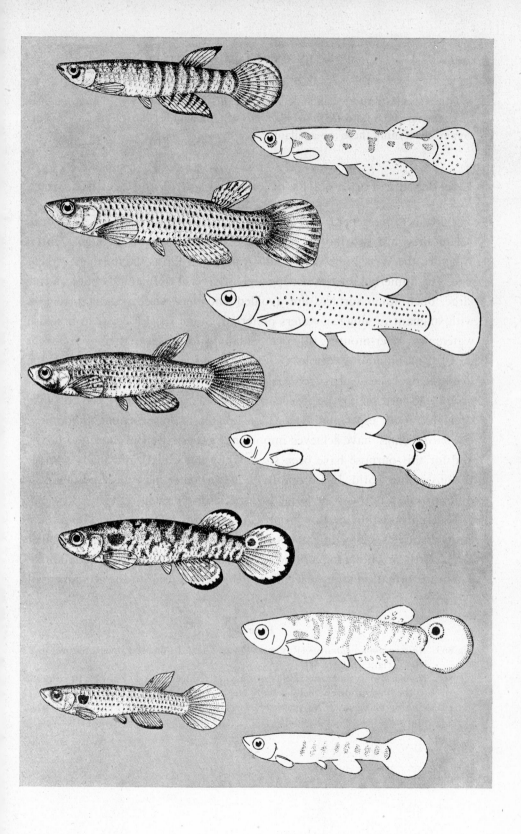

Other species imported include *Rivulus agilis* Hoedeman 1954, *Rivulus holmiae* (Eigenmann 1909) and *Rivulus micropus* (Steindachner 1863), but no further details concerning these are available.

Live-Bearing Tooth-Carps of North, Central and South America

The live-bearing genera of Tooth-Carps are confined to the New World, where they are distributed from the southern U.S.A. through Central America, the West Indies and South America as far as the northern Argentine. The numerous species occupy a great diversity of habitats but as a rule large, open water-surfaces are avoided and very weedy, shallow regions with stagnant or sluggish waters preferred. Some species occur in brackish waters near river-mouths; others are adapted to the clear streams and clear lakes of mountainous regions. With the exception of a few species all the live-bearing Tooth-Carps are shoaling-fishes which live in the surface water-layers and feed mainly on insects and insect-larvae, although they do take vegetable food, especially algae, to a greater or lesser extent. Some, e.g. *Gambusia affinis*, have achieved importance as destroyers of mosquito-larvae and for this purpose have been successfully introduced into many warmer regions of the world. In Europe Italy, in particular, has mastered the mosquito problem in this way. Some few species are predators.

The reproduction of this group is of especial interest. The ♂ and ♀ are easily distinguished by differences in the anal fin which, in the usually smaller ♂♂, is partly or wholly transformed into a copulatory organ, the gonopodium. The transformation takes place during the period prior to the attainment of

Plate 149

Fig. 863. *Apistogramma ramirezi* (Ramirez' Dwarf Cichlid); fine specimens, natural size; left ♂, right ♀. (Original)

Fig. 864. *Nannochromis nudiceps;* adults, somewhat reduced; left ♀, right ♂. In contrast to the illustration the belly usually has an emerald green lustre.

Fig. 865. *Apistogramma agassizi* (Agassiz' Dwarf Cichlid); ripe breeding pair, natural size; above ♂, below ♀. (Original)

Plate 149

Plate 150

Plate 150

Fig. 866. *Aequidens portalegrensis* (Black Acara); ripe ♂, natural size. (Original)
Fig. 867. *Pelmatochromis kribensis;* ripe young, natural size; left ♀, right ♂. (Original)

sexual maturity and is usually combined with a forward displacement of the anal fin as well as of the sexual opening, anus and ventral fins. At the end of the metamorphosis these organs often come to lie in the pectoral region, and the body-cavity is correspondingly shortened. The form of the gonopodium in sexually mature ♂♂ is an important systematic character, by means of which sub-families and genera, as well as species, may be distinguished. The simplest gonopodium occurs in representatives of the related Central Mexican family *Goodeidae*, in which the first 6(–8) anal rays are simplified, shortened, crowded together and delimited by a notch from the posterior portion of the fin. This gonopodium does not migrate forwards during development. In the genus *Jenynsia* of the family *Cyprinodontidae* the anal fin is concentrated by a ring-fold which develops into a tube. Apart from these peculiarities the gonopodium consists as a rule of the 3rd, 4th, and 5th rays of the anal fin which thicken and become prolonged and sometimes take on very distinctive forms. In some cases, for example, sickle- or spoon-shaped appendages may be formed at the end of the 3rd anal ray (Fig. 743). With the gonopodium, moreover, goes a musculature specialised for its movement. The result of this development is, in contrast to its structural diversity, always the same; the gonopodium is a movable external extension of the sperm-channel which serves for the transference of free spermatozoa or of spermatophores.

The extent to which Nature can elaborate such developments is shown by the genera *Jenynsia* and *Anableps*, in which the gonopodium can only be moved to one side. Since, furthermore, the sex-opening of the ♀♀ comes by a peculiar development to lie either to the right or the left, the unusual situation arises that ♂♂ with a leftward-moving gonopodium can only pair with ♀♀ having the sex-opening on the right side, and vice versa.

The ♀♀, as a rule, are able to store the sperm resulting from one sex-act for a considerable time and so fertilise several successive series of eggs without further pairing. The eggs are usually fertilised in the ovarian cavity and there develop on nourishment exclusively derived from their own yolk-material. When they are eventually extruded the eggs are ready to hatch (ovo-vivipar-ity) and in such a condition of internal pressure that the least contact, even falling to the bottom, causes them to burst and release the contained embryos. In the genus *Anableps* the development beyond this stage is so far advanced that the fertilised eggs no longer develop in the ovarian cavity but directly in the ovary, so that the wall of the follicle is specially transformed and serves for gaseous exchange as well as for the intake of nourishment. In *Heteran-dria* the embryos do not develop in batches, with each new batch, as it were, taking for granted the birth of a previous one, but a natural superfoetation is produced; the eggs are fertilised in the order in which they are developed so that embryos in all stages of development are found in the ovary and are shed over a birth period of many days. Finally, in *Jenynsia* even trophonemata are present; the embryos lie, without egg-membranes, in the ovarian cavity and are nourished by means of long nipple-like processes of maternal tissue.

The colouring of the sexes is in some cases similar. As a rule, however, the ♂♂ are more distinctly marked and more intensely coloured. The ♂ is express-ly polygamous and always the more active partner. Pregnant ♀♀ may be recognised by the pregnancy-mark, a black spot in front of the anal fin. The duration of pregnancy is not fixed, but depends on temperature, nourishment, season and also upon the age of the ♀. As a rule the period varies between 30–40 days. Usually a short pause follows pregnancy, during which the eggs

Figs. 868–871

♂♂ on the left; sketches of the corresponding ♀♀ to the right

Fig. 868. *Rivulus santensis* (Santos Rivulus); maximum size.
Fig. 869. *Rivulus strigatus* (Herringbone Rivulus); adults, enlarged.
Fig. 870. *Rivulus urophthalmus* (Golden Rivulus); natural size.
Fig. 871. *Rivulus xanthonotus* (Yellowback Rivulus); natural size.

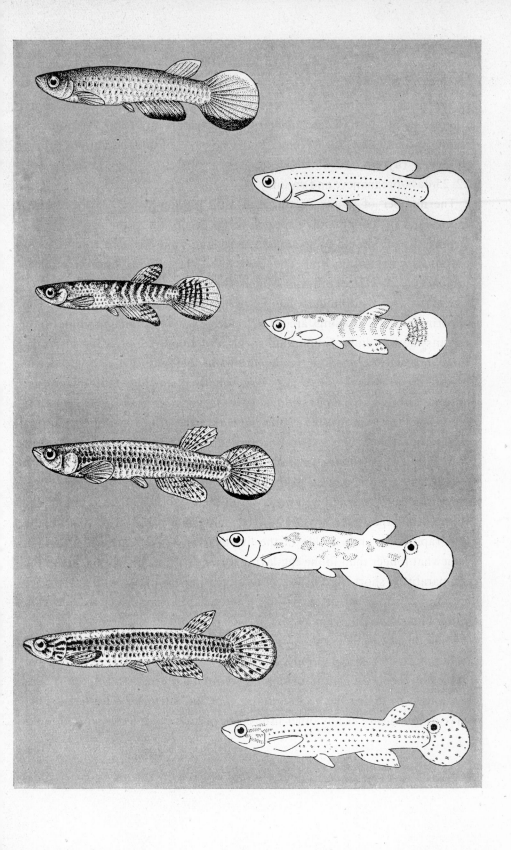

in the ovary ripen and are ejected as a new series into the ovarian cavity where they are fertilised and begin their development. These relationships result, in the Guppy, for example, under normal constant conditions, in the following rhythm: 22–25 days pregnancy, birth, 7–9 days resting-phase, 22–25 days pregnancy, and so on.

The number of young produced at a birth differs widely in the various species and in the individual species varies according to the age of the ♀♀, feeding conditions, etc. While most species under the constant conditions of the aquarium reproduce all the year round there is in Nature, in many *Mollienesia* spp. for example, a winter pause.

Tooth-Carps with similarly-shaped gonopodia may easily be crossed. The offspring of these crossings are often fertile, a state of affairs which not only permits the breeding of numerous form- and colour-varieties but also provides material for scientific investigations in the field of heredity. Even in Nature crossings are not so very rare. Finally it should be mentioned that in some Tooth-Carps a change of sex from ♀ to ♂ can take place during the course of life, often in ♀ fishes after several birth periods, with full transformation into functional ♂♂ (for further details see Fig. 700 and legend).

At birth the young are generally already fully developed and independent and, if they are not shot up to the surface during the process of being born, they strive hard to reach it in order to fill their swim-bladders with air. The young of all species commence to feed immediately and growth is usually very rapid. The span of life in the live-bearing Tooth-Carps is, as a rule, somewhat longer than in the egg-laying forms, but both groups belong to the comparatively short-lived fishes. With increasing age the ♂♂ of many species become very deep-bodied, particularly in the nape-region which may develop into a hump-like enlargement.

Many live-bearing Tooth-Carps are extremely hardy and very adaptable to the most diverse conditions. It is, however, to misunderstand the art of aquarium-keeping if – as unfortunately so often happens – these peculiarities are abused by giving the fishes reduced care and attention. Live-bearers deserve as much care as any other fishes. They require old, well-matured tanks standing in sunny positions, with dense plant growth as well as areas of free swimming-space. A loose covering of floating plants *(Riccia* or *Salvinia)*, or even hanging root-systems, are very beneficial to shy species. Water-quality as a rule plays quite a subordinate role; medium-hard to hard water, well worked-through biologically, is better than very soft or even acid water. For live-bearers from coastal waters a small addition of sea-salt is recommended. Temperature requirements are too diverse for generalisation; many species are quite well suited to the unheated domestic aquarium. These fishes take live food of all kinds, especially midge-larvae and small crustaceans, also such plant materials as algae, boiled spinach, lettuce, softened oat-flakes, etc. Many species may be kept together with one another or with fishes of different families.

Most live-bearers are easy to breed. In well planted single-species tanks with a loose floating plant-cover the young can usually find refuge from the cannibalistic desires of their parents. In serious breeding ♀♀ from which a birth is shortly expected should be isolated and placed in spawning-cases hanging in the breeding tank. At birth the young then fall through the bars of the cage and are well protected against seizure by the mother. It must, however, be emphasised that not every species will bear under these conditions and even that, in many Tooth-Carps, the slightest disturbance during pregnancy results in premature births. Information on these matters is to be found under the several species descriptions. The young are born hungry and feed on the finest-grade food immediately after birth. Growth is rapid. In the interests of the hobby as a whole one should try to maintain the quality of the stock by selecting only the strongest and best-coloured fishes for breeding.

Alfaro cultratus *(Regan* 1908) (Fig. 872)   Knife Live-bearer
Costa Rica, Nicaragua and the Atlantic slope of Panama, in small waters; ♂ to 4 cm., ♀ to 9 cm.
    D 7–9; A 8–10; P 12; V 6; LL 32–35. Body thick-set, strongly compressed. Lower part of caudal peduncle compressed to a sharp-edged keel; anal fin inserted closely before this keel. Ventral fins larger in the ♂♂.

♂ Pale brown to clay-colour, with a bluish sheen on the flanks; back darker. A usually indistinct narrow dark band along the side. The whole body is sprinkled with fine black spots, these being especially prominent on top of the head. Fins colourless or faintly yellowish. Caudal fin with dark edge. Gonopodium of older ♂♂ golden yellow.

♀ More modestly coloured.

Care and breeding, as given on p. 556. A hardy, agile predator, somewhat pugnacious and therefore best confined to a tank with its own kind. Temperature around 24 °C. Very long gestation period. Brood few. 1910/ −.

Belonesox belizanus *Kner* 1860 (Fig. 873)   Pike Top Minnow
Eastern Central America; ♂ to 10 cm., ♀ to 20 cm. The largest species of live-bearer.

D 8–10; A 10; P 14–16; V 6; LL 52–65. Body thick-set, compressed. Snout long and pointed. Mouth deeply-cleft, with pointed teeth. Eyes large.

♂ Back grey-olive; flanks grey-yellow to olive-green, with a bronze lustre by reflected light; breast and belly dirty white. Rows of more or less distinct spots on the flanks. A dark, round, pale-bordered blotch on the caudal fin. Fins colourless or faintly yellowish, the edges touched with dark.

♀ Smaller, with a reddish anal fin-base.

A predatory, surface-living fish which is not suitable for the community aquarium and is best kept in large, richly-planted heated outdoor establishments. Feeding is not easy; the ripe adults are often choosy and frequently accept only the larger live foods, such as fishes, dragonfly-larvae, tadpoles and worms. *Belonesox* of 12–18 cm. can overcome full-grown Platy or Guppy females without difficulty. Temperature 25–30 °C. Prolific; up to 100 young in a brood. The young fishes are 25–30 mm. long at birth and are immediately able to eat small *Daphnia* and Enchytraeids. The mothers will often greedily swallow their own young. 1909/ −.

Figs. 872–875

♂♂ on the left; sketches of corresponding ♀♀ to the right

Fig. 872. *Alfaro cultratus* (Knife Live-bearer); maximum size.
Fig. 873. *Belonesox belizanus* (Pike Top Minnow); natural size.
Fig. 874. *Brachyrhaphis episcopi* (Bishop); somewhat enlarged.
Fig. 875. *Cnesterodon decemmaculatus* (Ten-spotted Live-bearer); slightly enlarged.

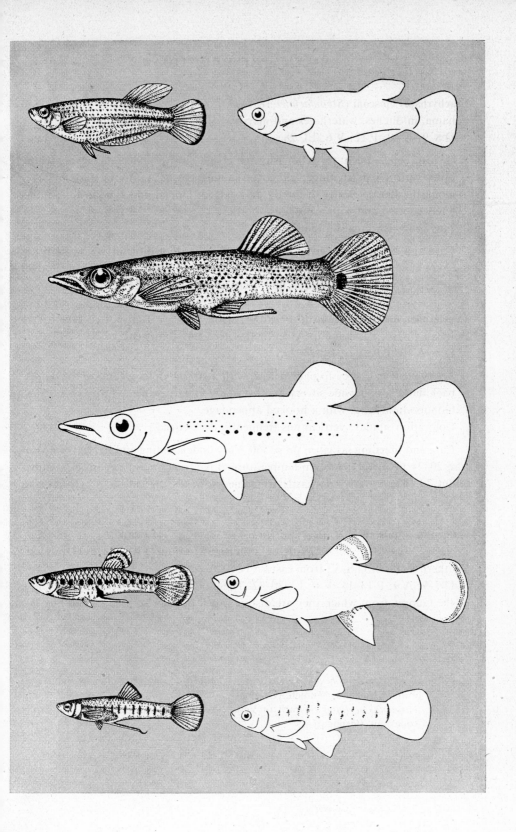

Brachyrhapis episcopi (*Steindachner* 1878) (Fig. 874)   Bishop

Panama, in ditches, waterholes and marshes; ♂ to 3 cm., ♀ to 5 cm.

  D 8–9; A 10; P 12; V 6; LL 28.

♂ Delicate olive-green to yellowish; upperside fawn; underside silvery-white, often with a reddish tinge; gill-cover shining green. A row of dark blotches along the flanks. Scales distinctly dark-edged. Dorsal and caudal fins yellow, finely spotted and with a brownish border.

♀ Fins yellowish; anal fin reddish.

Care and breeding, as given on p. 556. Breeding not difficult when the fishes are kept in very slightly brackish water in tanks thickly overgrown with algae. Not suitable for the community aquarium. Very warmth-loving (24–26°C.). 1911/–.

Cnesterodon decemmaculatus (*Jenyns* 1842) (Fig. 875)   Ten-spotted Live-bearer

Bolivian Chaco, Paraguay to Argentina; ♂ to 3 cm., ♀ to 5 cm.

  D 8; A 10; P 9; V 6; LL 24–25.

♂ Translucent pale grey to pale yellow, with a strong violet gleam on the flanks; back darker; underside silvery. 6–12 (usually 9) narrow black transverse bands. Gonopodium long, with a hooked appendage.

♀ Coloration similar; vertical fins frequently dark-edged.

Care and breeding, as given on p. 556. Very undemanding and hardy. Temperature 20–24°C., or about room-temperature. Live food and algae. Brood-number about 20. The ♀♀ are very easily frightened towards the end of pregnancy and liable to miscarry. 1902/–.

Gambusia affinis affinis (*Baird* and *Girard* 1854) (Figs. 745, 880)

                Spotted Gambusia, Mosquito Fish, Texas Gambusia.

Southern States of U.S.A., from eastern Texas to Alabama; ♂ to 3·5 cm., ♀ to 6 cm.

  D 7–9; A 9; P 13–14; V 6; LL 30–32. The ♀♀ of this species are very like those of the Guppy, from which they are distinguished by their spotted caudal fin.

Plate 151

Fig. 876. *Cichlasoma hellabrunni* (Hellabrunn Cichlid); 25 cm. specimen in the Hellabrunn Aquarium, Munich. (Original)

Fig. 877. *Astronotus ocellatus* (Oscar's or Velvet Cichlid); 20 cm. specimen in the Erfurt Aquarium. (Original)

Plate 151

Plate 152

Plate 152

Fig. 878. *Cichlasoma biocellatum* (Jack Dempsey); fine ♂, natural size. (Original)
Fig. 879. *Cichlasoma cyanoguttatum;* ripe young, natural size. (Original)

♂ Translucent grey, with a bluish sheen on the flanks; back olive-brown; belly silvery. A dark transverse bar across the eye. Isolated black spots occasionally present on the body. Fins colourless to yellowish; dorsal and caudal with black spots. Gonopodium about as long as the head.
♀ Similarly coloured, but with a larger anal fin.

Black-checked ♂♂ varieties occasionally occur in natural populations, very similar to the Black-checked Molly ♂♂. Similar ♀♀ can also be produced by selective breeding. The checked type are more commonly met with in the trade than the simple wild form. *Gambusia affinis affinis* and *G. a. holbrooki* (see below) were originally regarded as separate species. *G. a. affinis* is without a doubt pre-eminent among the temperature-resistant *Gambusia* spp., and is quite as happy at temperatures around freezing-point as it is at 30°C. These fishes are likewise almost indifferent to the oxygen-content and quality of the water.

The Gambusias are particularly well-known for their prediliction for mosquito-larvae, of which each fish can destroy its own weight daily. *G. a. affinis* has on this account been introduced into all the warmer parts of the world for mosquito control. The natural breeding season is from April to early October, but in the constant conditions of the aquarium the ♀♀ throw young all the year round. In natural populations the proportion of ♀♀ is greatly in excess of the ♂♂. In captivity best kept at room-temperature. Live food of all kinds. Breeding not difficult. Brood-number up to 60 in grown ♀♀. The parents often eat their young. Growth with good feeding very rapid; sexual maturity may be reached within 3 months.

Not suitable for community aquaria; not only pugnacious but still more liable to nibble fins of other fishes. 1914/+.

Gambusia affinis holbrooki (*Girard* 1859) (Figs. 740, 880)   Mosquito Fish
From New Jersey to Florida; widely introduced elsewhere; ♂ to 3 cm., ♀ to 6 cm.
D 6–8; A 9–10; P 13–14; V 6; LL 30–32. The ♀♀ are practically indistinguishable from those of the typical subspecies; the ♂♂, however, are irregularly blotched with black.

Care and breeding, as given for the typical subspecies.

Gambusia dominicensis *Regan* 1913 (Fig. 881) Domingo Gambusia
Haiti; ♂ to 2·5 cm., ♀ to 6 cm.
  D 9; A 10–11; LL 26–29.

♂ Translucent brownish to clay-colour; underside yellowish to white. An indistinct dark band along the side, with a few isolated dark spots above it. Dorsal and caudal fins orange with rows of dark spots; remaining fins yellowish.
♀ Similarly coloured; usually no lateral band.

Care, breeding and other matters, as given for *G. affinis affinis*. This species, however, is considerably more warmth-loving than the North American forms; temperature 20–24 °C. The ♀♀, no less than those of other species, are especially irritable shortly before the termination of pregnancy. 1912/ – .

Gambusia nicaraguensis *Günther* 1866 (Fig. 882) Nicaragua Gambusia
Atlantic slope, from Mexico to Panama; ♂ to 3·5 cm., ♀ to 6·5 cm.
  D 7; A 9–10; P 13; LL 29.

♂ Translucent pale brown to greenish-brown; whitish towards the belly; flanks shining blue-silver. Eye-stripe conspicuous. Fins colourless; the dorsal, caudal and anal with rows of dark spots. In many races the caudal fin is entirely black.
♀ Similarly coloured. Pregnancy mark dark orange.

Care and breeding, as given for *G. affinis affinis*. This species, however, is not so resistant to low temperatures and should not be kept below 14–15 °C.; otherwise it is very undemanding and voracious. Breeding very easy, but the adults have a great appetite for their own young. 1906/ – .

Gambusia punctata *Poey* 1855 (Fig. 883) Blue/Spotted Gambusia
Cuba, very common; ♂ to 5 cm., ♀ to 9 cm.
  D 8–10; A 11; P 15; V 6; LL 31–35.

Figs. 880–884

♂♂ on the left; sketches of corresponding ♀♀ to the right

Fig. 880. *Gambusia affinis affinis* (Spotted Gambusia); below, a figure of the ♂ *G. affinis holbrooki;* both, like the ♀, enlarged.
Fig. 881. *Gambusia dominicensis* (Domingo Gambusia); somewhat enlarged.
Fig. 882. *Gambusia nicaraguensis* (Nicaragua Gambusia); maximum size.
Fig. 883. *Gambusia punctata* (Blue Gambusia); natural size.
Fig. 884. *Gambusia yucatana* (Yucatan Gambusia); adults, natural size.

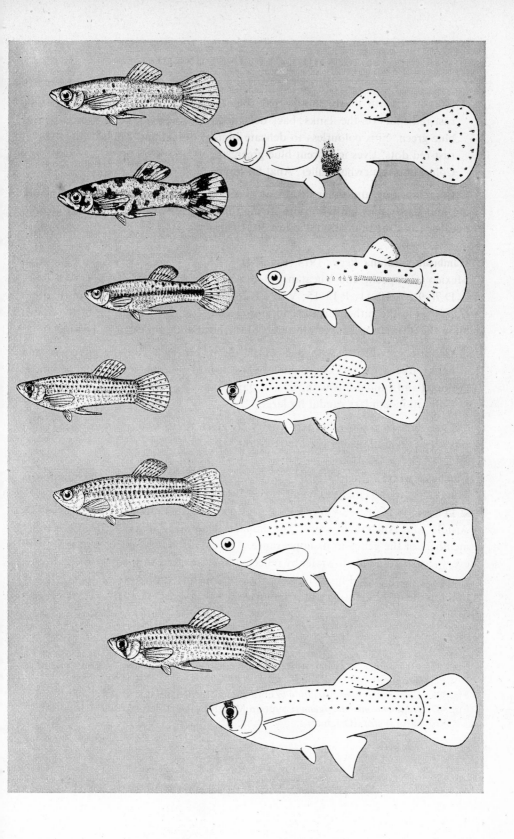

♂ Grey-blue, with lovely shining pale blue areas and longitudinal rows of fine rust-red spots on the flanks; back delicate fawn; underside yellowish; gill-cover blue-green. Fins colourless to delicate bluish; dorsal and caudal with rows of rust-red dots. Eyes iridescent blue-green.

♀ Coloration somewhat duller. Anal fin large.

Care, breeding and other details, as given for *G. affinis affinis*. Very undemanding and hardy, but more warmth-loving than *G. a. affinis* itself; 12–20°C. Brood-number for a medium-sized ♀ about 30. 1930/+.

Gambusia yucatana *Regan* 1914 (Fig. 884)   Yucatan Gambusia
Mexico (Campeche and Yucatan); ♂ to 5·5 cm., ♀ to 7·5 cm.

D 7(–9); A 10–11; P 13–15; V 6; LL 28. This species differs from most other *Gambusia* in the rather larger head and the more anterior insertion of the dorsal fin in the ♂ (midway between the ends of the head and of the caudal peduncle).

♂ Delicate grey-brown with a greenish sheen, especially on the gill-cover and flanks. Eye-stripe very conspicuous. Fins clear to delicate grey. Caudal peduncle, dorsal and caudal fins with rows of dark spots.

♀ Coloration similar; caudal fin larger.

Care, breeding and other particulars, as given for *G. affinis affinis*, except that this species is not as temperature-resistant; 18 – 23°C. Very prolific. 1912/–.

Gambusia wrayi *Regan* 1913   Jamaica Gambusia
Jamaica; ♂ to 3·5 cm., ♀ to 6 cm.

D 8; A 10–11; P 13; V 6; LL 31–33. Concerning this species, imported in 1933, Arnold and Ahl (1936) say:–'The Jamaica Gambusia diverges from the other members of the genus in its appearance. The colour is grey-green, iridescent with every shade from blue to violet by reflected light, marked with blackish and brown spots on the flanks. Fins yellowish, the vertical fins with rows of spots.' In my opinion the determination of the imported fishes in question as *G. wrayi* is open to

Plate 153

Fig. 885. *Cichlasoma facetum* (Chanchito, Chameleon Cichlid); young, enlarged. (Original)
Fig. 886. *Cichlasoma nigrofasciatum* (Zebra Cichlid); ♂, natural size. (Original)
Fig. 887. *Haplochromis strigigena* (Egyptian Mouthbrooder); left ♀, right ♂, ripe young, natural size. (Original)

Plate 153

Plate 154

Plate 154

Figs. 888–890. Nest-building and brood-care in *Tilapia zillii* (Zilli's Cichlid). For the continuation of this sequence, see Plate 155.

Fig. 888. (above) The ♂ excavates the nesting hole by himself. Sand and small stones are carried away in his mouth; larger stones are pushed to one side.

Fig. 889. (centre) The same scene, after the completion of the nesting hole. The large stone at the back is now freely exposed. At the bottom of the hole is the spawn, which is at first fanned and guarded by the ♀.

Fig. 890. (below) The ♂ (right) joins in the care of the spawn at a later stage, but at first the ♀ (left) attacks him. Eventually the ♀ herself is driven away.

doubt. We are probably dealing here with *G. affinis*, imported into Jamaica and subsequently offered in the European market as *G. wrayi*.

Girardinus metallicus *Poey* 1854 (Fig. 904)   Girardinus
Cuba; ♂ to 5 cm., ♀ to 8 cm.

D 9–10; A 10–11; P 10; V 6; LL 29–31. Mouth upwardly directed. Gonopodium very long, with two curved, horn-like appendages at the end.

♂ Yellow-brown to grey-green, with a strong metallic glint by reflected light. An alternating series of silvery transverse stripes and dark blotches along the middle of the side. Several shining greenish spots on the gill-cover and underneath the eye. Upper edge of the eye golden yellow. Fins grey to yellowish. Leading-edge of dorsal fin black; a round black blotch on the hinder part, near the base.

♀ Dorsal fin with nearly vertical black stripes.

Care and breeding, as given on p. 556. Peaceful, hardy and undemanding. Temperature 22–25°C. This species requires supplementary plant food (algae, lettuce, softened oat-flakes). Brood-number up to 60. The young should be isolated. 1927/+.

Glaridichthys falcatus *Eigenmann* 1903 (Fig. 905)   Yellow Belly
Cuba, in shallow, rapid waters; ♂ to 6 cm., ♀ to 8 cm.

D 7–9; A 10; P 11; LL 29–30.

♂ Gonopodium very long and slender, with two horn-like appendages. Body translucent, pale yellowish-green. Back a fine green by reflected light, lower half of the side sulphur-yellow; belly yellowish. A fine shining silver band along the side. Mid-line of caudal peduncle deep black above and below. Fins pale yellow to bright yellow. Large, very brilliant eyes, shining bronze to pale green.

♀ Similarly coloured. Anal fin large.

Care and breeding, as given on p. 556. A very peaceful, lively and contented species. Temperature 22–25°C. Gestation period 30–130 days, depending on temperature. Brood-number 25–60, according to the size of the mother. Young very small. 1935/ −.

Heterandria formosa *Agassiz* 1853 (Fig. 741) Dwarf Top Minnow, Mosquito Fish

North Carolina and Florida; ♂ to 2 cm., ♀ to 3·5 cm. The ♂♂ of this species are among the smallest vertebrate animals.

D 7–8; A 10–11; P 12; V 6; LL 27–31.

♂ Yellowish to reddish-brown, with a pearly lustre by reflected light, iridescent violet at certain angles. An irregular broad band from the tip of the snout to the root of the tail, intersected by 8–12 dark transverse bars. In healthy fishes the whole body is blotched and marbled with dark. Fins yellowish. A deep black blotch at the bases of the dorsal and anal fins; the dorsal blotch is also bordered with orange.

♀ Similarly coloured. Anal fin large.

This species is a very lively and aggressive little fish, despite its tiny size, and makes a very rewarding pet which can be kept in the smallest aquarium. These fishes prefer to remain among loose, fine-leaved plants, and especially among the hanging roots of floating plants. Their diet consists chiefly of small waterfleas and other small creatures which they find among the plants. Temperature 20–24°C. *H. formosa* is easily the smallest live-bearing Tooth-Carp and, as regards its breeding, one of the most interesting. Whereas as a rule several eggs are fertilised at a time, and develop together into young which are born simultaneously, followed by a repetition of the same cycle, *H. formosa* develops numerous embryos of different ages which are delivered (2–3 daily) over a period of 6–10 days. With good feeding it is possible to induce such a pregnancy-period every 4–5 weeks. The adults hardly ever molest the young. 1912/ +.

Heterophallus rachovi *Regan* 1914 (Fig. 906) Rachow's Live-bearer

Vera Cruz (Mexico); ♂ to 3 cm., ♀ to 4·5 cm.

D 7; A 10; LL 30. Very similar to the *Gambusia* spp.

♂ Translucent, delicate greenish; back fawn; underside silvery. A sharply-delimited dark band along the flanks, broadening posteriorly and ending in a dark blotch at the root of the tail. Fins greenish.

♀ Similarly coloured, with a larger anal fin.

Care and breeding, as given on p. 556. A peaceful, hardy species, loving sunshine and loose plant-growth like most live-bearers. Temperature 18–23°C. Brood-number up to 30. 1912/−.

Jenynsia lineata (*Jenyns* 1842) (Fig. 838)　　　　　　　　One-sided Live-bearer
Southern Brazil and northern Argentina, in the basins of the Rio Grande do Sul and La Plata; ♂ to 4 cm., ♀ to 12 cm.

D 8–9; A (8)–9–10; P 13; V 6; LL 25–29. This species is mainly distinguished from those of other genera by the peculiar origin of its gonopodium. Whereas the gonopodium as a rule is morphologically derived from the modified 3rd–5th anal fin-rays, in *Jenynsia* it arises as a ring-shaped outgrowth from the skin of the anal fin-base. This outgrowth lengthens all around until finally it forms a tube quite enclosing the anal fin. During this process the anal fin and anal opening are not carried forward; there is no shortening of the body-cavity such as is characteristic of many genera (see also p. 553). There is also a very peculiar relationship between the mobility of the gonopodium and the location of the ♀ sex-opening. The ♂♂ can be divided into those with gonopodia movable to the left and those with gonopodia movable to the right; a corresponding distinction can be made in the ♀♀ in which, through the sex-opening being partially occluded by a large scale, the aperture is forced either to the right or to the left. These peculiarities decree that ♂♂ with leftward-movable gonopodia can only mate with ♀♀ having the sex-opening on the right side, and vice-versa. (See also p. 554.)

Body elongate, only slightly compressed. Coloration delicate olive-grey to olive-green. The flanks are shining cobalt-blue by reflected light and have various transverse streaks which are usually brown in colour but extraordinarily variable in form and arrangement. Fins greenish, without markings.

The sexes are similarly coloured.

Care and breeding, as given on p. 556. Older ♂♂ are very quarrelsome and pugnacious, but otherwise undemanding.

Omnivorous. Temperature 16–23°C. The adults pursue the young a great deal. Prolific. 1905/−.

Lebistes reticulatus (*Peters* 1859) (Figs. 742–744, 772, 891)   Guppy, Millions Fish
Venezuela, Barbados, Trinidad, parts of northern Brazil and Guiana; ♂ to 3 cm.,
♀ to 6 cm.

D 7–8; A 8–9; P 13–14; V 5; LL 26–28.

As is to be expected from its wide area of distribution, this species shows a
great number of form- and colour-varieties, which have been further intensified
and fixed by selective breeding under domestication. In its natural habitat the
Guppy occurs in great numbers (Millions Fish) and is very useful for mosquito
control.

♂ Large, black ocelli on the flanks. The intervening areas shimmer with all the
  colours of the rainbow, with red, blue or green dominating in various individuals. Especially beautiful colour-varieties are found in the West Indian islands.
  Fins very diversely shaped and coloured (see Fig. 891).

♀ Unpretentious, yellowish to green-yellowish, with some rows of scales shining
  bluish by reflected light. Fins grey; some domesticated varieties with coloured
  blotches on the caudal.

Care and breeding, as given on p. 556. While the Guppy can tolerate temperatures around 15°C. for short periods, it seems happiest at 22–24°C. Live and artificial foods. Very prolific. 1908/+.

In captivity this lovely live-bearer often falls victim to its own contentedness
and hardiness. Under conditions which no other species could sustain the Guppy
flourishes, always cheerful, always on the move and breeding incessantly. Thought-
less aquarists, too, often carelessly cross colour-strains which other breeders
have taken ten years to perfect, and continue to propagate feeble stock.

Guppy-breeding is, above all, a problem involving the laws of heredity. The object is to obtain a pure-breeding strain, that is to say, a strain in which every individual shows practically identical inherited characteristics. In such a stock all the
members of one sex would be uniformly shaped and coloured. Only such fishes
enable the objectives of the breeder – finer form and coloration – to be attained,
and the production of such strains often involves laborious selective-breeding over
a long period of years until finally an almost pure stock is isolated.

In doing this the breeder first of all keeps his eye on certain chosen characters,
such as a colour or the shape of the caudal fin, and from among the young fishes
isolates those ♂♂ which show these characters clearly and are at the same time especially robust and vigorous, all the others being destroyed. These ♂♂ of the desired type are then mated with virgin ♀♀ from the same brood, and the first gene-

ration from this mating are further treated in the same way, and so on. Slowly the proportion of the desired type is increased until ultimately the desired pure strain is achieved.

Such uniform strains with homozygous (pure) hereditary material may be crossed with other new strains with the object of building up a new combination of beautiful characters, this, of course, in a further new strain. In other words, by applying our knowledge of the laws of inheritance and using our pure strains of fishes we can produce strains showing new combinations of characters which can be transmitted almost indefinitely to subsequent generations. These laws, which indeed are not only effective but especially striking in the Guppy, are known as Mendel's Laws and may be stated essentially as follows: if one crosses pure-bred adults (Parental or P Generation) of two strains, then the resulting offspring (First Filial or F_1 Generation) will either be hybrids with characters intermediate between those of the parents (Intermediate Hybrids) or will show characters deriving entirely from one or other parent (Dominants). The character carried over from a parent to the whole F_1 generation is said to be Dominant; the corresponding character which is not carried over from the other parent is said to be Recessive. Sometimes the hereditary material (Mendelian Factors, or Genes as they are now called) interacts in such a way that the F_1 generation exhibits characters which are not present in either parent or are intermediate, and we then say that we are dealing with Blending Inheritance.

In general all the fishes of the F_1 generation should be alike, but this ideal state of affairs is seldom achieved in the Guppy. If one crosses members of the hybrid F_1 generation, too, one often finds that the resulting offspring (F_2) show all kinds of combinations of the characters inherited from their grandparents, although the characters which are dominant will, of course, be carried right through. The breeder must now, from this motley family, again select those fishes which approximate most closely to this desired ideal combination of characters, cross them and so continue until his goal is reached. Even then he remains unsuccessful in many cases, because even in the Guppy hereditary processes are at work which have a decidedly modifying effect upon the easy-seeming system which we have just outlined.

Here only the dominant and recessive characters are dealt with. As the following table from Ostertag (1955) shows, unfortunately almost all the attractive characters are recessives, which means that they are obscured in the F_1 generation:−

569

Dominant	Recessive
Wild Grey	'Gold'
Wild Grey	'Blond'
'Gold'	'Blond'
Wild Grey	Albino
Round Tail	Pointed Tail
Round Tail	Flagtail
Round Tail	Veiltail
Round Tail	Swordtail
Swordtail absent	Swordtail
Normal Caudal Fin-colour	Black blotches on the Caudal Fin in ♀♀
Normal Caudal Fin-colour	Chess-board Tail in ♀♀
Normal or Stunted Growth	Gigantism

The Guppy-breeder takes heed of the following important guiding principles:–

1. When buying fine Guppies always acquire them in pairs.

2. Never keep pure strains together in the same aquarium, but always isolate them in separate tanks.

3. Always separate the offspring from the adults immediately after birth and segregate the sexes.

4. Eliminate poor specimens.

5. Inbreed brothers and sisters, or back-cross father × daughter or mother × son.

Further information can be obtained from the Deutsche Guppygesellschaft, Hanover. In conclusion it must be emphasised that any Guppy, just like any other fish, needs proper care and attention; anything is *not* good enough for a Guppy! Proper care is not only an inescapable condition of every attempt at breeding; it is also essential to the preservation of the now almost universally distributed fine strains of these very interesting fishes.

Lebistes melanzonus (*Eigenmann* 1911) (Fig. 907)
Arnold (1939) expresses his opinion, from personal observations on living material, that *L. melanzonus* is a true species; Regan (1913), on the other hand, regards *L. melanzonus* as a synonym of *L. reticulatus*.
Guiana; ♂ to 3 cm., ♀ to 4·5 cm.
 D 6; A 9; LL 28–30. Coloration, according to Arnold:–

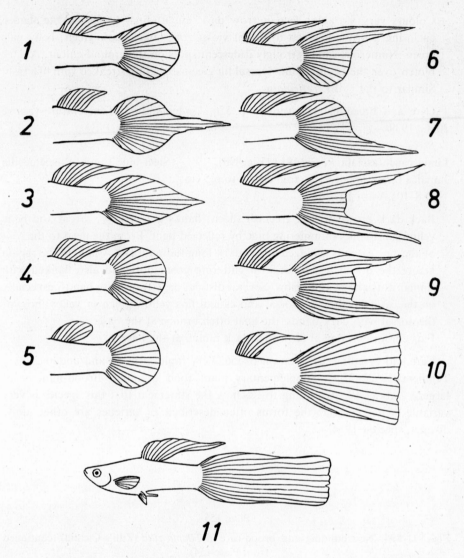

Fig. 891. Established Standards for the various recognised varieties of Caudal Fin in Guppies. (1) Spade-tail or Cofer-tail; (2) Pintail; (3) Pointed Tail or Speartail; (4) Robson-Roundtail; (5) Roundtail; (6) Top Sword; (7) Bottom Sword; (8) Double Sword; (9) Lyretail; (10) Veiltail; (11) Flagtail. (From *Die Aquarien-und Terrarien-Zeitschrift*, 3.Jg., H.10)

♂ Colours very variable. Two narrow dark longitudinal bands on the flanks, enclosing a brilliant green to bright violet zone. Back dark green; belly pale green. Numerous small, strongly iridescent spots on the ground-colour. A dark blotch over the pectoral fin. Dorsal fin greenish, lightly streaked with blackish.
♀ Similar to the ♀ of *L.reticulatus.*

Care and breeding, as given on p. 556. Undemanding. Temperatures above 20°C. 1939/−.

Limia caudofasciata *Regan* 1913 (Fig.898)   Steel-blue Limia, Blue Poecilia
Jamaica (Cuba, Haiti?); ♂ to 5 cm., ♀ to 6·5 cm.
  D 8–10; A 10; LL 26.

♂ Back dark brown with a greenish sheen; flanks grey-yellow; throat and belly yellowish. Flanks shimmering blue by reflected light. From the head to the root of the tail extends a ragged-edged dark longitudinal band which, in the region before the dorsal fin, is set with glittering green dots and also flanked with similar dots above and below. Several distinct dark transverse bands, especially on the caudal peduncle. Dorsal and caudal fins yellow-green or yellow-brown; the dorsal with dark bands, the anal often orange at the base.
♀ Fins colourless; dorsal fin with a dark blotch at the base.

Care and breeding, as given on p. 556. Very rapid-growing and undemanding. Temperature 22–25°C. Supplementary plant food essential. Brood-number of larger ♀♀ about 60. According to Rachow the statement that this species is very variable is not correct: the forms often described as varieties are other, quite distinct, species. 1914/+.

Plate 155

Figs.892–894. Nest-building and brood-care in *Tilapia zillii* (Zilli's Cichlid) (continued from Plate 154)

Fig.892. (above) The ♂ takes sole responsibility for guarding the nest of eggs. Resting obliquely over the spawn he fans fresh water over it with his pectoral fins.

Fig.893. (centre) The hatching young are taken up in the mouth of the ♂, completely freed from their egg-membranes and spat out into a newly prepared pit.

Fig.894. (below) The young fishes swim freely after 4 days and are then protected either by both parents or predominantly by the ♀.

Plate 155

Plate 156

Plate 156

Fig. 895. *Cichlasoma festivum* (The Festivum); young, enlarged. (Original)
Fig. 896. *Cichlasoma festivum;* adult ♂, reduced. (Original)
Fig. 897. *Teleogramma* sp. a Cichlid imported in 1957 from the Congo, where it lives in rapids; reduced. (Photo Dr. Foersch)

Limia heterandria *Regan* 1913 (Fig. 899)   Dwarf or Haiti Limia
Haiti; ♂ to 2·5 cm., ♀ to 4·5 cm.
   D 8; A 9; P 13; V 6; LL 26.

♂ Dark olive; flanks yellow-olive, with a dull silver gleam and closely-approximated transverse bands under the dorsal fin; belly pale to orange. Fins yellow; dorsal fin with two curved dark bands.
♀ No transverse bands. A dark band along the side, distinct only under the dorsal fin. Fins colourless to yellowish. Dorsal fin with a round black blotch.

Care and breeding, as given on p. 556. Warmth-loving, like all *Limia* spp.; temperature 22–25°C. Likes sunshine. Brood-number of larger ♀♀ about 50. Very prolific if healthy and well-fed. 1908/−.

Limia melanogaster (*Günther* 1866) (Fig. 746)   Black-bellied Limia, Blue Limia
Jamaica; ♂ to 3 cm., ♀ to 6 cm.
   D 8–10; A 10; P 13; V 6; LL 26–27. Very similar to *L. caudofasciata*, but more intensely coloured and with a very much larger, very striking, pregnancy-mark.

♂ Back olive-green; flanks with a steel-blue lustre in adult fishes. Several indistinct dark transverse bars on the caudal peduncle. A deep black, often triangular, blotch at the root of the tail. Throat and belly dark orange, in young ♂♂ bright green-blue. Fins yellowish. Dorsal, and often the caudal too, with a deep black border; the former has a black band parallel to the outer edge. Eye golden.
♀ Transverse bars very distinct, their hinder edges silver. Caudal blotch only indistinct. No black border to the dorsal fin.

The name '*melanogaster*' (black belly) is given in allusion to the extraordinarily large pregnancy-mark, which persists after delivery and spreads over almost half the belly.

Care and breeding, as given on p. 556. Needs warmth and sunshine. This species develops its full colour only in well-planted, well-matured aquaria. Prolific. Brood-number in larger ♀♀ up to 80. 1933/+.

54 Sterba   573

Limia nicholsi *Myers* 1931 (Fig. 900) Nichols' Limia
Haiti, Dominican Republic near Bonao; ♂ to 4·5 cm., ♀ to 5·5 cm.
D 9; A 9; LL 27–28. Coloration according to Roloff (1940):–

♂ Ground-colour olive-yellow. Throat and some other parts of the body bright
  yellowish. Several dark, short transverse bars on the flanks, more or less blending with one another. Gonopodium sometimes black. Dorsal fin red-brown,
  bordered with black and with a black blotch on the upper leading-edge. Caudal
  fin yellowish; all other fins colourless.
♀ Unpretentious, sometimes with dark but not very conspicuous blotches on the
  dorsal and anal fins.

Care and breeding, as given on p. 556. Roloff states that always only a proportion of the ♂♂ are well-coloured, an observation which suggests further studies.
1938/–.

Limia nigrofasciata *Regan* 1913 (Fig. 754) Hump-back Limia
Black-barred Limia
Haiti; ♂ to 4·5 cm., ♀ to 6 cm.
D 10–11; A 9–10; P 13; LL 26–28. In the ♂ the shape of the body changes with
age, becoming increasingly deep and more strongly compressed; the back also becomes more strongly arched than in other species. The dorsal fin becomes greatly
enlarged and fan-like. In the ♀ the shape of the body shows no such changes.

♂ (Adult) Back bronze-green; flanks yellow, often with a metallic green glint;
  breast and belly (including the ventral fins and gonopodium) deep black. Several narrow black transverse bands on the flanks, reaching to the ridge of the
  back. Rays of dorsal fin black; caudal fin dark-edged.
♂ (Young) Back brown; flanks olive-brown to yellowish with indistinct grey
  transverse bands. Ventral fins and gonopodium grey.

Figs. 898–903
♂♂ on the left; sketches of corresponding ♀♀ on the right
Fig. 898. *Limia caudofasciata* (Steel-blue Limia); maximum size.
Fig. 899. *Limia heterandria* (Dwarf Limia); enlarged.
Fig. 900. *Limia nicholsi* (Nichols' Limia); somewhat enlarged.
Fig. 901. *Limia ornata* (Ornate Limia); slightly enlarged.
Fig. 902. *Limia vittata* (Cuban Limia); natural size.
Fig. 903. *Limia versicolor* (Olive Limia); slightly enlarged.

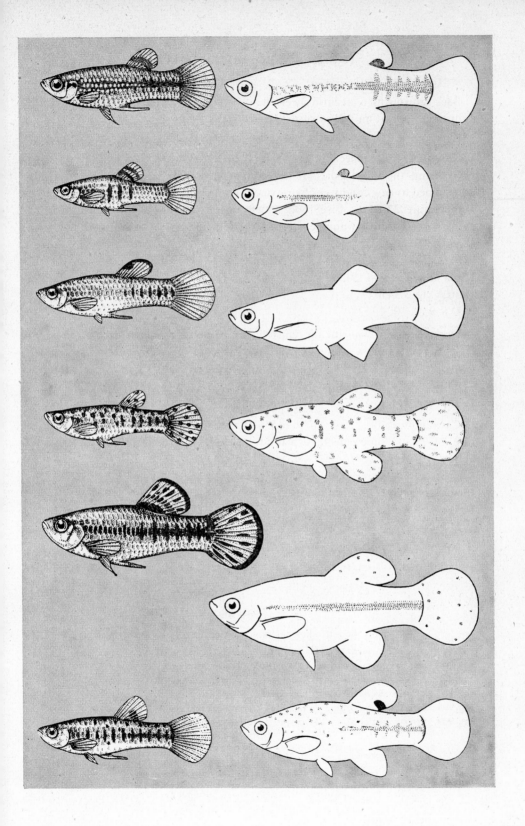

♀ Back brown with a greenish sheen; flanks olive; belly whitish. Transverse bands distinct. Dorsal fin yellowish with black spots.

Care and breeding, as given on p. 556; not exactly easy. This species is very sensitive and frail; especially great care is necessary when changing the water or transferring the older fishes. It is recommended that these fishes be gradually accustomed to new conditions by mixing the water over a period of days. Peaceful. Temperature 22–25°C. Live food, chiefly insect-larvae, but also algae. The ♀♀ easily miscarry. Brood-number up to 30. The young are already 10–12 mm. long at birth. 1912/+.

Limia ornata *Regan* 1913 (Fig. 901)   Ornate Limia
Haiti; ♂ to 3·5 cm., ♀ to 6 cm.
    D 8–9; A 10; LL 28.

♂ Dark yellow-brown with a greenish lustre; belly paler. Numerous blurred-edged spots and blotches scattered over the body and the pale vertical fins; on the middle of the body these markings may aggregate into transverse bars. Dorsal fin orange, sprinkled with dark markings.
♀ Similarly coloured, with a large anal fin.

Care and breeding, as given on p. 556. Warmth-loving and rather shy. Temperature 24–28°C. Supplementary plant food needed. Brood-number in larger ♀♀ about 30. 1912/–.

Limia versicolor (*Günther* 1866) (Fig. 903)   Olive Limia
Haiti; ♂ to 4 cm., ♀ to 6·5 cm.
    D 8–9; A 9–10; P 13; V 6; LL 26–28.

♂ Pale brown, with a greenish lustre; back darker; belly silvery-white. Numerous dark blotches; some indistinct transverse bars, especially on the caudal peduncle,

Figs. 904–909
♂♂ on the left; sketches of corresponding ♀♀ to the right
Fig. 904. *Girardinus metallicus* (Girardinus); maximum size.
Fig. 905. *Glaridichthys falcatus* (Yellow Belly); maximum size.
Fig. 906. *Heterophallus rachovi* (Rachow's Live-bearer); enlarged.
Fig. 907. *Lebistes melanzonus;* enlarged.
Fig. 908. *Micropoecilia branneri* (Branner's Live-bearer); adults, enlarged.
Fig. 909. *Micropoecilia parae* (Two-spot Live-bearer); adults, enlarged.

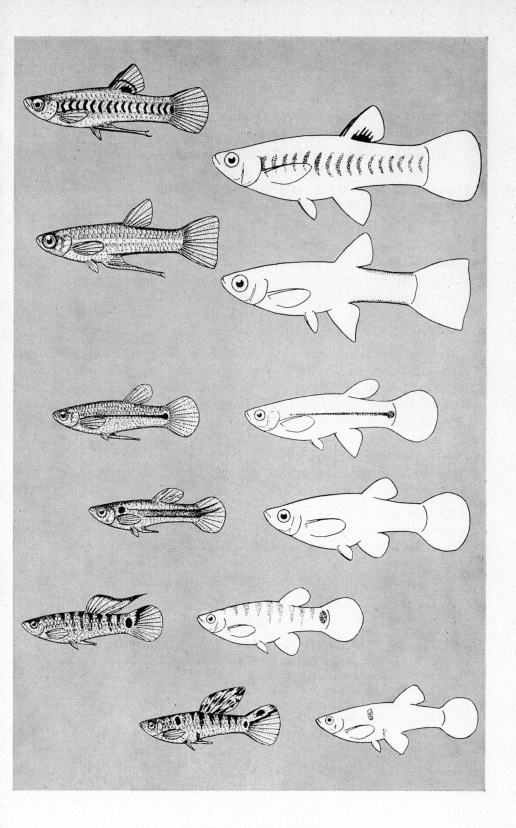

and a vague-edged dark blue band along the flanks. Fins delicate yellowish or brownish; dorsal fin with a black blotch at the base.

♀ Similarly coloured, with a large anal fin.

Care, breeding and other particulars, as for *L. caudofasciata* (see p. 572). 1913/ −.

Limia vittata (*Guichenot* 1853) (Fig. 902)   Cuban Limia
    D 9–11; A 10; P 13–14; V 6; LL 26–28.

♂ Back delicate yellow; flanks yellow; belly yellowish to pink. Both sexes have a bluish shimmer by reflected light. A usually indistinct dark band along the flanks and several narrow dark transverse bands which may be especially prominent on the caudal peduncle. Dorsal and caudal fins lemon-yellow, with irregularly arranged black blotches; often with a dark border.

♀ Unpretentiously coloured, without transverse bars. Dorsal and anal fins only yellowish, with a few small dark dots.

Care and breeding, as given on p. 556. Peaceful and warmth-loving, like most *Limia* spp. Temperature 23–26°C. Together with live food of all kinds *L. vittata* also takes dried foods and fresh plant food. This species is very hardy and also relatively resistant to water-changes and lowered temperatures. Large ♀♀ are exceedingly prolific and may produce up to 200 young at a birth. 1913/ −.

Micropoecilia branneri (*Eigenmann* 1894) (Fig. 908)   Branner's Live-bearer
Lower Amazon region, also in brackish water; ♂ to 2·5 cm., ♀ to 3 cm.
    D 6–7; A 8; P 13; V 6; LL 27–28.

♂ Back olive-green; flanks pale brown; belly silvery-white. The flanks show a pearly iridescence by reflected light. 6–8 dark transverse bands on the flanks. A conspicuous round, black, yellow-bordered blotch at the root of the tail. Vertical fins orange or yellow. Dorsal fin produced, flag-like.

♀ Rather more soberly coloured. Dorsal fin rounded.

Figs. 910–914

♂♂ on the left; sketches of the corresponding ♀♀ to the right

Fig. 910. *Mollienesia caucana* (South American Molly); adults, enlarged.
Fig. 911. *Mollienesia dominicensis* (Domingo Molly); maximum size.
Fig. 912. *Mollienesia elegans;* maximum size.
Fig. 913. *Mollienesia latipunctata;* maximum size.
Fig. 914. *Mollienesia sphenops* (Molly); adults, natural size.

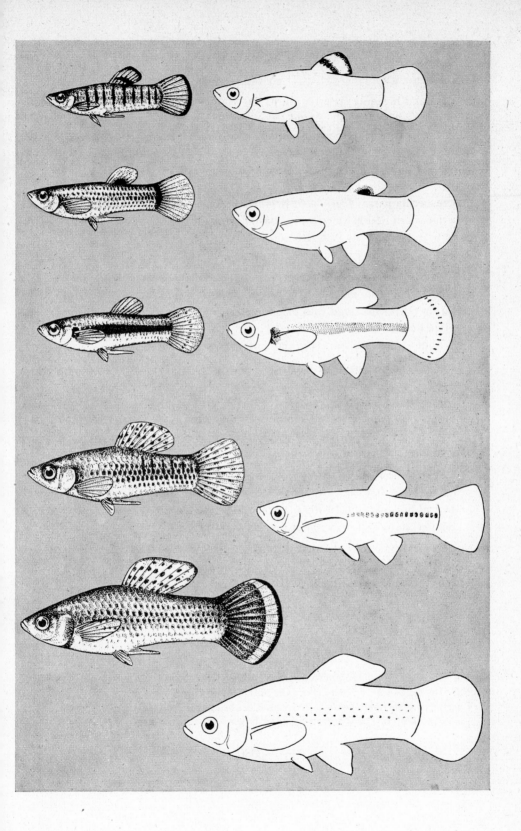

Care and breeding, as given on p. 556. Rather delicate. Temperature 24–26 °C. Common salt or sea-salt should be added (2–3 teaspoons to 10 litres of water). Supplementary algal food absolutely necessary. Pregnancy period lasts several days; total brood 10. Stunting observed in the first generation bred in captivity is probably caused by lack of plant nourishment. 1930/−.

Micropoecilia parae (*Eigenmann* 1894) (Fig. 909)   Two-spot Live-bearer
North-eastern South America, in coastal waters; ♂ to 2 cm., ♀ to 2·5 cm.
  D 6–7; A 8–9; P 13; V 6; LL 26–28.

♂ Delicate yellowish or greenish with a silvery gleam on the upperside and a violet to brown-red sheen, especially on the caudal peduncle. Belly pale. A dark, pale-bordered shoulder-blotch. Several dark transverse bars on the flanks. Dorsal fin fawn, checkered with black. A dark blotch on the caudal fin; upper edge often bright red.
♀ Without transverse bars. Fins colourless or yellowish.

Care, breeding and other particulars, as given for *M. branneri*. 1910/−.

Mollienesia caucana (*Steindachner* 1880) (Fig. 910)   South American Molly
South-east Panama, eastern Colombia; ♂ to 2·5 cm., ♀ to 6 cm.
  D 8; A 9; P 12; V 6; LL 26–27. Dorsal and anal fin-insertions opposite in ♀♀. Dorsal fin not enlarged to a sickle-shape.

♂ Orange-yellow, with a strong violet sheen on the flanks. Gill-cover brass-coloured to blue. 6–8 narrow, dark transverse bands on the flanks. Fins orange. Dorsal fin dark-edged with an arched blue band.
♀ Similar, more yellow, without distinct transverse bands.

Care and breeding of this lovely species, as given for *Mollienesia latipinna*. Warmth-loving. Temperature 22–25 °C. Brood small, 10–25, according to the age of the ♀♀. The parents attack the young fishes. 1906/−.

Plate 157

Fig. 915. *Crenicara maculata;* half-grown, somewhat enlarged. (Original)
Fig. 916. *Crenicichla lepidota* (Pike Cichlid); young, natural size. (Original)
Fig. 917. *Steatocranus casuarius* (African Blockhead); natural size; above ♂, below ♀. The hump on the forehead becomes larger with age. (Original)

Plate 157

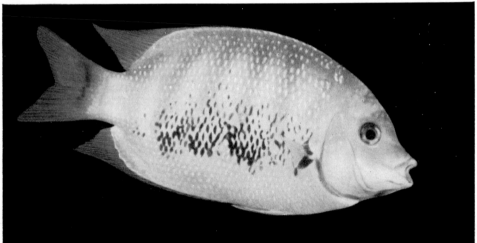

Plate 158

Plate 158

Fig.918. *Etroplus maculatus* (Orange Chromide); adult, natural size. (Original)
Fig.919. *Etroplus suratensis* (Green Chromide); 20 cm. specimen, in the Hellabrunn Aquarium, Munich. (Original)
Fig.920. *Geophagus brasiliensis* (Pearl Cichlid); 12 cm. ♂, in the Erfurt Aquarium. (Original)

Mollienesia dominicensis (*Evermann* and *Clark* 1906) (Fig.911)   Domingo Molly
Haiti, Dominican Republic; ♂ to 4 cm., ♀ to 6 cm.

D 8–9; A 10; LL 26–28. Coloration very dull.

♂ Dorsal fin not enlarged. Coloration (according to Roloff): matt olive-green, the back darker. Rows of glittering silver spots on the flanks, faint transverse stripes occasionally present. Fins colourless; the dorsal with a dark blotch outlined in pale red. Older ♂♂ also occasionally have a dark-coloured transverse stripe on the caudal peduncle.

Care, breeding and other particulars, as given for *Mollienésia latipinna*. A contented species. 1938/–.

Mollienesia elegans *Trewavas* 1948 (Fig.912)
Haiti, Dominican Republic near Jarabawa; ♂ to 4 cm., ♀ to 6 cm.

D 9; A 9; LL 28. Dorsal and anal fin-insertions opposite in ♀♀. Dorsal fin of ♂♂ not enlarged. Coloration (according to Roloff): –

♂ Ground-colour olive-yellow; throat and belly shining white. A dark blotch near the insertion of the pectoral fin. Behind this begins an intense black longitudinal band which gradually tapers towards the root of the tail. Fins colourless; dorsal and anal with a few dark spots. Eyes turquoise blue.
♀ Similarly coloured; longitudinal band less distinct and narrower.

Care, breeding and other particulars, as given for *M.latipinna*. Probably mainly herbivorous. Withstands very low temperatures. Brood-number small, about 25 according to Roloff. 1938/–.

Mollienesia latipinna *Le Sueur* 1821 (Figs.699, 921)   Sail-fin Molly
Eastern states of U.S.A., from Carolina to Yucatan, in coastal regions and near the mouths of rivers; to 12 cm. in the wild, 9 cm. in aquaria.

D 13–14; A 9–10; P 13; V 6; LL 26–28. Dorsal fin inserted well in front of the anal.

581

♂ Dorsal fin enlarged, sail-like. Back dark olive-green to brown. Flanks brownish above, pink or blue below, with a pearly iridescence and 5–6 longitudinal bands of red, blue and dark green spots. A few transverse bars are barely apparent. Throat and belly whitish. Dorsal fin pale blue, with rows of black spots and a yellow border. Centre of caudal fin bluish-grey, lower part blue, upper part orange-red spotted or with a pearly gleam.

♀ Coloration considerably duller; dorsal fin small.

Care and breeding, as given on p. 556. All *Mollienesia* spp. are warmth-loving; temperature 24–28°C. Large, richly-planted, sunny aquaria. Well-being usually considerably furthered by the addition of common salt, or better still sea-salt (1 teaspoon to 10 litres of water).

The finely-coloured varieties at least are best kept in an aquarium to themselves and furnished according to their natural needs, or in company with other *Mollienesia* species. Together with different kinds of animal-food all *Mollienesia* spp. require nourishing supplementary plant-food, such as algae, cooked and finely-shredded spinach, lettuce and softened oat-flakes. In the absence of such plant-food these fishes, especially the ♂♂, remain small and poorly-coloured. ♂♂ of the species with large, sail-like dorsal fins *(M.latipinna, M.velifera)* as a rule only develop this lovely embellishment when they are bred in spacious, heated open-air establishments; the enlargement of the dorsal then commences during the second year. Only small-finned ♂♂ are so far known to have been bred in indoor aquaria. Large ♀♀ are generally very prolific and can produce a brood of up to 120 youngsters at a time, these being already quite large (to 12 mm.) at birth. *Mollienesia latipinna* was first imported in 1903/+.

Among aquarists special importance is attached to the black-checkered and entirely black varieties generally known by the name of 'Black Molly'. One brood of these fishes commonly includes both all-black and checkered young, but a proportion of the latter subsequently develop into all-black individuals. Among the all-black strains the sail-finned ♂♂ are again especially prized, such fishes being velvet-black with iridescent pale yellow eyes and a dorsal fin beautifully edged with orange. The instructions for the care of the wild form are equally applicable to the Black Molly; unfortunately the trade is becoming increasingly saturated with indoor-bred fishes which lack the magnificent enlargement of the fins.

Mollienesia 'formosa' = *M.sphenops* × *M.latipinna* hybrid.

This natural hybrid is found in Mexico and Central America, where both the parent species occur together, and shows characteristics of both (Intermediate

582

Hybrid). Hubbs refers to the interesting fact that in certain districts only ♀ hybrids occur. The offspring from the back-cross between the hybrid and either parent species are again exclusively ♀♀ and again resemble the hybrid.

Coloration similar to that of *M. latipinna*, but rather duller, brownish; the pearly gleam on the flanks is much less obvious. Fins colourless. Dorsal fin occasionally marked with brown-red spots. Caudal fin possibly with a yellow inner border and dark edge. The checkers which appear off and on become quite black with increasing age. Both sexes grow to 8 cm.

Care, breeding and other particulars, as given on p. 556. 1904/−.

Mollienesia latipunctata (*Meek* 1904) (Fig. 913)
Southern Mexico; to 6 cm.
Shape similar to that of *M. sphenops*.

♂ Dorsal fin rather larger than in the ♀, but not sail-like. Olive-green to brownish, with a bluish-silver sheen on the flanks; underside paler. The scales, especially those underneath the dorsal ridge, are dark-edged. Sundry narrow, dark, transverse bands at about the level of the dorsal fin. Rows of orange-coloured spots along the lower half of the body. Fins delicate greenish to pale yellow, the dorsal and caudal being spotted with brown.

♀ Dorsal and anal fins inserted opposite one another. Coloration similar to that of the ♂, but with a row of black spots along the middle of the side. Fins usually without markings.

Care, breeding and other particulars, as given for *M. latipinna*. Brood-number small, usually less than 10, but the young are correspondingly larger at birth (to 15 mm.). 1934/−.

Mollienesia petensis (*Günther* 1866) (Fig. 928)
Guatemala; to 9 cm.
D 15–16; A 9–10; P 12; V 6; LL 28–30. Shape similar to that of the better-known *M. velifera*.

♂ Dorsal fin very large, sail-like. Brownish, with a strong bluish to silvery gleam on the flanks; back darker; belly pale brown to yellowish. Each scale on the flanks has a black spot, with a further shining green spot immediately in front of it; the spots together form several distinct longitudinal lines. Dorsal fin coloured rather like that of *M. latipinna*; caudal fin black, ventrally produced to a sword-like point.

583

♀ Dorsal fin relatively small, inserted somewhat in front of the anal. Coloration paler.

Care, breeding and other particulars, as given for *M. latipinna*. 1938/ —.

Mollienesia sphenops (*Cuvier* and *Valenciennes* 1846) (Figs. 699, 755)   Molly
From Mexico to Colombia (northern South America), in fresh and brackish waters; ♂ to 8 cm., ♀ to 12 cm.

D 8–11; A 8–10; P 14; V 6; LL 25–30. *M. sphenops* is among the finest species of the genus, even though the ♂♂ do not develop such large dorsal fins as *M. latipinna*, *M. petensis* or *M. velifera*. Coloration very variable, in relation to the wide distribution.

♂ Upperside dark blue-grey to brown-olive. The flanks display numerous iridescent bluish-silver to greenish spots on a bright olive to blue ground. The whole body is a shimmering light violet by reflected light. Underside very pale, delicate bluish or very light pink. Dorsal fin quite translucent, with numerous dark spots. Caudal fin a lovely ultramarine at the base, the outer part with a broad orange transverse band, edged with black.

♀ The dorsal fin begins somewhat in front of the anal and is smaller than in the ♂. Altogether more violet, to some extent with rows of rust-red spots on the flanks. Caudal fin lacking orange transverse bar.

Care, breeding and other particulars, as given for *M. latipinna*. 1909/ —.

This species also produces, among others, black-checkered to black varieties. A very brilliant colour-variety from Yucatan ('Liberty', see Fig. 699) is especially worth mentioning; it is mainly kept in America where, according to Innes, it has greatly degenerated through improper care and unwise crossing. The 'Black Molly' kept in Germany is probably derived from the stem-form *M. sphenops* (Fig. 771).

Mollienesia velifera *Regan* 1914 (Figs. 699, 757, 922)   Sail-fin Molly
Coastal districts and river-mouths of Yucatan; to 15 cm. in the wild, 12 cm. in aquaria.

D 18; A 9; P 14; V 6; LL 26–28. One of the most attractive live-bearing Tooth-Carps. The colouring somewhat resembles that of *M. latipinna*, but is considerably finer and more intense.

♂ Dorsal fin very large (the largest of any species). Dark olive to blue. Flanks blue-green, set with iridescent green-silver to pale blue spots above and below. Throat and belly bluish to greenish or orange. Several dark blue-green streaks on the flanks. 3–4 dark transverse bars at the level of the ventral fins. Roots of the dorsal and caudal fins bluish, outer parts bluish to grey with brilliant spots and streaks and a magnificent pearly lustre. Dorsal fin broad, orange. Caudal fin bordered with orange and black.

♀ Dorsal fin large, beginning well before the anal, but still smaller than in the ♂. Bluish-grey with rows of dark spots.

Care, breeding and other particulars, as given for *M. latipinna*, from which *M. velifera* is most certainly distinguished by its higher dorsal fin-ray count. A very good leaper; cover the aquarium! This species also produces numerous varieties. 1913/+.

Phallichthys amates (*Miller* 1907) (Figs. 748, 929)   Merry Widow
Atlantic slope of Guatemala; ♂ to 3 cm., ♀ to 5 cm.

D 13; A 9–10; P 13; V 6; LL 26–28. In shape *P. amates* somewhat resembles a ♀ Swordtail. Gonopodium very long, reaching almost to the caudal fin. Translucent delicate yellow-greenish throughout, with a bluish sheen on the flanks by reflected light. Occasionally an indistinct band along the middle of the side; a bold black vertical stripe across the eye.

♂ 10–12 fine dark transverse lines. Fins yellowish. Dorsal fin bright yellow at the base with an arched black band and a black margin which is very narrowly edged with white.

♀ Transverse lines absent.

Care and breeding, as given on p. 556. Temperature 22–24 °C. Dried food and plant-food in the form of algae. Brood-number in large ♀♀ to about 40. The parents vigorously pursue the young, otherwise a peaceful species and well-suited to the community tank. 1937/+.

Phallichthys pittieri (*Meek* 1912) (Fig. 930)   Orange-dorsal Live-bearer
Costa Rica, Panama; ♂ to 4 cm., ♀ to 8 cm.

D 9–10; A 10; P 11; V 6; LL 26–28. Similar to the previous species. Back shining yellow-green; flanks metallic pale blue by reflected light; breast and belly silver-white. The dark edges to the scales form a network over the body, especially over the back. Several dark transverse lines on the flanks, usually indistinct. Dorsal fin dark at the base, outer part yellowish with an orange border and a fine black edge. Ventral fins tipped with blue-white. Remaining fins delicate yellowish.

♀ without transverse lines.

585

Care and breeding, as given on p. 556. Warmth-loving; temperature 22–25 °C. Peaceful. Feeds chiefly on algae, also dried food. Brood-number of larger ♀♀ up to 100. Well-suited to the community tank. 1906/–.

Phalloceros caudomaculatus (*Hensel* 1868) (Fig. 747) Caudo, One-spot Live-bearer

Dusky Millions Fish

From Rio de Janeiro to Uruguay and Paraguay; ♂ to 2·5 cm., ♀ to 6 cm.

D 7–8; A 9–10; P 10; V 5; LL 28–30. Gonopodium deeply forked. Coloration of freshly-imported fishes:–

♂ Back olive-green; sides bright yellow; throat and belly yellowish. On the caudal peduncle, underneath the dorsal fin, there is a black, transverse comma-shaped blotch surrounded by a shining golden or silver patch. Fins yellowish; dorsal fin with a black border.

♀ Dorsal fin without black border.

Care and breeding, as given on p. 556. A very peaceful and easily satisfied species. Resistant to low temperatures and can be kept in unheated aquaria at 12–18 °C.; the best temperature, however, is 20–24 °C. Live and dried foods. Brood-number in larger ♀♀ about 80.

There are numerous varieties of this species. The best-known is the black-checkered form, *Phalloceros caudomaculatus reticulatus* Köhler, which occurs especially around Rio de Janeiro. This should be treated like the typical sub-species, but remains rather smaller and should not be kept at temperatures below 20 °C. Varieties without markings are also known. 1898/+.

Phalloptychus januarius (*Hensel* 1868) (Fig. 931)   Barred/Striped Millions Fish

South-eastern Brazil, La Plata; ♂ to 2·5 cm., ♀ to 3·5 cm.

D 9; A 9; P 10–11; V 5; LL 28–29. Altogether very translucent. Gonopodium very long.

♂ Back olive-brown; flanks delicate greenish to greenish-yellow, with a violet sheen and 8–12 very narrow transverse lines. Underside silvery to white. Fins

Figs. 921–922

Sketch of corresponding ♀ under the ♂ in each case

Fig. 921. *Mollienesia latipinna* (Sail-fin Molly); fine large specimens.

Fig. 922. *Mollienesia velifera* (Sail-fin Molly); fine large specimens.

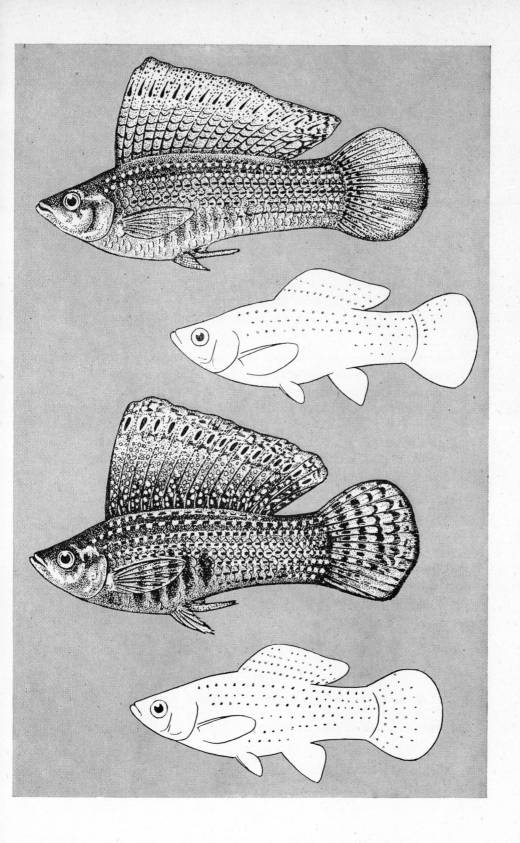

colourless, but often brownish at the base. Dorsal fin with numerous fine brown dots.

♀ Translucent yellowish; anal fin large.

Care and breeding rather difficult. Richly-planted aquaria, standing in not too bright a position. Temperature 21–25°C. The addition of common salt or sea-salt (1 teaspoon to 10 litres of water) is beneficial. Live foods and algae. The pregnancy period lasts for many days. Brood-number about 25. The young are very susceptible and often perish without any apparent reason a few days after birth. This species is readily kept in company with other tiny species (see also p. 556). 1907/–.

Poecilia vivipara *Bloch* and *Schneider* 1801 (Fig. 945) One-spot Live-brearer
From Venezuela to the La Plata Basin, Puerto Rico; ♂ to 4 cm., ♀ to 7·5 cm.

D 8–10; A 7–8; P 13–14; V 6; LL 25–27. As regards shape this species is rather like a slim Platy.

♂ Fawn-grey to yellowish, with a silver sheen on the flanks; back darker; underside silvery-white. A black shoulder-blotch surrounded by a shining golden patch underneath the anterior edge of the dorsal fin. Narrow dark transverse bands, usually distinct only on the caudal peduncle. Dorsal fin of older ♂♂ bright orange at the base, outer parts pale yellow bordered with black; usually a bold dark band across the middle of the fin. All other fins colourless. A colour-variety with black-red-white dorsal fins has been imported from the R. Amazon.

♀ More soberly coloured. Dorsal fin yellowish at the most.

Care and breeding, as given on p. 556. Warmth-loving; temperature 23–25°C., otherwise undemanding. Brood-number in larger ♀♀ about 150. A peaceful species, well-suited to the community aquarium. 1904/–.

Poecilistes pleurospilus (*Günther* 1866) (Fig. 946) Porthole Fish
Atlantic and Pacific slopes of Mexico and Guatemala; ♂ to 3 cm., ♀ to 5 cm.

D 8; A 8–10; P 12–14; V 6; LL 26–29. This species is rather elongate.

Plate 159

Fig. 923. *Pterophyllum eimekei* (Angelfish); longfinned mutation or so-called Veiltail Angel, reduced. (Original)
Fig. 924. Young Veiltail Angels. (Original)

Plate 159

Plate 160

Plate 160

Fig. 925. *Pterophyllum eimekei* (Angelfish); black mutation, the so-called 'Black Angel'; adult, somewhat reduced. (Original)
Fig. 926. *Aequidens pulcher* (Blue Acara); adult, somewhat reduced. (Original)

♂ Fawn, often with a greenish lustre; back darker; underside silvery. A longitudinal row of large dark blotches on the flanks, often elongated into transverse bars. Fins brownish. Dorsal and anal fins in fine specimens with a dark border, the anal often also with rows of spots.
♀ Coloration similar; anal fin large.

Care and breeding, as given on p. 556. Warmth-loving; temperature 22–24°C., but otherwise an undemanding species which breeds readily and does not molest its young. Omnivorous. 1913/–.

Poeciliopsis turrubarensis (*Meek* 1912) (Fig. 947)
North-western Colombia and western Central America; ♂ to 4 cm., ♀ to 8 cm.
D 8; A 8–9; LL 27–29. Shape similar to that of the Platies.

♂ Pale brown to clay-yellow, slightly translucent, with a greenish lustre on the flanks and 6–7 narrow dark brown transverse bands. Back darker. Belly pale yellow to white. Fins colourless, occasionally yellow in old ♂♂.
♀ Similarly coloured; anal fin large.

Care and breeding, as given on p. 556. Warmth-loving; temperature 23–25°C. Brood-number of larger ♀♀ to about 40. Suitable for the community aquarium. 1939/–.

Priapella bonita (*Meek* 1904) (Fig. 948)
Mexico, Rio Papaloapam; ♂ to 4 cm., ♀ to 6 cm.
D 7–9; A 9–10; LL 30–32.

♂ Grey-green to smoke-grey, with a greenish sheen and a dark longitudinal band along the side extending from the tip of the snout to the root of the tail. Back very dark; belly whitish. Fins yellowish. Dorsal and anal fins with rows of dark spots, and with brownish edges in old ♂♂.
♀ Coloration similar; anal fin large.

Care and breeding, as given on p. 556. Peaceful. Temperature 20–23°C. Brood-number of larger ♀♀ about 35. 1935/–.

56 Sterba

Pseudoxiphophorus bimaculatus (*Heckel* 1848) (Fig. 950)   Two-spot Live-bearer
Southern Mexico, Guatemala, Honduras; ♂ to 4·5 cm., ♀ to 9 cm.

D 13–17; A 9–11; P 15; V 6; LL 30–32. Lower edge of caudal fin in ♂♂ briefly produced, not as long as a proper sword-tail. Very variable in form and colour, with numerous local races.

♂ Back brownish-olive; flanks yellowish-green; belly yellowish-white. Owing to the pattern created by the dark edges of the scales the body appears to be covered by a dark network. Flanks metallic green by reflected light. Gill-cover shining bluish-green with an orange blotch. A vague black blotch over the pectoral insertion; a very bold one at the root of the tail. Dorsal fin yellowish-green marked with very attractive spots and streaks. The other fins are colourless, but the anal has a yellowish base, and the caudal a red border below. The coloration here described is chiefly found in fishes from the lowland regions of the distribution; populations in the higher regions are usually more soberly coloured.

♀ No red border to the lower edge of the caudal fin; base of anal yellow-green.

Care and breeding, as given on p. 556. A very hardy, predatory species, not suitable for the community aquarium. Brood-number in larger ♀♀ up to 160. The young are quite 16 mm. long at birth. 1909/+.

Quintana atrizona *Hubbs* 1934 (Fig. 949)   Black-barred Live-bearer
Cuba, near Havana and Baracoa; ♂ to 2·5 cm., ♀ to 4 cm.

D 8–9; A 10; P 8–9; V 7; LL 27–29. Body thick-set, strongly compressed, translucent to transparent.

♂ Yellowish-green, with a bluish sheen by reflected light. 7–8 irregular transverse bars on the flanks, more or less distinctly contrasted. Fins colourless. Dorsal fin with a dark blotch at the base and a black leading-edge. Caudal fin yellowish.

♀ Coloration similar; anal fin with a dark leading-edge.

Care and breeding, as given on p. 556. A very beautiful species. Warmth-loving; temperature 23–28 °C. Live food and algae. Peaceful; the adults only disturb the young when short of food. Brood-number of larger ♀♀ to about 40. 1935/−.

Xiphophorus helleri *Heckel* 1848 (Figs. 699, 700, 756, 927)   Swordtail
Atlantic slope of southern Mexico, Guatemala; ♂ (less sword) to 8 cm., ♀ to 12 cm.

D 11–14; A 8–10; P 12–13; V 6; LL 26–30. One of the most popular aquarium fishes.

♂ Lower rays of caudal fin very strongly produced. Back olive-green; flanks green-yellowish; belly yellowish. Has a greenish to bluish lustre by reflected light. From the tip of the snout, across the eye, to the root of the tail there extends a dark violet or purple to cinnabar zig-zag band, accompanied above and below by a narrow brilliant greenish zone which is further delimited by a more or less distinct carmine-red line. The scales are edged with delicate brown, so that the whole fish appears thereby to be covered with a delicate net. Fins yellow-greenish. Dorsal fin with fine red to brownish streaks and blotches. Sword orange-yellow, edged with black above and below, the lower border being continued forward along the caudal peduncle.

♀ Upper edge of dorsal fin rounded; no sword.

Xiphophorus undergoes a quite remarkable and always astonishing sex-reversal. One often observes that a good Swordtail female, which has already given birth to numerous families, gradually loses her dark pregnancy-mark while at the same time the whole shape of her body begins to alter. Careful observation reveals that the whole female anal fin becomes transformed into that of a male, complete with gonopodium, that the lower caudal fin-rays become lengthened and the whole body becomes slimmer and typically male. This period of transformation usually lasts quite a long time; at the end of it there results a typical male which is fully-functional as such and capable of mating with a female just like any other male.

Such a peculiar occurrence is far from infrequent among Swordtails; in certain strains 30% of the ♀♀ in a brood eventually change into ♂♂. Sex-reversal does occasionally occur in the Guppy, too, and, very rarely, in the Paradisefishes (*Macropodus* spp.).

This apparent bisexuality arises in the following manner, The young fish is sexually indifferent; that is to say, it contains the potentialities of both sexes. Certain influences tip its development towards one sex or the other while not at the same time eliminating the latent potentiality of the opposite sex. The developing ovary of the future ♀, working through hormones which it secretes itself, invests the body with the characteristics of a typical ♀. Through processes which are not yet quite clear the hormone production of the ovary may then decrease or entirely fail. The consequence of this is that the male potentiality, formerly inhibited, now begins to obtrude itself and the ♀ gradually changes to a ♂ whose testes supplant the former ovary. No reverse transformation from ♂ to ♀ has been observed.

Care and breeding, as given on p. 556. Very peaceful, hardy and lively, though the ♂♂ are quarrelsome among themselves. Temperature 22–25°C.; can be lower for short periods. Omnivorous, preferring live foods but also accepting dried food.

591

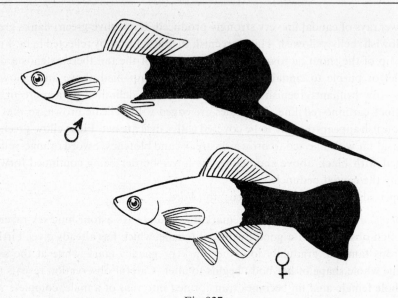

Fig. 927
A new domesticated strain of Swordtail. The fishes are red anteriorly and black posteriorly.

Brood-number of larger ♀♀ up to 180. The species is very variable and can be crossed with other species, attributes which have led to the production of numerous cultivated strains. Some of the best known are:–Red Swordtail (Hybrid: green *X. helleri* × red *X. maculatus*); Green Wagtail Swordtail (Hybrid: green *X. helleri* × Wagtail Platy); and the Yellow Swordtail (a partly albino mutation).

All the artificially-produced strains and hybrid crosses need to be kept at a slightly higher temperature than the wild form. See also Fig. 699.

X. helleri was first imported in 1909.

Figs. 928–931

♂♂ on the left; sketches of corresponding ♀♀ to the right

Fig. 928. *Mollienesia petensis;* adults, enlarged.
Fig. 929. *Phallichthys amates* (Merry Widow); somewhat enlarged.
Fig. 930. *Phallichthys pittieri* (Orange-dorsal Live-bearer); maximum size.
Fig. 931. *Phalloptychus januaris* (Barred/Striped Millions Fish); adult, enlarged.

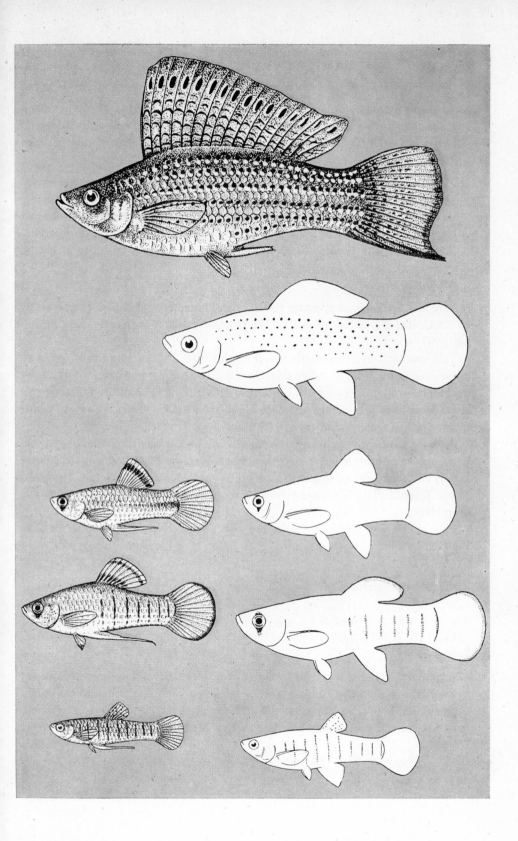

Xiphophorus maculatus (*Günther* 1866) (Figs. 699, 760, 761, 771)   Platy
Atlantic slope of Mexico and Guatemala; ♂ to 4 cm., ♀ to 6 cm.

D 10; A 8–9; P 10–11; V 6; LL 25–27. Shape similar to that of the previous species, but the ♂♂ have a rounded caudal fin. Wild form:–

♂ Nape and back brownish-olive to dark olive; flanks with a bluish to blue sheen by reflected light. Throat and belly whitish, with the edge of the belly gleaming greenish to yellowish. Two round black blotches on the caudal peduncle. A blackish shoulder-blotch is often present. Fins almost colourless, transparent. Pectoral fins with bluish tips. Caudal and anal fins with a bluish to greenish-white band.

♀ All fins colourless.

Care and breeding, as given on p. 556. Very contented and hardy. Temperature 20–25°C. Brood-number up to 100. The young are usually born early in the morning. 1907/+.

This species is extraordinarily variable, and black-checkered and red varieties occur even in the wild. Through suitable selective-breeding numerous other varieties can be produced. Two favourite forms are the 'Golden' and 'Red' Platies, the latter being known in orange and deep blood-red varieties; fishes with ivory-white tips to the fins are especially prized. (Fig. 699)

Another group of varieties are the various colour-forms of the 'Wagtail Platies'. Gordon obtained this lovely variety through crossing the wild Platy with the golden variety and after prolonged and exacting breeding succeeded in fixing it. The body of the Wagtail Platy is orange-yellow or red and the dorsal and caudal fins are deep black.

Pure yellow and all-black Platies are also known, and many others; see also Fig. 699.

Xiphophorus montezumae *Jordan* and *Snyder* 1900 (Fig. 762)

Montezuma Swordtail

Southern Mexico; ♂ to 5·5 cm., ♀ to 7 cm.

D 11–13; A 6–8; P 12; V 6; LL 27–29. Body more thick-set than in *X. helleri*. Sword short.

♂ Back dark olive-brown; flanks olive-brown to greenish; belly brownish-white. From the eye to the root of the tail extends a chain-like longitudinal band, pale-edged above, which, especially at the level of the dorsal fin, is intersected by several indistinct transverse bands. Dorsal fin very large, yellowish-green with brownish blotches and streaks. Caudal fin pale yellow; sword sea-green, with dark edges.

♀ No transverse bands. Dorsal fin yellowish, without markings. No sword.

Care and breeding, as given for *X. helleri*. This species, too, is often crossed with others of the same genus. Suitable for the community aquarium. 1913/+.

Xiphophorus variatus (*Meek* 1904) (Fig. 699)   Variegated Platy
Southern Mexico; ♂ to 5·5 cm., ♀ to 7 cm.

D 10–11; A 8–9; P 12; V 6; LL 25. Another species which is very variable in shape and colouring. The following is the variety which is most commonly met with in Central Europe:–

♂ Back brown-yellow; gill-cover and anterior part of flanks yellowish-green; hinder half of body, especially the caudal peduncle, bluish to blue-greenish; throat and underside orange. The flanks are sprinkled with numerous black to brownish spots which may combine to form an irregular band of spots along the middle of the side. Usually 3–4 indistinct transverse bands over the ventral fins. Sometimes two deep black blotches at the root of the tail. A curious peculiarity of this species is that the 'pregnancy-mark' is also present in the ♂, lying just behind the gonopodium, but not in any way related to the breeding cycle. Dorsal fin reddish at the base, outer parts with brown spots and streaks, border black. Caudal fin yellowish to reddish; remaining fins yellow-greenish.

♀ Olive-green or brownish-grey, with two rows of zig-zag lines on the flanks.

Care, breeding and other particulars, as given for *X. maculatus*. An especially beautiful species which, again, has numerous different strains some of which are extraordinarily attractively coloured (see also Fig. 699). 1931/+.

Recently *Xiphophorus xiphidium* Hubbs and Gordon has been imported. (Figs. 758, 759)

Family Goodeidae

The Family *Goodeidae* are confined to Central Mexico and are especially interesting for the peculiarities in their reproductive biology. The *Goodeidae* are live-bearers, like many other Tooth-Carps, but exhibit a vital difference in that the gonopodium is not constructed from specialised anal fin-rays as in

595

the other genera, but is formed from the anterior part of the fin which is delimited by a notch. The first 6(–8) fin-rays are reduced, simplified and very tightly crowded together; in some species the gonopodium is at least partly sheathed by a ring-fold (see also p. 553). The development of the embryo does not take place in the ovarian cavity, as in many other live-bearers, but in a specially modified section of the oviduct. The eggs are rather poor in yolk. Storage of sperm does not occur and a fresh sex-act is necessary for the fertilisation of each succeeding batch of eggs. The lack of yolk in the eggs necessitates nourishment of the developing embryos by the mother, as in the mammals, and cord-like embryonal appendages (Trophotaenia) are accordingly developed for the purposes of food-transport and gaseous exchange. The embryos are born without egg-membranes. The *Goodeidae* are thus truly viviparous fishes (see also p. 554).

The care and breeding of these interesting, but also very delicate, fishes has not been very successfully managed so far, quite apart from the fact that living specimens have seldom been imported into Europe. Their natural habitat is in stony upland streams and lakes which support very little vegetation and almost dry out during the dry season but during the rainy season become transformed into torrential rivers.

Plate 161

Fig. 932. *Tilapia nilotica* (Nile Mouth-brooder); 15 cm. specimen in the Hellabrunn Aquarium, Munich. (Original)
Fig. 933. *Tilapia tholloni* (Thollon's Cichlid/Mouth-brooder); 12 cm. specimen in the Hellabrunn Aquarium, Munich. (Original)
Fig. 934. *Tilapia mossambica* (Mozambique Cichlid/Mouth-brooder); adult ♂ at the beginning of the breeding season. (Original)

Plate 162 (overleaf)

Fig. 935. *Tilapia* sp.; 15 cm. specimen in the Hellabrunn Aquarium, Munich. (Original)
Fig. 936. *Tilapia heudeloti* (Senegal Cichlid/Mouth-brooder); adult ♀ in breeding dress, in the Hellabrunn Aquarium, Munich. (Original)
Fig. 937. *Tilapia* sp.; adult ♂ in breeding dress, in the Hellabrunn Aquarium, Munich. (Original)

596

Plate 161

Plate 162 (see page 596)

Plate 163 (see page 597)

Plate 164

Plate 163 (overleaf)

Fig. 938. *Tilapia heudeloti* (Senegal Cichlid/Mouth-brooder); ♂ and ♀ (left) in the nesting hole; reduced. In the Hellabrunn Aquarium, Munich. (Original)

Fig. 939. *Tilapia lepidura* (Pearly Cichlid/Mouth-brooder); ♀ in breeding dress; reduced. In the Hellabrunn Aquarium, Munich. (Original)

Fig. 940. *Tilapia lepidura;* ♂ in breeding dress. (Original)

Plate 164

Fig. 941. *Stigmatogobius hoeveni* (Celebes Goby); maximum size; left ♂, right ♀. (Original)

Fig. 942. *Brachygobius xanthozona* (Bumblebee Fish); maximum size. The fishes illustrated are atypical in markings (see Fig. 1139). (Original)

Fig. 943. *Stigmatogobius sadanundio;* maximum size. (Original)

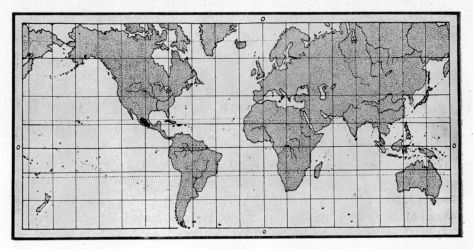

Fig. 944
Distribution of the *Goodeidae;* note Mexico.

Goodea gracilis *Hubbs* and *Turner* 1939 (Fig. 957)
Tributaries of the upper Rio Panuco; to 9 cm.

Body rather elongate, robust; caudal peduncle strongly compressed. Fins small. Intestine very long (4 times as long as the body), repeatedly coiled.

♂ Olive-coloured with shining fawn to bluish zones, especially on the caudal peduncle. Underside yellowish. Scales dark-edged, with brown blotches in older fishes. Medium sized fishes have a dark lateral band, increasingly distinct to-

wards the tail, extending from the hinder end of the gill-cover to the root of the tail. Fins yellowish or quite colourless, often dark in sexually mature fishes.
♀ Coloration similar; anal fin undifferentiated.

Care: large, moderately planted aquaria, standing in not too dark a situation. Undemanding as regards water-conditions but needs periodic additions of fresh water. Preferred temperature 22–24°C.; resistant to cooling. Feed well; plant material as well as live food. Peaceful. Brood-number in larger ♀♀ about 20. The young are already about 20 mm. long at birth and grow rapidly. 1936/–.

Lermichthys multiradiatus (*Meek* 1904) (Fig. 959)
Rio Lerma basin; to 6 cm.

D 26–30; A 26–30; LL 42–47. Body elongate, compressed. Dorsal and anal fins very long-based.

♂ Dorsal fin larger than in the ♀. Delicate brownish with a green lustre on the flanks. Back darker to fawn; underside whitish. Numerous dark blotches with blurred edges on the flanks; these may combine to form irregular transverse bars. Fins delicate yellow-green, the vertical fins with dark edges. According to Rachow older ♂♂ are often entirely dark.
♀ Dorsal fin smaller than in the ♂; vertical fins without dark edges; blotches more sparsely distributed.

Care, as given for *Goodea gracilis*. Probably not yet bred in captivity. 1934/–.

Neotoca bilineata (*Bean* 1887) (Fig. 958)
Central Mexico (Rio Lerma basin); ♂ to 3·5 cm., ♀ to 5 cm.

D 13–15; A 23–24; P 15–16; V 6; LL 29–33. As regards body-form this species is rather like a ♀ Guppy. The first 6 anal fin-rays in the ♂♂ are separated from the remainder by a notch and form a small lobe (the gonopodium) in front of the anal fin.

Figs. 945–950

♂♂ on the left; sketches of corresponding ♀♀ to the right

Fig. 945. *Poecilia vivipara* (One-spot Live-bearer); maximum size.
Fig. 946. *Poecilistes pleurospilus* (Porthole Fish); maximum size.
Fig. 947. *Poeciliopsis turrubarensis;* natural size.
Fig. 948. *Priapella bonita;* very slightly reduced.
Fig. 949. *Quintana atrizona* (Black-barred Live-bearer); adults, somewhat enlarged.
Fig. 950. *Pseudoxiphophorus bimaculatus* (Two-spot Live-bearer); somewhat enlarged.

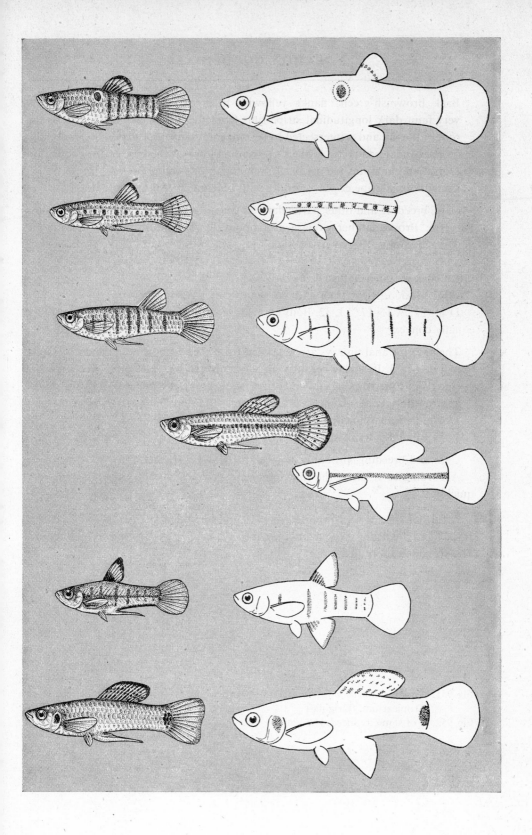

♂ Back brownish-green; flanks yellowish to greenish; belly yellowish-grey. A very faint dark longitudinal stripe runs from the mouth, across the eye, to the root of the tail and is intersected by several short dark transverse bars, especially on the caudal peduncle. A black crescentic blotch at the base of the caudal fin. Dorsal and anal fins almost black; remaining fins colourless.

♀ Longitudinal stripe edged ventrally with blue-green. All fins colourless.

Care, breeding and other particulars, as given for *Goodea gracilis*. Omnivorous. Peaceful. Brood-number of larger ♀♀ about 30. The adults seldom disturb the very small young. 1935/−.

Ollentodon multipunctatus (*Pellegrin* 1901) (Fig. 960)
Central Mexico, Rio Lerma and Santiago; ♂ to 5·5 cm., ♀ to 6 cm.

D 15–17; A 15–17; LL 32. Body elongate, compressed; upper and lower profiles equally convex.

♂ The anterior anal fin-rays are separated from the rest by a notch and enveloped in a ring-fold. Pale clay-colour with a greenish sheen. Back olive-green; underside pale. Fine rows of indistinct dark spots along the upper part of the flanks and on the caudal peduncle. A dark blotch often present at the root of the tail. Dorsal and anal fins delicate fawn, edged with green-yellow.

♀ Longitudinal rows of spots stronger and always clearly apparent.

Care and breeding, probably as given for *Goodea gracilis*. 1939/−.

According to Rachow the four imported species mentioned above perish very quickly.

A further species was imported in 1914 and identified as *Characodon encaustus* Jordan and Snyder by Arnold, but described as *Chapalichthys encaustus* by Rachow. The specimen soon died.

Plate 165

Fig. 951. *Symphysodon aequifasciata axelrodi* (Brown Discus); ♂, reduced. In the Frankfurt Tropicarium. (Original)
Fig. 952. ♀ of same, reduced. (Original)

Plate 165

Plate 166

Plate 166

Fig. 953. (above, left) *Scatophagus argus* (Scat); half-grown fishes, reduced. (Original)
Fig. 954. (above, right) *Pterophyllum scalare* (Angelfish); adult, reduced. (Original)
Fig. 955. *Cichlasoma severum* (Banded Cichlid); adult, reduced. The specimen figured is
paler in tone than the usual form. (Original)

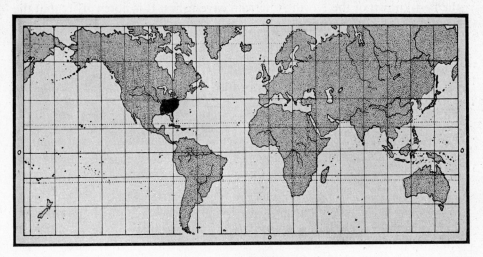

Fig. 956
Distribution of the *Amblyopsidae*

Family Amblyopsidae

Small, Tooth-Carp-like freshwater fishes from southern North America,
belonging to the Order *Microcyprini*, which live to some extent in subterranean waters and have lost their sight. All the species are elongate and spindle-
shaped, only slightly compressed or compressed only in the hinder region of
the body. Head scaleless. Mouth large. The lower jaw usually projects. Jaws
and bones of the palate toothed. Ventral fins small or absent. Dorsal fin
inserted about opposite the anal. Scales cycloid, irregularly arranged. No
lateral line. The *Amblyopsidae* are ovoviviparous like many genera of the
Cyprinodontidae, that is to say, the eggs are retained within the body of the
mother until the embryos are fully developed and the young emerge from the

57a Sterba

egg-membranes immediately after the eggs are laid. The stem-form of the cave-dwelling species must have been a *Chologaster*-like ancestor, possessing ventral fins and functional eyes and living in a variety of surface waters. The most highly-specialised member of the group is *Amblyopsis spelaeus*, the best-known of the North American cave-fishes. It is noteworthy that the embryos of this species, like those of many other blind fishes, develop almost normal eye-rudiments. Despite the lack of eyes these fishes are well able to orientate themselves, probably through the sense of touch developed in the very numerous sensory papillae embedded in folds of the naked skin on the crown of the head.

Amblyopsis spelaeus *De Kay* 1842 (Fig. 982)   Blindfish
Subterranean waters of North America, not infrequent; occasionally also in springs. The best-known locality is Mammoth Cave, Kentucky. To 13 cm.

D 9; A 8–9; P 11; V 4. Body elongate, spindle-shaped. Ventral fins very small. Eyes very much reduced, unpigmented, deeply embedded in the skin. Numerous sensory papillae (vibration receptors) on the head and body. Delicate translucent yellowish to faint flesh-colour.

♀ (according to Arnold) considerably more robust.

Care in aquaria not difficult; the fishes are very tenacious of life and eat almost any food. Temperature 12–16°C. They are best kept in large-surfaced aquaria with a sandy bottom and neither plants nor direct sunlight. It is essential that the aquarium be kept in a quiet undisturbed position, since fishes equipped with a heightened sense of touch react to the slightest vibration and often dash about madly in all directions.

The specimens imported into Germany in 1899 and 1935 unfortunately perished after a short time. Very probably the fishes were damaged in transit for the reason just given.

Figs. 957–960

♂♂ on the left; sketches of corresponding ♀♀ to the right

Fig. 957. *Goodea gracilis;* adults, natural size.
Fig. 958. *Neotoca bilineata;* somewhat enlarged.
Fig. 959. *Lermichthys multiradiatus;* adults, somewhat enlarged.
Fig. 960. *Ollentodon multipunctatus;* somewhat enlarged.

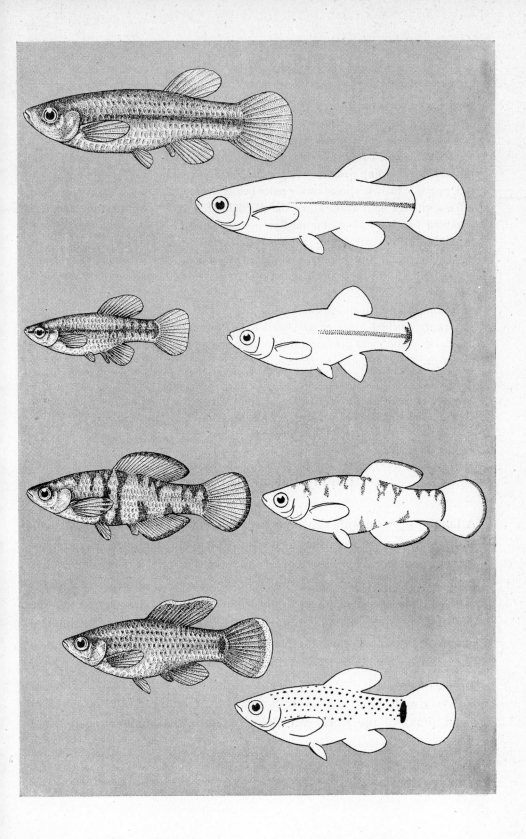

Chologaster cornutus *Agassiz* 1853 (Fig. 981)
Ditches, small ponds, shallows of larger rivers of the southern States of U.S.A., and occasionally in brackish waters; to 15 cm.

D 8–9; A 8–9; LL 60–62. Body spindle-shaped; caudal peduncle slightly compressed. Ventral fins absent. Eyes normal and functional.

Upperside brown, considerably paler below the middle of the body. Belly white, often sprinkled with dark. Three sharply delimited and very prominent dark longitudinal bands, of which the median one commences on the snout and extends to the root of the tail while the lowest occasionally breaks up into a row of spots beyond the middle of the body. Fins grey. Dorsal fin often spotted. Caudal fin with a dark blotch at the base, a pale centre often with two white blotches, and very dark outer parts.

No information available concerning care and breeding. This species is probably very easily satisfied, however, and likely to be quite easy to keep. Keep its aquarium in a dark position and provide a soft bottom-soil and suitable hiding-places among pieces of wood and stones. Worms, insect-larvae and small crustacea should be acceptable as food. 1934/–.

Another well-known North American blind fish is *Typhlichthys subterraneus* Girard 1859 which, however, has not yet been imported into Europe.

Family Belonidae (Garfishes)

A family of world-wide distribution, belonging to the order *Synentognathi* and mainly comprising fishes of coastal waters and the open sea, some of them of quite considerable size. Only a few species ascend rivers or even live permanently in brackish water. The following are some of the characteristics of the family: a very elongate, only slightly compressed body; a beak-like development of the strongly-toothed upper and lower jaws; dorsal and anal fins inserted opposite one another and very far back; pectoral and ventral fins relatively small; scales very small and to some extent irregular in their arrangement.

A very well-known species in Europe is the Garpike, *Belone belone* (Linnaeus 1758), of the North Sea, Baltic, Atlantic and Mediterranean, a fish which grows to 1 m. in length and is remarkable for the peculiar green colour of its bones.

Xenetodon cancila (*Hamilton-Buchanan* 1822) (Fig. 962)
Throughout India, Ceylon, Burma, Thailand and the Malay Peninsula; to 30 cm.
D 15–18; A 16–18; P 11; V 6; LL over 250. Body-form as given in the family description.

Dorsal and anal fins in ♂♂ deeply emarginate; caudal fin squarely truncated. Upperside dark grey-green; flanks green-silver; underside white, the throat often yellowish. A shining stripe along the whole length of the body, from the tip of the snout to the caudal fin; the anterior part of this stripe is usually tinged with rust-red and the whole stripe often edged with a fine dark line. Upper half of the body, as a rule, finely spotted with black.

♂ Dorsal and anal fins dark-edged.

An elegant surface-living fish, suitable for large public aquaria. Not choosy over food; large individuals prefer fishes and frogs. An accomplished leaper which can jump almost vertically. Temperature 22–26 °C. 1910/ − .

Potamoraphis guianensis (*Schomburgk* 1843)
A single specimen was imported from the Amazon in 1935 and described by Arnold and Ahl. The species needs similar treatment to the previous one. Description, according to Arnold:–the body is very elongate, spindle-shaped. Mouth deeply cleft; jaws provided with needle-sharp teeth. Coloration: upperside grey-green, sometimes with faint dark marbling. A broad, irregular black band extends from the tip of the snout, across the eye, to the root of the tail. Underside yellowish-white. Fins colourless, transparent.

In 1945 several further representatives of this family were imported from South-east Asia.

Family Hemiramphidae (Halfbeaks)

Fishes belonging to the order *Synentognathi*, with a world-wide distribution, mainly living in the sea and in brackish water, and usually having a produced lower jaw. A few species live in fresh water. Head usually elongate, almost

605

round in transverse section or only slightly compressed. The maxillary and premaxillary are almost fused with one another and movable about the cranium. Lower jaw fixed, very greatly produced (Fig. 961). Fins relatively small; dorsal and anal fins inserted well back. Some species are live-bearers; in these a part of the anal fin is modified as an intromittent organ.

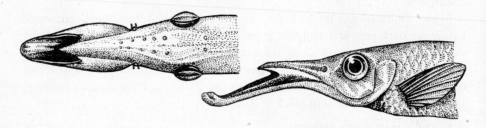

Fig. 961

Dorsal and lateral views of the head of *Dermogenys*, showing the peculiar extension of the mouth in the protruded position

Of this family of many species only members of the genus *Dermogenys* have so far been imported. This genus is chiefly distinguished by the insertion of the dorsal fin being a short distance behind that of the anal.

Dermogenys pusillus *von Hasselt* 1823 (Figs. 763, 961)
Thailand, Malay Peninsula, Singapore, Greater Sunda Islands, in fresh and brackish waters; ♂ to 6 cm., ♀ to 7 cm.
   D III/7–9; A I/12–15; P I/9–11; V 6; LL 45–50. Body elongate, only slightly compressed. Lower jaw almost twice as long as the fused upper jaw. The anterior,

Figs. 962–966

Fig. 962. *Xenetodon cancila;* adult ♂, greatly reduced.
Fig. 963. *Hemirhamphodon pogonognathus;* adult, reduced.
Fig. 964. *Microphis brachyurus;* adult, reduced.
Fig. 965. *Syngnathus pulchellus;* somewhat reduced.
Fig. 966. *Nerophis ophidion* (Straight-nosed Pipe-fish); somewhat reduced.

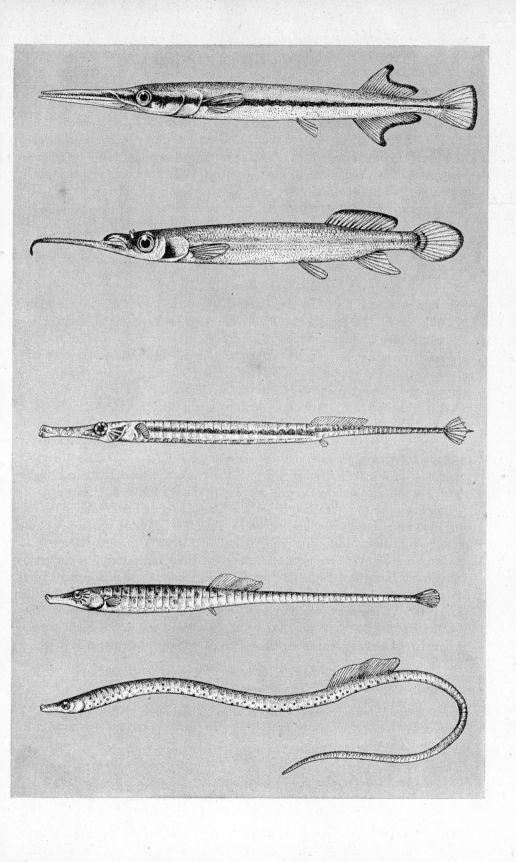

inferior part of the anal fin in the ♂ is modified as an intromittent organ. The ventral fins are inserted nearer to the caudal than to the head. Very variable in coloration, in relation to its wide distribution. Specimens from Java:–upperside delicate brown to olive-green; flanks brilliant silver, with a bluish lustre by reflected light; underside silver-white to light yellowish. Edge of lower jaw black, often with a fine red longitudinal stripe as well. A dark shoulder-blotch, as well as a blotch at the root of the pectoral fin, both usually indistinct. Fins colourless to bright lemon-yellow. Dorsal fin with a bright red blotch in the ♂♂. Leading-edge of anal fin occasionally black. Eyes brilliant greenish.

♀ Coloration similar, but without the red on the dorsal fin.

For these very lively surface-fishes large-surfaced tanks with plenty of swimming-space are necessary. For their health, especially of the pregnant ♀♀, the addition of a little sea-salt (2–3 teaspoons to 10 litres of water) is also essential. Rich feeding is needed if they are to be brought to sexual maturity, especially small insects such as *Drosophila*, mosquito- and other small insect-larvae of all kinds and supplementary waterfleas and springtails. Temperature 18–22°C. The ♂♂ are very quarrelsome among themselves and engage in prolonged battles in which they rush at one another with their beaks open and their gill-covers spread wide. In many cases they interlock their jaws and tug until one fish lets go or gives up in exhaustion. This propensity of the *Dermogenys* ♂♂ is commonly exploited in Thailand, where contests are arranged similar to those between the *Betta* ♂♂. The fishes are rather timid and often slightly damage their beaks, such wounds commonly resulting in death. On this account *Dermogenys* are kept in shallow dishes in Thailand.

Breeding of this live-bearing species is not easy, because the ♀♀ often miscarry. Imported fishes usually produce 1–2 viable generations and then proceed to throw entirely or predominantly stillborn young. The reason for this may lie partly in incorrect feeding or in keeping the fishes at too high a temperature. The courtship-behaviour is very interesting. The ♂ rests underneath the ♀ and nudges her ventral surface with his beak; during the sex-act the ♂ presses himself close against the side of the ♀. Pregnancy-period up to 8 weeks. Brood-number small, large fishes producing at most 12–20 young. The young are about 1 cm. long at birth and can at once be fed on fine-grade food. The lower jaw is the first to lengthen. 1905/+.

Plate 167

Fig. 967. *Hypseleotris cyprinoides;* adult, enlarged. (Photo Dr. Foersch)
Fig. 968. *Toxotes jaculator* (Archerfish); half-grown specimen, enlarged. (Original)

Plate 167

Plate 168

Plate 168

Fig. 969. *Melanotaenia maccullochi* (Black-lined Rainbowfish); half-grown specimens, natural size. (Original)

Fig. 970. *Telmatherina ladigesi* (Celebes Rainbowfish); adults, somewhat reduced. (Original)

Dermogenys sumatranus (*Bleeker* 1853)

Singapore, Sumatra, Borneo; ♂ to 5 cm., ♀ to 6 cm.

D III/7–9; A I/12–13; P I/8–9; V 6; LL 45–50. This species is very like the previous one, from which it is distinguished by the following characters:–ventral fins inserted midway between the head and the caudal fin; colouring altogether more brownish; no black or red stripes on the lower jaw; eyes silvery.

Sex-distinctions, care and breeding, as given for the previous species. 1935/–.

Hemirhamphodon pogonognathus (*Bleeker* 1853) (Fig. 963)

Malay Peninsula, Sumatra, Borneo, Banka, Biliton, in fresh and brackish waters; to 20 cm.

D 12–13; A 15; LL 65; TR 24. The genus *Hemirhamphodon* differs from all the other genera in the extreme elongation of the lower jaw, which is further provided with fine teeth. The dorsal fin is inserted in front of the anal and has a longer base. *H. pogonognathus* is mainly characterised by the median barbel-like projection of the tip of the lower jaw and by the insertion of the ventral fins being anterior to the dorsal. Overall shining silvery; upperside brownish to brown-olive; flanks light yellowish; throat delicate violet; belly white. Gill-cover shining brass-colour with a red blotch. Fins delicate brownish, to some extent with dark edges. The sexes are distinguished by the shape of the anal fin. ♀ as a rule larger. This species, too, is a live-bearer and should be treated like *Dermogenys pusillus*. 1939/+.

Family Syngnathidae (Pipe-fishes)

This is a family of world-wide distribution belonging to the Order *Solenich thyes*, whose members, the Sea Horses, Needle-fishes and Pipe-fishes, are generally well known. Almost all the species inhabit shallow, coastal regions and are especially common among seaweeds; several of them are found in

609

European seas. The number of species and their variety of form are greatest, however, towards the Equator.

The main characteristic of the whole family is the complete dermal armour, composed of large bony plates which unite into rings encircling the body and entirely envelop the whole fish. Other characters, such as the elongate, tubular mouth; the finnage (ventral fins, and sometimes the caudal, absent); the mobility of the eyes; the arborescent gills, emphasise the distinctiveness of this group of fishes. Locomotion is accomplished exclusively through the wave-like motion of the dorsal fin. Needle-fishes and Pipe-fishes certainly perform a serpentine movement of the body, but without any substantial improvement in locomotion thereby. Sea Horses swim – or more correctly hover – vertically in the water and can anchor themselves to plant-stems, etc., by their peculiar finless prehensile tails. Most Needle-fishes and Pipe-fishes can also assume a similar position. Prey, usually small crustacea, larvae of other animals, and small fishes, is sucked in, not snapped up. A sudden dilation of the narrow tubular mouth creates a suction which draws the prey in, and this suction, often accompanied by an audible muffled sound, is so strong that animals larger than the oral opening may be drawn through.

The reproduction and brood-care of these fishes are of special biological interest. The peculiar pairing is accompanied by characteristic swimming- and twining-movements and the ♀ transfers the eggs through her long ovipositor to the ♂, who assumes sole responsibility for brood-care. In some genera, as for example in the Straight-nosed Pipe-fish *(Nerophis ophidion)* of European seas, the eggs are simply attached in rows to glandular depressions in the skin of the belly of the ♂ before or behind the anal opening. In others, as in another European species, *Syngnathus rostellus*, a marsupial pouch is formed from the development and fusion of lateral skin-folds. The brood-pouch attains its highest development in the Sea Horses. The pouch is filled from in front and by peculiar movements the ♂♂ move the eggs backwards into the pouch to make room for further series until the pouch is full. The young fishes hatch in the pouch and leave it as soon as they are fully independent; this departure is especially amusing in some of the Sea Horses which expel the young in a series of puffs by repeated convulsive jerks rather like sneezes.

This large group contains only a very few freshwater species, and these only Pipe-fishes and Needle-fishes which invade fresh water in various quite different regions of the world. This adaptability is shown in one of the European species, the Straight-nosed Pipe-fish, which is not infrequently met with in the entirely fresh coastal waters of the Baltic Sea.

Nerophis ophidion (*Linnaeus* 1758) (Fig. 966)   Straight-nosed Pipe-fish
Mediterranean, Black Sea, northern European seas to Scandinavia, Baltic; to 28 cm.

D 33–34. The genus *Nerophis* is characterised by its reduced finnage; pectoral, ventral and anal fins absent; caudal fin occasionally present as a rudiment but usually absent. 30–31 bony rings on the trunk, 60–70 on the tail. The eggs are simply attached to the ventral skin of the ♂ between the throat and the vent.

Colour, rather translucent yellow-olive with numerous tiny white to bluish dots.

♀ with lovely iridescent blue to blue-green flanks during the breeding season.

First kept in an aquarium in 1841 in England. This native Pipe-fish is very hardy and easily contented and can be kept in an unheated planted domestic aquarium. Sea-salt should be added to the water (2–3 teaspoons to 10 litres) and fresh water provided from time to time. Aeration essential. The fishes breed readily in aquaria and have interesting courtship behaviour. Live foods only, especially small crustacea; worm foods are not accepted.

The following freshwater species have so far been imported from Asia:–

Microphis boaja (*Bleeker* 1851)
Southern China to Thailand, Greater Sunda Islands, common in fresh and brackish waters; to 43 cm.

D 47–61; A 3–5; P 23–27. 21–24 bony rings on the trunk, 30–40 on the tail. Anal-opening behind the middle of the body (in terms of total length). Snout longer than the remainder of the head. The eggs are carried on the ventral surface of the ♂ between the throat and the vent, this surface being only laterally delimited by projecting longitudinal ridges. Upperside grey-green; flanks yellow-grey; underside

611

a lovely yellow. The colour of the tail becomes increasingly dark posteriorly. Head with black blotches and dots. Anterior part of body with iridescent bluish transverse blotches. Caudal fin almost black; remaining fins colourless, transparent.

Fundamentally all tropical Needle-fishes should be kept in hard water to which sea-salt (2–3 teaspoons to 10 litres) has been added. They do best in aquaria with thin planting – *Vallisneria* is excellent – and some sunshine. Temperature 22–26 °C. Gentle aeration. Feed on small crustacea such as *Cyclops* and *Daphnia*. These highly interesting fishes can change colour to match their surroundings and can look deceptively similar to narrow leaves. Almost all the species do well in captivity, but essentially nothing is so far known about successful breeding. 1954.

Microphis brachyurus (*Bleeker* 1853) (Fig. 964)
Very widely distributed along the coasts of southern Asia, the Malay Archipelago, the Philippines, Japan and many groups of Pacific islands, in fresh, brackish and salt water; to 23 cm.

D 36–48; A 3–4; P 18–23. 19–22 bony rings on the trunk, 20–24 on the tail. General details as given for the previous species. The brown upperside is sharply delimited from the pale-blotched, dirty green flanks; underside yellowish. Gill-cover iridescent light green blotched with black. Caudal fin dark.

Care and breeding, as given for *M. boaja*. 1953.

Doryichthys deokhatoides (*Bleeker* 1853)
Thailand, Malay Peninsula, Sumatra, Borneo, in streams and rivers; to 18 cm.

D 30–35; A 3–4; P 18–23; C 8–10. 17–20 bony rings on the trunk, 31–35 on the tail. Anal-opening in front of the middle of the body (in terms of total length). The eggs are carried on the whole ventral surface of the ♂ anterior to the vent and entirely covered over by two lateral folds of skin. Colour greenish; underside darker. Sundry dark spots on the sides of the body anterior to the dorsal fin. A black stripe across the eye from the snout to the hinder edge of the gill-cover.

Weber and de Beaufort (1922) state that *Doryichthys fluviatilis* is a synonym of this species.

Care and breeding, as given for *Microphis boaja*. 1911/–.

The following freshwater species have so far been imported from Africa:–

Microphis smithi *Duméril* 1870 (Fig. 764)   Large Freshwater Pipefish
Lower reaches of the Niger and Congo, in thickly weeded shallows in fresh water; to 20 cm.

D 42–48; A 2–3. 21–22 bony rings on the trunk, 22–24 on the tail. Anal-opening behind the middle of the body (in terms of total length). Snout longer than the rest of the head. Upperside pale ochre; flanks bright brown. Snout dark, more or less thickly strewn with pale spots. Caudal rings occasionally black. Caudal fin black.

Care, as given for *Microphis boaja*. 1954.

Syngnathus pulchellus *Boulenger* 1915 (Figs. 765, 773, 965)
Congo, Ogowe, in fresh and brackish waters; to 15 cm.

D 25; A 2. 13 bony rings on the trunk, 35 on the tail. In the genus *Syngnathus* the whole or the greater part of the dorsal fin lies along the very long tail. The eggs are carried behind the anal opening of the ♂ and are covered over by two lateral skin-folds. Colour grey to very dark brown; flanks marbled with a filigree pattern; underside paler, often rust-red. Black stripes radiate from the eye. Caudal fin black or orange-red with black stripes.

Care, as given for *Microphis boaja*. 1933/+.

The following is the only freshwater species so far imported from America:–

Doryichthys lineatus *Kaup* 1856
Brazil to Mexico, in streams in coastal regions, also in brackish and salt water; not infrequent in the Atlantic between Africa and the West Indies; to 20 cm.

D 42–44; A 1–3. 19–22 bony rings on the trunk, 22–23 on the tail. The eggs are carried on the ventral surface of the ♂ in front the anal-opening and are protected by lateral skin-folds. Colour yellow-brown with dark spots over the whole body; underside yellowish. Snout with 5–6 black transverse bands.

Care, as given for *Microphis boaja*. 1913 (?)/–.

Family Aphredoderidae (Pirate-perch)

The *Aphredoderidae*, together with the *Percopsidae*, form the Order *Salmopercae* (Trout-perches). This name is given because in the family *Percopsidae* (of which no representatives have so far been imported) an adipose fin is present as in the Trout. The family *Aphredoderidae*, however, lack an adipose fin and contain only the single species described below.

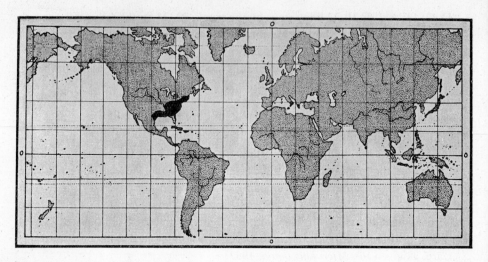

Fig. 971
Distribution of the *Aphredoderidae*

Aphredoderus sayanus (*Gilliams* 1824)·(Fig. 983)   Pirate-perch
Eastern States of U.S.A., in streams and standing waters; to 13 cm.

D III–IV/10–11; A II/6; V I/7; LL 45–60. Body elongate, slightly compressed. Head large, cheeks scaled. Lower jaw projecting. Jaws, vomer, palatines and pterygoids provided with fine rows of teeth. Scales ctenoid. Lateral line incomplete or absent. Dorsal fin tall, undivided; anal appreciably smaller than dorsal; caudal fin rounded. Especially characteristic of this species is the position of the anus, which lies immediately in front of the anal fin in the young and migrates forward onto the throat in the adult. Colour dark olive-green to brownish with dark spots and blotches which are not infrequently arranged in longitudinal rows. Underside yellow-brown. Fins opaque grey-green. Caudal fin with two dark transverse bars at the base, often with a pale interspace.

♀ usually deep black in the breeding season.

The Pirate-perch is best kept by itself in a planted and well-matured tank. It must be provided with suitable hiding-places among stones or under pieces of broken flowerpot. Room-temperature, not over 22 °C. Good aeration. Live food of all kinds, especially small fishes, worms and insect-larvae. Very quarrelsome, both with other species and with its own kind, like many station-holding fishes. 1904/ –.

614

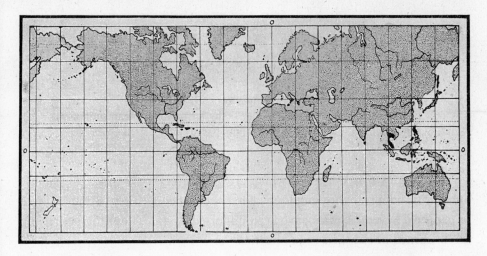

Fig. 972
Distribution of the *Phallostethidae;* note the Malay Peninsula and the Philippines.

Family Phallostethidae

Very small, Tooth-Carp-like fishes, belonging to the Order *Percomorphi*, which are found in fresh and brackish waters in parts of south-east Asia and in the Philippines and are well-known for their distinctive intromittent organ (and/or clasper?). This organ, the Priapum, is situated in the throat region and consists of a more or less erect basal stalk-like structure from which, in many species, one or two sabre-shaped processes project forwards (Fig. 973). This organ is primarily attached to the shoulder-girdle and is supported by various bones. The urinogenital and anal openings are situated on the priapum; the corresponding openings in the ♀♀ lie between the pectoral fins. The eggs are either fertilised within the maternal body and expelled in a fully-developed condition (ovoviviparity), or produced in the more normal way and fertilised in the water. According to Smith (1945) the ♂ can clasp the ♀ with his priapum. Other peculiarities of this family are the partly spinous dorsal fin and the absence of ventral fins.

615

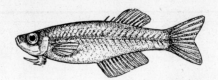

Fig. 973
♂ Phallostethid, showing the peculiar fleshy intromittent organ (priapum)
on the throat.

These pigmy fishes, most of which grow to barely 3 cm. in length, mainly inhabit standing, slightly muddy waters where they feed on various minute organisms. Several species have been imported, so far without much having been learned about their requirements.

Families Theraponidae, Serranidae, Lobotidae

The majority of the predatory *Theraponidae*, like the large and closely related family *Serranidae* (Sea-perches), are marine fishes. Their distribution extends from the Red Sea and the east coast of Africa over the whole of the Malay Archipelago and Australasia to many groups of islands in the Pacific. The family, belonging to the Order *Percomorphi*, is characterised by an elongate, perch-like body with a dorsal fin almost divided into two and a short anal fin. The *Theraponidae* are distinguished from some similarly-shaped *Serranidae* by the number of dorsal fin-spines (XII-XIV) as well as by the small scales and certain peculiarities of dentition. The mouth is quite large and protrusible. Many *Theraponidae* are valued as food-fishes.

Plate 169

Fig. 974. *Mogurnda mogurnda mogurnda* (Purple-striped Gudgeon); half-grown specimen, enlarged. (Original)
Fig. 975. *Dormitator maculatus;* young adults, reduced. (After Innes)
Fig. 976. *Carinotetraodon somphongsi;* 5 cm. specimen. (Photo Dr. Foersch)

Plate 169

Plate 170

Plate 170

Fig.977. *Eleotris lebretonis;* adult, natural size. (Original)
Fig.978. *Periophthalmus barbarus* (Mudskipper); adult, somewhat reduced. (Original)
Fig.979. *Periophthalmus barbarus;* front view of the head. (Original)

Undoubtedly kindred relations of the *Theraponidae* are the *Lobotidae*, a family of few species, whose representatives live predominantly in brackish waters at the mouths of the larger rivers of south-east Asia and penetrate into fresh water. Body deep, strongly compressed. Scales ctenoid. Lateral line complete, arched. Dorsal fin undivided, the anterior part composed of spines, the posterior of soft rays. Jaws toothed; vomer, palatines and tongue toothless.

One species of this family was imported in 1955: *Datnoides quadrifasciatus* (Sevastianov 1809), which is found at the mouth of the Ganges as well as in Thailand, Malaya, Borneo and New Guinea (Fig. 823). Coloration dusky olive-brown; underside paler. 8–10 dark, partially incomplete, transverse bars. A blackish blotch on the gill-cover. 3 dark bands radiate from the eye. A voracious predator, growing to 30 cm. in length; only young specimens are suitable for the domestic aquarium.

The very large, almost exclusively marine family *Serranidae* (Sea-perches) includes a few freshwater species which are chiefly native to Africa. Not at all infrequently, and no doubt quite unintentionally, young specimens of the Nile Perch, *Lates niloticus* (Linnaeus 1762), are imported, a species (Fig. 1040) native to the basins of the Nile, Senegal and Niger where it attains a length of 180 cm. The marbled grey-green young should be treated rather like the larger Cichlids.

Therapon jarbua (*Forskål* 1775) (Fig. 1039)   Saltwater Zebrafish
Widely distributed, from the east coast of Africa to northern Australia and the Philippines as well as southern China, very common in many river-mouths; to 35 cm.

D X–XIII/9–10; A III/8–9; P 13; V I/5; LL 80–90. A perch-like predator. Body grey-silver; upperside often light yellow-green; flanks gleaming faint violet. Gill-cover with a strong spine, often light brass-coloured. The upper half of the fish has several black longitudinal bands which resemble the contours of mountains on a map. These bands are especially prominent in the young, but often become quite indistinct in the ripe adults. Fins transparent; tip of dorsal black; caudal to some extent tipped with dark and with oblique bands.

The sexes are uniformly coloured, but the ♀ becomes very stout towards spawning time.

Care easy. *Therapon* is a very robust and hardy fish for the brackish or marine aquarium. While the young fishes school and are very peaceful at first, the larger ones are typical predators which even attack larger species and kill them by biting them in the belly. *Therapon* is very restless and keeps continually on the move in the aquarium. When in danger the fishes like to slip into crevices between stones and lie there fully quiescent for some time. Very voracious; almost any kind of food is taken greedily. Growth consequently rapid. Breeding already achieved in captivity. The eggs are laid on stones and guarded by the ♂. The young hatch after 24 hours and grow very rapidly. This species is very much to be recommended for first attempts at brackish or marine aquarium-keeping. *Therapon jarbua* plays an important role as a food-fish in some regions. 1908/+.

Family Centrarchidae (Sunfishes and Basses)

The Sunfishes (Order *Percomorphi*) are closely related to the true Perches. The body is egg-shaped as a rule, that is to say, thick-set, deep and strongly compressed. Only the genera *Aplites*, *Pomoxis*, *Elassoma* and *Micropterus* have a more elongate and relatively low shape. Dorsal and anal fins undivided and long-based. In the genera *Pomoxis* and *Centrarchus* these fins are about equally large; in all the other genera the anal fin is the smaller. Both fins are composed of anterior spinous and posterior soft-rayed portions, which may be almost divided by a shallow notch, as in *Micropterus,* for example. The lateral line is almost or quite complete, but absent in the genus *Elassoma*. Cycloid scales, or ctenoid scales as well. The sexes are usually not easy to distinguish. The young fishes are often very attractively coloured but in practically all the species the intensity of colour diminishes with age.

The Sunfishes are typical North American fishes, above all of the central and eastern regions, where they chiefly inhabit clear lowland waters over a sandy bottom. The smaller species school to some extent, but the larger ones are predatory individualists. In flowing waters quiet, weedy shallows are preferred. All the species practise very intensive brood-care. As a rule the eggs are laid in large, carefully-prepared hollows and the young are led by the ♂ when they hatch.

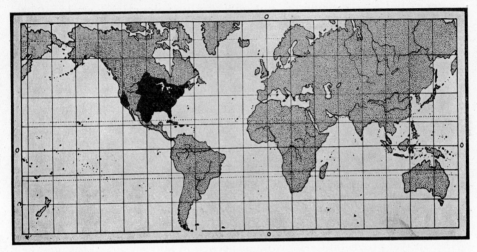

Fig. 980

Natural distribution of the *Centrarchidae*. Sunfishes have been successfully introduced and have multiplied in many other regions, particularly in Europe.

Sunfishes should be kept in large aquaria standing in a light position, and provided with a fine sandy bottom-soil and numerous possible hiding-places among thick clumps of plants or between root-tangles or pieces of wood. At the same time it is important that these very lively fishes should be allowed plenty of uninterrupted swimming-space. Especially suitable are open-air ponds, in which the fishes can remain all through the winter, provided the water does not freeze right to the bottom.

All Sunfishes, however, especially older individuals, are susceptible to abrupt alterations in environmental conditions, such as being transferred to water of a different character, sudden and considerable changes of temperature or rapid deterioration of the water; they are, moreover, exceedingly sensitive to medicines, metallic poisons and acid water. They are at their best in medium-hard to hard, matured water to which some fresh water is added from time to time. If soft water happens to be the only kind available, some marble chips can be added. Sunfishes should not be kept too warm; room-temperature (15–22°C.) in summer and, in contrast, as cool as possible in winter. After a cold wintering not only are the colours and markings improved in the subsequent warm season but the whole vitality of the fishes is increased; indeed the application of this kind of treatment is often the only way in which the spawning-drive can be stimulated. Only quiet species, best of all surface-living fishes, are suitable companions for community tanks. Peaceful species may, of course, be kept together with others of the same family, but the large predatory kinds must be isolated.

Live food of all kinds, especially midge- and other insect-larvae, small crustacea, and rarely dried food; large species also eat small fishes. Food is taken from the bottom only unwillingly. Many Sunfishes remain shy and fearful even after a prolonged acclimation, a peculiarity which must be taken into account through quiet management in aquaria.

No special provision for breeding is needed in tanks reserved for one species. The fishes will also spawn occasionally in the family tank. The best breeding tank is an old-established aquarium with fine bottom-soil, to which some fresh water has been added. Some species, like the Black-banded Sunfish, can also be induced to breed in all-glass tanks without bottom-soil, if one uses old water with an addition of fresh and provides algae or Perlon yarn to form a shallow nest in which the fishes can spawn. Finally, it must be admitted that many species have not so far been induced to breed in domestic

Figs. 981–985

Fig. 981. *Chologaster cornutus;* ripe adult, natural size.
Fig. 982. *Amblyopsis spelaeus* (Blindfish); adult, natural size.
Fig. 983. *Aphredoderus sayanus* (Pirate-perch); somewhat reduced.
Fig. 984. *Acantharchus pomotis;* half-grown specimen, reduced.
Fig. 985. *Chaenobryttus gulosus;* young, natural size.

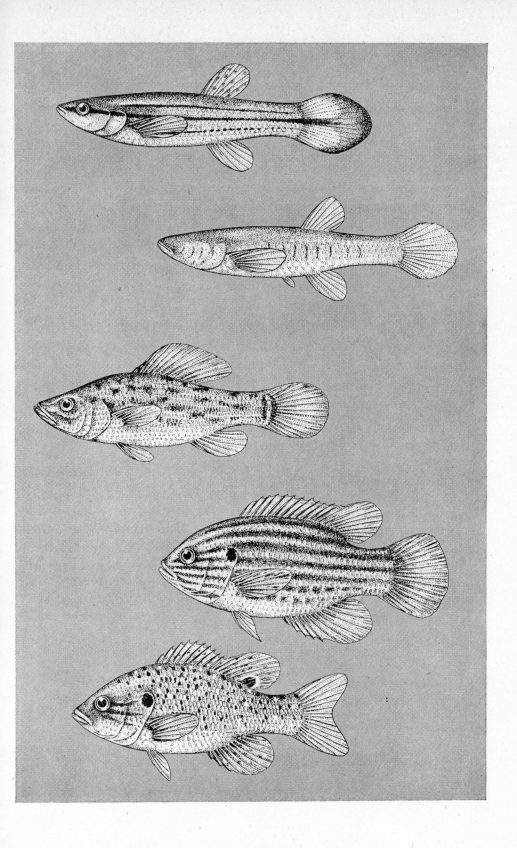

aquarium-conditions although they will breed quite well in open-air ponds. The ♂♂ fan depressions, usually in the shelter of plants or stones, and strengthen these to some extent with plant débris. In the actual spawning-act the ♂ is usually pale while the ♀ is resplendent in the most beautiful colours. The eggs are often sand-coloured and stick to one another and to sand-grains to form lumps of spawn; a spawning period can produce 1000 eggs. The ♀♀ should be carefully removed after spawning, leaving the ♂ to guard the nest and fan fresh water over the eggs. The young hatch after 3–6 days, according to temperature, and lie in the nest to begin with; later they attach themselves to plants and at this point the ♂, also, should be carefully removed. It should, however, be pointed out that the ♂ frequently takes care of the brood for 2–3 weeks, gathering the young into the nest at night, holding the shoal together, etc. As soon as the young swim freely they must be given rich, fine-grade food; Infusoria are not sufficient. The ♀♀ very soon recover and are once again ripe, but the ♂♂ usually require a resting phase of 6–8 weeks. There is usually one spawning season in spring and a second in late summer.

The colour-indications in the following species-descriptions apply always to the livery of young, sexually-ripe fishes.

Acantharchus pomotis (*Baird* 1854) (Fig. 984)
U.S.A., between New York and South Carolina, in waters near the coast and occasionally in brackish water; to 30 cm.

D XI-XII/10–11; A V/10; LL 43; TR 6/12. The genus *Acantharchus* is distinguished from other nearly-related genera of the *Centrarchidae* chiefly by the cycloid scales and dentition (among other features the tongue and pterygoids are toothed). Head large. Mouth deeply cleft. Caudal fin rounded. Ground-colour blackish-green. 5–6 dark parallel longitudinal bands extend along the rather paler flanks; there are also longitudinal stripes on the sides of the head, especially distinct under

Figs. 986–989

Fig. 986. *Elassoma zonatum* (Dwarf Sunfish); adult ♂, enlarged.
Fig. 987. *Lepomis auritus* (Red-bellied Sunfish); adult, reduced.
Fig. 988. *Lepomis cyanellus* (Green Sunfish); half-grown specimen, natural size.
Fig. 989. *Lepomis megalotis* (Long-eared Sunfish); adult, reduced.

the eye. A deep-black blotch on the gill-cover. Fins opaque blackish or grey-green. Old individuals are almost uniformly dark grey-green.

Sex-distinctions in coloration not known.

Care, as given in family description. A predatory species, best suited to large public aquaria. 1911/ — .

Ambloplites rupestris (*Rafinesque* 1817) (Fig. 811)
Great Lakes region to Louisiana, common in the upper Mississippi; to 25 cm.

D X–XI/10–12; A V–VII/9–11; LL 39–43; TR 6–8/11–13. Body elongate, rather deep, compressed. Mouth large, directed obliquely upwards. Scales ctenoid.

Ground-colour grey-green, with striking groups of rectangular black spots. Underside pale, whitish. Gill-cover gleaming brass-colour with a black blotch (rimmed with gold in the ♂) in the hinder corner. Vertical fins delicate greenish to brown-yellow, to some extent dark-edged. The pectoral fins, at least during the breeding season, are blackish in the ♂ and brownish in the ♀.

Care and breeding, as given in the family description. On the one hand this species is predatory and quarrelsome, even with fishes of the same size, yet on the other it is, at least initially, shy and fearful. It is valued as a food-fish and is economically important. 1887/ — .

Centrarchus macropterus (*Lacépède* 1802) (Fig. 820) Peacock-eyed Bass
Eastern States of U.S.A., from Illinois to Florida; to 18 cm., but remains considerably smaller in aquaria and becomes sexually mature at 8 cm.

D XI–XII(XIII)/12–14; A VII–VIII/13–15; LL 38–45. Body short, deep, strongly compressed. Lateral line complete. Dorsal and anal fins of about equal size. Upperside dark olive-brown to brown; flanks pale olive, bluish-silver by reflected light; underside yellowish to white. Several more or less distinct dark longitudinal bands on the flanks, often interrupted. A dark vertical stripe through the eye. Vertical fins transparent yellowish to reddish with orange-red and black spots.

Plate 171

Fig. 990. *Ophicephalus obscurus;* 30 cm. long specimen in the Hellabrunn Aquarium, Munich. (Original)
Fig. 991. *Anabas testudineus* (Climbing Perch); half-grown specimens, natural size. The photograph shows posed, dead fishes. (Original)
Fig. 992. *Belontia signata* (Comb-tail Paradisefish); half-grown specimen, natural size. (Original)

Plate 171

Plate 172

Plate 172

Fig. 993. *Betta bellica* (Slim Fighting Fish); ripe adults, slightly reduced. (Original)
Fig. 994. *Betta fasciata* (Striped Fighting Fish); maximum size. (Original)
Fig. 995. *Betta brederi* (Javan Mouth-brooding Fighting Fish); maximum size. (Original)

In young fishes only there is a large, black, orange-bordered ocellus near the hinder end of the base of the dorsal fin. Older fishes are, as a rule, unpretentiously coloured. The sexes are difficult to tell apart.

♀ often rather deeper and fuller. Anal fin usually bordered with white. Ocellus pronounced during the spawning season.

♂ anal fin usually bordered with black. The ocellus regresses during the spawning season.

Care and breeding, as given in the family description. This species is remarkable for its peculiar play instinct, in which two fishes lunge alternately at one another with lightning speed, reversing immediately in front of the opponent and suddenly resuming the old station. These movements, at first repeated in slow succession, become increasingly rapid until they eventually follow one another so quickly that the eye can scarcely follow them. Very lively fishes, which also become very tame. 1906/+.

Chaenobryttus gulosus (*Cuvier* and *Valenciennes* 1829) (Fig. 985)
Eastern States of U.S.A., from the Great Lakes region southwards to Carolina and Texas and westwards to Kansas and Iowa; to 20 cm.

D X/9–10; A III/8–9; LL 40–46; TR 6–11. The genus *Chaenobryttus* is distinguished from other *Centrarchidae* chiefly through certain peculiarities of dentition and finnage. Rather more elongate than *Lepomis*; head and mouth very large. Upperside olive-green to blackish-green; flanks paler green, often with a bluish sheen; underside yellowish to brass-coloured. Upper part of body thickly spotted with blue and red, less often with brass-colour. 3–4 bright red lines from the eye to the gill-cover. A deep black blotch in the upper corner of the gill-cover. Vertical fins sprinkled with dark. Dorsal fin with a pale-bordered black blotch on the proximal parts of the last fin-rays.

♀ less intensely coloured; very robust at spawning time.

Care and breeding, as given in the family description. 1896/−.

625

Elassoma evergladei *Jordan* 1884 (Fig. 818)   Dwarf or Pigmy Sunfish
From North Carolina to Florida; to 3·5 cm.

D II–IV/8–9; A III/5–7; P 13; LL 26–30. Body longish, rather compressed. Easily distinguished from other genera of the *Centrarchidae* by the lack of a lateral line. Scales cycloid, quite large. Clay-colour to grey-green with isolated silvery scales and black spots, occasionally with irregular dark transverse bars.

♂ at spawning time, including the fins, lovely velvet-black with numerous, though isolated, shining green scales.

♀ fins usually colourless; belly occasionally reddish; body in adult fishes deeper than in the ♂.

Care easy; the species is satisfied with a thickly-planted tank or one with plenty of algae. Outdoor ponds are certainly best of all. Pairs which have been put together in spring can be mated again in the autumn and will produce a further large brood of offspring, provided that they have been regularly fed. In the case of the domestic aquarium the instructions given in the family description should be followed. Very resistant to extreme temperature changes; healthy up to 30 °C. with good aeration, yet on the other hand can be kept as low as 4 °C. in winter; a cool wintering (8–12 °C.) is even to be recommended. Omnivorous, taking dried food and algae as well. The Dwarf Sunfish breeds readily in a tank reserved for the one species. After a charming courtship the eggs are laid, indiscriminately but usually thickly grouped, on plants. Each spawning produces 30–60 eggs. The young hatch after 2–3 days and should be provided with very fine-grade food as soon as they swim freely. The young fishes at first gather against the surface of the water and are not molested by the adults.

The Dwarf Sunfish has a peculiar method of locomotion over the bottom; rapidly advancing the left and right pectoral fins it achieves an unsteady 'gait'. 1925/+.

Elassoma zonatum *Jordan* 1877 (Fig. 986)   Banded Pigmy or Dwarf Sunfish
U.S.A., from southern Illinois to Alabama and westwards to Texas; to 3·5 cm.

D IV–V/9–10; A III/5; P 16; LL 38–45. This species is chiefly distinguished

Figs. 996–1000

Fig. 996. *Micropterus dolomieu* (Black Bass); young.
Fig. 997. *Stizostedion vitreum;* half-grown fish, reduced.
Fig. 998. *Etheostoma coerulea;* maximum size.
Fig. 999. *Beleosoma nigrum;* somewhat enlarged.
Fig. 1000. *Solenotoca papuensis;* half-grown fish.

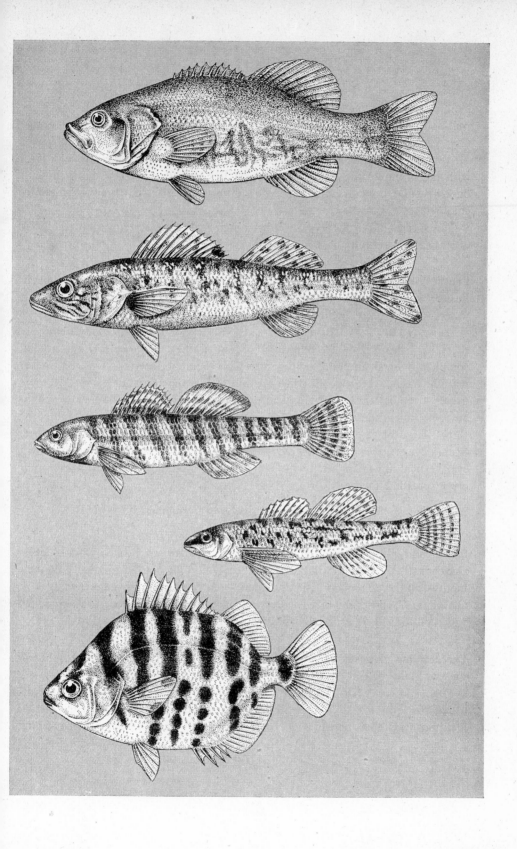

from the previous one by the differing longitudinal and transverse scale-counts, as well as by the coloration. The two species are the only members of their genus. Grey-green to olive-green with fine black dots over the whole body. Flanks with 11–12 dark transverse bars. A black blotch on the middle of the side on a level with the origin of the dorsal fin. Vertical fins with dark spots. Caudal fin with dark irregular transverse lines. The dorsal fin is larger in the ♂. ♀ less brilliantly coloured.

This species has probably not yet been imported into Germany, although it has often been successfully bred in other European countries.

Enneacanthus obesus (*Girard* 1854)   Blue-spotted Sunfish
Eastern States of U.S.A., from Massachusetts to Florida, in very weedy lowland waters; to 10 cm., remaining smaller in aquaria.

D IX(–X)/10–12; A III(–IV)/8–11; LL 32–35; TR 3–4/9–11. Body relatively short, very deep, strongly compressed. Mouth rather small. Lateral line usually complete. Dorsal fin appreciably larger than the anal, inserted about on a level with the base of the ventrals. Olive-brown to fawn, the upperside darker, with 5–8 usually irregular transverse bars and numerous green to brass-coloured, occasionally also blue, iridescent spots. Underside pale yellow to white. Flap of gill-cover with a large black blotch (gold-rimmed in the ♂) of the same size as the eye. A dark eye-stripe is usually distinctly apparent only underneath the yellow-brown eye. Vertical fins fawn, often with a strong red tinge, and covered with iridescent green spots like the body.

♀ usually less beautifully coloured; spots fewer in number; dorsal fin lower.

Care and breeding, as given in the family description. This species is very fearful and must be given the opportunity to bury itself in a plant thicket. Occasionally these fishes will burrow so deeply into the bottom-soil that only their mouths and eyes remain visible. Experimentally released in many localities in Germany. The fishes can breed successfully in normal years, but become completely wiped out during an especially cold winter. 1895/+.

Enneacanthus gloriosus (*Holbrook* 1855)   Banded Sunfish
Eastern States of U.S.A., from about New York to Florida; to 8 cm.

D IX(–X)/10; A III(–IV)/9; LL 30; TR 3/9. Very similar to the previous species as regards form, markings and colouring and hence very difficult to distinguish in life. In contrast to *E. obesus*, *E. gloriosus* has a small black blotch on the flap of the gill-cover, a blotch which is appreciably smaller than the eye. Furthermore, the transverse bars are wanting in the adults, the iridescent spots are usually blue and the black eye-stripe is indistinct under the eye.

Care and breeding, as given for the previous species.

Lepomis auritus (*Linnaeus* 1758) (Fig. 987)   Red-bellied Sunfish
U.S.A., east of the Alleghanies, from Maine in the north to Virginia; to 20 cm., remaining considerably smaller in aquaria.

D X–XI/11–12; A III/8–10; LL 43–48; TR 6–7/14–16. Body thick-set, deep and strongly compressed. Gill-cover flap ('ear') long and narrow. Dorsal fin larger than the anal. Young, sexually-ripe fishes are brown-olive to brown-violet on the upperside; flanks grey-green above, green-yellow below; underside, including the pectoral fins, bright orange-red. Head with attractive pale blue vermiform lines and spots, especially on the snout and around the eye; some spots on the body as well. Gill-cover flap deep black. Vertical fins transparent dirty yellow to brownish. The contrast of colours becomes reduced with increasing age; old fishes are predominantly brownish.

The ♀♀ are readily distinguished by their more homely colouring.

Care and breeding, as given in the family description. 1895/–.

Lepomis cyanellus *Rafinesque* 1819 (Fig. 988)   Green Sunfish
U.S.A., east of the Rockies from Canada to Mexico; to 20 cm., remaining considerably smaller (8 cm.) in aquaria.

D X–XI/10–11; A III/8–9; LL 45–55; TR 6–7/15–18. Grey-green to vivid shining green, often delicate brass-colour or occasionally even coppery further towards the belly. 8–10 dark transverse bands on the upper half of the body in the young. Blue stripes and spots on the flanks. A large, black blotch on the green gill-cover. Fins grey with a green lustre. Dorsal and anal fins sprinkled with brown-red in the young, the former with a dark blotch at the base of the hinder part of the fin. Eye blood-red. Old fishes are uniformly grey-green.

The sexes are difficult to tell apart; the ♀♀ are usually deeper and fuller.

Care and breeding, as given in the family description. Fishes imported from the southern part of the range are warmth-loving; 18–22°C. 1906/–.

Lepomis gibbosus (*Linnaeus* 1758) (Figs. 812, 813)   Pumpkinseed Sunfish
U.S.A., from the Great Lakes to Texas and Florida; to 20 cm., remaining considerably smaller in aquaria and especially beautiful and sexually ripe at 10–12 cm.

D X/10–12; A II/10–11; P 12; LL 40–47; TR 6/13–17. Body thick-set, deep, strongly compressed, altogether very robust. The colouring of fishes 4–8 cm. long is uniform grey-green with 5–8 shining pearly transverse bars. In older fishes the coloration is more brownish and the transverse bars are shining green-blue; there are also numerous dark red or reddish-yellow blotches and spots on the head. The gill-cover is shining green with bold dark red lines and spots. The gill-cover flap ('ear') is deep black, with an orange-red blotch on the hinder part. Throat and belly bright orange-red. Fins greenish to yellowish. Several dark spots on the hinder end of the dorsal. A very beautiful species.

♀ easily recognised by her less brilliant colouring.

Care, as given in the family description. First bred in the open in 1887. The species has been introduced into several districts of Germany and has been very well naturalised. 1877/+.

Lepomis megalotis (*Rafinesque* 1820) (Figs. 808, 989)   Long-eared Sunfish
East of the Rockies, from southern Canada to Mexico, in clear streams; to 20 cm., remaining considerably smaller in aquaria, and sexually ripe at 10–12 cm.
D X/10–12; A III/8–10; LL 36–45; TR 5/14. Body short and deep, strongly compressed. Coloration very variable. Upperside dark brown with a bluish sheen; flanks olive to dark blue-violet; belly greenish-yellow to orange. 7–10 more or less distinct dark transverse bands on the flanks. The whole body is sprinkled with greenish, blue or reddish-yellow spots. The gill-cover has green iridescent stripes and the large ear-like flap is blue-black edged with golden-green. Edges of lips green. Vertical fins greenish with white borders. Eye blood-red or black-red.

♀ more dully coloured; dorsal fin smaller.

Care and breeding, as given in the family description. Rather quarrelsome and snappy. Fond of direct sunlight. 1895/+.

Mesogonistius chaetodon (*Baird* 1854) (Figs. 798, 809)   Black-banded Sunfish
New Jersey to Maryland, in standing and sluggish waters; to 10 cm., becoming sexually ripe at only 5 cm. A favourite decorative species for the unheated aquarium.
D IX–XI/10–13; A III/12–13; LL 28–30. Body short and deep, strongly compressed. Grey-yellow to green-yellow with several more or less distinct, dark brown to black, broad, irregular-edged transverse bands. The areas between these bands

are quite irregularly blotched with grey to brown. Fins colourless with dark stripes and spots on the fin-rays. The anterior rays of the dorsal are either black or, like the succeeding ones, orange. The ventral fins are similarly coloured, but in this case the anterior rays are either orange or, like the rest, black. The whole fish has a pearly sheen by reflected light.

The sexes are difficult to distinguish but at spawning time the ♀♀ are more brilliantly coloured.

Care and breeding, as given in the family description. 1897/+.

Micropterus dolomieu *Lacépède* 1802 (Figs. 810, 996)   Black Bass
North America, from southern Canada to South Carolina and Arkansas, in quiet places in larger and smaller flowing waters and in lakes; to 50 cm.

D X/13–15; A III/10–12; LL 72–85; TR 11/25. The genus *Micropterus* is distinguished from other genera of the family chiefly by the more strongly elongate, relatively low body and by the low dorsal fin, which is almost divided into two by a median notch. Mouth large, lower jaw protruding. Scales usually ctenoid. Lateral line complete. Caudal fin somewhat forked. Young fishes are pale yellow-green and have cloudy dark blotches on the flanks. Gill-cover with black spots. Underside almost white. Old fishes are plain dark grey-green to blackish.

♀ rather paler and more robust.

The members of the genus *Micropterus* are typical predators and feed chiefly on smaller fishes, supplemented by small crustacea, snails, large aquatic insects, etc. They pounce upon their prey from chosen stations among roots or between stones and occasionally play with it, like a cat with a mouse. Sexual maturity is attained after 3–4 years. These brigands also build shallow nests, often as much as 1 m. in diameter, which they take great pains to keep clean; *M. salmoides* (below) even lines its nest with leaves. When the eggs have been laid the ♂ and ♀ take turns to guard them. The young hatch after about 8–10 days at 16–18°C. Only young specimens, at best, can be kept in domestic aquaria; one hardly keeps these fishes for amusement but rather more for their biological interest. Good aeration is essential. Very voracious. This, like the following species, has been successfully introduced, especially into southern Europe. 1883/+.

Micropterus (Aplites) salmoides (*Lacépède* 1802) (Fig. 797)
North America, widely distributed, from the Great Lakes region in the north to Florida in the south, Texas and Mexico; also found in brackish water; to 45 cm.

631

D X/12–13; A III/10–11; LL 65–70; TR 7/8. Similar to the previous species, but with a still larger mouth. The notch in the dorsal is so deep that the fin is often quite divided. The young may also be distinguished by their markings; in this species there is a distinct longitudinal band, though often composed only of a series of blotches; above this, and more rarely below also, are isolated dark blotches. Old fishes are uniformly dark olive-green to grey-green.

Biology and care, as given for *M. dolomieu*. In some parts of America *M. salmoides* is a popular food-fish. 1883/–.

Pomoxis nigromaculatus (*Le Sueur* 1829) (Fig. 796)
Widely distributed, from the Great Lakes region to Florida and Texas; to 27 cm., remaining considerably smaller in aquaria. Medium-sized individuals are popular as food-fishes.

D VII–VIII/15; A VI/16–18; LL 38–44. Body elongate, strongly compressed; upper profile considerably more convex than the lower. Lateral line complete. Dorsal fin about as large as the anal. Grey to delicate olive-green, with a striking silver sheen, especially on the flanks. Back usually quite dark. Numerous olive-green to blackish-green irregular blotches over the whole body, which are often scattered at random but may also be organised into transverse bars or longitudinal stripes. The fins are usually dark-bordered and similarly coloured throughout but do show isolated yellow blotches, however. The eye is large, blood-red anteriorly and posteriorly, blue-green above. The ♀♀ can be recognised with certainty only during the breeding season, when they have a greater girth.

Care and breeding, as given in the family description. Only young specimens are suitable for the domestic aquarium. Already bred in outdoor ponds. 1891/–.

Plate 173
Fig. 1001. *Betta* sp. *(Betta pugnax?)* imported from Java in 1956 by Dr. Schmidt; enlarged. (Original)
Fig. 1002. *Trichopsis pumilus* (Dwarf Gourami); left ♀, right ♂; slightly reduced. (Original)
Fig. 1003. (below, left) *Sphaerichthys osphronemoides* (Chocolate Gourami); young, about three times natural size. (Photo Dr. Foersch)
Fig. 1004. (below, right) Bubble-nest of *Trichopsis pumilus* (Dwarf Gourami) among fine-leaved plants. (Photo Dr. Foersch)

Plate 173

Plate 174

Plate 174

Fig. 1005. *Trichopsis vittatus* (Talking Gourami); ripe fishes, somewhat enlarged; above ♀, below ♂. (Original)

Fig. 1006. *Macropodus cupanus dayi* (Brown Spike-tailed Paradisefish); ripe fishes, somewhat enlarged; above ♂, below ♀. (Original)

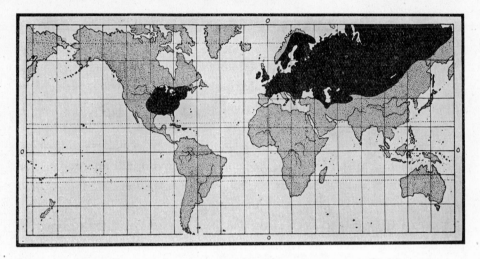

Fig. 1007
Distribution of the *Percidae*

Family Percidae (True Perches)

The true Perches are entirely dwellers in the inland waters of the North Temperate Zone. Especially characteristic of this family are the broad dorsal fins, separate as a rule but in rare exceptions united, of which the first is composed entirely of spinous hard-rays and the second chiefly of soft-rays. The anal fin is usually as large as the second dorsal and not infrequently lies directly beneath it. The ventral fins are inserted well in front of the anal. Head large. Mouth forwardly or somewhat downwardly directed, in some cases deeply cleft, not, or only slightly, protrusible. Jaws, vomer and palatines with rows of teeth. 2 nostrils on each side. Scales ctenoid. Lateral line usually incomplete.

The genera *Perca* and *Lucioperca* are particularly characteristic for Europe; *Stizostedion* and *Boleosoma* for America. The last-mentioned is related to the European genus *Aspro*.

European Perches and their Care

Our native European Perches, like those of North America, can be kept more or less successfully in large unheated aquaria. The ideal arrangement of course for these fishes is a tank with a continuous flow of spring- or artesian-water. Unchlorinated (!) mains water is also suitable. It should be emphasised, however, that in any case there should only be a moderate through-current. In general, at least for the amateur, only normal aquaria will be available and it is to these that the following instructions are intended to apply.

The easiest species to keep is the Perch. The essential thing to do is to procure young specimens from standing water which is not too rich in oxygen, such as a pond with muddy water. Perch taken from such conditions do very well in a planted and aerated domestic aquarium, feed readily and grow rapidly. Larger specimens have the habit of remaining motionless among plants and only become active when they are really hungry. Live food of all kinds, especially midge and other insect-larvae, worms and slugs; larger individuals will also take young fishes. After a cool wintering Perch can even be bred in large aquaria.

The Ruff *(Acerina cernua)* and the related *A.schraetzer* can also be kept successfully for a long time under the conditions just described. On the contrary, it is much more difficult to keep the species of the genus *Aspro* *(A.asper, A.streber* and *A.zingel)* and the Pike-perch *(Lucioperca lucioperca)*. As a rule it is quite difficult even to procure young fishes of these species, and data concerning their care are thus correspondingly scanty. *Aspro streber* probably requires soft, slightly muddy, bottom-soil in which worms and insect-larvae can burrow, and low temperatures attaining an absolute limit of

17°C. in summer. So far Spranger has achieved most success, using outdoor aquaria.

The Pike-perch needs a great deal of oxygen and can only be kept successfully with good aeration. It is a very voracious species and grows extraordinarily rapidly in captivity. Food for larger specimens is almost entirely a question of maintaining a supply of small fishes since, as a rule, meat is not accepted. Breeding has been successfully managed in large aquaria of several cubic metres capacity. The Pike-perch is very susceptible to injury.

Acerina cernua (*Linnaeus* 1758) (Fig. 833)   Ruff, Pope
Central and northern Europe, in various types of lowland waters, and also in the very fresh parts of the Baltic; to 25 cm., usually considerably smaller.

D XII–XVI/11–15; A II/5–6; P 13; V I/5; LL 35–40; TR 6–10/16–21. Body rather slimmer than in the Perch. First and second dorsal fins united. Gill-cover with a backwardly-directed spine. Preopercular spinous. Upperside dark grey-green sparsely scattered with black spots and blotches which also extend onto the rather paler, often shining pearly, flanks. Underside yellowish, often delicate scarlet anteriorly. Gill-cover with greenish to bluish reflexions, according to the light. Fins grey-green to clay-coloured. Vertical fins with irregular rows of black spots.

The ♀♀ may be recognised during the breeding season by their greater girth.

The Ruff lives in schools or shoals chiefly in the quiet parts of larger streams and pursues small prey of all kinds, especially crustaceans. The breeding season is from March to May. The strongly adhesive eggs are often laid in strings and stick to stones and aquatic plants. The colourless young hatch after 8–12 days and at first live by absorbing the material in their yolk-sacs. Up to 100,000 eggs may be produced at spawning.

Care, as given on p. 634.

Acerina schraetzer (*Linnaeus* 1758) (Fig. 834)   Schrätzer
Danube and some of its tributaries, parts of the Moldau basin in Southern Bohemia; to 30 cm.

D XVIII–XIX/12–14; A II/6–7; P 13–14; V I/5; LL 55–62. Body elongate. Head large, produced to a point. First and second dorsals united. Gill-cover with a pointed, posteriorly-directed spine. Skin very glandular and hence very slimy.

635

Altogether very pale, clay-yellow to dirty yellow-green with 3–4 very bold black longitudinal bands; the lower bands are commonly broken up into rows of spots. Fins very pale, yellowish. Dorsal fin with prominent rows of spots. At spawning time the coloration and markings of the ♂♂ are considerably brighter; the fishes often taken on a varnish-like gleam.

Acerina schraetzer is a bottom-living species which prefers deeper places where, at least to some extent, it holds station in a convenient crevice among stones, etc. With its relatively narrow mouth it is only able to take small prey, such as crustaceans, worms and also fish-spawn. The food is usually sucked up in a rather jerky fashion. Breeding season April to May. The eggs are laid in broad bands which the ♀ spreads thickly on the bottom. The young hatch after 6–10 days. Growth slow.

Care, as given on p.634.

Aspro asper (*Linnaeus* 1758) (Fig. 832)
Danube and some of its tributaries, in deep pebbly reaches, rare; to 18 cm.

D_1 VIII–IX, D_2 I/12–13; A I/10; P 14; V I/5; LL 70–81. Body very elongate, cylindrical. Mouth ventral. Dorsal fins widely separated. Ventral fins large, very strong. Squamation very complete. Eyes upwardly directed. Yellow-brown to clay-yellow; underside paler with prominent and very broad irregular brown transverse bars. Fins yellowish, without markings.

♀ very robust at spawning time.

Aspro asper is a typical bottom-living fish which, according to Spranger, as a rule lives in the deeper reaches and hunts worms, larvae, etc., both by day and by night. Its locomotion hardly resembles the swimming of other fishes; on the contrary, with the aid of its pectoral and caudal fins it hops forwards toad-fashion in a series of jerks. The eyes are independently movable and the head can also be turned from side to side to some extent. Spawning season March to April. At this season the fishes have a bright brassy tinge. The eggs are attached to the bottom. A very interesting aquarium fish.

Care, as given on p.634.

Aspro zingel (Linnaeus 1758) is very similar to *A. asper* in appearance and biology and has the same distribution.

Lucioperca lucioperca (*Linnaeus* 1758) (Fig. 829)   Pike-perch
Widely distributed through Central Europe, southwards to northern Italy, eastwards to the U.S.S.R., northwards to the Baltic, westwards to the River Werre;

in large rivers, very numerous in the lagoons of the Baltic; average length about 40–55 cm.

D_1 XIII–XV, D_2 I–II/19–23; A II/11–12; P 15; V I/5; LL 80–95. The largest of the European *Percidae*. Body elongate, moderately compressed. Mouth large but narrow, strongly toothed. Gill-cover with a posteriorly-directed spine. Dorsal fins separate. Caudal fin slightly forked. Upperside blackish to blackish-green. Flanks grey-green, with 7–11 irregular-edged cloudy brown transverse bars in the young. Underside dirty white. Head with numerous shining blue to brass-coloured zones on a marbled brown/grey-green ground. Fins grey to yellow-grey. Dorsal fins with longitudinal rows of dark brown spots; caudal fin usually with transverse rows of the same.

♀ more robust; head less pointed.

The Pike-perch lives in large open stretches of water, preferably over a hard bottom. In summer it resorts to slightly turbid, opaque waters which provide it with adequate shelter. The young fishes feed chiefly on small organisms, but when they are only about 15 cm. long (one year old) they become fish-predators and lie in wait for Bleak and Smelts in particular. Sexual maturity is usually attained in the third year. The spawning season is from April to the beginning of June and is determined by the temperature of the water (12–14 °C.). The eggs are large (about 1·5 mm.), and strongly adhesive, and are laid, often in clumps, on hanging roots, stones or pieces of waterlogged wood. Large ♀♀ not infrequently produce as many as 200,000 to 300,000 eggs. The parents are said to guard the spawn for some time. The young hatch after 8–12 days and, after a short resting-period, spiral to the surface in order to fill their swim-bladders with air. The Pike-perch ranks with the best food-fishes.

Care, as given on p. 634.

Perca fluviatilis *Linnaeus* 1758 (Figs. 830, 831)   Perch
Throughout Europe, with the exceptions of Spain, southern Italy and northern Scandinavia; also common throughout northern Asia and in North America; average size about 25 cm.

D_1 XIII–XVII, D_2 I–II/13–15; P 14; V I/5; LL 58–68. Body moderately elongate, deep, slightly compressed. Head obtuse. Mouth large. Posterior edge of gill-cover produced to a point. Dorsal fins separate. Caudal fin slightly forked. One of the most beautiful European freshwater fishes.

Coloration very variable in different parts of the range; the fishes also have the ability to change colour in relation to that of the bottom. Upperside blackish-green to dark blue-grey or even brown. Flanks paler, green-yellowish with something of a brassy glint, and also clay-coloured. Underside yellowish to silver-white. 6–10 dark transverse stripes are usually clear only in the young and when the fishes are excited. Sides of head with areas shining with a rainbow iridescence. Dorsal fins grey-green, D_1 with a lacquer-black blotch on the hinder part. Caudal fin usually dirty yellow-green, the lower edge brick-red. Ventral and anal fins orange to brick-red; pectoral fins dirty yellow. The sexes are similarly coloured.

The Perch occurs in clear and turbid flowing waters as well as in ponds and lakes, and up in the mountains to heights of 1000 m. and also, it must be mentioned, penetrates into the brackish waters of the Baltic. In contrast to the Pike-perch it avoids the more open waters and prefers to live in the weedy margins. Old individuals are lone-wolves as a rule and prey upon smaller fishes. Young ones gather in large shoals and hunt various small animals. The spawning season is from March to July. During the spawning-act the ♀♀ glide close over the spawning-substrate (stones, pieces of wood, water plants) with their fins depressed and shed the eggs which are fertilised immediately afterwards by the resplendently coloured ♂♂. Often more than one ♂ takes part in the spawning-act. The spawn is laid in a network of perforated ribbons. A large ♀ can produce up to 200,000 eggs. The young hatch after 8–10 days and are glass-clear; they spiral up to the surface first of all to fill their swim-bladders with air and then hang for a time from water plants. Growth is rapid.

North American Perches

Boleosoma, Etheostoma and other genera form an exclusively North American sub-family of the *Percidae*, the *Etheostominae*. The numerous species of this group inhabit the widest variety of waters and live under stones in much the same way as the Miller's Thumb *(Cottus gobio)* of Europe. The majority of the species are beautifully coloured. The smallest, *Microperca punctulata*, barely attains 2·5 cm. in length.

Boleosoma nigrum (*Rafinesque* 1820) (Fig. 999)
B. nigrum is extraordinarily widely distributed: Eastern States of U.S.A., northward to Manitoba, westward to Colorado; to 6·5 cm.

D_1 VII–XI, D_2 10–14; A I/6–9; P 10–14; V I/5; LL 38–52. Body elongate, little compressed, low. Head rather small, anteriorly conical. Mouth small, directed forwards or slightly upwards; premaxillaries protractile. Gill-cover scaled. Dorsal fins entirely separated; D_2 composed only of soft rays. Caudal fin squarely truncate. Pectoral fins very large. Upperside delicate olive-green to yellow-green, often spotted with a mosaic of brown. Flanks clay-coloured, spotted with dark and usually with a longitudinal row of W-shaped blotches. Underside pale. Crown of head blackish; a lacquer-black band from the eye to the tip of the snout. Vertical fins transparent with rows of dark spots. ♀ usually paler, very stout at spawning time.

An interesting coldwater fish which, like many other North American species, likes, from its youth up, to dig in like our Miller's Thumb. The fishes propel themselves like springs, with the large pectoral fins assisting the caudal. In this way they can avoid capture with lightning speed. They chiefly rest sitting near the high elevation of a stone, always ready to slip away. Spawning takes place in springtime, under stones, and the ♂ guards the spawn. This species does very well in a very well aerated aquarium with a gravel bottom and will also breed there. Peaceful and easily-contented. Live food of all kinds, especially red midge-larvae *(Chironomus)*. Numerous subspecies of *B. nigrum* are known. 1925/ –.

Etheostoma coerulea *Storer* 1845 (Fig. 998)
Mississippi Basin; the commonest fish in Ohio; to 8 cm.

D_1 IX–XII, D_2 12–14; A II/7–8; LL 37–50; TR 5/10. The genus *Etheostoma* is distinguished from the others (see also *Boleosoma nigrum*) chiefly by the pronounced vaulting of the cranium, the non-protrusible premaxillaries, the closely-approximated ventral fins, the naked crown and the large D_1. Coloration very variable, in relation to that of the bottom. *E. coerulea* ranks with the most beautiful members of a large genus. Upperside grey-green, with dark spots and often blotches. Flanks paler, with 12 shining deep-blue transverse bands, often sloping obliquely backwards; the interspaces between these bands are bright orange, especially on the caudal peduncle. Underside yellowish to dirty white. Fins very attractive. D_1 bright red at the base, orange in the centre and blue at the edge. D_2 orange-coloured, with a blue base and border. Caudal fin brilliant orange-red, edged with blue above and below. Anal fin likewise orange, tinged with blue at the front and back. Ventral fins deep blue. The head also shows lovely shades of orange and blue.

♀ considerably duller in colour; blue and red tints only faintly differentiated.

Care and breeding, as given for *Boleosoma nigrum*. 1903/ –.

Perca flavescens (*Mitchill* 1814)   Yellow Perch, American Perch
U.S.A., north-eastern States, Great Lakes region and thence south-eastwards to
the coast, Upper Mississippi Basin, and other localities; to 30 cm.

D_1 XIII–XV, D_2 II/13–15; A II/7–8; LL 74–88; TR 7/17. *P. flavescens* is very
similar to the European Perch as regards form and markings and on this account
has frequently been regarded as a subspecies of *P. fluviatilis*. *P. flavescens* is altogether more clay-coloured, with a strong golden-yellow glint on the flanks. The
gill-cover is often very conspicuously striped. Dorsal fins yellow-olive: D_1 with a
lacquer-black blotch as in *P. fluviatilis*. Ventral and anal fins orange to red.
Biology, as given for *P. fluviatilis*.

Care, as given on p. 634. 1938/ –.

Stizostedion vitreum (*Mitchill* 1818) (Fig. 997)
U.S.A., Great Lakes region, upper Mississippi, southwards to Georgia and
Alabama and eastwards to Pennsylvania; to 90 cm.

D_1 XIII–XV, D_2 II/13–15; LL 110–132; TR 10–25. Shape similar to that of the
European Pike-perch. Mouth large, jaws about equal; premaxillaries movable,
protractile. Gill-cover with a spine at the hinder end. Preopercular spinose.
Upperside dark olive-green, to some extent with blackish blotches. Flanks paler
with numerous small brassy spots. Underside, including the ventral and anal fins,
delicate pink to light violet. Dark vermiform lines on the sides of the head. Dorsal
fins ochre-coloured or light greenish: D_1 with a black blotch across the last fin-
rays; D_2 and the caudal fin sprinkled with brown on a yellowish ground. Pectoral
bases dark. Eyes large, peculiarly transparent (hence *vitreum*).

This very predatory species is very difficult to keep in captivity; it requires a
large tank with a continuous circulation, such as is only at the disposal of a
public aquarium. Feeds almost entirely on fishes. In general to be treated according
to the instructions given on p. 634. 1938/ –.

Plate 175

Fig. 1008. *Colisa fasciata* (Giant Gourami); adults, somewhat reduced; above ♂, below ♀.
(Original)
Fig. 1009. *Macropodus chinensis* (Round-tailed Paradisefish); natural size; left ♂, right ♀.
Fig. 1010. Mouth of *Luciocephalus pulcher*, showing the protruded folds; greatly enlarged.
(Photo Dr. Foersch)

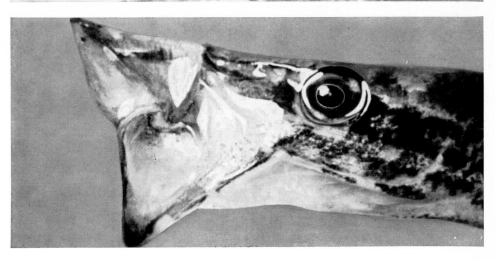

Plate 175

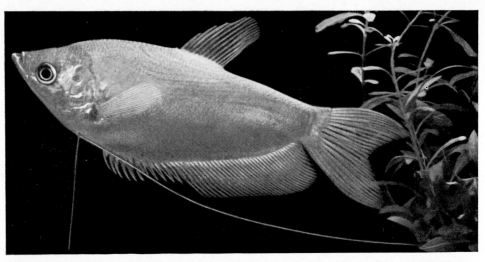

Plate 176

Plate 176

Fig. 1011. *Trichogaster microlepis;* natural size. (Original)
Fig. 1012. *Trichogaster pectoralis* (Snake-skinned Gourami); ripe young, natural size. (Original)
Fig. 1013. *Trichogaster trichopterus trichopterus* (Three-spot Gourami); natural size. (Original)

Family Centropomidae (Glassfishes)

(This family has often been known as the *Ambassidae*, but since the name *Ambassis* has been invalidated under the International Rules of Zoological Nomenclature it seems logical to discourage the popular use of that name and its compounds.)

The Glassfishes are widely distributed, from East Africa to the larger groups of Pacific islands. The majority of the species live in the sea or in brackish water and only a few small forms inhabit fresh water. The transparent, glass-clear body is usually relatively deep and strongly compressed. The vertebral column and swim-bladder are easily visible in the living fish; the latter is often produced to a posterior point in the ♂ but rounded in the ♀. Dorsal fin divided into two parts usually separated by a very deep notch. D_1 is composed entirely of hard rays; D_2 contains one hard ray and 8–18 soft rays. Caudal fin rounded, or deeply forked (genus *Chanda*). Scales usually cycloid, rarely finely ctenoid. Lateral line complete. So far only species belonging to the genus *Chanda* (formerly *Ambassis*) have been imported.

For care and breeding, see under *Chanda ranga*.

Chanda agassizi (*Steindachner* 1867) (Fig. 1014)
Eastern Australia, in brackish and fresh water; to 6·5 cm.

D_1 VIII, D_2 I/8; A III/8; P 13; V I/5; LL 26–29. Rather more elongate than the better-known Indian Glassfish *Chanda ranga*. 9 scales between the end of the head and the dorsal fin. Lateral line complete. The fish is honey-yellow and strongly transparent, mainly shining like brass by reflected light. The region of the body-cavity is silver. Belly white. Snout and nape with a slight dark tinge. Vertical

641

Fig. 1014
(1) *Chanda nama;* ripe ♂;   (2) *Chanda ranga;*
(3) *Chanda buruensis;*   (4) *Chanda agassizi.*
All drawings actual size

fins delicate yellowish, in the ♂ especially quite light rust-red. Leading-edge of D_1 blackish; D_2 and anal fin with a dark band. Lower edge of caudal peduncle black.

The sexes are often not easy to distinguish; see family description.

Care, as given for *Chanda ranga.* Breeding probably not yet achieved in captivity (according to Meinken). 1936/−.

Chanda buruensis (*Bleeker* 1856) (Fig. 1014)　　　　East Indian Glassfish
Thailand, Malay Peninsula, Sumatra, Celebes, Philippines and other localities;
to 7 cm.

D_1 VII, D_2 I/8–9; A III/8–10; P 14; V I/5; LL 27–29. Rather more elongate than
the better-known Indian Glassfish *Chanda ranga*. 13–16 scales between the end of
the head and the dorsal fin. Lateral line briefly interrupted beneath the origin of the
second dorsal. Transparent honey-yellow, shining silver in the region of the body-
cavity. An especially strongly iridescent zone along the middle of the side. Fins
glass-clear to bright yellow. Anterior rays of dorsal blackish.

Ripe adult ♀♀ more robust and uniform yellowish.

Care and breeding, as given for *Chanda ranga*. The ♂♂ are usually rather
quarrelsome among themselves. 1953.

Chanda commersoni (*Cuvier* and *Valenciennes* 1828) (Fig. 822)
Very widely distributed: from the Red Sea and the east coast of Africa to northern
Australia; also in fresh water in Thailand, the Greater Sunda Islands, and New
Guinea; to 10 cm.

D_1 VII, D_2 I/9–10; A III/9–10; P 13; V I/5; LL 27–29. Rather more elongate
than the better-known Indian Glassfish *Chanda ranga*. The two dorsal fins are
very similar in shape. The second ray of the anal fin is the longest. 17–22 scales
between the end of the head and the dorsal fin. Lateral line complete.

♂ transparent, delicate amber-coloured. Flanks shining brass-colour by reflected
light. Crown of head commonly with small black spots. Vertical fins in healthy
fishes bright orange. Tip of first dorsal and tips of caudal lobes lacquer-black.
Ventral fins delicate iridescent greenish.
♀ transparent yellowish; fins without black tips.

Care and breeding, as given for *Chanda ranga*. The addition of sea-salt (50–60 g.
to 10 litres of water) is essential. To stimulate breeding, however, it is necessary to
put the fishes into pure seawater from time to time and then, over a period of days,
to reduce the salinity gradually. The tiny eggs are laid among fine-leaved plants.
Very prolific. The young should be fed with brine-shrimps *(Artemia)* or red *Cyclops* nauplii. 1912/+.

Chanda nama *Hamilton-Buchanan* 1822 (Fig. 1014)　　　　Elongate Glassfish
India and Burma, in fresh and brackish waters; to 11 cm.

D_1 VII, D_2 I/16–17; A III/16–17; P 11; V I/5. Body relatively strongly elongated, strongly compressed. Mouth large, deeply cleft. Lower jaw considerably produced. Scales minute, often irregularly arranged. Lateral line partly distinct, partly absent. Transparent green-yellow with numerous tiny black dots which concentrate into a lengthy transverse blotch behind the gill-cover. Eye dark. Crown of head blackish. Vertical fins bright orange, especially in sexually ripe ♂♂. Outer half of D_1 and tip of D_2 deep black. Caudal fin black and orange with a pale outer border.

♀ fins uniformly yellow.

Care, as given for *Chanda ranga*. A very quarrelsome species, only to be kept together with fishes of the same size. *Chanda nama* is a station-holding fish, which defends its chosen territory against all comers. Very voracious, eating insect-larvae especially. Breeding in captivity probably not yet achieved. 1908/+.

Chanda ranga (*Hamilton-Buchanan* 1822) (Figs. 821, 1014)   Indian Glassfish
India, Burma, Thailand, in fresh and brackish waters; to 7 cm., remaining appreciably smaller in captivity.

D_1 VII, D_2 I/12–15; A III/13–15; P 10–11; V I/5; LL 60–70. Body thick-set, deep, strongly compressed. D_2 rounded. Third ray of anal usually the longest. Transparent as glass.

♂ greenish-yellow to yellowish by direct light, shining gold to iridescent bluish-green by reflected light. Flanks with more or less distinct transverse lines composed of the tiniest black dots. A dark or delicate violet stripe from the gill-cover to the root of the tail. Fins yellowish to delicate rust-red. Dorsal and anal fins with black fin-rays and bordered with pale blue. Pectoral and ventral fin-spines reddish to red or bluish. Caudal fin gleaming gold by reflected light.
♀ coloration considerably duller, yellowish.

Long-established, richly-planted aquaria with a dark soil and not too fresh water. Temperature 18–25°C. The tank should stand in the sunniest place possible. Only such other fishes should be admitted as are peaceful and quiet. Glassfishes are shy to begin with and remain among plants, but soon become tame. Their welfare is enhanced by the addition of common salt, or better sea-salt (3–6 teaspoons to 10 litres of water). Live food, not too coarse, especially small crustacea and Enchytraeids.

Under such conditions the fishes usually spawn readily; rearing the young is the more difficult matter. Willingness to spawn is aroused by morning sunshine, raising the temperature, fresh water and a brief separation of the sexes. It is often a good plan to place several pairs in one tank. The eggs are laid among plants, to which they adhere at once. Each spawning-act produces 4–6 eggs and several such acts follow in rapid succession. As spawning substrates fine-leaved plants, roots of floating plants and Perlon yarn are especially suitable. A spawning produces a grand total of 200 or more eggs. The parents take no interest either in the eggs or in the young. The young hatch within the first 24 hours and are very small. They hang at first on the sides of the tank or on water plants and swim freely after 3–4 days. It is wise to remove the parents at this point. On the second day feeding of the free-swimming young may be commenced, providing them with red *Cyclops* nauplii; Infusoria are not nourishing enough. The problem of feeding now resolves itself into that of so arranging the aeration apparatus that the resulting water-movements continually drive the food past the young as they rest in their shoal. Most failures in breeding can be traced back to the death of young through under-feeding, a danger which is particularly prevalent in this species because the young do not go in search of food as a rule but merely take that which is whirling in front of their mouths. The more often they are fed, the greater will be the survival rate and consequent success. 1905/+.

Chanda wolfii (*Bleeker* 1851) (Fig. 819)
Thailand, Sumatra, Borneo, in fresh water; to 20 cm., remaining considerably smaller in aquaria.

D_1 VII, D_2 I/10(–11); A III/9–10; P 17; V I/5; LL 43–46. Body rather thick-set, deep, strongly compressed. *C. wolfii* is mainly distinguished from other species by the longitudinal scale-count and by the very long second fin-ray of the anal. Young fishes are entirely pale yellow, transparent, with a pronounced silver sheen on the flanks, especially in the region of the body-cavity, and a delicate greenish iridescent lateral band. The mouth is light reddish in healthy fishes.

Sex-distinctions in coloration not yet described.

Care, as given for *Chanda ranga*. Imported fishes remain relatively small even with good feeding. Not yet bred in captivity. 1955.

Gynochanda filamentosa *Fraser-Brunner* 1954 (Fig. 787)
First imported from Singapore by the Frankfurt Tropicarium; original locality unknown; to 5 cm.

D_1 VII; D_2 I/14 (1–6 very elongate, a greatly reduced soft ray between 5 and 6); A III/15 (1–5 very elongate); P 11; V I/5. Body moderately elongate, strongly compressed. Depth of body (at D_1) contained 2·6–2·8 times in the body-length (without caudal). Head-length contained 3·3 times in the body-length. Eye large, 3 times in the head-length. No scales visible. Jaws and vomer toothed. Very beautifully coloured.

♂ Transparent, honey-yellow to delicate yellow-green. Region of body-cavity silvery. 6–10 delicate dark transverse lines on the flanks. Mouth reddish. Fins yellowish, glass-clear. Fin-rays of dorsal and anal fins marked with brown. The short fin-membranes between the elongated rays are often almost entirely black. D_1, as well as the elongated rays of the dorsal and anal fins, with brilliant blue-white tips; hinder parts of these fins similarly coloured.

♀ D_2 and anal fins without produced rays.

This attractive species does very well in brackish water and may be kept in the same manner as *Chanda ranga*. Breeding has been managed successfully, but unfortunately the normally produced fin-rays are much shorter in captive-bred fishes. Breeding, as for *Chanda ranga*. I have not been able to induce my fishes to spawn despite many changes in the water-conditions. Generally very hardy. 1955.

Family Toxotidae (Archerfishes)

The Archerfishes, as their popular name implies, are famous for their abilities as marksmen, being capable of spitting a powerful jet of water at insects crawling about on leaves and twigs above the water and so shooting them down as prey. The most accomplished spitters are the fully-grown adult fishes, which are able to bring down targets 150 cm. above the surface of the water. If the first shot fails then several others follow in rapid succession. This remarkable accomplishment is learned in youth. When the fishes are only about 2–3 cm. long they begin to spit small drops of water which scarcely attain a height of 10 cm. and from these first undirected and unskilled shots a practised skill very soon develops. Insect-shooting is only an accessory means of obtaining food, however, and the fishes feed mainly on swimming or floating water animals. It is therefore easier to persuade hungry fishes to exhibit their art than those which have just eaten, but even so a certain residual 'spitwillingness' must also be present as a rule. Cockroaches make the best prey.

The spitting capacity is made possible by certain peculiarities in the shapes of the tongue and roof of the mouth and by their relationships with one another. The water is expelled, by a powerful contraction of the gill-covers, through a tube formed between the tongue and the roof of the mouth and receives its final deflection in the desired direction from the thin anterior end of the tongue. In spite of many opinions, the question as to how these surface

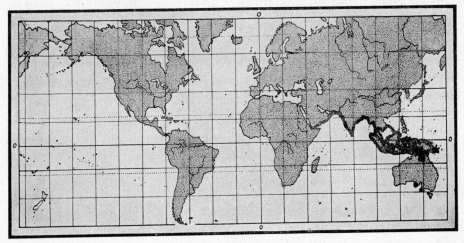

Fig. 1015

Distribution of the *Toxotidae;* note coastal waters of south-east Asia, including the islands.

fishes can estimate the distance of the target out of the water, and still more how they can aim at it, has not been satisfactorily answered.

A second peculiarity is provided by the so-called 'light-flecks' which only occur in the young of this family. These are yellow, iridescent, very strongly refractive flecks near the middle of the back, between or above the broad, black transverse bars. As Lüling has suggested (1956) these flecks must enable the fishes to maintain contact with one another. This view is strengthened by the fact that the young *Toxotes* occur in turbid, mangrove water, and further, by the fact that the older fishes are solitary and exhibit no such light-flecks. Ladiges (1950) observes that one is first aware of the young

647

mainly through their 'lights', for even in turbid water the green iridescent spots are easily recognised. Grown fishes more often betray their presence by the feather-lines drawn by the lower jaw as it rests at the surface of the water.

The area of distribution of the Archerfishes is very large, including as it does the Philippines, Australia, the whole Malay Archipelago, Thailand, southern China, Burma and India, where the fishes chiefly inhabit the turbid, brackish mangrove belt. The young are said to occur where the water is fresher, but it is accepted that the adult fishes spawn far from land in the regions of dead and living coral.

The shape betrays the typical surface-fish. Body elongate, deep, strongly compressed. The upper profile of the head and back as far as the dorsal fin is almost a straight line. Mouth large, deeply cleft, directed obliquely upward. Eyes large. Dorsal and anal fins inserted well back. Pectoral fins very powerful. Ctenoid scales. Lateral line complete. A genus with 5 species, of which so far only 2 have been imported.

Toxotes chatareus (*Hamilton-Buchanan* 1822) (Fig. 1021)
India, Malay Peninsula, southern Thailand, Indo-China, Philippines, Malay Archipelago, northern, western and southern Australia, mainly in brackish water at the mouths of rivers; to 27 cm.

D V/13; A III/17; LL 33–34; TR 5/11–13. Body as in family description. *T. chatareus* is very similar to the following species, but the following distinctions can be made between living fishes: D V in contrast to D IV in *T. jaculator;* head not quite as pointed (Fig. 1021); a black spot dorsally between the first and second broad bars behind the gill-cover which, according to Lüling, is a constant character in southern Malayan fishes; similar spots are commonly found in the other interspaces. Dead specimens are easily distinguished by the longitudinal scale-counts.

Coloration and care, as described for the following species. 1949.

Plate 177

Fig. 1016. *Trichogaster trichopterus sumatranus* (Blue Gourami); sexually-ripe young, natural size. (Original)
Fig. 1017. *Helostoma temmincki* (Kissing Gourami); half-grown, natural size. (Original)
Fig. 1018. *Osphronemus goramy* (Gourami); 50 cm. long, in the Hellabrunn Aquarium, Munich. (Original)

Plate 177

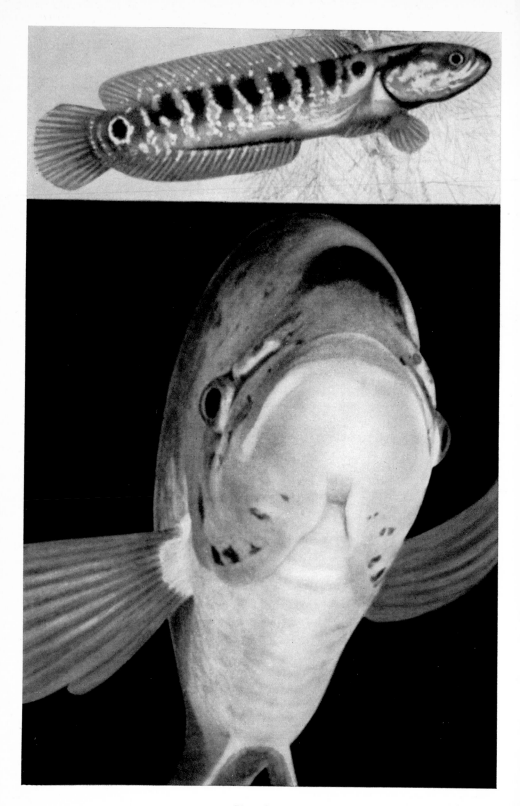

Plate 178

Plate 178

Fig. 1019. *Channa asiatica*; half-grown, reduced.
Fig. 1020. *Osphronemus goramy* (Gourami); head-on view of a 50 cm. specimen in the Hellabrunn Aquarium, Munich. (Original)

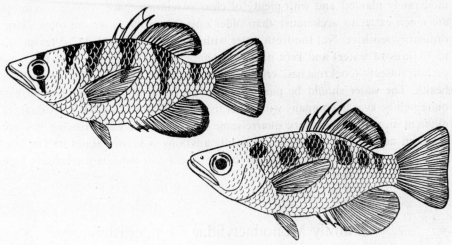

Fig. 1021
Basic patterns of *Toxotes* spp. Left: *Toxotes jaculator* (Archerfish); right: *Toxotes chatareus*

Toxotes jaculator (*Pallas* 1766) (Figs. 968, 1021)   Archerfish
Very widely distributed through the whole of southern and south-eastern Asia, including the Philippines and the Malay Archipelago, also in Australia and in many groups of islands in the Pacific, chiefly in brackish water at the mouths of rivers; to 24 cm., becoming sexually mature at about 10 cm.

D IV/12–13; A III/15–16; LL 28–30; TR 4/9–10. Body as in family description. Very similar to the previous species, which see for discriminating characters. Very variable in coloration and markings owing to its wide distribution.

Younger specimens from south-east Asia are more or less yellow-green to brown on the upperside; flanks delicate grey-green, gradually changing to a pure white-silver ventrally. 4–6 broad black transverse bars may extend far down the body in young fishes but become shorter with increasing age and eventually restricted to the upper half of the body. No dark blotches in the interspaces between the transverse bars, as a rule. Eyes large, silvery, black above and below. Dorsal fin yellow-green

649

with a black border to the soft-rayed portion. Caudal fin dirty yellow-green. Anal fin silver with a broad black margin.

Sex-distinctions not known.

This very interesting species (for an account of its biology see family description) should be accommodated in an aquarium with the largest possible surface-area, moderately planted and with plenty of clear swimming-space. Young specimens are much easier to acclimatise than older ones, since the latter are often extraordinarily sensitive. Not too fresh water with a little sea-salt added (2–3 teaspoons to 10 litres of water) and kept at a high temperature (26–28 °C.). Live food, especially insects (cockroaches, crickets, grasshoppers, flies) is essential to their health. The water should be partly replenished from time to time. *Toxotes* can quite well be kept in company with other fishes of the same size, but individuals of different sizes are often very quarrelsome among themselves. Breeding has not yet been achieved in captivity and hardly anything is known about it. The liveliness, alertness and entire behaviour of the Archerfish indicate a relatively high intelligence for a fish. 1899/+.

Family Monodactylidae / Fingerfishes

Fishes with rather unusual, very deep, strongly compressed bodies, which are only distantly related to the Angelfishes *(Pterophyllum)*. The head and mouth are relatively small. Dorsal and anal fins undivided, to some extent thickly scaled. The anterior spines of the dorsal are short and, as a rule, detached. Small ctenoid scales. Lateral line complete, arched.

The Fingerfishes inhabit the seas and brackish waters of Africa, southern Asia and Australia and sometimes ascend rivers.

Monodactylus argenteus (*Linnaeus* 1758) (Figs. 844, 1023)   Fingerfish
Very widely distributed, from the Malay Archipelago to the east coast of Africa, common in the Red Sea; to 23 cm., remaining considerably smaller in the aquarium.

D VII–VIII/28–30; A III/27–32; P 17; V I/5; LL 55–60. Body discoidal, not quite as deep as long. Ventral fins very small. Silver, with a yellowish-green sheen on the upperside. Healthy fishes have two prominent deep black bands, of which the first begins at the nape and curves forward and downward across the eye, and

650

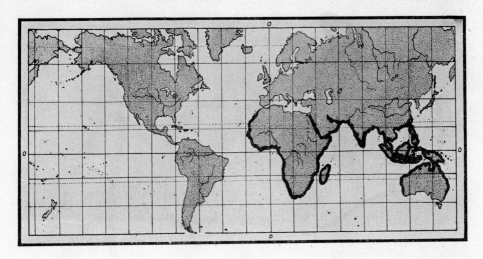

Fig. 1022
Distribution of the *Monodactylidae;* note the coastal waters of southern Asia and Africa.

the second starts at the front end of the dorsal fin and descends in a wide curve across the body and back along the edge of anal fin. Both the dorsal and anal fins are yellow to a lovely orange, with more or less black tips. Caudal fin yellowish.

Sex-distinctions unknown.

M. argenteus can be kept equally well in brackish or in seawater; pure fresh water, however, is not recommended, at least for any considerable period. This lovely shoaling fish requires adequate swimming-space in which its lively, rapid and elegant movements can be shown off to best advantage. Temperature 24–28 °C. Live foods of all kinds, especially large *Daphnia, Tubifex* and Enchytraeids; very voracious. Unfortunately these fishes, like many of the disc-shaped fishes offered for sale, usually remain shy in captivity and are liable to rush madly in all directions when frightened. *M. argenteus* is a very suitable species to keep in an aquarium of coral-fishes. Breeding not yet achieved in aquaria. 1908/+.

Monodactylus sebae (*Cuvier* and *Valenciennes* 1831) (Fig. 1023)
Tropical West Africa, from the mouth of the Senegal to the Congo, in the sea, brackish water and also temporarily in fresh water; to 20 cm.

D VIII/32–36; A III/37; P 17; V I/5; LL 50. Body extraordinarily deep, pointed

651

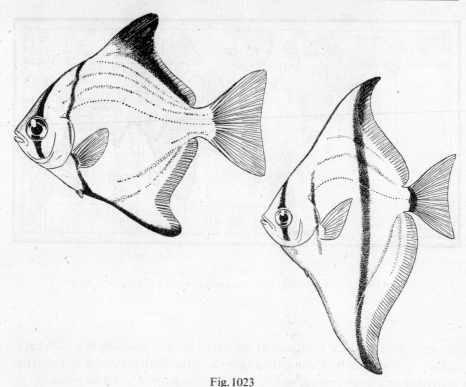

Fig. 1023

Left: *Monodactylus argenteus* (Fingerfish); reduced. Right: *Monodactylus sebae* (Striped Fingerfish); reduced.

in front and behind; the dorsal and anal fins emphasise this shape and are likewise pointed in their soft-rayed portions. Ventral fins reduced to a few small rays. Body silver, light brown on the upper half of the body. 2–5 dark transverse bands, of which 3 are especially prominent; a curved band across the eye, a band from the tip of the dorsal to the tip of the anal and one across the caudal peduncle. These markings become indistinct with age. Vertical fins delicate yellow, rarely orange. According to Arnold dark young also occur.

Sex-distinctions not known.

Care, as given for the previous species. 1914/—.

A few specimens of *Monodactylus falciformis* (Lacépède), whose distribution is similar to that of *M. argenteus*, have also been imported from the Red Sea.

Family Scatophagidae ('Scats', Argus-fishes)

The *Scatophagidae* are coastal fishes, native to south and south-east Asia and the adjacent islands where they may be found in the sea as well as in brackish and fresh water. It is generally believed today that these fishes, like the Archer-fishes, spawn in the neighbourhood of coral reefs, but the young migrate to

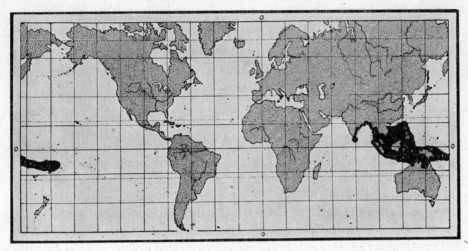

Fig. 1024
Distribution of the *Scatophagidae*

the fresh waters at the mouths of rivers and estuaries until they grow large enough in their turn to go back to the sea. The name *Scatophagus* signifies 'dung-eater' in allusion to the observation that the gut-contents of these fishes always consist of mud and excrement. In fact 'Scats' feed not only on plants and animals but on any mud, decomposing refuse, etc., which can possibly be digested. They collect in great numbers about the sewerage out-falls of large towns and anywhere else where the water brings down human refuse.

Body disc-shaped, deep, strongly compressed. The small ctenoid scales cover not only the head and body but also to some extent, as in the nearly-related *Chaetodontidae* (Coral-fishes), the soft dorsal and anal fins. Lateral line distinct, running about parallel to the profile of the back. Head and mouth small. Dorsal and anal fins composed of both hard- and soft-rayed portions which are almost separated. The anal fin is shorter-based, elevated and banner-like.

Young *Scatophagus* pass through a larval phase called the *Tholichthys* stage, in which a strong bony armouring of the head and nape is developed, which regresses later. Little is known about reproductive biology in general. Rachow put a pair together in a marine aquarium and observed a Cichlid-like spawning in a crevice in a rock, but later lost the newly-hatched larvae through an accident. All subsequent attempts to date have been unsuccessful. The ♂ and ♀ undertake brood-care.

Care in aquarium, as given under *Scatophagus argus*.

Scatophagus argus (*Gmelin* 1788) (Figs.953, 1025)   Scat, Argus-fish
Tropical Indo-Pacific, in sea, brackish and fresh water, locally very common; to 30 cm., remaining considerably smaller in captivity.

D XI/14–15; A IV/14; P 17; V I/5; LL over 100. Shape as given in family description. Coloration variable and very different in various parts of the range. Young fishes of about 2 cm. are usually quite dark in colour. The finest coloration and markings are attained in fishes of about 5–6 cm. total length: uniform greenish-silver, bluish-silver or coffee-brown with a distinct delicate golden sheen, especially on the back. In many fishes increasing age brings an extension of the pale, often red-golden, colour of the back down onto the brown of the flanks to form transverse bars. Transverse rows of large, round blackish spots or irregular transverse bars are superimposed on this ground. The fins may also be very variously coloured. From several localities fishes have been imported which have red spots arranged in various patterns on the back; such forms are known as *Scatophagus rubrifrons*, a name which is quite incorrectly given, since these are merely varieties of *S. argus* and should at most be called 'Red Argus'. Old fishes are usually green-

Fig. 1025
From the top: *Scatophagus argus* (Argus-fish); *Scatophagus tetracanthus* (African Scat); *Solenotoca multifasciata; Solenotoca papuensis.*

654

silver with large black blotches and often yellow-brown and black markings on the fins. Fishes from the sea show especially beautiful colouring.

Sex-distinctions so far unknown.

Scatophagus should be kept in large tanks with plenty of swimming-space. Add sea-salt: 3–4 teaspoons to 10 litres of water. Temperature 20–28 °C. Omnivorous: live food in huge quantities, as well as fine-leaved plants, algae, lettuce, cooked spinach and softened oat-flakes. Aquarium plants are eaten right down to the root-stocks. A very lively and perfectly peaceful species which as a rule leaves even the tiniest fishes unmolested. The locomotion of the Argus-fish is often very peculiar; its swimming can only be described as unsteady and resembles that of the Coral-fishes. A great deal of mulm soon accumulates in a *Scatophagus* tank and should, if possible, be removed by continual filtration. Older fishes should gradually be acclimatised to pure seawater. 1906/+.

Scatophagus tetracanthus (*Lacépède* 1800) (Fig. 1025)   African Scat
Northern Australia, northern New Guinea, East Africa including the neighbouring islands, in salt, brackish and fresh water; to 40 cm., remaining considerably smaller in captivity.

D XI/15–18; A IV/14–15; P 17; V I/5; LL 90–95. This species is distinguished from the previous better-known one by the almost complete division of the dorsal fin and by the transverse bands. Bold black-brown bands on a yellow to blue-silver ground. The number of bands and their extent is very variable, but as a rule the number of bands is inversely correlated with their breadth and their length with the age of the fish. In the young the bands usually extend to the edge of the belly and with increasing age they shrink until they are restricted to the upper half of the body. Dorsal and anal fins brownish; caudal fin yellowish at the base; ventral fins dark brown.

Sex-distinctions unknown.

Care, as given for the previous species. 1939/+.

Plate 179

Fig. 1026. *Ctenopoma oxyrhynchus* (Sharp-nosed Climbing Perch); natural size. (Photo Dr. Foersch)

Fig. 1027. *Ctenopoma ansorgei;* natural size. (Original)

Fig. 1028. *Ctenopoma congicum* (Congo Climbing Perch); maximum size. (Original)

Plate 179

Plate 180

Plate 180

Fig. 1029. *Ctenopoma kingsleyae;* adult, somewhat reduced. (Photo Dr. Foersch)
Fig. 1030. *Ctenopoma ocellatum* (Eye-spot Climbing Perch); somewhat enlarged. (Photo Dr. Foersch)
Fig. 1031. *Ctenopoma acutirostre;* half-grown, natural size. (Photo Dr. Foersch)

Solenotoca multifasciata (*Richardson* 1844) (Fig. 1025)
In quite isolated cases imports of *Scatophagidae* also include specimens belonging to the genus *Solenotoca* which is mainly distinguished from *Scatophagus* by the rather more elongate shape and by the soft dorsal and anal fins. These fins are banner-like and posteriorly straight-edged in *Scatophagus;* relatively long-based and low in *Solenotoca. S. multifasciata* is native to the coasts of Australia, excluding the south coast; to 10 cm.

D XII/16; A VI/16; P 16; V I/5. Uniformly greenish-silver, with a faint brassy glint on the upperside especially. 9–15 very sharply contrasted transverse bands on the flanks which break up into rows of spots below the lateral line. Crown and nape brownish. Fins to some extent marked with black.

Sex-distinctions unknown.

Care and breeding, as given for *Scatophagus argus.* 1954.

The import of a further *Solenotoca* sp., *S. papuensis* Fraser-Brunner 1935, into Central Europe is very questionable. The species comes from New Guinea and Celebes, grows to 10 cm. in length and is mainly distinguished from the previous species by the fewer and broader bars and by the larger spots (Figs. 1000, 1025).

Family Nandidae

The present discontinuous distribution of the *Nandidae* in South America, West Africa and Southern Asia (Fig. 1032) indicates that they are the survivors of a formerly more widespread family. As with the *Cichlidae,* their presence in South America and Africa requires a closer connexion between these two continents, at least by a chain of islands (since both families include brackish-water species) in the Late Mesozoic. (The connexion that accounts for the distribution of the modern *Characidae* may have been earlier.)

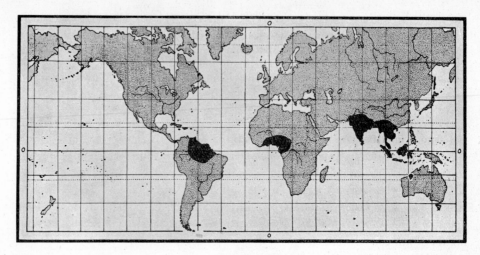

Fig. 1032
Distribution of the *Nandidae*

The *Nandidae* are all relatively small and often very robust in appearance. Body stocky, very deep in some genera, more or less strongly compressed. Head large; mouth often deeply cleft and as a rule highly protrusible. Dorsal fin large; spinous and soft portions united. Caudal fin rounded. Ctenoid scales. Lateral line incomplete or absent.

The sexes are often not easy to recognise, but distinctive markings and colourings do appear to some extent at the beginning of the breeding season. In some species the shape of the anal papilla provides a useful indication, that of the ♀ usually being larger.

The *Nandidae* are biologically very interesting predatory fishes, with a viciousness and greed excelled by few other groups. Most of the species are able to overcome and devour prey measuring up to three-quarters of their own body-length, and many of them consume about their own body-weight in food daily. Similar-sized members of the same species can often be kept together quite satisfactorily as long as suitable hiding-places among stones or root-systems are provided for them. On the other hand, with the possible exception of *Badis badis*, none of the species are suitable inmates for the community tank. The *Nandidae* do best in aquaria standing in a dark position, provided with thick clumps of plants and suitable hiding-places; if these conditions are not fulfilled their initial shyness and timidity generally persist. Live food of all kinds, preferably small fishes, but also beef and horseflesh. Almost all the species spawn in hollows on the bottom, but *Polycentropsis abbreviata* builds a bubble-nest. Brood-care is undertaken by the ♂♂, less often by the ♀♀. The young are very cannibalistic and since, moreover, they tend to grow at different rates, the serious breeder is advised to undertake some sorting and segregation.

Afronandus sheljuzhkoi (*Meinken* 1954)
Africa, Ivory Coast near Abidjan and Agboville, in springs; to about 5 cm. (Maximum length?).

D XV–XVI/9–10; A IV/6–7; V I/4; LL 31. Very closely related to the *Nandus* spp. of south-east Asia and on this account especially interesting from the zoogeographical point of view. Body elongate, moderately deep, compressed. Head large. Mouth deeply cleft and directed obliquely upwards. Lateral line absent. Anal fin-base relatively short. Coloration of a preserved specimen, according to Meinken *(Die Aquarien- und Terrarien-Zeitschrift 54)*: dark brown-olive, darker on the head, nape and along the back. Belly paler. A pale, yellowish-white band, as broad as the diameter of the eye, runs across the body from the origin of the soft dorsal to the origin of the soft anal; the caudal peduncle behind this band is somewhat lighter than the rest of the body. A large, round and rather vague-edged blotch on the gill-cover, joined to the hinder edge of the orbit by a black to blackish bridle-band. Edges of jaws blackish-brown. All fins uniformly black-brown, the ventrals and caudal being somewhat paler.

Sex-distinctions unknown.

According to Sheljuzhko, live imported fishes did very well at first in a small aquarium with flowerpots in which they lived singly, but later they perished through no apparent reason. It seems likely, however, that they are fishes which require a great deal of oxygen. 1952.

Badis badis (*Hamilton-Buchanan* 1822) (Fig. 843)   Badis
India, widely distributed in standing water; to 8 cm.

D VI/VIII/6–10; A III/6–8; LL 26–33. Body elongate, relatively low, a little compressed. Mouth small. Lateral line interrupted. The most beautifully coloured of all the *Nandidae*. The colouring of an individual fish changes extraordinarily rapidly and considerably; in fact quite contrasting colours can appear in a few minutes. Clay-yellow, brownish or green with a bluish sheen; back olive-colour to black-blue; belly greenish or bluish. 6–10 dark transverse bands are often present on the flanks in the young, but older fishes almost invariably lack these markings. A black stripe runs from the mouth across the eye to the origin of the dorsal fin. A dark, pale-bordered shoulder-blotch is usually only indistinctly visible. Especially fine ♂♂ display a mosaic-like arrangement of greenish, yellowish, red and lacquer-black scales on the flanks. The scales of the lateral line are often reddish with golden edges. Fins yellowish-green, bluish or dark blue. The dorsal often has red or green longitudinal stripes and the anterior part is occasionally edged with rose-red.

♀ more plainly coloured. Ventral profile strongly convex, whereas that of the ♂ is always inclined to be concave.

Care and breeding, as given in the family description. In contrast to other *Nandidae*, *Badis badis* is quite peaceful, even towards other members of its own kind when kept in a community tank; in a tank restricted to the one species, on the other hand, it becomes very quarrelsome. Temperature 26–28 °C. Live food of all kinds. The welfare of *Badis* depends very largely on the availability of hiding-places, and if the fishes are provided with crevices among stones, reclining flower-pots or tangles of roots, and thick clumps of plants they lose their proverbial shyness. The spawn is usually deposited on the upper side of a hollow stone or flowerpot, and the ♂ guards the brood. Not very prolific. The young are rather delicate to begin with. 1904/+.

A brown-red variety with longitudinal rows of dark spots, imported from Burma, was described as *Badis badis burmanicus* by Ahl (1936).

Monocirrhus polyacanthus *Heckel* 1840 (Fig. 847)   South American Leaf-fish
Basins of the Amazon and Rio Negro, western Guiana; to 8 cm.
D XVI–XVII/11–13; A XII–XIII/11–14; P 18–20; V I/5; LL 34–38. Body deep,

Plate 181

Fig. 1033. *Betta splendens* (Fighting Fish); various domesticated colour-varieties. (Original)
Fig. 1034. *Luciocephalus pulcher;* ripe adults, somewhat reduced; above ♂, below ♀. (Original)

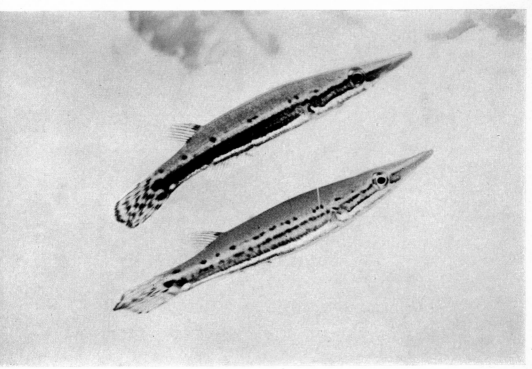

Plate 181

Plate 182

Plate 182

Fig. 1035. *Macropodus opercularis* (Paradisefish); ripe young, natural size. (Original)
Fig. 1036. *Sphaerichthys osphromenoides* (Chocolate Gourami); half-grown fishes, somewhat enlarged. (Original)

egg-shaped. Front of head pointed. Mouth highly protrusible. A short, barbel-
like flap on the lower lip, erected when the fish is excited. The coloration is very
variable, depending in the first place on the bottom and conditions in the tank.
When among plants, the fish is marbled with green and yellowish; in the open water
it is usually clay-yellow to brownish, also marbled with dark brown. Three fine
dark lines radiate from the eye; one across the gill-cover to the root of the tail, a
second obliquely upwards and a third obliquely downwards to the edge of the
belly. The spinous parts of the dorsal and anal fins are greenish to yellowish; the
soft-rayed parts of these fins, together with the caudal, glass-clear.

Sex-distinctions unknown.

A very interesting but also extraordinarily predatory species. The fishes rest
obliquely, head-down in the water and preferably among plants, looking deceptively like drifting dead leaves. Leaf-fishes are very bad swimmers. Large, long-
established aquaria, thickly planted. Temperature 22–25°C. Since this species
feeds almost exclusively on fishes, of which it requires daily a quantity about equal
to its own weight, it is not easy to keep; live-bearing Tooth-Carps are the most
acceptable food. Very soft, slightly acid water (2–4° German Hardness Scale,
pH 6–6·5) is essential for its health. The Leaf-fish spawns on large plant leaves,
stones or on the glass sides of the aquarium which it meticulously cleans beforehand. Courtship is a very straightforward affair; the pair proceed straight to the
actual spawning. The few, large eggs are guarded and fanned by the ♂; the ♀ should
be removed. The young hatch after 3–4 days and are at first almost colourless and
quite large; as soon as they swim freely they may be fed with *Cyclops* and other
Copepods. After a month the fishes should be isolated since they try to swallow
one another. During this phase of development the young become covered with
white spots which look rather like those of the *Ichthyophthirius*-disease of the same
name, but these soon disappear of their own accord. 1912/+.

Nandus nandus (*Hamilton-Buchanan* 1822) (Fig. 845)   Nandus
India, Burma, Thailand; to 20 cm.

D XII–XIV/11–13; A III/7–9; P 15; V I/5; LL 46–57. Body elongate, perch-
like. Head large, scaled. Mouth very large, protrusible. Lower jaw projecting.

661

Hinder end of gill-cover pointed. Preopercular serrate. Coloration sombre, marbled with large blotches of yellow-green/olive-green/dark brown. Upperside especially dark; underside often light reddish. Fins greenish to yellowish. Dorsal fin as a rule included in the marbled pattern of the body; the other fins to some extent with rows of greenish spots.

♀ altogether paler in tone; fins smaller.

Care, as given in family description. This very predatory species is best kept in slightly brackish water (1–2 teaspoons of sea-salt to 10 litres of water). Not yet bred in captivity. 1904/+.

Nandus nebulosus (*Gray* 1830)
Thailand, Malay Peninsula, Greater Sunda Islands; to 12 cm.

D XIV–XV/11–12; A III/5–6; P 16; V I/5; LL 34–35. Shape similar to that of the previous species, from which *N. nebulosus* is mainly distinguished by its obviously larger scales and by the fin-formula. Ground-colour fawn to grey-brown, with irregular transverse band-like blotches of dark brown or occasionally even blackish. A very conspicuous dark band, posteriorly pale-edged, extends from the mouth across the eye and thence in an arch to the leading edge of the dorsal fin. Spinous portions of dorsal and anal fins brown; remaining parts of these fins, like the caudal, pale and transparent.

Sex-distinctions unknown.

Care, as given in family description. Like *Nandus nandus*, very predatory. Not yet bred in captivity. 1934/+.

Polycentropsis abbreviata *Boulenger* 1901 (Fig. 1037)   African Leaf-fish
Tropical West Africa, Lagos, Niger, Ogowe; to 8 cm.

D XV–XVII/9–11; A IX–XII/8–9; P 18–19; V I/5; LL 31–35. Shape similar to that of the better-known *Polycentrus schomburgki*, but rather shorter. Pointed snout still further produced. Soft portions of dorsal and anal fins short-based,

Figs. 1037–1040

Fig. 1037. *Polycentropsis abbreviata* (African Leaf-fish); adult, reduced.
Fig. 1038. *Pristolepis fasciata;* adult, reduced.
Fig. 1039. *Therapon jarbua* (Saltwater Zebrafish); young, natural size.
Fig. 1040. *Lates niloticus* (Nile Perch); greatly reduced.

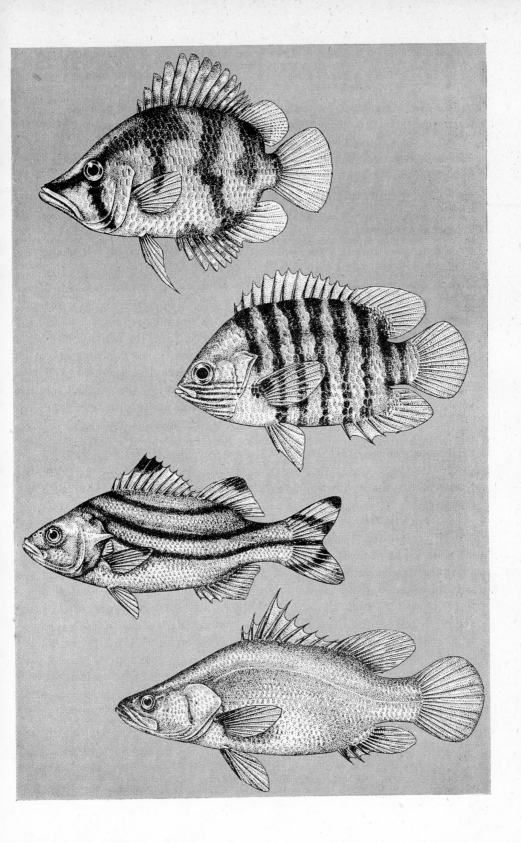

banner-like, elevated above the adjacent spinous rays. Lateral line very short. Coloration very variable but always dark. Ochre to dark grey-green with large brown to blackish blotches, to some extent like transverse bands. A conspicuous dark band from the snout across the eye to the origin of the dorsal fin; a similar band from the eye upwards. Spinous portions of dorsal and anal fins dark; soft-rayed parts occasionally faint rust-red at the base but usually transparent and colourless.

♀ paler at spawning time.

Care, as given in family description. Reproduction very interesting. The African Leaf-fish builds a large bubble-nest, preferably underneath floating leaves or alternatively among *Riccia*. In the actual spawning-act the ♀ turns onto her back underneath the nest and lays a single egg in it from time to time, up to a total of about 100 eggs in all. The ♀ should be removed when she has finished spawning. The ♂ undertakes the care of the brood; at first he keeps the nest together and later, when the young hatch (after about 48 hours at 28 °C.), he gathers them into a depression on the bottom or among stones and guards the little shoal after the fashion of most Cichlids. The serious breeder should remove the ♂ as soon as the young are swimming freely about the tank. The young are very voracious and, in soft slightly peaty water, they grow rapidly and without casualties. 1906/+.

Polycentrus schomburgki *Müller* and *Troschel* 1849 (Fig. 846)   Schomburgk's or
South American Leaf-fish
North-eastern South America and Trinidad; to 10 cm., remaining smaller in captivity.

D XVI–XVIII/8–9; A XIII/6–8; P 15; V I/5; LL 25–27. Body thick-set, deep, strongly compressed. Mouth very large, protrusible. A spine at the hinder edge of the gill-cover. Soft-rayed portions of dorsal and anal fins banner-like, elevated above the spinous parts. Lateral line absent. A beautiful and interesting species. Coloration very variable, depending in the first instance upon temperature and degree of excitement. Pale grey, brownish grey, leather-brown to deep black with dark spots and dots which often have a silvery glint. 3 dark brown to black, usually yellow-edged, wedge-shaped bands radiate from the eye to the snout, the nape and the lower edge of the gill-cover. Spinous portions of dorsal and anal fins olive-green to dark blue, bordered with bluish-white and with large pale-bordered blotches at their bases. The soft dorsal and anal fins, like the caudal and pectorals, are colourless and glass-clear. Ventral fins produced to long points, greenish with yellow leading edges.

♀ duller in colour, the basic colour more brown; very pale at spawning time.

♂ at spawning time velvet-black with silvery-blue or turquoise spots and dots. At this time, too, the hinder parts of the dorsal and anal fins, as well as the caudal, are black.

Care and breeding, as given in the family description. 1907/+.

Pristolepis fasciata (*Bleeker* 1851) (Fig. 1038)
Burma, Thailand, Indo-China and sundry islands of the Malay Archipelago; to 21 cm.

D XIII–XVI/14–16; A III/8–9; V I/5–6; LL 26–28. Body thick-set, very deep, compressed. In contrast to the genus *Nandus*, with which *Pristolepis* has much in common, the latter has a narrow, only slightly protrusible, mouth. Gill-cover with two flattened spines. Lateral line interrupted under the soft dorsal fin and displaced further ventrally. Greenish to yellow-green with 8–12 rather regular dark transverse bands, which are especially prominent in the young. Upperside darker; belly pale, usually yellowish. Several dark longitudinal lines beneath the eye, extending from the mouth to the gill-cover. Fins greenish; pectoral fins yellow.

Little is known of the behaviour of this species in captivity. Probably they are territorial fishes and liable to be quarrelsome among themselves. Live food of all kinds. 1932/–.

Pristolepis and *Badis* form a distinct sub-family of the *Nandidae*, which some authors elevate to the rank of a distinct family.

Family Cichlidae / Cichlids

Altogether attractively coloured fishes of Perch-like appearance, chiefly native to Africa, Central America and tropical South America. The Cichlids are distinguished from the true Perches (*Percidae, Centrarchidae, Nandidae*) by, among other characters, the presence of only one nostril on each side of the head which serves simultaneously as entrance and exit for the nasal cavity. In the true Perches, on the other hand, these two nasal openings are separate so that two nostrils are to be observed on each side of the head. The body is usually deep to very deep, often even disc-shaped and strongly compressed, rarely elongate and low (e.g., in *Crenicichla*). The almost invariably large head becomes further accentuated in the ♂♂ of many species (both sexes in some) through the development with age of swollen cushions of fatty tissue in the snout region and the hinder part. The mouth is protrusible, usually broad and often bordered by swollen lips. The long-based dorsal fin and shorter-based anal always consist of anterior spinous and posterior

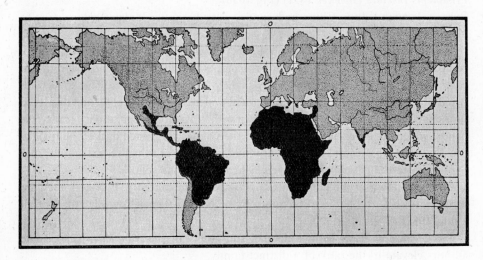

Fig. 1041
Distribution of the *Cichlidae*

soft-rayed portions and their hinder ends, especially commonly in ♂♂, may be pointed or even considerably produced. In some Cichlids, as in the genus *Pterophyllum*, these fins may be extremely large and are carried spread out like sails. Caudal fin rounded posteriorly or squarely truncated, more rarely emarginate. The lateral line in Cichlids is usually in two parts; the upper portion extends from the gill-cover to below the soft dorsal while the lower portion appears as though the hinder part of the upper lateral line has been broken off and transposed to a lower level.

In their natural habitats Cichlids frequent standing or sluggish waters in which there are good hiding-places under banks or among waterlogged branches, between stones or in plant thickets. Many species are pronounced station-holding or territorial fishes which, in the breeding season at least, annex a clearly-defined living-space which they defend against all comers and from which they forage for prey. Apart from some *Geophagus* and *Tilapia* spp. and a few specialised lake genera which feed almost exclusively on plant materials, almost all Cichlids are predatory fishes which in nature feed predominantly upon smaller fishes (even their own species), upon insect-larvae, water-beetles, worms, etc. Some are specialised mollusc-eaters. Many Cichlids, like the genus *Pelmatochromis* and some species of *Tilapia* and *Cichlasoma*, enter brackish water.

Keeping Cichlids is one of the most interesting problems in the aquarium hobby. In general these fishes, with the possible exception of the so-called Dwarf Cichlids *(Apistogramma, Nannacara, Pelmatochromis, Nannochromis)* and the disc-shaped Cichlids *(Pterophyllum, Symphysodon, Uaru)*, are quarrelsome with their own kind and towards other species, and also have an annoying tendency to grub up the bottom and devastate the plants. For all that, Cichlid keeping has much to recommend it and will certainly attract much more attention from serious hobbyists in the future than hitherto. Furthermore, the undesirable peculiarities of many species can be diminished by thoughtful furnishing of the aquarium, for very often their awkwardness is nothing more than the reaction of very intelligent fishes to unsuitable conditions. Since the special requirements of the various species will be dealt with in the individual descriptions only the essentials will be summarised here.

For all large Cichlids, such as *Aequidens, Cichlasoma, Geophagus, Hemichromis, Tilapia*, etc., the largest possible aquaria should be made available. In the case of genera which stir up the bottom a great deal *(Cichlasoma, Geophagus* and *Tilapia)* planting should be avoided at the outset and a natural biotope should be built up from an artificial rock background with numerous corners or groups of stones or hollow root-systems in which the fishes can hide. Coarse-grade gravel or basalt chips will serve quite well for the bottom. This arrangement may be enlivened by tough hanging roots and a loose cover of floating plants which further contributes very much to the welfare of most species. For species which dig very little, or only at spawning time, one can also provide tough aquatic plants or marsh plants in flower-pots. Quite a different furnishing is required for species which do not dig and which are found mainly among loose plant-stands in their natural habitat. For *Apistogramma* spp., see under *A.agassizi;* for *Pelmatochromis*, under *P.annectens,* and for *Pterophyllum* and *Symphysodon,* under the corresponding genera.

The feeding of Cichlids usually presents no difficulties. Large live food of all kinds; occasionally dried food is also greedily accepted provided mono-tony in the diet is avoided. Many species can be accustomed to horseflesh or veal. *Tilapia* spp., as well as some *Cichlasoma* and *Geophagus,* require supplementary vegetable food in the form of green lettuce, algae, softened oat-flakes and boiled spinach,

The juxtaposition of pairs ready to spawn is difficult and in many species has not yet been achieved. While young fishes are generally peaceful towards one another at first and even remain together in schools, they always become more independent with increasing size and even cannibalistic, not infre-quently feeding on their weaker brethren. Grown fishes are often extraordin-arily hostile towards one another; and a strong fish may kill all its compan-ions of the same species. Large tanks with numerous hiding-places help to diminish this rivalry. Putting the ♂ and ♀ together is an operation which always requires foresight. Success can sometimes be achieved by at first separating the partners by a pane of glass and after some days removing the pane experimentally during the daytime and, after a further period, at night as well. Even this precaution, however, often enough ends with the death of the ♀. There is less risk in selecting harmonising pairs from a shoal of young fish, for frequently such pairs separate themselves and prove highly com-

Plate 183

Fig. 1042. *Trichogaster leeri* (Pearl Gourami); ripe young, natural size. (Original)
Fig. 1043. *Colisa lalia* (Dwarf Gourami); natural size. (Original)

Plate 183

Plate 184

Plate 184

Fig. 1044. *Tetraodon miurus;* maximum size. (Original)
Fig. 1045. *Tetraodon palembangensis;* half-grown, natural size. (Original)

patible on reaching sexual maturity. In almost all Dwarf Cichlids, on the other hand, the choice of pairs is considerably easier, but some large Cichlids are also quite peaceful in this regard, as for example *Pterophyllum eimekei, Cichlasoma severum*, most *Aequidens* spp., some *Tilapia* and *Haplochromis* spp., etc.

Breeding and care of young: pairs of many Cichlids reproduce easily in aquaria and are further very prolific. Some, on the contrary, like *Symphysodon discus, Uaru*, some *Apistogramma*, can only be bred with difficulty even in the tanks of experienced breeders. In the typical case the partners begin to clean a previously selected place with their mouths, very likely a flat stone, a dark hollow or the broad leaves of some aquatic plant. All day long in this way the chosen place is worked over again and again. Other species, like many *Haplochromis* and *Tilapia*, prepare shallow depressions in advance and even peaceful species now drive off every animal which approaches the future spawning-place. During this time the fishes don their usually very gay spawning-livery and the ♀ as a rule becomes very portly. A further characteristic of the courtship period is the prominence of the genital papilla, which in the ♀ is almost always bluntly conical in contrast to that of the ♂ which is pointed (often the only certain external sexual character).

The behaviour of the two sexes at pairing-time is quite characteristic. The courtship may include a gracefully-swum dance as well as nuptial biting. Rival ♂♂ often seize one another by the mouth and pull their opponents hither and thither. The ♀ lays her eggs in regular rows or groups in the chosen place, usually 3–8 at a time, and they are at once fertilised by the ♂ who glides down upon them with extended genital papilla. This process is repeated many times. The size and number of the eggs are very distinctive. Mouthbrooders and Dwarf Cichlids lay the largest eggs, though usually not more than 100 (far more in the large mouth-brooding *Tilapia* spp.). The eggs are adhesive at first and generally both partners look after them and fan them with their pectoral fins. In *Apistogramma* spp. – with the exception of *A. ramirezi* – the ♀♀ alone undertake the care of the eggs (for Mouth-brooders see below). After an average of 2–4 days the young hatch – many Cichlids chew the young out of the eggshells – and are now brought to previously prepared pits, crevices in rocks or large leaves and are several times re-transferred before they are ready to swim. The parents also deal with the problem of fresh water and, indeed, the often soiled young are chewed over and so cleaned. Once the fry are ready to swim the parents begin to lead the little shoal. At first the whole swarm remain timidly close together; strays are picked up in the mouth and spat back, laggards driven forward into the group. The parents direct the movements of the shoal by definite patterns of swimming and in times of danger many species (*Apisotogramma, Etroplus*, etc.) have a striking signal-and-reaction system. Thus when the ♀ makes certain movements with her mouth the whole shoal 'freezes' and becomes almost invisible.

Frequently the parents help their brood to feed, seizing large prey in the mouth and masticating it and then either spitting the finely-divided particles out among the brood or whirling them out through the gill-openings in the respiratory stream. Since the young also begin to forage for fine-grade food once they commence to swim, such food (*Cyclops* nauplii, Rotifers, chopped Enchytraeids, etc.) must now be introduced into the tank. Growth of the young is usually rapid and gradually the cohesion of the shoal decreases until it finally disappears; at the same time the parents lose their instinct for brood-care and must be removed. This operation is not necessary with *Pterophyllum*.

Brood-care, which is exhibited in various ways – young *Symphysodon discus*, for example, cling to the bodies of their parents – is most intensely developed in Mouth-brooders. Mouth-brooding Cichlids, such as the African *Haplochromis* and many *Pelmatochromis* and *Tilapia* spp., also *Geophagus cupido* from the Amazon, usually lay their eggs initially in shallow depressions and subsequently take them, or more rarely the young fish, up into the mouth where they are accommodated in a broadening of the floor of the buccal cavity (throat-sac). In *Geophagus cupido* the eggs are carried against the roof of the mouth. The parents effect a continual shuffling of the layers by means of chewing-movements and thereby ensure a good aeration of all the eggs. Even the young are sheltered in this way, at least until their yolk-sacs have been absorbed, and later still they are only allowed to go free for short periods. At night, or when danger threatens, they are again stowed in the mouth. Usually only the ♀♀ concern themselves with mouth-brooding; in a few cases the ♂ takes full responsibility (e. g. *Tilapia heudeloti*) or takes some share of responsibility *(Tilapia galilaea)*. Finally, in *Pelmatochromis guentheri*, the sexes relieve one another in mouth-brooding. During the brooding period, a maximum of 4–5 weeks, the parent concerned takes no food.

In conclusion, it must be said, in this matter of breeding and the care of the young, that frequently the first clutch is devoured by the parents but that in this event a subsequent one is all the more intensively cared for. Any intrusion during the period of brood-care is to be avoided, since disturbed fishes readily respond by destroying the eggs or young.

Unfortunately there is a commercial approach to be considered, even in such a highly interesting case as the breeding of Cichlids. The serious breeder frequently takes the clutch away from the parents and hatches the eggs in an all-glass tank with moderate aeration. Practical as this method may be for professional breeders, it should not be at all to the taste of amateurs who would thereby deprive themselves of the opportunity of making very interesting observations.

Cichlids are generally not dependent on the composition of the water, although many species have a very low tolerance of transfer to fresh water. Where water factors are important they will be dealt with under the individual descriptions.

The coloration and markings of all the species are highly susceptible to change in relation to the emotional condition and life-phase of the fish (Fig. 1046).

671

Cichlids of North, Central and South America

Acaropsis nassa (*Heckel* 1840) (Fig. 1053)
Guiana, northern Amazon Basin; to 20 cm.

D XII–XIV/9–11; A III/7–9; LL 22–24. Body deep, strongly compressed. Mouth extraordinarily large and highly protrusible. Coloration very attractive but very variable in relation to age and emotional condition. Ground-colour dull greenish-silver to yellow-brown with a greenish sheen. Back rather dark; flanks paler, with rows of pale blue, silver or green-golden spots especially on the lower part. On the gill-cover, underneath the eye, are two black blotches which, in younger fishes especially, are ringed with golden spots. Similar blotches are to be found on the gill-cover at the level of the eye (a small blotch), on the middle of the side (a large blotch) and at the root of the tail. A dark longitudinal band and several transverse bands are not always distinctly apparent. Fins delicate red-brown or greenish, to some extent marked with dark spots and streaks.

♂ dorsal and anal fins produced, pointed; coloration as given above.
♀ dorsal and anal fins rounded or pointed, but never produced. Coloration less brilliant.

Care, as given in family description. A very snappish and predatory species which can only be kept in company with predatory fishes of similar size. Fishes of the same species are compatible almost only when a sufficiency of hollow stones or other hiding-places allows each individual to take station in a definite territory. Temperature not less than 22 °C. Live food, with small fishes at least occasionally.
Nothing is known about reproduction. 1909/+.

Aequidens curviceps (*E. Ahl* 1924) (Fig. 854)　　　　　　　Flag Cichlid
Amazon Basin; to 8 cm.

D XV/7; A III/7; P 15; LL 23–24; TR 2½–3/8–9. Body deep, strongly compressed. Head large.

Fig. 1046
Patterns of markings in *Apistogramma reitzigi*. In each pair of figures the ♂ is shown on the right, behind the ♀. (1) Basic colour-pattern; (2) Fright-pattern; (3) Threat-pattern; (4) Breeding-dress; (5) Assembling-pattern, adopted by the ♀ when guarding and collecting the brood; ♂ intrasexual combat-pattern. (After D. Vogt)

672

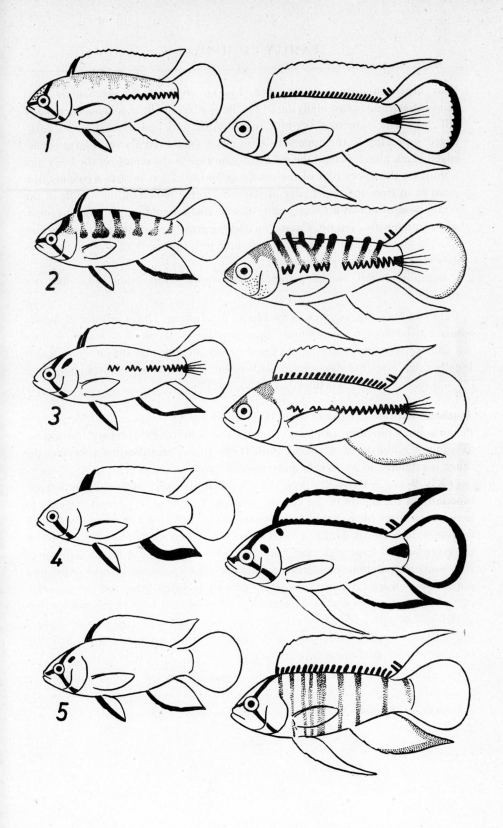

♂ Back brownish-green to olive-green. Flanks silver-grey to green-silver, also yellow-green and occasionally dark blue. Belly silvery to light golden. Cheeks and gill-cover with numerous sky-blue to turquoise dots and streaks. Scales dark-edged, especially on the upperside. Iris golden, blood-red above. A large vague-edged black blotch behind the gill-cover, another in the middle of the body and a third on the upper part of the caudal peduncle. There is often a pale longitudinal band from the upper edge of the orbit to the blotch on the middle of the body. Base of dorsal fin blue-green, middle shining gold, upper edge greenish-white, often with a red tip. Caudal fin and the greatly produced anal fin greenish to olive-green with curved rows of pale-blue to turquoise dots. Ventral fins delicate blue-green; pectorals greenish.

♀ Coloration duller; caudal peduncle more grey. Dorsal and anal fins not produced.

Care and breeding, as given in the family description. This is a peaceful species which can be kept in a community aquarium out of the breeding season. It does not damage plants even during the breeding season. The first spawning of eggs is usually eaten after 1–2 days, but a further clutch is then very meticulously cared for and reared. A very worthwhile Cichlid. 1911/+.

Aequidens latifrons (*Steindachner* 1878) (Figs. 852, 926)
Panama and Colombia; to 15 cm. Axelrod and Schultz (1955) regard this species as a junior synonym of *A. pulcher* (Gill 1858). If this identification is correct the range is extended to Venezuela and Trinidad.

D XIV/9–10; A III/7(–8); P 14; LL 23–24. Body deep, strongly compressed, especially in the region of the caudal peduncle. Forehead very broad. Yellow- to grey-brown; back olive; flanks with a bluish sheen; belly paler. 5–8 vaguely defined transverse bars on the flanks; a black lateral blotch on the 4th bar. Each scale on the body bears a large iridescent blue, pale blue or blue-green blotch. Gill-cover with numerous shining blue-green to metallic blue spots and streaks. Anal and dorsal fins bluish to greenish; caudal fin delicate to bright wine-red. All fins with curved rows of sky-blue dots. Dorsal fin with a pale red to dark red border. Iris golden-yellow with a red periphery. Lips pale blue. All the colours become beautifully iridescent at spawning time; simultaneously a further 6–8 longitudinal rows of shining green-gold spots become very prominent.

♂ the produced and curved rays of the dorsal and anal fins often reach to the caudal.

♀ finnage less strongly developed.

674

Care and breeding, as given in the family description. Since the excreta of this species make the water very turbid, frequent additions of fresh water are necessary. In old water the fishes become susceptible to diseases. They spawn very readily and several times a year. They do not grub up the bottom to any extent nor damage the plants. Sexually ripe at 7–8 cm. An attractive species. 1906/+.

Aequidens maroni (*Steindachner* 1882) (Fig. 853)   Keyhole Cichlid
Guiana; to 10 cm.

D XV/10; A III/9–11; P 15; LL 22–24. Body deep, short, compressed. Forehead strongly convex. Coloration very attractive and variable. Yellowish, cream-coloured to pale brown, occasionally chocolate-brown. 12–13 rows of dark spots on the flanks. A blackish band, edged with a pale stripe above, runs in an arc to the eye and thence, becoming increasingly broad, to the lower, hinder end of the head. A dark, pale-rimmed blotch under the last three spines of the dorsal fin, continued ventrally as a broad transverse band. A dark longitudinal band extending from the gill-cover is usually only faintly apparent. Fins brownish to green-yellow. Dorsal and anal fins with pale green spots on the posterior, soft-rayed portions; these same fins have white edges also.

Sexes not easily distinguished.

♀ dorsal and anal fins not as strongly produced as in the ♂.

Care and breeding, as given for *Aequidens curviceps*. One of the most peaceful Cichlids. The young can be left with their father for over six months. This species does not grub up the bottom. 1936/+.

Aequidens portalegrensis (*Hensel* 1870) (Fig. 866)   Port or Black Acara
Southern Brazil, Bolivia; to 25 cm., remaining appreciably smaller in captivity.

D XV/10; A III/9; P 14–15; LL 24–26. Body deep, compressed. Head large. Coloration very variable, depending on age and locality.

♂ Younger fishes are greenish or bluish to brownish, with a bluish, yellowish or reddish sheen by reflected light. The scales are dark-edged, especially on the upperside of the body. A more or less prominent broad dark band extends from the hinder edge of the orbit to a black-brown, greenish- to yellowish-bordered blotch in the upper part of the caudal peduncle. When the fish is excited the whole body may become quite dark. Dorsal fin blue-grey. Caudal and anal fins pale green to brownish-green. The soft-rayed hinder parts of the dorsal and anal fins, as well as the caudal are adorned with alternately black and pale

675

green vermiform flecks and spots. Pectoral fins delicate wine-red. Both sexes are often black in the breeding season.

♀ Basic tint more reddish; fins brownish.

Care and breeding, as given in family description. Rather tolerant as regards temperature; 16–20°C. in winter, up to 22°C. in summer. This species likes to dig up the bottom, especially at spawning time, and continually turns over the soil around the nest. No rooted plants; on the contrary pieces of wood, stones, and flowerpots, with a surface covering of floating plants. The young are often really pugnacious but well-adjusted fishes are peaceful enough. 1913/+.

Aequidens pulcher (*Gill* 1858) (Fig. 1055)　　　　　　　　　Blue Acara
Trinidad, northern Venezuela; to 17 cm.

D XIV/10; A III/8; P 14; LL 23–25. Body deep, egg-shaped, strongly compressed. Delicate olive-green to yellow-green; underside grey-silver to bluish. On the flanks there are 8 vaguely-delimited transverse bands and numerous narrow longitudinal bands, the latter separated by longitudinal rows of grass-green or brass-coloured scales. A deep black blotch under the eye and another about in the middle of the body; a vertical black stripe also on the caudal peduncle. Numerous shining green vermiform lines on the head and similar spots on the body. Dorsal and caudal fins clay-colour with dark spots. Ventral and anal fins to some extent blue-green, likewise delicately spotted.

Care, as given in the family description. Nothing is known about breeding, but according to Regan there are no especial peculiarities. 1934/−.

Axelrod and Schultz (1955) regard *Aequidens latifrons* (Steindachner 1878) as a junior synonym of *A. pulcher*. If this synonymy is correct then the range of the present species becomes extended to Panama and Colombia.

Aequidens tetramerus (*Heckel* 1840) (Fig. 1054)　　　　　Saddle Cichlid
Throughout central and north-eastern South America; to 25 cm., remaining appreciably smaller in captivity.

Plate 185

Fig. 1047. *Cottus gobio* (Miller's Thumb); natural size. (Original)
Fig. 1048. *Cottus gobio;* ♂ resting on the ball of spawn. (Original)
Fig. 1049. *Melanotaenia nigrans* (Australian Red-tailed Rainbowfish); ripe young, natural size; above ♂, below ♀. (Original)

676

Plate 185

Plate 186

Plate 186

Fig.1050. *Evorthodus breviceps;* ripe adults, natural size. (After Innes)
Fig.1051. *Pygosteus pungitius* (Nine-spined Stickleback); maximum size, left ♂, right ♀.
(Original)
Fig.1052. *Achirus fasciatus;* half-grown, enlarged. (Original)

D XV–XVI/10; A III/8; P 15; LL 26–27. Body rather more elongate than in the previous species, strongly compressed. Head and back thick. Coloration very variable, in relation to the wide distribution.

♂ Back usually greenish to brownish; flanks yellowish to grey; underside delicate reddish; throat usually brilliant violet. A dark longitudinal band runs from the eye to a black, gold-rimmed blotch at the root of the tail. Irregular transverse bands, as well as a dark, vaguely-delimited blotch at about the middle of the side, are not always clearly apparent. A small and always distinct black triangle underneath the eye is especially characteristic. Fins greenish-brown or yellowish or blue-grey, with rows of dark spots. Dorsal and anal fins greatly produced.

♀ Ends of dorsal and anal fins usually blunt. Colouring duller, fishes occasionally almost uniformly clay-coloured.

Care and breeding, as given in the family description. This species does not generally grub up the bottom and is therefore quite suitable for a planted aquarium. The young are not only more beautifully coloured but also at the same time more peaceful than the adults. The Saddle Cichlid is esteemed as a food-fish in its native countries. 1909/−.

Aequidens thayeri (*Steindachner* 1875)
A species from the Amazon Basin which has probably not yet been imported. Specimens so described almost invariably prove to belong to *Aequidens curviceps*.

Apistogramma agassizi (*Steindachner* 1875) (Fig.865)　　　Agassiz' Dwarf Cichlid
Amazon Basin, southwards to Bolivia; to 7·5 cm., ♂♂ often somewhat larger.

D XV/7; A III/6; P 14; LL 23. Body elongate, compressed. Dorsal fin very long-based. Back brown-yellow to green-blue; flanks orange, becoming greenish-blue posteriorly. Gill-cover with shining blue streaks and vermiform markings. Back and flanks set with numerous glittering green-blue spots. From the mouth to the root of the tail (omitting the eye) there extends a sharply-contrasted brown-black longitudinal band. A second line, which is curved, runs obliquely upwards from the mouth. The base of the dorsal fin is blackish, its centre blue-green in front, marbled smoke-grey to pale behind; its margin and its greatly produced posterior point are poppy-red. Anal fin yellow-green with pale fin-rays and a red tip. The upper edge of the heart-shaped caudal fin is grey-green, with a smoke-grey zone underneath it, the centre is marbled with ivory and blue-green, with a brilliant orange zone beneath it which extends to the tip of the fin; the lower part is blue-green. Ventral fins long, sabre-like, orange-red with black rays. Pectoral fins colourless. Unfortunately these attractive colours of the wild fishes as imported are often not retained in captivity.

♀ smaller; dorsal and anal fins rounded or only slightly pointed and never long drawn-out. Lemon-yellow, with a dark longitudinal band from the eye to the root of the tail, often indicated only by a few long streaks. Gill-cover with blue-green spots and stripes. Dorsal and anal fins yellowish, the former with a red border. Ventral fins short, yellowish, distally black.

Care: the Dwarf Cichlids are considerably more demanding in captivity than their more robust relatives *Cichlasoma* and *Tilapia*. An aquarium suited to their special needs must include numerous suitable hiding-places, such as stones, tangles or roots, hollow branches, dense groups of plants, even inverted or reclining flowerpots and coconutshells with small holes giving them a resemblance to the nesting-boxes provided for birds. This provision is especially important when breeding is anticipated. The water should be soft, slightly acid and somewhat peaty; an ideal arrangement is to have filtration through a partially peaty bottom-soil. It is further important to draw off a little of the old water now and then and substitute fresh. Average temperature 23–25°C.; many species, like *A. agassizi*, tolerate lower temperatures (17–19°C.) without damage during the winter months. Abundant and varied live food. Even in an aquarium with numerous hiding-places these fishes are not infrequently aggressive towards one another. All Dwarf Cichlids are susceptible to medicines and poisons, so that care must be taken in the treatment of sickness or in dealing with invasions of *Hydra*.

The hobbyist, at least, will generally make no special provision for breeding

Figs. 1053–1055

Fig. 1053. *Acaropsis nassa* (Basket-mouthed Cichlid); reduced.
Fig. 1054. *Aequidens tetramerus* (Saddle Cichlid); adult, aquarium specimen.
Fig. 1055. *Aequidens pulcher* (Blue Acara); adult, reduced.

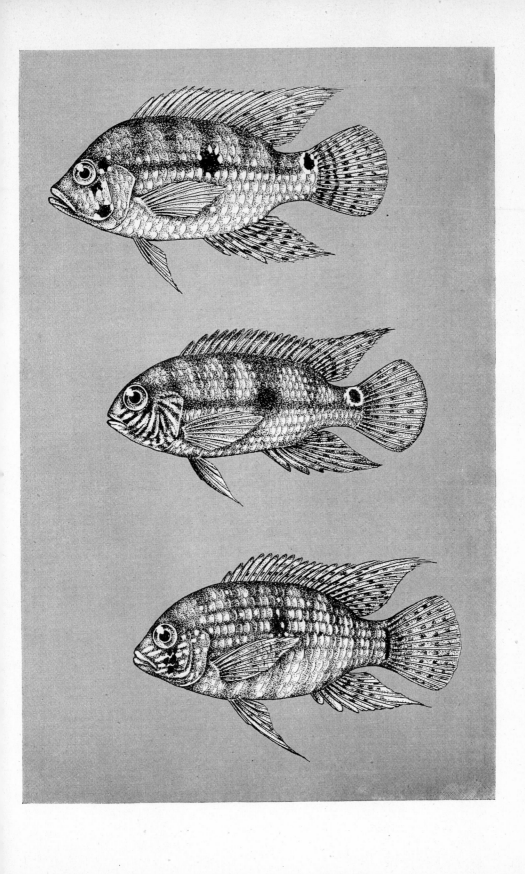

since most species, under favourable conditions, spawn readily enough and often several times a year. Preferred spawning-places are the undersides of stones or still more 'caves' with narrow entrances, which is where our flowerpots and coconut-shells are especially useful. First of all both sexes clean the selected place, then the ♀ attaches the eggs which are immediately fertilised by the ♂. The eggs are generally elongate, yellow or brown-red or – in *A. agassizi* – dark cherry-red. In the Dwarf Cichlids the care of the brood is almost exclusively undertaken by the ♀; often one's first intimation of a spawning comes from the behaviour, colouring and markings of the ♀ which suddenly takes to biting and driving away her usually considerably larger partner, and even other fishes, from her normal station. (Many species, moreover, assume such a gay breeding-dress that this period can hardly be overlooked.) It is best now to remove the ♂.

The young hatch, as a rule, after 2–5 days and require a further 4–6 days for the absorption of the yolk-sac, until when they are unable to swim freely. Up to this time the young are brought by the ♀ into pits or clefts between stones, or onto leaves, and usually changed about several times. Once the young swim freely the ♀ leads the moderately numerous, and often by no means small, shoal on excursions around the tank. At this time many species show interesting protective behaviour; upon certain movements made by the ♀ the young sink motionless to the bottom or move closer to her. After 2–4 weeks the young become independent and separate from the ♀. Feeding commences with the smallest *Cyclops* nauplii as soon as the young swim freely.

Pairs of many species reproduce again after 4 weeks. Often, too, the first clutch of eggs are devoured and only the young from a later spawning are carefully reared. As a rule the ♀ removes dead eggs from the clutch. In many species, e.g., *A. reitzigi*, the young are chewed out of the eggshells by the ♀.

In the case of serious breeding in hatcheries it is usual to remove the eggs at the sacrifice of parental care of the brood.

In *Apistogramma agassizi* a very high proportion of the offspring are ♂♂, a phenomenon whose causes have not yet been elucidated. This species is very susceptible to *Ichthyophonus*-disease. 1909/+.

Plate 187

Fig. 1056. *Tetraodon cutcutia;* natural size. (Photo Dr. Foersch)
Fig. 1057. *Tetraodon leiurus brevirostris;* half-grown, somewhat enlarged. (Original)
Fig. 1058. *Tetraodon schoutedeni;* adult, enlarged. (Photo Dr. Foersch)

Plate 187

Plate 188

Plate 188

Fig. 1059. *Tetraodon fluviatilis;* variety with dark transverse bars; young, enlarged. (Original)

Fig. 1060. *Tetraodon fluviatilis;* inflated fish lying on its back in the hand. (Original)

Fig. 1061. *Tetraodon fluviatilis;* variety with dark, round blotches; young, enlarged. (Original)

Apistogramma borelli (*Regan* 1906) (Fig. 1062)   Borelli's Dwarf Cichlid

Matto Grosso region, Rio Paraguay, southwards to the Argentine; to 7·5 cm., ♀♀ remaining smaller.

D XVI/5–6; A III/6–7; LL 18–22. Body elongate, but stockier than in the previous species; strongly compressed, especially in the hinder part. Upper and lower profiles almost equally convex.

♂ Upperside quite dark brown-olive; flanks paler with a lovely blue sheen; throat and belly delicate clay-colour. Like many other *Apistogramma* spp., *A. borelli* has a very dark, sharply-contrasted cheek-band extending from the eye to the throat. Less distinct, on the other hand, are bands running from the upper jaw across the eye to the nape and a longitudinal band along the side. The latter usually consists only of isolated blotches which at times lie on transverse bands extending up to the base of the dorsal fin. Dorsal, anal and ventral fins delicate bluish with a dark edge and often with white tips; the soft dorsal and anal occasionally spotted with blue-green. Caudal fin usually yellowish.

♀ Usually smaller and less intensely coloured. Fins not produced to points.

Care and breeding, as given for the previous species. Said to be temperature-sensitive; not less than 22°C. 1936/+.

Apistogramma commbrae (*Regan* 1906) (Fig. 1063)   Corumba Dwarf Cichlid

Paraná Basin; to 5·5 cm.

D XVI/6; A III/6–7; P 11; LL 22. Body elongate, strongly compressed. Coloration very variable in relation to health, age and locality.

♂ Yellow-brown to yellowish; back with a greenish sheen; belly yellowish-white. A black longitudinal band from the tip of the snout to a distinct round blotch at the root of the tail; this band may occasionally be broken up into several elongate streaks. 6–7 more or less transverse bars on the flanks. 2–4 parallel rows of black spots under the broad longitudinal band, beginning behind the pectoral fins. A black, curved band from the nape across the eye. Fins smoke-

grey to yellowish. Dorsal and anal fins with dark bands on their soft-rayed portions. Caudal fin similarly marked. Dorsal fin long and produced to a point.
♀ Dorsal fin only moderately produced posteriorly, rounded.

Care and breeding, as given for *A. agassizi*, except that this species is rather more warmth-loving. In winter the temperature may be reduced at most to 19°C. Brood-care is taken over entirely by the ♀; the ♂ should therefore be removed after spawning. Eggs elongate, yellow-brown. 1906/−.

Apistogramma ornatipinnis *E. Ahl* 1936 (Fig. 1064)
Western Guiana; to 7 cm., the ♀♀ remaining smaller.
D XV/7–8; A III/6; LL 21–24. Body elongate, strongly compressed.

♂ Clay-yellow to fawn; upperside more rust-brown with irregular dark areas. A dark longitudinal band from the eye to the root of the tail, usually only indistinctly visible. A bold deep black band from the eye to the throat. A dark blotch at about the middle of the body and another at the root of the tail. 2 vermiform shining silver stripes on the gill-cover. A double row of shining spots under the dark lateral band. Dorsal and anal fins greatly produced, orange with a dark border; the anterior fin-rays are deep black and the hinder parts of the fins with light and dark bands. Centre of caudal fin orange; upper and lower parts more reddish with several, usually distinct, transverse bands. First ray of the smoke-coloured ventral fins bright red.
♀ Dorsal and anal fins rounded.

Care and breeding, as given for *Apistogramma agassizi*, except that *A. ornatipinnis* requires to be kept somewhat warmer. Eggs yellowish. 1936/−.

Apistogramma ortmanni (*Eigenmann* 1912) (Fig. 1065)   Ortmann's Dwarf Cichlid
Western Guiana and central Amazon Basin; to 7 cm.
D XV/7; A III/6–7; P 12; LL 22–24. Body elongate, strongly compressed, upper

Figs. 1062–1066

Fig. 1062. *Apistogramma borelli* (Borelli's Dwarf Cichlid); natural size.
·Fig. 1063. *Apistogramma commbrae* (Corumba Dwarf Cichlid); enlarged.
Fig. 1064. *Apistogramma ornatipinnis*; maximum size of ♂.
Fig. 1065. *Apistogramma ortmanni* (Ortmann's Dwarf Cichlid); somewhat enlarged.
Fig. 1066. *Apistogramma pertense* (Yellow Dwarf Cichlid); adult ♂, enlarged.

and lower profiles equally convex. The coloration is very variable, depending on locality of origin and conditions in captivity. In general the markings and colouring are similar to those of *A. commbrae*. Meinken gives the relative positions of the longitudinal bands as a discriminating character, stating that in *A. commbrae* all the longitudinal bands (including the longitudinal rows of spots) lie *above* a line drawn from the pectoral fin to the lower corner of the caudal. In *A. ortmanni*, on the other hand, there is always one, and usually two, longitudinal bands lying below this imaginary line.

♀ usually rather smaller and less brightly coloured; dorsal fin not produced.

Care and breeding, as given for *A. agassizi*, except that this Dwarf Cichlid is very warmth-loving; 26–28 °C. 1934/+.

Apistogramma pertense (*Hasemann* 1911) (Fig. 1066)   Yellow Dwarf Cichlid Amazon, between Manaõs and Santarem; to 5 cm., the ♀♀ remaining somewhat smaller.

D XVI/6; A III/6; P 12–13; LL 23. Coloration very changeable. Grey to yellowish-brown with a greenish sheen. All the scales, especially those of the back, have dark edges. A dark longitudinal band from the eye to a vertical blotch at the root of the tail. 7–8 blackish transverse bands on the flanks. Both the longitudinal and transverse bands may be reduced to two dark blotches, one in the middle of the side and the other at the root of the tail. An intense black bar, extending in a curve from the eye to the throat. Several green and red-brown lines and spots on the head and gill-cover. The belly of the ♂ is orange during the breeding season. Vertical fins grey, green or blue-green. Soft-rayed parts of dorsal and anal fins with rows of blue-green and reddish spots. Anterior part of dorsal fin orange; front spines black. Caudal fin violet at the base. Leading-edge of pectoral fins black.

♀ golden yellow to orange, with a row of spots on the side; fins yellowish.

Care and breeding, as given for *A. agassizi*, but rather more warmth-loving than that species. Eggs orange. 1911/−.

Figs. 1067–1070

Fig. 1067. *Apistogramma pleurotaenia* (Chequered Dwarf Cichlid); somewhat enlarged.
Fig. 1068. *Chaetobranchopsis bitaeniatus;* adult ♂, reduced.
Fig. 1069. *Cichla ocellaris;* adult, greatly reduced.
Fig. 1070. *Cichlasoma arnoldi;* adult ♂, reduced.

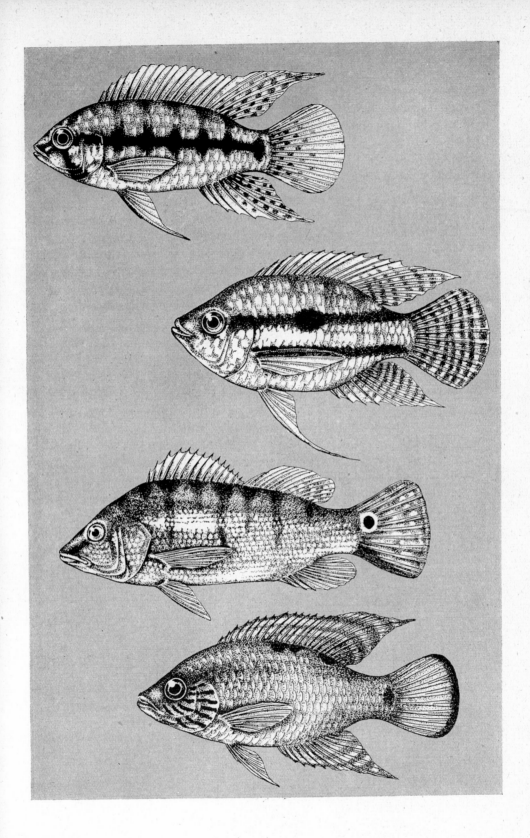

Apistogramma pleurotaenia (*Regan* 1909) (Fig. 1067)   Chequered Dwarf Cichlid
Amazon Basin, especially southwards to La Plata and south-eastwards to Bolivia
(Rio Paraguay); to 7·5 cm.

D XVI/6; A IV/5; LL 23. Shape similar to that of the better-known *A. reitzigi*.
Coloration and markings very variable.

♂ Yellowish-grey to brownish. Brownish, bluish or greenish spots and streaks,
according to locality of origin, on the gill-cover. A quite irregularly-shaped,
often necklace-like, dark band extends from the gill-cover to the root of the
tail. 6 more or less distinct transverse bands on the flanks. Vertical fins yellowish-brown; bases of soft-rayed portions of dorsal and anal, also caudal, often
with a chessboard pattern. First ray of dorsal black, of the ventrals brown-red.
♀ Coloration duller, outside the breeding-season. Fins without chessboard pattern.

During the breeding-season these fishes assume an especially pleasing colouring
of harmoniously matched shades of golden-yellow, orange and black.
   Care and breeding, as given for *A. agassizi*. Eggs yellowish. 1905/—.

Apistogramma ramirezi *Myers* and *Harry* 1948 (Fig. 863)

Ramirez' Dwarf Cichlid
Venezuela, tributaries of the Rio Apure and Rio Meta; to 5 cm.

D XIV–XV/9; A III/8; P 11–12; LL 26–29. Body thick-set, deeper than in
other *Apistogramma* spp., strongly compressed. Dorsal fin tall, its second ray produced. Ground-colour delicate crimson, with rainbow reflexions on the flanks
depending on the lighting. A dark blotch under the dorsal fin, surrounded by electric blue to blue-green spots. There are similar groups of spots on the head, gill-
cover, at the root of the tail and on the caudal and anal fins. A dark band from the
nape, over the eye, to the throat. Iris shining pale blue above, red below. Dorsal,
caudal and anal fins pink with blood-red fin-rays. Ventral fins blood-red. First
three spines of dorsal deep black. One of the most beautiful of the Cichlids.

♂ coloration as above. 2nd spine of dorsal very long.
♀ coloration rather fainter. 2nd spine of dorsal only moderately produced.

Figs. 1071–1074

Fig. 1071. *Cichlasoma aureum* (Golden Cichlid); adult ♂, reduced.
Fig. 1072. *Cichlasoma bimaculatum* (Two-spotted Cichlid); adult ♂, reduced.
Fig. 1073. *Cichlasoma coryphaenoides* (Chocolate Cichlid); adult ♂, reduced.
Fig. 1074. *Cichlasoma crassa;* adult ♂, reduced.

Care and breeding, as given for *A. agassizi*. This species also spawns in small pits, however. Brood-care is undertaken by both parents alternately. One spawning produces 150–200 young. This species must be regarded as delicate and may well attain no great age (to 2 years). Very susceptible to *Ichthyophonus* disease. 1948.

Apistogramma reitzigi *E. Ahl* 1939 (Figs. 855, 1046) Yellow Dwarf Cichlid
Middle Basin of the Rio Paraguay; to 5 cm., ♀ usually appreciably smaller.

D XVI/5; A III/5; LL 21. Body not so strongly elongated as in the better-known *A. agassizi*, strongly compressed.

♂ Back greenish-grey; flanks grey-yellowish; throat and belly bright yellow. Flanks with a bluish sheen in healthy fishes. Numerous bright green spots and streaks on the gill-cover and beneath the eye. Anterior parts of dorsal and anal fins grey-green with a bluish sheen; posterior parts more yellowish. At the base of the dorsal, and to a greater extent on the flanks, there are overlapping dark blotches. Caudal fin pale yellow; ventral fins yellow, produced to points. Several dark transverse bands and longitudinal stripes, apparent only when the fishes are excited. There is usually an especially bold black bar from the eye to the nape (Fig. 855).

♀ Smaller, usually darker in colour; intense yellow at spawning-time.

Care and breeding, as given for *A. agassizi*. Eggs brick-red, very large but not numerous (40–70). In this Dwarf Cichlid, especially, the maternal instinct for brood-care may be extended to larger waterfleas, which are herded together like a shoal of young fish and likewise protected from any aggressor! This behaviour may be observed almost invariably when the eggs do not hatch. In that event, as in normal brood-care, the ♀ develops a characteristic colouring during this period. 1936/+.

Apistogramma weisei *E. Ahl* 1935 Weise's Dwarf Cichlid
Middle Amazon Basin; to 7 cm.

D XVI/6; A III/4; LL 22; TR 2½/8. Very elongate and compressed, like *A. agassizi*. Coloration, according to Arnold:

Plate 189

Fig. 1075. *Tetraodon fluviatilis;* variety with spotted underside; adult, somewhat reduced. (Original)
Fig. 1076. *Colomesus psittacus;* half-grown fish, enlarged. (Copyright P. Chlupaty)
Fig. 1077. *Tetraodon mbu;* 30 cm. fish in the Hellabrunn Aquarium, Munich. (Original)

Plate 189

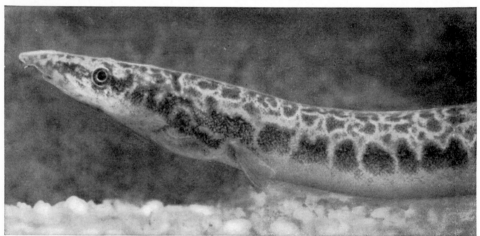

Plate 190

♂ Ground-colour olive-green; back brilliant grass-green. A bold black longitudinal band, edged above and below by a brilliant golden-yellow stripe, extends from the upper lip across the eye to the root of the tail. Shining green spots and lines on the gill-cover. Anterior part of dorsal fin in older ♂♂ with strongly produced fin-membranes (?). Fins bluish-green, bordered with red, and spotted with carmine-red in the hinder portions. Caudal fin green with bright red fin-rays. Anal fin brown-red anteriorly, greenish with red spots posteriorly. The whole fish has a reddish sheen when it is excited and during the breeding-season.
♀ Rather smaller, altogether more yellowish, almost lemon-yellow during the breeding season, with a reddish sheen by reflected light.

Care and breeding, as given for *A. agassizi*. Temperature not lower than 20°C. in winter. 1913/−.

Astronotus ocellatus (*Cuvier* 1829) (Fig. 877) Oscar's or Velvet Cichlid
Amazon, Paraná, Rio Paraguay, Rio Negro; to 33 cm.
D XII–XIV/19–21; A III/15–16; LL 36–38. One of the most beautiful Cichlids. The coloration is extraordinarily variable, depending in the first instance upon health, upon age and upon locality of origin. For domestic aquaria young specimens are more suitable and these also are generally more beautifully coloured than the adults. Body rather deep, elongate-oval, moderately compressed. Upper and lower profiles about equally convex. Fishes of 10–15 cm. length are dark olive-green to a fine chocolate-brown, with, on the flanks, attractive irregular band-like markings which may be ivory or reddish in colour and are usually edged with black. Fins olive-green with more or less distinct black and gold streaks and dots. A large round ocellus bordered with bright red on the upper part of the caudal fin-base; further similar ocelli may also be present on the dorsal fin-base, especially in older fishes.
The sexes are occasionally easy to distinguish and the ♂♂, indeed, often have three prominent round blotches (ocelli) at the base of the spinous dorsal.

Care and breeding, as given in the family description. Relatively peaceable despite its size. Sexually mature at 10–12 cm. The brood-care is peculiar in that the newly-hatched young are carried about attached to the flanks of the parents. 1929/+.

Chaetobranchopsis bitaeniatus *E. Ahl* 1935 (Fig. 1068)
Middle Amazon Basin; to about 12 cm.

D XV–XVI/11; A VI/14–16; LL 25–27. Body deep, strongly compressed, oval in side-view. A very attractive species. Coloration, according to Meinken: yellow-grey with a golden glint; back rather darker. Each scale with a glittering gold edge. Two bold dark longitudinal bands, of which the upper extends from the eye to the upper corner of the caudal peduncle and bears a large dark blotch at about the middle of the side. The interspace between the bands has an intensely golden gleam. Vertical fins yellowish with wine-red bands and wavy lines. Iris bright red.

Sex-distinctions not yet described.

Care, as given in family description; said to be very peaceful and not to grub up the bottom. Nothing is known about breeding. 1934/−.

Cichla ocellaris *Bloch* and *Schneider* 1801 (Fig. 1069)
Almost everywhere in tropical South America, mainly in standing waters; to 60 cm.

D XIII–XVI/16; A III/10; LL 83–102. Perch-like in shape, strongly compressed. Scales very small. Dorsal fin almost divided into spinous and soft-rayed portions. Coloration very variable at different growth-stages. The grey-green ground-colour, deeper on the back, changes to a silver-white tone with increasing age, when the back also becomes pure leaf-green; throat and belly often golden. Young fishes have a longitudinal band, usually composed of isolated blotches; older fishes have several transverse bands as well but these markings entirely disappear with increasing age. At all stages there is a deep black blotch on the upper part of the caudal fin-base, with a golden edging which increases with age; a similar blotch may be present below the anterior part of the soft dorsal fin. Fins greenish with dark blotches, often united to form bands. In older fishes the lower fins and the lower part of the caudal become yellowish and finally brick-red.

Sex-distinctions not yet described.

This species is markedly predatory and only young specimens are suitable for domestic aquaria. Very voracious and also needs plenty of oxygen. It does not grub up the bottom. Temperature not less than 20°C. Nothing is known about breeding. 1912/−.

690

Cichlasoma arnoldi *E. Ahl* 1936 (Fig. 1070)
Southern tributaries of the lower Amazon; to 13 cm.

D XV/11; A V/9; LL 28–31. Body elongate, strongly compressed, somewhat cherry-leaf-shaped in lateral view. Coloration, according to Meinken:–almost uniformly dark brown with blackish streaks on the cheeks. Several dark blotches on the back, close to the dorsal fin-base. A bold vertical spot on the caudal peduncle. Fins dark grey with blackish bands; caudal edged with black. Iris deep red. By artificial light yellow bands are to be seen on the upper half of the body, especially on the back. With similar lighting the gill-cover is shining green.

Sex-distinctions not yet described.

Care and breeding, as given in the family description. Said to be quite peaceable towards other fishes but very unmannerly with related Cichlids. Warmth-loving; at least 22°C. 1933.

Cichlasoma aureum (*Günther* 1862) (Fig. 1071)   Golden Cichlid
Southern Mexico and Guatemala; to 16 cm.

D XV–XVII/9–12; A VI–VIII/7–8; LL 29–32. Typically Cichlid in shape. Coloration very variable, depending on locality of origin. Depending on health greenish to brownish with a lovely golden or reddish glint, especially on the flanks. Throat and breast blood-red. A longitudinal band and several transverse bands are usually distinct only when the fishes are excited. On the other hand, a rhomboidal gill-cover blotch outlined with golden spots, as well as a blotch on the middle of the side and a smaller one at the root of the tail, at least are almost always clearly visible. The large fins are always carried fully spread out. Dorsal and anal fins brownish at the base, externally yellow-green and bordered with red and black. Caudal fin yellow-green. Pectoral fins fine blue distally.

♀ Usually smaller and also not so brilliantly coloured as the ♂; the intense golden gleam, especially, is often absent.

Care and breeding, as given in the family description. Often but not invariably given to grubbing up the bottom. Rather snappy and often very quarrelsome with its own kind. These fishes eat a lot of plant-material from time to time; feed lettuce occasionally. The Golden Cichlid in its natural habitat lives in very weedy waters. Becomes very tame in captivity. 1910/–.

Cichlasoma bimaculatum (*Linnaeus* 1754) (Fig. 1072)   Two-spotted Cichlid
Throughout northern South America, with the exception of the R. Magdalena; to 20 cm.

D XIV–XVI/9–11; A IV(–VI)/8–9; P 13–14; LL 26–27. Body, especially in old fishes, very deep, strongly compressed. Coloration very variable, depending on age and locality of origin. Ground-colour usually grey-brown with a dark back having a light greenish sheen. Lower half of flanks and underside usually silvery-white. A large, bold, black blotch about in the middle of the side and another at the root of the tail; the latter blotch often outlined in pale blue. Several dark transverse bands and a longitudinal band from the eye to the root of the tail are often not clearly apparent; on the other hand several rows of spots on the lower half of the body are usually quite distinct. Fins grey-green or bluish, often with cloudy markings. At spawning time the colouring becomes altogether brighter; the blue colours especially make a lovely contrast with the golden yellow of the belly. Throat bright blue at spawning time.

♀ not difficult to distinguish by the rounded dorsal and anal fins.

Care and breeding, as given in the family description. Mated pairs should be of equal size if this is possible. Well-matched pairs are usually quite peaceful with one another. A very undemanding species which will stand a temperature below 20°C. in winter. 1912/+.

Cichlasoma biocellatum *Regan* 1909 (Figs. 857, 878)　　　　　　Jack Dempsey
Middle Amazon Basin, Rio Negro; to 18 cm., ready to breed at 8–10 cm.

D XIX/9; A VIII/8; P 13; LL 31. Typically Cichlid in shape. Grey-brown to fawn, when healthy dark blue to black. 7–8 more or less distinct dark transverse bands which vanish completely with age. A black longitudinal band from the hind end of the gill-cover to the middle of the side where it ends in a black blotch which is edged with yellowish. A similar blotch in the upper corner of the caudal peduncle. Lower lip brilliant blue. Numerous large, pale blue to dark blue spots around the lower half of the orbit and on the gill-cover. Each scale on the flanks has a brilliant blue-green to blue spot. Fins dark. Dorsal, anal and caudal fins spotted with blue; dorsal with a fine red border. Iris reddish-yellow. At the breeding season the colouring is intensified to a brilliant deep dark blue.

Plate 191

Fig. 1081. *Macrognathus aculeatus;* half-grown, somewhat reduced. (Original)
Fig. 1082. Head of *Macrognathus aculeatus*, greatly enlarged. (Original)
Fig. 1083. *Protopterus dolloi;* 80 cm. specimen in the Hellabrunn Aquarium, Munich. (Original)

Plate 191

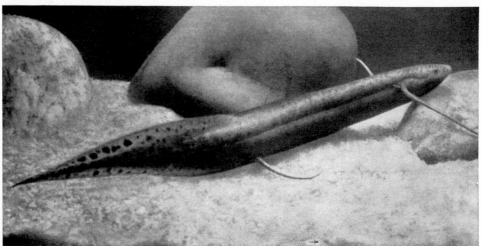

Plate 192

Plate 192

Fig. 1084. *Protopterus dolloi;* larva, natural size. (Original)
Fig. 1085. *Protopterus aethiopicus;* larva, natural size. (Photo Dr. Foersch)
Fig. 1086. *Protopterus aethiopicus;* 110 cm. specimen in the Hellabrunn Aquarium, Munich. (Original)

♀ coloration duller; the brilliant spots are merely indicated. Dorsal fin rounded posteriorly.

♂ forehead bulges with increasing age.

Care and breeding, as given in family description. Unplanted tanks! An unmannerly creature in the breeding season. 1904/+.

Cichlasoma coryphaenoides (*Heckel* 1840) (Fig. 1073)   Chocolate Cichlid
Amazon Basin; to 22 cm.

D XVI/12–13; A VI–VII/9–11; LL 31–33. Body deep, strongly compressed. Forehead tuberous with increasing age, especially in ♂♂. According to Meinken young fishes are dark clay-colour to blackish yellow-olive with a delicate reddish sheen on the flanks and underside. A not always distinct longitudinal band from the eye to the root of the tail. On the other hand, a W-shaped blotch behind the eye and a black blotch at about the middle of the side are usually prominent. Fins brownish-red. Ventral fins with black leading-edges. A very marked capacity for colour-change. Older fishes are quite uniformly brown-violet, with a dark-red and gold-rimmed iris.

♀ Easily distinguished by the less pointed dorsal and anal fins.

Care, as given in family description. An extraordinarily snappish species which, however, according to Meinken's observations, does not damage plants. Attempts at breeding have so far been unsuccessful because the prospective partners are always so incompatible that usually one of them is killed by the other. Warmth-loving. 1911/−.

Cichlasoma crassa (*Steindachner* 1875) (Fig. 1074)
Mainly in the region of the middle Amazon; to 20 cm.

D XVI–XVII/12; A VII/9; LL 29–30. Body deep, strongly compressed, upper profile considerably more convex than the lower. Forehead steep. According to Arnold very variable in coloration, like many other Cichlids, in relation to the various growth-stages and locality of origin. Uniform beautiful brown with a greenish or often reddish sheen, or more clay-coloured. A very irregular band from the eye to a small blotch in the upper corner of the caudal peduncle. A hazy dark blotch at about the middle of the side. Several longitudinal rows of spots, especially on the lower half of the body. Fins yellow-brown, occasionally almost pure orange; dorsal fin with a dark border; caudal with dark transverse bands.

Sex-distinctions in form and colouring practically unknown.

Care, as for other pugnacious and bottom-grubbing Cichlids. Not yet bred in captivity. Warmth-loving. 1933/−.

Cichlasoma cutteri *Fowler* 1952 (Fig. 1087)   Cutter's Cichlid
Honduras; to 12 cm.

D XVIII–XIX/10; A IX(–XI)/8; P 15; LL 32–33. Typically Cichlid in shape. The colouring is strongly influenced by the health of the fish. Bluish-green to olive-green with an attractive coppery glint on the shoulder and belly regions. 7–8 irregular black transverse bars on the flanks which more or less overlap the dorsal fin. A large, black, transverse-oval blotch at the root of the tail. A dark band from the mouth across the eye to the nape. Pectoral and ventral fins yellowish; all other fins a beautiful wine-red. Anal fin usually dark-edged. Iris emerald-green, rimmed with gold.

♂ coloration as given above. Olive-green during the breeding season, with a poppy-red throat and wine-red fins.
♀ fins pink; clay-yellow at the breeding season.

Care, as given in the family description. A beautiful species, *C. cutteri* is almost always very peaceful toward other fishes and to its own kind. Out of the breeding season plants are little disturbed, but during the breeding season it digs great pits and naturally uproots most of the plants. Apparently resistant to comparatively low temperatures (hardly below 20°C.). Eggs grey-yellow with slender stalks. 1933/+.

Figs. 1087–1090

Fig. 1087. *Cichlasoma cutteri* (Cutter's Cichlid); adult ♂, somewhat reduced.
Fig. 1088. *Cichlasoma fenestratum;* adult ♂, reduced.
Fig. 1089. *Cichlasoma friedrichsthali* (Friedrichsthal's Cichlid); adult ♂, reduced.
Fig. 1090. *Cichlasoma tetracanthus* (Cuban Cichlid); adult ♂, reduced.

Cichlasoma cyanoguttatum (*Baird* and *Girard* 1854) (Fig. 879)
Northern Mexico, Texas; to 30 cm., remaining considerably smaller in captivity and sexually ripe at 8–10 cm.

D XV–XVIII/10–12; A V/8–9; LL 27–30. Body rather deep, almost egg-shaped, strongly compressed. Whereas the young merely exhibit several dark transverse bands and the usual dark mid-lateral and caudal blotches on a clay-coloured ground, the adults rank with the most attractively coloured of all Cichlids. The whole body, including the fins, is thickly set with glittering sky-blue to sea-green spots or streaks on a blue-grey or fawn ground. Anal fin with magnificent blue-green fin-rays. Ventral fins often pure blue-green. Pectorals colourless.

♀ usually not quite as brilliantly coloured and often smaller than the ♂.

Care and breeding, as given in the family description. Unfortunately this so very lovely species is one of those Cichlids which are not very compatible with other species or with their own kind. *C. cyanoguttatum* also likes to rearrange the bottom-soil, especially during the breeding season, so that all the plants that are not actually chewed up are nevertheless thoroughly uprooted. Furthermore, this species is rather sensitive to old water although it can comfortably withstand temperatures as low as 14–15°C. without harm. The parents are not conscientious over the duties of brood-care and, as a final vice, often eat their newly-hatched young. 1902/+.

Cichlasoma facetum (*Jenyns* 1842) (Fig. 885)   Chanchito or Chameleon Cichlid
Southern Brazil, Paraguay, Uruguay and northern Argentina; to 30 cm., sexually mature at 8–10 cm.

D XV–XVII/9–11; A VI–VIII/7–9; P 13–14; LL 26–28. 'Chanchito' (= Piglet) in allusion to the low forehead. Coloration very changeable. Brassy-yellow to brownish-yellow, greenish, ashen or deep black. Several deep black transverse bands on the flanks which overlap the dorsal and anal fins. Fins usually dark olive-green to black, occasionally even colourless.

The sexes can only be distinguished with difficulty outside the breeding season. During the breeding season it is best to rely on the genital papilla, which is pointed in the ♂, blunt in the ♀. At this time, too, the ♂ displays the finer colouring. The transverse bands appear deep black on a golden-yellow ground. The fins are black to dark olive-green at the base and reddish to scarlet distally. The iris is blood-red during the breeding season, golden yellow at other times.

Care and breeding, as given in the family description. Pugnacious and a great digger, yet very solicitous over its brood-care. Quarrelsome with its weaker brethren. Very resistant to lower temperatures. Soon becomes tame. 1894/+.

Cichlasoma fenestratum (*Günther* 1860) (Fig. 1088)
Very widely distributed and common in Mexico; to 22 cm.

D XVII–XVIII/11–13; A VI–VII/8–9; LL 31–33. Typically Cichlid in shape. Rather monotonously grey-green, often with numerous dark blotches especially in the region of the back. A dark longitudinal band and several transverse bands are not always distinct; however, the dark blotch on the caudal peduncle is almost always prominent. Gill-cover marbled with blue-green in fine fishes. Lips pale blue. Fins uniform greenish with black-red borders. At the breeding season the underside, especially in the ♂, becomes blood-red.

Sexes almost equal in size; ♀ hard to distinguish from the ♂ outside the breeding season.

Care, as given in the family description. Becomes very tame with its keeper but is very snappish with other species and towards its own kind. A vigorous digger. Stands temperatures as low as 15°C. very well. 1912/–.

Cichlasoma festivum (*Heckel* 1840) (Figs. 895, 896) Barred/Flag Cichlid; Festivum Western Guiana and Amazon Basin; to 15 cm.

D XIV–XVI/10–12; A VIII–IX/10–12; P 11–12; LL 27–29. Body lime-leaf-shaped. Dorsal, anal and ventral fins strongly produced. Coloration very changeable. Ground-colour brass-yellow, clay-yellow or greenish-yellow, with a metallic gleam. A broad black band runs obliquely upwards from the corner of the mouth across the eye to the hinder end of the dorsal fin-base and is continued into the produced hinder tip of the soft dorsal. The upper third of the body, as delimited by this band, is usually black-brown to velvet-black and more rarely set with greenish or pale brownish dots. A large, black to black-violet blotch rimmed with golden yellow in the upper corner of the caudal peduncle. A similar blotch is occasionally present at the middle of the longitudinal band already described. Gill-cover iridescent yellow to green. Iris golden yellow to blood-red. Fins yellowish with white and often brownish markings.

Outside the breeding season the sexes cannot be distinguished by any difference in coloration, and only with difficulty during the breeding season. The ♂ is often more boldly marked.

Care and breeding, as given in the family description. In its natural habitat this species lives in association with *Pterophyllum scalare* and is a very serene and usually also rather timid Cichlid which has similar requirements to the Angelfishes. It only becomes tame when provided with hiding-places among tangles of roots or thick plant-stands and even then, however, never entirely loses its shyness. A quiet position for the tank is essential. This species prefers to spawn on stones or in large flowerpots; unfortunately the association of suitable pairs is not always easily arranged. This species needs plenty of oxygen and is warmth-loving. The serious breeder transfers the spawn into shallow dishes which must be provided with good aeration. 1911/+.

Cichlasoma friedrichsthali (*Heckel* 1840) (Fig. 1089)   Friedrichsthal's Cichlid
Central America; to 25 cm., remaining considerably smaller in captivity.

D XVIII/9–10; A VII–VIII/8; LL 30. Body moderately deep, elongate, strongly compressed. Coloration, according to Meinken: pale brown to dirty yellow-green with numerous dark blotches strewn over the whole body. From the gill-cover to the root of the tail there extends a row of irregular, usually lacquer-black, blotches of which those in the centre, at least, often lie on indistinct transverse bands. A deep-black spot, bordered with green, in the lower corner of the gill-cover. Fins dark brown, often with blackish spots. Dorsal fin with a yellow-red border anteriorly and a yellow one posteriorly. Pectoral fins yellow.

Care, as given in the family description. Snappish and a great digger, but at the same time resistant to quite low temperatures (15°C. upwards). 1914/–.

Cichlasoma haitiensis *Tee-Van* 1935   Haiti Cichlid
Haiti, Dominican Republic; to 14 cm.

D XII–XIV/11–13; A III–IV/9–10; LL 32–38. Typically Cichlid in shape. Coloration of adult fishes, according to Roloff:

♂ Ground-colour yellowish pale grey, with a dull gold glint by reflected light. The whole body, including the dorsal and caudal fins and the proximal part of the anal, is spotted with dark brown. Ground-colour of fins yellowish-green.

♀ Outside the breeding season brownish with an indistinct longitudinal band and some transverse bands. Dorsal and anal fins rounded. During the breeding season very dark to velvet-black.

Care, as given in family description. Like most *Cichlasoma* spp., *C. haitiensis* is very quarrelsome, snappish and a great digger. This species spawns on stones. In the spawning observed by Roloff the ♀ took over the brood-care and drove the ♂ away by biting him. 1938/–.

Cichlasoma hellabrunni *Ladiges* 1942 (Fig. 876)   Hellabrunn Cichlid
According to Ladiges, Upper Amazon Basin ?; to 30 cm.

D XVI–XVII/11–12; A VII–VIII/10–11; LL 17–18/11–12. Body deep, egg-shaped, strongly compressed, especially in the caudal region. Upper profile considerably more convex than the lower. Forehead strongly tuberous, steeply sloping. Upperside velvety olive-green, often with a rusty sheen. Flanks and underside a lovely wine-red. Forehead with irregular, broad, yellowish bands. An often indistinct longitudinal band from the gill-cover to the root of the tail; on the other hand the usual large blotch in the middle of the side and the smaller one on the caudal peduncle are almost always prominent. Fins wine-red, often light greenish towards the edges. Iris dark orange-red with a vertical black streak. According to Zoll and Mohr, the young are unpretentiously coloured, predominantly green-reddish wi'h bold transverse bands and 4 yellow spots at the base of the dorsal fin.

♀ head relatively narrower than in the ♂ (according to Ladiges).

Care and breeding, as given in the family description; a peaceful species. 1939/+.

Cichlasoma maculicauda *Regan* 1905 (Fig. 1091)   Spotted Cichlid
Central America, also in brackish water; to 25 cm.

D XVI–XVII/12–14; A VI–VII/9–10; LL 32–35. Shape similar to that of the better-known *C. severum*. Coloration, according to Meinken: back yellow-brown; flanks somewhat paler with a lovely green glint. The large dark blotch on the caudal peduncle is especially characteristic of this species. Numerous sharp-edged black-brown blotches on the sides which may run together into necklace-like longitudinal rows. Several transverse bars, usually not very distinct. Spinous dorsal and anal dark green or blue-green, the former with a wine-red tip; soft parts of the same coppery or yellowish with brown spots and yellowish tips. Base of caudal fin colourless, centre yellowish, outer parts fine red. Ventral fins blackish; pectorals reddish. The throat and breast are brick-red during the breeding season.

Sex-distinctions not known.

Care, as given in the family description. This species is said to be relatively peaceful. Resistant to low temperatures. Breeding apparently not yet achieved. Further imports of this attractive species are much to be desired. 1912/–.

Cichlasoma meeki (*Brind* 1918) (Fig. 789)   Fire-mouth Cichlid
Guatemala and Yucatan, also in subterranean connexions between natural springs; to 15 cm., sexually mature at 8 cm.

D XV–XVI/9–10; A VIII–IX/7–9; LL 28–32. Body rather deep, strongly compressed. Upper profile considerably more convex than lower. One of the most beautiful *Cichlasoma* spp. Bluish-grey with a violet sheen; back darker; belly yellow-olive to orange; throat and lower jaw brilliant brick-red. 5–7 more or less distinct transverse bands on the flanks. All the scales, especially those of the flanks, have red edges so that the whole body appears covered by a red network. A very prominent intense black band, often merely composed of isolated blotches, extends from the upper edge of the gill-cover to a blotch at the root of the tail, the said blotch being black, transverse-oval and edged with gold fore and aft. The band is interrupted at the centre of the side by a large, round, deep black, grey-rimmed spot. The root of the pectoral is surrounded by a deep black, gold-bordered blotch; there is a similar blotch on the lower edge of the gill-cover. All fin-rays, with the exception of those of the pectorals, brown-red; distally yellowish. Fin-membranes to some extent blue-green. Dorsal fin with a bluish border, anal with a black one; the produced points of these two fins are gleaming blue-green.

♀ coloration rather duller; dorsal and anal fins not greatly produced posteriorly.

Care and breeding, as given in the family description. The Fire-mouth Cichlid is often quite peaceful, and tough plants, at least, are not disturbed by it outside the breeding season. Now and then, however, one encounters individuals of extraordinary pugnacity and snappishness, characteristics which are very often displayed against smaller members of the same species. Well-matched pairs spawn readily and undertake exemplary brood-care. Not sensitive to temperatures a little below 20°C., but needs at least 24°C. for breeding. 1937/+.

Cichlasoma nigrofasciatum (*Günther* 1869) (Fig. 886)   Zebra or Convict Cichlid Guatemala, in Lakes Atitlán and Amatitlán; Salvador, Costa Rica, Panama; to 10 cm., sexually mature at 8 cm.

D XVII/7–8; A IX/6; P 13–14; LL 29–30. Typically Cichlid in shape. Back dark grey to bluish; flanks mouse-grey, often with a violet sheen; belly pale grey. 8–9 more or less prominent dark transverse bars on the flanks, which commence on the ridge of the back and nearly encircle the body. The most anterior band, commencing on the nape and head, is somewhat oblique. A more or less distinct black blotch on the upper part of the gill-cover; another at the root of the tail. Fins fine green with a metallic glint; dorsal and anal fins bordered with red, the former with dark bands on the hinder part.

♂ coloration as above. The transverse bars regress during the breeding season and are replaced by gleaming metallic areas.

♀ coloration duller, without bands on the dorsal fin. Transverse bars deep black during the breeding season.

Care and breeding, as given in the family description. Very snappish and incompatible, both with other fishes and its own kind. Supplementary plant food necessary (lettuce, algae, softened oat-flakes). 1939/+.

Cichlasoma octofasciatum (*Regan* 1903) (Fig. 1092)　　　Eight-banded Cichlid
Southern Mexico, Guatemala, Yucatan, Honduras; to 20 cm., sexually ripe at 7–8 cm.

D XVII–XIX/8–10; A VIII–X/7–8; LL 28–31. Body moderately elongate, strongly compressed. Usually rather dark, brownish or grey, with a bluish sheen on the flanks. Several transverse bars and a short longitudinal band are usually conspicuous in the young but only faintly indicated in the adults. A bold black blotch, usually ringed with gold, at the upper edge of the gill-cover; a second on the anterior part of the flanks and a third in the upper corner of the caudal peduncle. Older fishes have numerous shining silvery or green dots on the head, flanks and fins. Fins usually quite dark, the dorsal having a yellow border.

♀ usually considerably duller in colour; the silver dots are at best faintly indicated. The tips of the dorsal and anal fins are not as strongly produced as in the ♂.

Concerning care and breeding hardly any information is available. The fact that these fishes, at least when young, frequent thickly weeded waters probably points to a partly herbivorous diet. Snappish and quarrelsome. 1934/−.

Cichlasoma salvini (*Günther* 1864) (Fig. 1093)　　　Salvin's Cichlid
Southern Mexico, Guatemala and Honduras; to 15 cm.

D XVI–XVII/9–12; A VIII–IX/7–9; LL 28–31. Typically Cichlid in shape. Front of head rather produced, pointed. Coloration, according to Meinken: body rather dark olive-green or brown-yellow. A vaguely-delimited band runs from the snout across the eye, arches around a dark blotch on the middle of the side, and continues to a dark blotch in the upper corner of the caudal peduncle. An especially peculiar curved band runs forward from the origin of the dorsal fin to the forehead enclosing, with its partner of the other side, a pale blotch at the nape. Further very irregularly orientated dark bands on the upper half of the flanks. Numerous shining blue-green spots and streaks on the gill-cover; longitudinal rows of similarly coloured spots along the lower half of the body. Dorsal fin green with a bright red border and a clay-yellow produced posterior tip. Caudal and anal fins clay-yellow at their bases, red externally. Ventral fins pale blue with black fin-rays. Iris blood-red.

701

Sex-distinctions unknown.

Care, as given in the family description. Snappish and quarrelsome. Like all Mexican Cichlids, not sensitive to temperatures barely less than 20°C. 1913/−.

Cichlasoma severum (*Heckel* 1840) (Fig. 955)   Banded Cichlid
Northern Amazon Basin and Guiana; to 20 cm.

D XVI–XVIII/13–14; A VII–VIII/12–13; P 14; LL 28–30. Body very deep, nearly oval, strongly compressed. Upper profile considerably more convex than lower. Coloration variable, depending on health and locality of origin. Brassy-yellow, brownish, greenish or very dark; belly always paler; head and nape usually greenish. Head with red-brown or blue-green spots and streaks. Each scale on the flanks bears a red-brown spot, especially in the ♂. Half-grown fishes display 8–9 more or less prominent black bands on the flanks which, with the exception of the last two on the caudal peduncle, disappear in the adults. The anterior band of this surviving pair crosses the body between the hind ends of the dorsal and anal fin-bases and overlaps onto each fin to end in a black ocellus rimmed with pale yellow or brownish. Dorsal fin olive-green to black; caudal grey-green; anterior part of anal fin reddish-brown, posterior part olive-green; ventral fins brown-red to blackish. Iris blood-red.

♀ usually rather paler in colouring. Dorsal and anal fins often not so strongly produced.

Care, as given in family description. Out of the breeding season the Banded Cichlid (chiefly known as *Heros spurius* in Germany) is a very peaceable Cichlid which hardly takes any notice even of small fishes and disturbs plants only in exceptional cases. During the breeding season, however, its behaviour changes a great deal; henceforth it drives away other fishes and has to be kept by itself in an unplanted tank. Unfortunately, too, the matching of compatible pairs is often not easily achieved since *C. severum* is very choosy over its mating. On this account breeding is not as easy as in most other *Cichlasoma* spp. Spawning, guarding of the spawn and care of the young are carried out in typical Cichlid fashion. A good

Figs. 1091–1094

Fig. 1091. *Cichlasoma maculicauda* (Spotted Cichlid); adult ♂, reduced.
Fig. 1092. *Cichlasoma octofasciatum* (Eight-banded Cichlid); adult ♂, reduced.
Fig. 1093. *Cichlasoma salvini* (Salvin's Cichlid); adult ♂, somewhat reduced.
Fig. 1094. *Cichlasoma spectabile;* adult ♂, reduced.

702

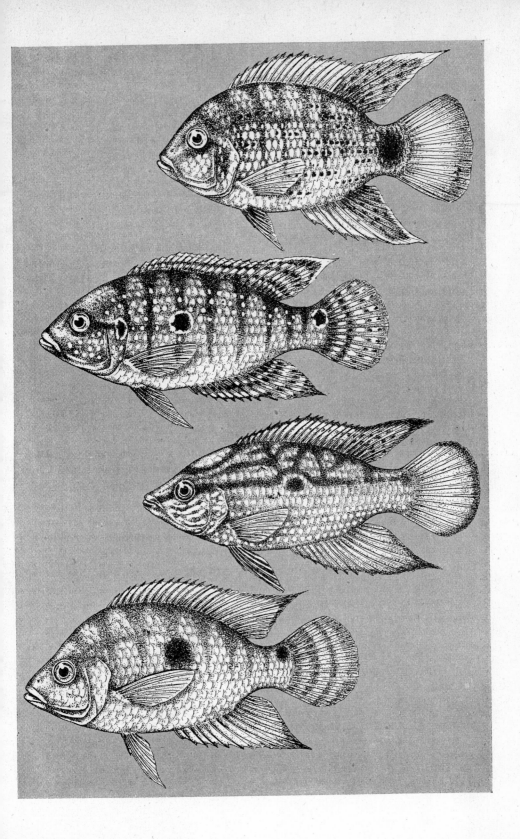

mating can produce 1000 or more eggs. Warmth-loving; not less than 22 °C. even in winter. This species becomes very tame. 1909/+.

Cichlasoma spectabile (*Steindachner* 1875) (Fig. 1094)
Middle and lower Amazon; to 20 cm.

D XV/12–13; A VI/9–10; LL 30. Body thick-set, deep and strongly compressed; upper profile considerably more convex than the lower. Mouth highly protrusible. Coloration, according to Meinken: grey-brown to yellow-brown with 7–9 dark transverse bands which are most conspicuous in the young and with increasing age become increasingly shorter and eventually almost disappear. A large dark blotch at about the middle of the side; another smaller one in the upper corner of the caudal peduncle. Fins brownish, the tips often light violet. Caudal fin with curved transverse bands.

Sexes easily distinguished by the considerably longer prolongation of the hinder tips of the dorsal and anal fins in the ♂♂.

Care and breeding, as given in the family description. A very unmannerly and quarrelsome species. 1935/−.

Cichlasoma tetracanthus (*Cuvier* and *Valenciennes* 1831) (Fig. 1090) Cuban Cichlid
Cuba and Barbados, also in brackish water; to 20 cm.

D XV–XVI/10–12; A IV/8–10; LL 28–31. Typically Cichlid in shape. A special characteristic of this species, commented on by several authors, is its capacity for cryptic colour-change. The self-same fish can adopt an almost completely contrasting coloration and pattern in a few moments. Various growth-stages may display quite different ground-colours. Furthermore, the sexes are usually equally intensely marked and coloured so that discrimination is only possible through the shapes of the dorsal and anal fins which are considerably more produced in the ♂♂. The only constant character, present in almost all growth-stages, at least in healthy fishes, is a dark network which extends over the whole body and vertical fins and on the head becomes thickened into a pattern of vermiform lines and irregular blotches. Occasionally this network over the body assumes more of the character of an irregular pattern of spots. Three dark blotches may be present, one behind the eye, one on the middle of the side and one on the caudal peduncle. Occasionally, also, transverse bands appear, especially on the caudal peduncle.

Care and breeding, as given in the family description. Unfortunately this often attractively coloured species is one of the quarrelsome, snappish Cichlids and likes to have its special needs catered for in the furnishing of the tank. During the daytime the fishes like to rest among root-tangles or stones and only become active towards nightfall. The Cuban Cichlid is very warmth-loving and should not be kept below 22°C., even in winter. Pairs are not easily matched. Very thorough brood-care. 1933/−.

Cichlasoma urophthalmus (*Günther* 1862) (Fig. 1104)
Central America, north of the Panama Canal; to 20 cm.

D XV–XVII/10–12; A VI/8; LL 28–31. Typically Cichlid in shape. Coloration, according to Meinken: brownish to yellowish-green, with 6–7 black transverse bands which taper to points towards the underside. A deep black, yellowish-rimmed blotch at the root of the tail. Dorsal and caudal fins brownish at their bases, externally wine-red with pale red borders. Anal fin bluish anteriorly, wine-red posteriorly. Ventral fins bluish. Iris blood-red or yellowish.

Sex-distinctions unknown.

Care, as given in the family description. Snappish and quarrelsome. Probably not yet bred in captivity. 1913/−.

Crenicara maculata (*Steindachner* 1875) (Fig. 915)   Chessboard Cichlid
Middle Amazon; ♂ to 10 cm., ♀ to 5 cm.

D XIV/9; A III/7; LL 26. Body elongate. Fins of ♂ produced to points. Head of adult ♂ strikingly blunt. Coloration, according to Ladiges: ground-colour ochre-yellow with shining orange-red spots. An especial characteristic of this species is a double row of large, dark, quadrangular blotches which together form a chessboard pattern. A dark longitudinal band runs forwards from the upper row of blotches across the brilliant orange eye. Vertical fins with wine-red margins and rows of spots, which form 10–12 narrow transverse bands across the caudal fin. Ventral fins strongly produced and longitudinally striped with blue and orange-red.

♀ ochre-yellow; fins intense orange yellow at spawning time.

Care and breeding, as given for *Apistogramma agassizi* (see p.678). 1938/+.

Crenicichla dorsocellata *Hasemann* 1911 (Fig. 1095)   Two-spot Pike Cichlid
Middle Amazon Basin and Rio Parahyba; to 20 cm.

D XX–XXIII/10–13; A III/8; LL 62–65. Body elongate, Pike-like, moderately compressed. Head broad. Back dirty green-blue, less frequently brilliant green-blue; flanks paler greenish; underside usually delicate bluish. 7–9 transverse bands are always distinctly visible in the young but only prominent in the adults when the fishes are excited. Several brown blotches behind the eye which may run together

705

into a longitudinal band. An especial characteristic of this species is a large black blotch, rimmed with white and brilliant red, about in the middle of the dorsal fin. Dorsal fin bluish or more brownish. Lower part of caudal greenish, upper usually reddish spotted with brown; a dark blotch is often present at the upper corner of the base. Anal fin bright sky-blue in fine fishes.

♂ dorsal and anal fins produced to long points.
♀ dorsal and anal fins rounded; at the most pointed but never produced.

The members of the genus *Crenicichla* are typical predatory fishes which lie in wait for prey after the manner of the European Pike, seize it with a lightning rush and swallow it head-first. With their very large, deeply cleft mouths the Pike Cichlids can overcome fishes little smaller than themselves.
Crenicichla spp. require especially large aquaria with thickets of plants or tangles among which they can hide. They cannot be kept together with other species even of the same size.
Breeding is generally not as easily induced as in the *Cichlasoma* and *Tilapia* spp. The spawn is deposited in shallow pits. Brood-care is chiefly undertaken by the ♂♂; removal of the ♀♀ is not absolutely necessary. The eggs are remarkably small and whitish. Plentiful and varied feeding is essential during the period of brood-care; chiefly fishes, large dragonfly-larvae and water-beetles.
In contrast to most Pike Cichlids *Crenicichla dorsocellata* is normally quite peaceable. Fishes from the Amazon should not be kept below 20°C.; those from south-eastern Brazil are rather more resistant to lower temperatures. 1913/−.

Crenicichla lepidota *Heckel* 1840 (Figs. 916, 1095)　　　　　Pike Cichlid
Generally distributed, from the Amazon to the northern Argentine; to 20 cm.
D XVII–XVIII/13–14; A III/8–10; LL 45–60. Shape similar to that of the previous species. Coloration very variable, depending on locality of origin. Striking capacity for colour-change. Back grey-green or dark olive-green, passing on the flanks into a pearly greenish or more yellowish leather-coloured tint. Belly slate-brown, white-silver, yellowish or delicate wine-red. The body and vertical fins may be strewn with pearly or greenish or shining golden spots, among usually indistinct short transverse bars or a longitudinal band from the mouth to the root of the tail or merely isolated dark blotches. An especial characteristic of this species is a large, often multiple, lacquer-black blotch behind the gill-cover, which may also be ringed with golden or silvery spots. There is usually a similar blotch on the caudal peduncle. Fins very variably and often very attractively coloured with harmoniously

706

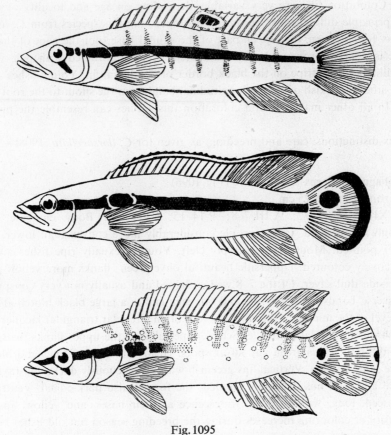

Fig. 1095

Basic patterns of *Crenicichla* spp. From above downwards: *C. dorsocellata* (Two-spot Pike Cichlid); *C. saxatilis* (Ring-tailed Pike Cichlid); *C. lepidota* (Pike Cichlid).

alternating faint green and yellow tones. All the colours become more intense during the breeding season. See also previous species.

Sex-distinctions, care and breeding, as given for the previous species. 1907/+.

Crenicichla saxatilis (*Linnaeus* 1758) (Fig. 1095)   Ring-tailed Pike Cichlid
Widely distributed, from Trinidad over the whole central and eastern Amazon Basin to southern Brazil; to 35 cm.

D XVII–XX/13–16; A III/8–10; LL 50–62. Shape similar to that of *C. dorsocel-*

707

lata. Coloration likewise very variable, depending on age and locality of origin. The principle differences in colouring distinguishing this species from *C. lepidota* are as follows:–on the upper part of the caudal base (not the root of the tail!) there is a large, brown-red to black blotch, broadly bordered with pale yellow. A brilliant white stripe on the black border of the dorsal fin. Young fishes always have a bold blackish or brown longitudinal band from the snout to the root of the tail. In all other markings and coloration this species can resemble the previous one.

Sex-distinctions, care and breeding, as given for *C. dorsocellata*. 1908/ +.

Geophagus acuticeps *Heckel* 1840 (Fig. 1096)
Amazon Basin; to 25 cm.

D XIII–XIV/11–12; A III/7–8; P 14–15; LL 30–31. Body elongate, deep, strongly compressed. Upper profile considerably more convex than lower. Head rather pointed. Mouth large, deeply cleft. Young, sexually ripe fishes are very attractively coloured. Upperside beautiful olive-green; flanks more yellow-green; underside dull silver. Of the 7–8 wedge-shaped and usually not very conspicuous transverse bands, the 2nd, 4th and 6th each end in a large black blotch at about the level of the middle of the side. There is often a regular triangular lacquer-black blotch on the caudal peduncle. Scales, especially on the upper flanks, with large shining bright grass-green and silver spots. Head with shining lines and blotches of the same colours. Vertical fins greenish with conspicuously darker fin-rays. Soft dorsal and anal fins delicately banded; the former also dark-edged. Ventral fins produced, long, with a bluish iridescence at their bases, and yellow tips. The intensity of colouring increases during the breeding season but old fishes become somewhat paler.

♀ dorsal and anal fins pointed but not produced.

Care: *Geophagus* spp. are generally very quarrelsome and great diggers. Although such characteristics can hardly be altered they can at least be mitigated through a natural arrangement of the tank. These are fishes which, in their natural habitat, take up a station in a hollow tree-stump, under a bank or among stones from whence they control a definite territory. If they are provided with corresponding environmental conditions in captivity they tend to lose some of their roughness. To this end Meinken recommends a large tank in which the rear wall is arranged as a steep bank and provided with numerous holes while the foreground serves as hunting-space. Large, hollow tree-stumps are still more suitable in my opinion.

Among these, in dishes at least, coarse-leaved plants can be introduced. Suitable pairs are often more easily matched than in the case of *Cichlasoma* spp. The fishes spawn preferably on or among stones. Rearing of the young as given in the family description. Both sexes take part in brood-care. *Geophagus acuticeps* is warmth-loving and should not be kept below 22 °C. even in winter. 1913/ —.

Geophagus australe *Eigenmann* 1907 (Fig. 1097)
Neighbourhood of Buenos Aires, chiefly in La Plata; to 18 cm.
D XII–XIV/10–11; A III/8; LL 25–27. Shape similar to that of the previous species. Coloration, according to Meinken: bluish to grey-green with a strong pearly lustre. Scales dark-edged, especially those of the upper half of the body. 6–9 irregular dark transverse bands and a dark blotch on the middle of the side are usually not very distinct; however, a curved band from the nape across the eye and cheek is almost always boldly indicated. Gill-cover with dark blotches and inter-vening shining blue and green areas. Fins grey-green. Dorsal and anal fins anteriorly with blue-green, posteriorly with pearly, spots and dots. Dorsal fin also with a brown longitudinal stripe parallel to the margin. Caudal fin with dark spots at the base. Ventral fins with shining green membranes.
Sex-distinctions unknown.
Care, as given for *Geophagus acuticeps*. Resistant to low temperatures; can be kept at room-temperature (12–15 °C.) in winter. 1936/ —.

Geophagus brasiliensis (*Quoy* and *Gaimard* 1824) (Figs. 920, 1098)   Pearl Cichlid
Eastern Brazil, in coastal streams, standing waters and in brackish water; to 28 cm., sexually mature at 8–10 cm.
D XIV–XVI/10–13; A III/8–9; LL 27–30. Body, especially in older fishes, rather deep, elongate and strongly compressed. Head pointed in young but developing a protuberant forehead in the adult. Coloration very changeable. Grey-yellow to clay-yellow, more yellow-brown on the caudal part, often with a green sheen. Several large pearly blotches on the sides of the head and the gill-cover. 5–7 more or less distinct dark transverse bands are present in the young; older fishes have a large, cloudy, dark blotch on the middle of the side. A dark curved band from the nape across the eye. Vertical fins yellow-green to brownish with wine-red, silvery or yellowish spots and blotches. During the breeding season the coloration of both sexes becomes more intense; during this period especially the iridescent shining spots become more prominent.
The sexes cannot always be distinguished with certainty on the shapes of the dorsal and anal fins.

709

♀ genital papilla conspicuously blunter during the breeding season. The ♀ is also not infrequently more finely coloured than the ♂.

Care and breeding, as given for *Geophagus acuticeps*. Temperature not less than 20 °C. 1899/+.

Geophagus cupido *Heckel* 1840 (Fig. 1099)
Middle Amazon Basin, western Guiana; to 13 cm.

D XV/(9–)10; A III/9; LL 29–31. Body elongate, moderately deep, strongly compressed. Upper profile considerably more convex than the lower. Coloration usually rather dark. Upperside chocolate-brown, often with a greenish sheen. Flanks more yellow-brown, with indistinct transverse bars in the young and usually with rows of shining blue-green spots in older fishes. Underside light yellowish. An especially characteristic feature of this species is a large lacquer-black blotch, broadly bordered with pearly or rosewood colour, immediately below the centre of the dorsal fin; the pale surround often contains two tiny white streaks. A bold black band from the nape through the eye to the edge of the gill-cover; several brilliant blue lines underneath the eye. Dorsal and anal fins brownish, less frequently yellowish, and banded in their hinder parts. Caudal fin yellow-green, sharply edged above and below by black fin-rays between which white longitudinal bands may be present. Pectoral and ventral fins cream-coloured. Iris brown, often delicately rimmed with gold.

Sex-distinctions unknown.

Care, as given for *Geophagus acuticeps*. Remains incorrigibly quarrelsome, despite all attempts to reproduce its natural environment, and usually grubs up the bottom a great deal. Breeding in captivity not yet achieved. According to Eigenmann and Kennedy this species is said to be a mouth-brooder which takes up its eggs and young into its gill-chamber. 1935/–.

Geophagus gymnogenys *Hensel* 1870 (Fig. 1100)
Southern Brazil and La Plata region; to 21 cm., sexually ripe at 12 cm.

D XIII–XIV/10–11; A III/(8)–9; LL 27–30. Body elongate, rather deep, strongly

Figs. 1096–1099

Fig. 1096. *Geophagus acuticeps;* adult ♂, reduced.
Fig. 1097. *Geophagus australe;* adult ♂, reduced.
Fig. 1098. *Geophagus brasiliensis* (Pearl Cichlid); adult ♂, reduced.
Fig. 1099. *Geophagus cupido;* adult ♂, reduced.

compressed. Forehead and nape strongly protuberant in older fishes. Dark olive-green to coffee-brown; anterior part of body more yellow-brown. Each scale on the flanks bears a large iridescent bright pale blue or pearly spot. The head is often more clay-coloured with numerous shining spots and lines in pale blue to greenish shades. A large, dark blotch, usually indistinct, at about the middle of the side; a smaller but considerably clearer one at the root of the caudal fin. Fins brownish, often rosewood-coloured or greenish with bright blue bands or spots. Vertical fins to some extent bordered with fine rust-red. All the colours are intensified at spawning time.

♀ often more finely coloured than the ♂♂ and easily distinguished by the less produced dorsal and anal fins.

Care and breeding, as given for *Geophagus acuticeps*. An attractively coloured species which is very resistant to lower temperatures (12–14°C.). 1900/+.

Geophagus jurupari *Heckel* 1840 (Fig. 1101)
North-eastern Brazil, Guiana; to 25 cm., sexually ripe at 10–15 cm.

D XV–XVI/9–10; A III/6–7; LL 29–31. Body elongate, quite slim and low, strongly compressed. Head large. Back dark olive-yellow; flanks yellowish with a green lustre; belly pale grey-yellow. In young fishes several dark transverse bars on the flanks and a dark longitudinal band from the hind end of the gill-cover to the root of the tail are more or less distinctly present. In front of the eye, running obliquely upward from the upper jaw, are several stripes which vary in colour from yellow to brown. Each scale on the flanks has a small shining pearly spot at its base. Fins grey-brown with paler spots and streaks. A pronounced capacity for colour-change. No sexual differences in coloration.

In contrast to its thoroughly predatory relatives, *G. jurupari* is quite a peaceful Cichlid which even leaves considerably smaller fishes almost unmolested. Also, even among several individuals of the same species, there is hardly any serious biting. It compensates for these virtues by grubbing up the bottom well and truly and liking it, although without damage to tough and well-rooted plants. In the aquarium, as in its natural haunts, *G. jurupari* almost systematically works through the bottom-soil in search of eatables (the generic name *Geophagus* (= 'earth-eater') can be applied almost literally in this case). This requirement must be implicitly accepted through the provision of the most fine-grained sand obtainable. The principal foods are small worms, midge-larvae and large waterfleas; no earthworms, on the other hand. Temperature not less than 22°C.; this species readily succumbs to fungus disease at too low a temperature. The eggs are laid on stones, for preference, and covered with a fine layer of sand. The newly-hatched young are taken up in the mouth of the ♀ and brooded for about 14 days; the ♂ should be discreetly removed after the young have hatched. 1909/+.

Geophagus surinamensis (*Bloch* 1791) (Fig. 1102)
North-eastern South America; to 24 cm.

D XVII–XIX/11–12(–13); A III/7; LL 33–36. Body rather deep, especially anteriorly, strongly compressed. Upper profile strongly convex, lower almost straight. Head very large; forehead slightly concave in front of the eyes. Coloration very variable, depending on locality of origin and state of health. Coloration, according to Meinken: younger fishes are yellow-olive to brown-olive; upperside rather darker; underside yellow. The scales of the flanks, especially, have large shining green to bluish spots which in their collective entirety may form longitudinal lines. A large dark blotch at about the middle of the side. A bold dark band from the nape across the eye. Fins delicate rust-colour, to some extent with blue bands, rows of spots or blue fin-membranes. At spawning time the ♂♂ especially develop a reddish breast and more or less red fins with bright blue spots. One of the most beautiful of the *Geophagus* spp.

♀ Altogether more silvery. Fins usually rust-brown.

Care and breeding, as given for *G. acuticeps*. A quarrelsome species. 1914/–.

Nannacara anomala *Regan* 1905 (Fig. 788)   Golden-eyed Dwarf Cichlid
Western Guiana; to 8 cm.

D XVI/8; A III/8; P 12–14; LL 23–24. Body elongate, compressed. One of the most beautiful Cichlids. Coloration very changeable.

♂ Forehead, nape and back olive-brown. Flanks metallic green to olive-green, golden or deep copper-colour, depending on lighting. Each scale bears a small triangular spot. Sides of head with irregular brilliant green and black blotches and stripes. Iris orange, becoming red towards the pupil. When the fish is excited two dark longitudinal bands, and often some transverse bars as well, become visible on the flanks. The very large and always fully spread dorsal fin is usually rather darker, orange-red to brilliant green, and bordered with deep black or pale. Upper and lower parts of caudal fin reddish. Ventrals yellow-green. Anal fin bordered with orange-red.

♀ Smaller, duller in colouring, more clay-yellow. 2 dark longitudinal bands and some transverse bars on the flanks may be present or absent, depending on whether or not the fish is excited. Fins without any special markings.

713

The colouring becomes more intense at spawning time.

Care and Breeding: a richly planted aquarium with suitable hiding-places under stones or flowerpots. Temperature 24–25 °C., not less than 20 °C.! Live food only, especially midge-larvae and worms. Quite peaceful outside the breeding season, even towards other species. Does not grub up the bottom. Very suitable for the community aquarium. See also instructions for *Apistogramma agassizi*. The breeding tank for *Nannacara anomala* should be furnished in the same way as has already been described, and if the species has been kept in a tank by itself no special breeding tank is necessary.

The eggs are laid in typical Cichlid fashion upon a substrate previously cleaned by either or both partners, preferably in a hollow (flowerpot) and guarded by the ♀. The ♂ should be removed after spawning. The young hatch after 2–3 days and are gathered into a pit by the ♀ where they remain for about 5 days on the bottom. They begin to swim freely about the tank then, and to seek food, and should be fed fine-grade food as recommended for the Indian Glass-fish *Chanda ranga* (see p.645). Rearing does not present any special difficulties after these first few days. 1934/+.

Nannacara taenia *Regan* 1912 (Fig.1105)   Lattice Dwarf Cichlid
Amazon; to 5 cm.

D XVI/7; A III/7; LL 24. Shape similar to that of the previous species. Coloration and markings very variable. Grey-brown or yellow-brown, also yellowish to old-gold. Throat yellowish to dark brown, rarely blue or deep black. A broad deep-black longitudinal band from the eye to the root of the tail, accompanied by sundry further dark lines above and below. Fins colourless, bluish or violet with red borders and to some extent tipped with black. Some transverse bars may appear when the fishes are excited.

♀ coloration duller, more grey-yellowish or green-yellowish. Throat blackish to black.

Care and breeding, as given for *N. anomala*. 1911/–.

Genus Pterophyllum

Pterophyllum altum *Pellegrin* 1903   Deep Angelfish
Orinoco; usually not quite as large as *P. scalare*.

D XII–XIII/28–29; A V–VI/28–32; LL 41–47. Body, even without dorsal and anal fins, deeper than, or about as deep as, long. Dorsal and anal fins very long-based and steeply erected. Profile of head and back steeply inclined, snout strongly concave. Coloration similar or identical to that of *P. scalare*, except that there are brown to black blotches on the flanks, which commonly have a light bluish sheen.

Care, as given for *P. eimekei*. 1950.

The genus *Pterophyllum* so far comprises three species *(P. eimekei, scalare* and *altum)*, which are markedly distinguishable by their body-form and colouring. Admittedly the question whether these are really species or subspecies has not yet been resolved. The fact that crosses give fertile offspring, and further, that specimens are frequently imported which are intermediate between the three forms, makes it probable that they are subspecies. A final decision, however, can only be arrived at by investigations in the field. Pure lines of Angelfish are scarcely ever found in captivity; almost all the specimens in Central Europe are products of crosses between *P. eimekei* and *P. scalare* which resemble one or other form. This pheno-menon is occasioned by the simple fact that pure specimens of both species pair much more readily with members of the other than with their own, and also by the fact that it is easier to interbreed the hybrids than to back-cross a hybrid with a pure form. Moreover, the hybrids are hardier. *Pterophyllum altum* has not yet reproduced in captivity, but has probably been imported although not recognised as such. *P. scalare* and *P. altum* are more closely related to one another than *P. scalare* and *P. eimekei*.

Pterophyllum eimekei *Ahl* 1929 (Figs. 923–925)   Lesser Angelfish
Middle Amazon, R. Tapajoz and other tributaries; including fins, 12 cm. long and 23 cm. tall, remaining smaller in captivity.

D XII–XIII/21–25; A VI–VII/22–27; P 11–13; LL 29–36. Body very deep, strongly compressed. Body-depth, without dorsal and anal fins, contained 1·5 times in standard length (tip of snout to root of tail). The profile of the head and back rises in an even curve, without any sharp indentation over the snout. Old fishes have a strongly protuberant forehead. The coloration of pure-bred specimens is markedly different from that of *Pterophyllum scalare*.

Back, nape and snout blackish brown-yellow; flanks silvery with a bluish sheen; nape and back with small, more or less confluent, brown-red blotches; gill-cover silvery with gleaming greenish blotches. 5–6 black transverse bands on the flanks, more or less prominent depending on emotional condition; usually only the 2nd, 4th and 6th bands (the last on the caudal peduncle) are distinctly visible. A further band runs in an arc across the eye from the nape to the insertion of the ventral fin. The 4th and broadest band runs from the tip of the dorsal to the tip of the anal fin.

715

Ventral fins fine steel-blue towards the bases, distally black with long bluish-white produced tips. Pectoral fins colourless. The anterior short spines of the dorsal fin are yellowish; the soft dorsal is faintly patterned with greyish-white.

Sexes not easily distinguished.

Care: large, deep tanks, well planted and providing sufficient free swimming-space. Warmth-loving; temperature in winter 22–24°C. and may temporarily fall to 20°C., but not below 18°C. At too low temperatures dimming of the cornea of the eye and fungus infections appear, but are easily cured by warmth and good aeration. *P. eimekei* is very sensitive to chemicals; baths with medicaments should therefore be kept to a minimum and at least it should first be discovered whether the disease to be combatted cannot be cured by warmth (up to 33°C.). Live food: midge-larvae, worms, water-beetle-larvae and dragonfly-larvae, small crustacea and young fishes. Do not give too much food and vary the diet as often as possible. Over-feeding with one kind of food may result in refusal to feed. This state of affairs may often be overcome by frequent changes of food and of water, also by the addition of salt to the water. Peaceful, not a digger, and a good community fish.

Breeding: The sexes should be allowed to find each other. In pure *P. eimekei* the recognition of sex is very difficult since at the breeding season both ♂♂ and ♀♀ possess rounded genital papillae. The fishes spawn for preference on broad-leaved water plants *(Cryptocoryne, Echinodorus)* which they first free from algae and sediment. The eggs are cared for by both parents and continually fanned with fresh water. The young hatch after 24–36 hours at 26–30°C., and, since the parents eventually bring them into the bottom-soil, the breeding tank should have the least possible mulm. The young are chewed out of the eggshells by the parents and spat onto leaves, where they at first hang by short threads. Later the young are brought down into shallow pits and the first efforts at swimming follow after 4–5 days. After a further 2 days the parents lead the brood out. Rearing is not difficult since the young at once devour fine-grade food. A successful spawning can produce 1000 young.

In serious breeding an Aspidistra leaf should be introduced into the tank, on which the fishes usually prefer to spawn. After about 24 hours the leaf and clutch

Figs. 1100–1103

Fig. 1100. *Geophagus gymnogenys;* adult ♂, reduced.
Fig. 1101. *Geophagus jurupari;* adult ♂, reduced.
Fig. 1102. *Geophagus surinamensis;* adult ♂, reduced.
Fig. 1103. *Pelmatochronis annectens;* adult ♂, somewhat reduced.

are transferred to an all-glass tank with the same kind of water, or spring water which has been allowed to stand and been well worked-through by plants. No soil or plants should be provided, but an aerator-diffusor should be so positioned that there is a continual slow stream of water over the clutch.

Rival or courting ♂♂ emit loud creaking noises which are produced by the jaws. 1924/+.

Pterophyllum scalare (*Lichtenstein* 1823)   Scalare or Angelfish
Amazon; including fins to 15 cm. long and 26 cm. tall.

D XI–XII/24–25; A VI/26–28; P 11–13; LL 38–40. Body little longer than deep, even without the fins; strongly compressed. Profile of head and back with a saddle-shaped indentation over the snout, then rising steeply. Greenish-grey to olive-grey with a brilliant silver sheen. Back brownish-olive with yellowish to rust-coloured tones, often with a brown-red blotch in front of and beneath the dorsal fin. Belly paler. Four bold transverse bands on the flanks and a further three shorter and less conspicuous ones; all the transverse bands vary between deep black and dull grey, depending on the emotional condition of the fish. The 5th band, which is the strongest and darkest, extends from the tip of the dorsal fin across the body to the tip of the anal. Dorsal fin bluish-grey to lead-grey; fin-rays of the anterior part black, of the posterior whitish. Soft dorsal banded with delicate white-grey. Anal fin similarly marked but somewhat darker throughout. Ventral fins yellow-green at the base, blue-green distally with lemon-yellow to orange tips. Iris blood-red or dark red. Occasionally the body has a bluish sheen.

The sexes can only be distinguished with certainty during the breeding season, when the genital papilla of the ♂ is pointed, that of the ♀ rounded.

Care and breeding, as given for *P. eimekei*. This species is still more warmth-loving, however, and should not be kept below 23 °C. Breeding is successful only with well-matched pairs. 1909/+.

Genus Symphysodon (Discus or Pompadour Fishes)

Much confusion has hitherto existed in the treatment of the genus *Symphysodon* in aquarium literature, and this was reflected in the German edition of this book. The revisor has borrowed heavily from a study by Dr. L.P. Schultz (*Tropical Fish Hobbyist*, June 1960, p. 5) in preparing the English edition.

Professor Sterba commenced his account thus: As a preface to the description of this magnificent fish I would like to quote the appreciation of it which has been written by Dr. Ladiges, one of the best authorities in the world of tropical fishes:–'For sheer magnificence of colouring this is undoubtedly the noblest among all aquarium fishes; indeed, I would say that against these aristocratic tints the Neon Fish fades like a revue star before a queen. Recently I have often had the opportunity to display this precious fish to real connoisseurs and authorities on aquarium fishes. These people, so often blasé, invariably stand amazed like worshippers before it. It must be made to succeed one day, to the universal benefit of aquarium fanciers.'

Body disc-shaped, strongly compressed. A single pair of nasal openings. Scales ctenoid, rather small. Gill-cover and cheeks scaly. Mouth small, with thick lips. Teeth small, conical, in a single row.

Symphysodon aequifasciata aequifasciata *Pellegrin* 1903   Green Discus
Amazon and tributaries; to 15 cm.
D VIII–X/29–34; A VIII–IX/27–32; P 13–15; LL 52–61. Shape as given in the genus description. Coloration, according to Schultz: background coloration dark brownish green with nine dark brown vertical bars, all of about the same intensity except that the last is darkest; these dark bars have the same positions as the homologous dark bars in the other species of *Symphysodon*. Basal three-fourths of dorsal and anal fins blackish; distally these fins are light olive-green with scattered light spots basally. Caudal fin translucent with scattered light spots. Horizontal blackish streaks on head, dorsally on body and on dorsal fin, mostly absent on midsides, but distinct ventrally on anal fin. Alternating light blue and dark oblique streaks on cheek; three vertical, dark or light blue streaks on opercular; iris reddish brown. Pelvic fin dark green, outer ray blue and tips of rays dark brown. Pectoral fin translucent, its base dark green.

Sex-distinctions not yet described.

Care and breeding, as given under *Symphysodon discus*, below.

Symphysodon aequifasciata axelrodi *Schultz* 1960 (Figs. 951, 952)
                                  Brown Discus, Yellow-brown Discus
Amazon, Rio Urubú; to 14 cm.
D VIII–X/30–32; A VII–IX/26–32; P 12–14; LL 50–59. Shape as in genus description. Coloration, according to Schultz: background coloration light

yellowish-brown to dark brown, overlaid with nine vertical bars; the first, through the eye, is dark purplish-brown to blackish and the last, through the base of the caudal fin-rays, blackish; these two (first and last) notably darker than the other seven, all of which are light purplish to purplish brown. The second band, at the origin of the spinous dorsal fin, ends at the upper edge of the opercular opening; the third passes through the base of the pectoral fin thence ending at the base of the pelvic fin; the next four across the body; the next to last vertical bar occurs on the caudal peduncle and extends from the rear edge of the base of the dorsal fin to that of the anal fin. Soft dorsal fin and soft anal fin basally with a broad dark purplish band that is continuous with the dark crossbar at the base of the caudal peduncle and contrasts notably with the light background colour of the body. Soft dorsal and anal fins distally light olive, with scattered lighter spots mostly basally. Pelvic fin reddish-brown with distal tips of rays yellow or orange. Anal spines blue, membranes brownish. Pectoral fin light blue to light purplish; bases of rays purple. Operculum dark purple. Iris red. Forehead with about four horizontal light blue streaks. Anal fin with blue streaks basally.

♂ blue streaks carried right to the base of the anal fin.
♀ blue streaks carried only to the dark longitudinal band on the outer part of the anal fin.

Care and breeding, as given under *Symphysodon discus*, below. A long account of the breeding of *S. a. axelrodi* by O. Wagner appears in the *Tropical Fish Hobbyist* of November 1960, p. 44.

Symphysodon aequifasciata haraldi *Schultz* 1960   Blue Discus
Amazon; to at least 12 cm.

D IX/31; A VIII/29; P 14; LL 53. Shape as given in the genus description. Coloration, according to Schultz: background coloration of body brownish anteriorly, darker brown posteriorly; head purplish. Head and body crossed with nine dark blue vertical bars, first and last darkest; first bar through eye across cheek to isthmus; second from spinous dorsal origin to upper edge of opercle; third across base of pectoral fin to base of pelvic fin; next across body; next to last from rear edge of dorsal fin base across caudal peduncle to rear edge of base of anal fin; last bar almost black across base of caudal fin-rays. Basal three-fourths of dorsal and anal fins dark blackish purple that blends in with the background coloration of the body; distal areas of soft dorsal and anal fins light yellowish with scattered light spots, mostly basally. Caudal fin translucent, also with scattered light spots basally. Pelvic fin dark brown, outer ray blue; distally the tips of the rays are pinkish. Pectoral fin purple, its base brown. Horizontal wavy blue streaks, irregularly interrupted, cover the entire body, except breast and behind head, and distal parts of median fins. Forehead with four or five blue horizontal streaks; two oblique blue streaks below eye and two vertical blue bars on operculum.

Sex-distinctions not yet described.

Care and breeding, as given under *Symphysodon discus*, below.

Symphysodon discus *Heckel* 1840   Discus

Amazon, Rio Negro, Rio Cupai and other tributaries; to 20 cm.

D IX/31; A VII/29; P 13; LL 44. Shape as given in genus description. Coloration, according to Schultz: background coloration of the body composed of alternating horizontal light reddish brown and bluish streaks, numbering about 15 to 18; these streaks, beginning behind the operculum and on the forehead at the midantero-dorsal line, continue a somewhat wavy course posteriorly, thence disappearing at the base of median fins. The usual 9 vertical bars are present, three of which are dark blue, the others scarcely distinct; the first is a broad one through the eye to the isthmus, the next three very light tan, the fifth is a broad dark blue one, attaining its greatest intensity on lower midside of body but not reaching to base of anal fin; the next three are very light tan; the last is a broad bar across the base of the caudal sharply contrasting with the general background coloration as do numbers one and five; the usual dark band on bases of dorsal and anal fins indistinct. Distal parts of median fins light blue with scattered light blue spots. Pectoral fin light blue. Oblique light streaks on cheek, and two or three vertical ones on opercle. Outer pelvic ray blue; other rays yellowish.

Sex-distinctions not yet described.

Care: *Symphysodon* species at present rank among the fishes which are very delicate and consequently difficult to keep. For this reason the fishes imported are usually very small and require very careful attention up to sexual maturity. Large aquaria, standing in a quiet position, soft soil, loose planting and some pieces of rock or large, well-rotted pieces of root provide the closest approximation to the natural environment. A few floating plants may be used as shelter against too strong incident light. Plenty of attention should be paid, especially, to the composition of the water and its regular renewal. Very soft, slightly acid water (2–3° German Hardness Scale, pH about 6·5) is indicated, at least for the young. For older fishes I consider a slight addition of sea-salt (1 tablespoon to 10 litres of water) beneficial. I have myself kept half-grown Discus in almost neutral, medium-hard water (10–12° German Hardness Scale) without noticing any ill effects. It appears to me that the content of micro-organisms is more important than the very soft, slightly acid water. In any case the welfare of the fishes is considerably increased by the inclusion of substances such as peat-extracts which prevent the multiplication of bacteria. It is further very important to renew regularly a certain quantity of the water; as a start exchange about a quarter of the water for fresh every three weeks.

Feeding should be as varied as possible; in addition to *Daphnia*, white and black midge-larvae, mayfly-larvae, small dragonfly-larvae and large brine shrimps are especially recommended. On the other hand, red midge-larvae and *Tubifex* should only be fed if they come from pure waters or have been well cleaned. Occasionally dry food is accepted. Discus will take food from the bottom and worms are often pulled or washed out of the soil. The species are warmth-loving (26–30 °C.), very peaceful with other fishes, and do not dig up the bottom.

The Discus Cichlid has several times been bred in captivity. Especially valuable in this context are the observations of E. Schmidt of the Tropicarium, Frankfurt, where imported young fishes were systematically reared with the object of breeding. The fishes spawn in winter and the first months of spring (breeding season!) after the manner of Cichlids several times in succession on stones or large plant leaves which previously have been meticulously cleaned. The young hatch after about 50 hours and are then transferred to leaves where they hang by short threads. During this period both partners relieve one another, taking turns to fan the brood. After a further 60 hours the young fishes are able to swim about freely and they now attach themselves to the fins and body of the parents (usually of the ♀). The observation, that after the absorption of the yolk-sac the bellies of the young are full while at the same time the skin of the parents has a cloudy appearance, suggests that at first the young feed on a parental skin-secretion. There is, of course, evidence against any such hypothesis in the fact that Armbruster reared young Discus in the absence of the parents and, furthermore, that a similar attachment has been observed occasionally in other Cichlids, such as *Astronotus* and *Etroplus*, without the young feeding on skin-secretion. The parents relieve one another in brood-care and whenever a young one is shaken off by too strong a motion of the fins a parent rushes to the straggler and re-attaches it, either to itself or to its mate. The young become independent after a few days and should now be fed with very fine-grade food. Their shape, at first elongate, becomes noticeably more disc-like and eventually, after about 3 months, the typical form is attained. The species requires at least 2 years to reach sexual maturity. An excellent account has been given by O. Wagner (*Aquarien und Terrarien*, 4 Jg., H. 11., 1957, translated in *Tropical*

Fish Hobbyist, Nov. 1960). See also G. Wolfsheimer in the *National Geographic Magazine,* Vol. 117, p. 675, May 1960. 1921/+.

Uaru amphiacanthiodes *Heckel* 1840 (Figs. 1106, 1107)
Amazon and Guiana; to 25 cm.

D XV–XVI/14–16; A VIII/13–15; LL 40–42. Body egg-shaped, strongly compressed. The coloration is very variable and also very different in the young and the adult. Young fishes of 3–5 cm. length: head, body, breast and ventral fins, as well as the anterior spinous portions of the dorsal and anal fins, uniform black-brown. Soft dorsal and anal, also caudal fin, colourless, transparent. Tips of the dorsal and anal spines milky.

Adult fishes: Yellowish to brownish, with 3 large black blotches on the flanks; the first of these is round and situated immediately behind the eye, the second and largest is wedge-shaped and extends broadly along the lower flanks, the third is situated in the upper corner of the caudal peduncle. Fins yellowish with a greenish sheen. Eye pale red.

Reliable sex-distinctions are given only by the shape of the genital papilla.

The care of this very interesting, but unfortunately also delicate, species is not easy. Since it is often found in association with *Pterophyllum* or *Symphysodon* in its natural habitat, it calls for similar treatment (see p. 716). *Uaru* prefers to spawn in especially dark places (cavities among stones, hollow tree-stumps, etc.). Spawning procedure and brood-care as for *Pterophyllum eimekei.* Very warmth-loving, 27–28°C.; up to 30°C. for breeding. If necessary the spawn can be transferred to an all-glass tank and provided with gentle aeration. The rearing of the young is rather difficult. Generally peaceful with one another and towards other species; the ♂♂, however, are often very quarrelsome during the breeding season. 1913/+.

Cichlids of Africa and Southern Asia

Etroplus maculatus (*Bloch* 1795) (Fig. 918)   Orange Chromide
India and Ceylon, in fresh and brackish water; to 8 cm.

D XVII–XX/8–10; A XII–XV/8–9; P 15–16; LL 35–37. Body of adult fish disc-shaped, very deep, strongly compressed. Back grey-blue to brown-black, becoming pale orange to golden yellow on the sides. On the flanks there are 3 large, round, brown-black, black or bluish blotches, bordered by yellowish areas; the centre one of the three is very prominent. Numerous gold-red or bright red spots in rows along the flanks. Dorsal fin orange with dark brown or reddish spots and a red border. Anal and caudal fins yellow, the former with a deep black border to the spinous part, the latter with a reddish edge. Ventral fins black, the first ray being iridescent pale blue. Iris golden to brilliant red. Some rows of bluish scales under the eye. Out of the breeding season both sexes are dark and not so finely coloured; the fins are also more blackish at this time.

Sex-distinctions often difficult. The ♀♀ are usually duller in colouring and their dorsal and caudal fins merely with reddish borders.

Care and breeding, as given in the family description. *E. maculatus* is usually quite a peaceful Cichlid, not given to digging, and thrives in an aquarium with loose plant-stands and, especially, with pieces of decaying wood. This species is generally sensitive to changes in water-conditions and to fresh water. The addition of a little sea-salt (1–2 teaspoons to 10 litres of water) makes the fishes hardier. Temperature not below 20°C., 25–26°C. for breeding. Spawning takes place for preference on stones or in hollow pieces of wood, and the eggs hang by short threads. Both parents undertake brood-care, Cichlid-fashion. The serious breeder is recommended to isolate the spawn shortly before hatching and to treat it in much the same manner as has been described for *Pterophyllum eimekei* (see p. 716). The young require a plentiful and varied diet. Even in *E. maculatus* the young occasionally attach themselves to the flanks of the parents before they attain the free-swimming stage. 1905/+.

Etroplus suratensis (*Bloch* 1790) (Fig. 919)   Green Chromide
Ceylon, in brackish waters; to 40 cm., remaining considerably smaller in captivity.

D XVIII–XIX/14–15; A XII–XIII/11; LL 35–40. Body very deep, short oval, strongly compressed. Blue-grey to grey-green with a fine pearly gleam on the flanks and 6–8 usually not very prominent transverse bands. Scales on the flanks with large shining green or bluish spots; often numerous broad, lacquer-black-edged scales below the lateral line. Fins bluish or dirty green. Pectoral fins yellowish with

Figs. 1104–1107

Fig. 1104. *Cichlasoma urophthalmus;* adult ♂, reduced.
Fig. 1105. *Nannacara taenia* (Lattice Dwarf Cichlid); maximum size.
Fig. 1106. *Uaru amphiacanthoides;* adult ♂, reduced. Below, right, a young specimen of 3–5 cm. in length.
Big. 1107. *Uaru amphiacanthoides;* half-grown.

a lacquer-black blotch at the base. According to Day the fishes, in seawater during the breeding season, are banded with bright crimson and deep black.

Sex-distinctions unknown.

E. suratensis is a brackish-water fish and can only be kept in freshwater temporarily. On the other hand, a prolonged sojourn in seawater does no harm and even appears to be beneficial to health. Coloration considerably brighter in seawater. Warmth-loving, not below 23–24 °C. Probably not yet bred in captivity. 1905/ +.

Haplochromis desfontainesi (*Lacépède* 1802) (Fig. 1108)

Generally distributed through north Africa, also in oases and artesian wells; to 15 cm., the ♀♀ remaining considerably smaller.

D XIV–XVI/9–10(–12); A III(–IV)/8–10(–11); LL 28–36; TR 3–5/11–13. Body elongate, compressed. Head and mouth large. Coloration, according to Kirchshofer:–delicate brownish to olive-green. Scales with a pearly to bluish lustre by reflected light. Several dark transverse bands and a longitudinal band from the eye to the root of the tail may be either quite prominent or completely absent. On the other hand, a dark band from the eye to the corner of the mouth and a black, gold-rimmed blotch on the gill-cover are almost always obvious. Dorsal and caudal fins with numerous tiny orange to brown dots, the former also bordered with orange. Anal fin with 4–8 orange, black-bordered ocelli. Ventral fins black. During the breeding season overall steel-blue, with the fins almost black, the markings brilliant orange-red and the lips blue.

♀ smaller; coloration similar but not so intense as in the ♂.

Care and breeding, as given for *H. multicolor*, below. A very warmth-loving species, 26–28 °C. Eggs yellow. The mouth-brooding lasts about 16–20 days. The ♂ is pugnacious during the breeding season towards other members of his own kind. This characteristic is less frequently displayed in very large aquaria. 1953.

Haplochromis multicolor (*Hilgendorf* 1903) (Figs. 887, 1111)

Small or Egyptian Mouth-Brooder

Throughout eastern Africa and northwards to the lower Nile; to 8 cm.

D XIII–XV/8–10; A III/6–9; P 12; LL 25–29. Body elongate, strongly compressed in the hinder part especially. The coloration of the ♂♂ is especially attractive. Against a clay-coloured to pale rust-coloured ground the different parts of the body shine, according to the lighting, golden, greenish or, especially on the back, bluish. Gill-cover gleaming grass-green with a lacquer-black, gold-rimmed blotch posteriorly. Fins extraordinarily colourful. Dorsal usually bright rust-red with

726

green fin-rays, or at least green dots at the bases of the fin-rays, a pale green to blue border and a black edge. Anal fin similarly coloured, but usually rather darker and with a characteristic brilliant red spot at the hinder end. Caudal fin more yellow-green with attractive rows of spots. Pectoral fins yellowish, the second fin-ray brilliant blue-green.

♀ coloration considerably duller, altogether more yellowish, with dark transverse blotches.

Mouth-brooding is established in practically all the *Haplochromis* spp. which have been imported. They are exclusively African fishes, without exception quite peaceful, and can be kept quite well in the company of other not too small species; indeed, life in a community tank even seems to be good for them. Obviously there must be exceptions to such a rule; thus older ♂♂, especially, occasionally become quite pugnacious towards their own kind and with other fishes and may even ill-treat the ♀♀ during the breeding season, but such mischief-makers can easily be recognised and removed in good time.

The pairs spawn with whirling movements in shallow pits. Number of eggs 30–80, seldom more. Immediately after spawning the eggs are taken up in the mouth of the ♀ and accommodated in a widening of the floor (throat-sac). It is best now to remove the ♂. The eggs can usually be seen through the stretched skin of the throat, and the ♀ constantly rearranges the layers by means of chewing movements. The young hatch after about 10 days and now, at first only temporarily, are released from the mouth. The ♀ at once commences to feed again; the young, also, must find the finest possible food available on their first excursion. In *Haplochromis multicolor* the ♀ offers the young the shelter of her mouth in times of danger and at night-time for a period of about a week. Later the young become quite independent and should then be isolated from the ♀. It is especially interesting to observe that in the early days the young take refuge in the wide-open maternal mouth in response to quite definite signals from the mother. Thanks to the researches of Peters it is now known that this drive to seek the maternal mouth is inherited. This also explains the phenomenon that the mouth of an artificial dummy serving as a mother-mimic is also sought out. The brood-care drive of the mother, on the other hand, is occasionally also directed towards other young fishes. This species is best kept in well-matured aquaria with thin plant-stands, top lighting screened to some extent by floating plants, and a soft bottom-soil. If possible include some water-logged wood. *H. multicolor* should not be kept below 20°C.; 25–26°C. at least for breeding. 1902/+.

H. strigigena (Pfeffer 1893) is a synonym of this species.

727

Haplochromis pectoralis (*Pfeffer* 1893) (Fig. 1110)
East Africa, Korogwe, Kilimanjaro, R. Pangani system; to 10 cm.

D XV–XVI/8–9; A III/8; LL 28–30. Body elongate, rather deep, strongly compressed. Coloration, according to Meinken: upperside dark olive-brown; flanks more reddish-brown, also yellowish towards the belly; belly pale yellow. The whole body has a reddish sheen by reflected light. Several irregular transverse bands are usually not very distinct. Gill-cover with a dark blotch. Dorsal and anal fins anteriorly yellow-green with pale and dark stripes across the membranes between the spines; the soft hinder parts of these fins each bear a pale ocellus encircled by several curved pale and dark violet bands. Caudal fin yellow-green with pale and dark spots which may unite into transverse bands. Coloration of the ♀ unknown.

Care, as given for *Haplochromis multicolor;* probably a mouth-brooder. So far only ♂♂ have been imported. 1911/−.

Haplochromis philander (*Weber* 1897) (Fig. 1109)
South-west Africa, Transvaal, Rhodesia, Angola, Katanga; to 11 cm.

D (XIII–)XIV/9–11; A III/8–10; LL 26–28; TR 3/10–12. Shape similar to that of *Haplochromis multicolor*. Three forms of this species have been imported, which can be distinguished to some extent by their maximum sizes and more markedly by their colouring.

Large form from Beira (Portuguese East Africa): Coloration similar to that of *H. multicolor*, except that the golden gleam on the sides of the body is considerably brighter. Back and belly in the ♂ iridescent bluish. Some dark transverse bands, as well as a longitudinal band which breaks up into a series of disconnected blotches posteriorly, are usually not very clearly apparent. Vertical fins bright red with brilliant blue tips. When the fish is excited the anterior part of the anal fin is cobalt–blue, the posterior part reddish, as in *H. multicolor*, with a brilliant red blotch. Lower lip brilliant blue. Throat and belly reddish to crimson when the fish is excited. Coloration of ♀ considerably less pretentious. To 11 cm.

Figs. 1108–1111

Fig. 1108. *Haplochromis desfontainesi;* adult ♂, reduced.
Fig. 1109. *Haplochromis philander;* adult ♂, somewhat reduced.
Fig. 1110. *Haplochromis pectoralis;* adult ♂, somewhat reduced.
Fig. 1111. *Haplochromis multicolor* (Small or Egyptian Mouth-brooder); about natural size.

Small form from Beira: more yellowish to yellowish-olive with quite indistinct transverse bands, but usually with a bold longitudinal band. Scales on the flanks shining green to dull golden. Fins yellowish with rows of shining green spots. A blood-red blotch on the hinder part of the anal fin. ♀ uniformly clay-yellow. To 8 cm.

Small form from Lake Otjikoto (South-west Africa): considerably like the previous form in colouring, but with strongly emphasised blue tones. Mouth bordered with brilliant blue below. The throat of the ♂ is dark blue when excited. ♀ greenish-grey. Fins colourless; dorsal and caudal with faint reddish border. To 8 cm.

Care and breeding, as given for *Haplochromis multicolor*. This species is unfortunately not quite as peaceful. Resistant to temperatures close below 20°C., but requires 24–26°C. for breeding. The large form from Beira is the most attractively coloured mouth-brooder so far imported. 1911/+.

Hemichromis bimaculatus *Gill* 1862   Red Cichlid, Jewelfish

Niger, Nile, Congo, common everywhere; to 15 cm., sexually mature at 7 cm.

D XIII–XV/9–13; A III/7–9; P 14–15; LL 25–29; TR 2–3/9–11. Body elongate, compressed. One of the loveliest of the African Cichlids during the breeding season. Back dark olive to grey-brown with a greenish sheen; flanks greenish-yellow; belly yellowish. A dark longitudinal band along the flanks, passing through still darker blotches on the gill-cover, flanks and the root of the tail. 5–6 dark transverse bands are often suggested. Fins yellowish-brown to greenish.

Coloration during the breeding season: underside brilliant lacquer-red. Forehead and back olive-green with a reddish sheen. The blotches on the gill-cover and flanks are now blue-black and between them appear 6–7 rows of sky-blue spots; similar spots also on the gill-cover. A black stripe over the eye, forked posteriorly. On the dorsal fin a double row of shining bluish spots divides the wine-red base from the pale red centre; the margin is wine-red again. Pectoral, ventral and anal fins pale olive; ventral and anal with blue spots and black anterior edges. Caudal fin dark olive at the base, pale olive in the centre and dark red at the edge.

♀ usually more attractively coloured during the breeding season, the red colours becoming more prominent.

Care and breeding, as given in the family description. Older fishes must be kept as isolated pairs. Quarrelsome and likes to dig up the bottom, especially much so during the breeding season. Brood-care very striking. Temperature 22–28°C. 1907/+.

730

Hemichromis fasciatus *Peters* 1857   Five-spot Cichlid, Banded Jewelfish
Central West Africa; to 30 cm., remaining considerably smaller in captivity.

D XIII–XV/11–13; A III/8–10; P 15; LL 29–32. Body elongate, rather low, compressed. Head large. Profile of snout-nape slightly concave. Mouth large, deeply cleft.

Coloration out of the breeding season: yellowish with a green sheen. Back olive; flanks brass-yellow; underside dirty white to light yellowish. Throat grey-blue to deep blue. A distinct blue-green blotch on the gill-cover. Several transverse bands, usually not very distinct or appearing merely as large dark blotches on the middle of the side. Fins delicate greenish or yellowish.

Coloration during the breeding season: shining brassy overall, with a reddish sheen on the back and a blood-red underside. Gill-cover with a brilliant blue-green blotch ringed with gold. 5 large, lacquer-black oval blotches on the flanks. In fine specimens each scale bears a large brick-red spot. Fins clay-yellow, the dorsal with a red border and white tip, the anterior parts of the ventrals blue-green. Iris blood-red with a gold inner border.

♀ usually smaller and – at least during the breeding season – more robust. Anal fin rounded.

Care and breeding, as given in the family description. Unfortunately this species is one of the quarrelsome, digging Cichlids. Pairs are not too difficult to put together. Spawning takes place preferably on stones. Both parents take part in the extraordinarily careful brood-care and look after the young until they are 2–3 cm. long. Warmth-loving. 1905/+.

Nannochromis nudiceps (*Boulenger* 1899) (Fig. 864)
Congo (Stanley Pool, among other localities); to 7·5 cm.

D XVIII–XIX/8; A III/7; LL 28–29; TR 18–19. Body elongate, low, moderately compressed. Head rather obtuse; forehead relatively steep. The scales on the upper part of the lateral line lie immediately under the dorsal fin (a character of the genus).

♂ Ochre-colour with pale blue flanks and an emerald-green belly. Gill-cover bronze-coloured. An iridescent pale blue area under the eye; a small rust-red stripe over the eye. Narrow, dark, transverse bands, as a rule normally present only in the young but shown in sexually mature fishes when they are greatly excited. Dorsal fin orange-brown with a white margin and a black tip. Caudal fin ochre, longitudinally striped with orange and brown, with a white upper edge and a violet lower part. Anal fin violet to iridescent green. Ventral fins bright green

731

with white leading-edges. The green and violet colours, especially, become intensified during the breeding season.

♀ Smaller, on the whole, but likewise brilliantly coloured. The emerald-green belly is brighter.

N. nudiceps is one of the more beautiful of the smaller Cichlids and can very well be kept in a planted aquarium. ♂♂ snappish with one another but usually peaceful enough with ♀♀. Like most Cichlids this species is a typical territorial fish which likes to retire to a private hiding-place in the aquarium from which it can keep watch on its surroundings. Breeds readily in a tank reserved for the one species. In my experience the fishes prefer to spawn on the sloping face of an upright flowerpot which has been provided with a round entrance-hole like that of a starling's nest-box. Eggs oval, yellow, about 80–120. Brood-care is undertaken by the ♀. The young hatch after about 3 days and swim freely after a further 3. Temperature 24–28 °C. Soft, slightly peaty water. Live food of all kinds. 1952.

Pelmatochromis annectens *Boulenger* 1913 (Fig. 1103)
Africa, from Liberia to Nigeria, also in brackish water; to 10 cm., the ♀♀ remaining somewhat smaller.

D XV/9–10; A III/7–8; LL 28–29; TR 2/10–11. Body elongate, rather deep, strongly compressed. Upper profile rather more strongly convex than the lower. A marked capacity for colour-change. Healthy fishes in a not-too-light aquarium are blackish-yellow with a lovely sea-green sheen on the flanks. Throat light blue; belly pink in the ♀, bright red in the ♂. Several irregular transverse bands and a longitudinal band are usually indistinct; on the other hand, 4 dark blotches at the intersections between these longitudinal and transverse bands are almost always quite conspicuous. A large, blue-green, red-rimmed blotch on the gill-cover. Anterior parts of dorsal and anal fins greenish or yellowish, posterior parts checkered with delicate greenish and red. Caudal fin checkered, light and dark. Ventral fins long, blue-black.

♀ Coloration rather duller. Ventral fins shorter. Dorsal and anal fins usually slightly rounded. Sexually ripe fishes have a brilliant white spot on each side of the vent.

The exclusively West African genus *Pelmatochromis* comprises fishes which chiefly inhabit collections of water in coastal regions which are brackish from time to time, or which are even dwellers in large river-mouths and the lower reaches of rivers. These fishes, often attractively coloured, are found mostly in shallow, thickly-weeded places or where waterlogged wood or tangles of roots provide good

732

hiding-places. Their welfare in captivity largely depends on the successful imitation of such conditions. As compared with other Cichlids the majority of *Pelmatochromis* spp. may be described as quite peaceful; some species dig to some extent during the breeding season, but usually without damage to well-rooted plants. The addition of a little sea-salt to the water (1–2 tablespoons to 10 litres) is often vitally necessary to their health. It is best in this case, as with other Cichlids, to let the pairs select themselves among a shoal of young fishes. Popular spawning-places are inverted flowerpots, provided with holes about the size of that in a starling's nest-box, coconutshells, etc. Generally both partners take part in brood-care. Some *Pelmatochromis* spp. are even mouth-brooders which, like *P. guentheri*, carry the developing eggs in the mouth. Occasionally it is recommended (especially with *P. kribensis*) that the fishes be kept in very soft, peaty water, a provision which I regard as unnecessary, since biologically well-matured water should be sufficient for all requirements.

P. annectens is quite warmth-loving, yet on the other hand quite resistant to brief drops in temperature. These fishes will occasionally accept dried food. Eggs pale-brown, of the size of a millet-seed. The young hatch after 3 days. 1913/ −.

P. annectens may prove to be a junior synonym of *P. arnoldi*, the following species.

Pelmatochromis arnoldi *Boulenger* 1912 (Fig. 1114)
Distribution as given for the previous species; to 9 cm.

D XV–XVI/10–11; A III/8–9; LL 28. Shape similar to that of *P. annectens*, with which it may well be identical. Head deeply indented in front of the forehead. Usually overall ochre-coloured to grey, to some extent with a silver sheen. Especially characteristic of this species are a row of bold blotches along the flanks and a further similar blotch, usually bordered with shining green, on the gill-cover. Fins delicate greenish. Dorsal and anal fins checkered dark on the hinder parts, the former often bordered with red. During the breeding season the underside of the ♂ is a fine brick-red or, depending on health, orange-red.

Sex-distinctions in coloration not so far described.

Care and breeding, as given for *Pelmatochromis annectens*. 1911/ −.

Pelmatochromis guentheri (*Sauvage* 1882) (Fig. 1113)
West Africa, from Ghana to Gabon; to 16 cm., the ♀♀ remaining considerably smaller.

D XV–XVII/9–12; A III/7–8; LL 28–30. Head rather pointed. Olive-green, with a bluish sheen on the flanks; back appreciably darker. A usually bold but

733

very irregular band from the snout to the root of the tail. Parallel to this, but always considerably narrower, is a dark line from the upper edge of the orbit to the upper edge of the caudal peduncle. Both longitudinal bands are intersected by irregular and usually very indistinct transverse bands. Gill-cover with a shining brilliant blue-green blotch. Dorsal fin delicate greenish with a pearly longitudinal band and a blood-red border. Caudal fin somewhat yellowish with red spots and streaks towards the outer edge. Anal fin fine red in healthy fishes. Ventrals brilliant green-silver. Iris brilliant red.

♀ more beautifully coloured when full-grown. Fins dark-bordered; dorsal fin with a row of black spots at the base.

Care, as given for *Pelmatochromis annectens*. Unfortunately not as peaceful as the other species of the genus; keep them in pairs. Very voracious but not choosy. A mouth-brooder; in fact, according to Arnold, both parents take part in brood-care. (See *P. annectens*.) 1913/−.

Pelmatochromis kribensis *Boulenger* 1911 (Fig. 867)
Tropical West Africa, mouths of the Niger delta; ♂ to 9 cm., ♀ to 7 cm.

D XVI–XVIII/7–9; A III/7–8; LL 27–29; TR 2/9. Body elongate, moderately compressed. Upper profile more strongly convex than lower. Coloration very changeable, markings also very variable in the same brood. Upperside brownish with a handsome bluish to violet sheen. Flanks and belly ivory-coloured, delicate bluish to bright violet, often with shining greenish areas. Especially characteristic of this species are a large, vaguely-delimited brilliant wine-red blotch on either side of the belly and a dark brown blotch (usually edged with bright red above and steel-blue below) on the gill-cover. A dark band along the back and a broader one along the side are especially distinct in the young. Fins most attractively coloured. The ♂♂ are characterised by 1–5 round dark blotches, bordered with pale yellow, in the upper part of the caudal fin, although these may be entirely absent. The ventral fins are wine-red in the ♀, violet in the ♂, with steel-blue leading-edges in both sexes. The ♀♀ are commonly more brightly coloured than the ♂♂.

Figs. 1112–1116

Fig. 1112. *Pelmatochromis pulcher;* half-grown, somewhat enlarged.
Fig. 1113. *Pelmatochromis guentheri;* adult ♂, somewhat reduced.
Fig. 1114. *Pelmatochromis arnoldi;* adult ♂, reduced.
Fig. 1115. *Pelmatochromis subocellatus;* adult ♂, somewhat reduced.
Fig. 1116. *Pelmatochromis subocellatus;* ♀, natural size.

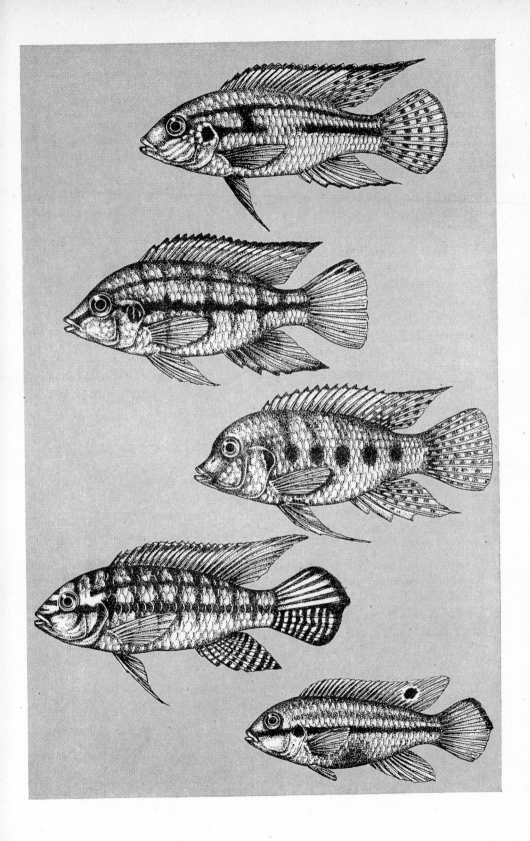

Care and breeding, as given for *P. annectens*. Warmth-loving, 25–28 °C. Adults should be kept in pairs if possible. Both parents take part in brood-care. The red-brown eggs are laid in flowerpots for preference. In serious breeding the spawn is transferred to an all-glass tank with gentle aeration. The young hatch after 2–3 days and swim freely after a further 4–5 days. 1951.

Pelmatochromis pulcher *Boulenger* 1901 (Fig. 1112)
Niger, mouths of the delta; to 10 cm.

D XVI/9–11; A III/7–8; LL 27–29; TR 2–2½/10. Coloration very variable and differing in the various growth-stages, as in most *Pelmatochromis* spp.

Adult fishes: upperside dark green; flanks brilliant green, with a blue sheen; underside reddish to bright carmine. Occasionally the red colour extends as far as the back. Gill-cover with brilliant shining green-blue stripes and a large black to coppery blotch. Dorsal fin beautiful dark violet at the base, externally delicate greenish with a red border. Caudal fin greenish with brown-red spots and a black upper edge. Anal fin a lovely violet, bordered with black. Ventral fins black-blue.

Young fishes: altogether more yellowish and displaying two longitudinal bands which are united by a dark blotch shortly before the middle of the body.

♀ (according to Arnold) with a reddish blotch in the middle of the lower half of the body, at least at the onset of sexual maturity.

Care, as given for *P. annectens*. Very peaceful. Not yet bred in captivity. 1913/ – .

Pelmatochromis subocellatus (*Günther* 1871) (Figs. 1115, 1116)
West Africa, Gabon to about the mouth of the Congo; to 10 cm.

D XIV–XVI/8–10; A III/6–8; LL 25–28. A very attractive species, sometimes rivalling the Coral-fishes in its colouring. An extraordinary capacity for colour-change.

Coloration, out of the breeding season: upperside grey-green to green-black; flanks olive-green to ochre-colour, often with a light brassy glint; underside delicate reddish, with a large red-violet blotch in the ♀. An almost always distinct longitudinal band from the snout to the root of the tail; on the other hand, 2 longitudinal bands in the upper half of the body and numerous transverse bands are only occasionally apparent. Fins very gay, usually all shades of yellowish to rust-red, with pale blue spots and lines.

♀ Ventral fins considerably shorter. Dorsal and anal fins rounded posteriorly. More brilliant than the ♂ during the breeding season. A deep-black ocellus on the dorsal fin, rimmed with gold, becomes especially distinct at this time. In the

736

spawning-act the ♀ is velvet black, with the exception of the middle upper part of the body (including the central part of the dorsal fin) which is chalk-white.

Care and breeding, as given for *P. annectens*. This species digs up the bottom at spawning time and prefers to lay its eggs under stones. No mouth-brooding. 1907/−.

Pelmatochromis taeniatus *Boulenger* 1901
Tropical West Africa, Niger delta, lower Calabar; ♂ to 9 cm., ♀ to 7 cm.

D XVII–XVIII/7–8; A III/7; LL 28–29; TR 2/9. Shape similar to that of *P. kribensis*, which this species is also not unlike in markings and colouring. As a distinguishing character Ladiges gives the blotch on the belly, stating that in *P. taeniatus* this is not wine-red but always emerald-green. *P. taeniatus* is said also to be even more brilliantly coloured than *P. kribensis*. Coloration, according to Ladiges: from the tip of the snout to the root of the tail there extends a broad olive-brown band which, in ♂♂ especially, is sometimes broken up into blotches or even absent. Lips and cheeks golden yellow. Particularly in the ♀♀ the region above the longitudinal band is intensely golden; in the ♂♂ more yellow-grey to blue-grey. Below the longitudinal band the flanks are delicate violet to turquoise-blue in the ♀, with a bright emerald-green blotch on the belly; in the ♂ they are yellow anteriorly, brownish posteriorly, often with a greenish sheen. Fins very handsome. The marking of the caudal is characteristic: in the ♂ it is orange above with 5–6 dark ocelli and below it is blue-green with dark wavy lines; in the ♀ uniformly orange with a few ocelli in the upper part and black fin-rays in the lower. Ventral fins emerald-green. Eyes delicate green-blue.

Care and breeding, as given for *P. annectens;* see also *P. kribensis*. 1911/+.

Steatocranus casuarius *Poll* 1939 (Fig. 917)   African Blockhead
Lower and Middle Congo, in rapids; to 9 cm.

D XIX–XX/8; A III/6. Body elongate, relatively low, rather compressed. Dorsal fin long-based. Caudal fin rounded. Cycloid scales. Forehead and nape of mature ♂♂ with a large hump-shaped or dome-shaped adipose outgrowth which becomes still higher with increasing age. Coloration almost uniformly brownish to grey-olive, occasionally with dark transverse bands. Fins opaque, coloured similarly to the body. Iris bright iridescent emerald-green.

♀ smaller.

Chlupaty (1956) has given some interesting information on the care and breeding of this peculiar African fish, saying that it is quite undemanding and, outside the breeding season, very peaceful. It hardly digs at all, so that plants are generally

737

undisturbed out of the breeding season and only a very little during that period. Not choosy over food. Temperature 24–28°C. The fishes will spawn in an inverted flowerpot provided with a narrow entrance. First of all the ♂ and ♀ carry away the sand from the artificial breeding-cave and clear a precinct about 25 cm. in diameter. Brood-care is chiefly undertaken by the ♂, who fans the eggs and masticates food for the young when they hatch. About 3 weeks after spawning both parents dig a hole in front of the 'cave' and bring the young into it during the daytime. Later the shoal is led for a long time by the ♀. Towards nightfall both parents concern themselves in transporting the young back to the cave. 1956.

Tilapia galilaea (*Linnaeus* 1758) (Fig. 1117)   Galilee Cichlid/Mouth-brooder
Widely distributed, from Jordan over the whole of East and Central Africa to Liberia; to 40 cm., remaining considerably smaller in captivity and becoming sexually mature at about 12 cm.

D (XV–)XVI–XVII/12–14; A III/10–12; LL 30–34. Body rather deep and rather strongly compressed. Back olive-brown; flanks silvery with a fine bluish sheen; underside white-silver. Gill-cover bronze-coloured with a brilliant pale blue or blackish blotch. Fins pale pink, the dorsal often with a black tip and dark spots on the hinder part. According to Meinken the young of this species are very similar to those of *T. nilotica*. Those of *T. galilaea* have the typical juvenile transverse bands rather oblique; there is also usually a dark blotch on the dorsal fin, and the caudal is never transversely banded.

Sex-distinctions in coloration not known. The ♀♀ become very stout towards spawning time, as in all *Tilapia* spp.

Care, as given for *T. heudeloti*, below. There is no definite information about a successful spawning in captivity. 1934/–.

T. galilaea is probably the fish from which the tribute-money was taken in the Biblical story.

Tilapia guinasana *Trewavas* 1936 (Fig. 1118)
Lake Guinas, in northern South-west Africa; to 14 cm.

D XII–XIV/10–11; A III/8–10; LL 27–28. Body moderately deep, compressed.

Figs. 1117–1120

Fig. 1117. *Tilapia galilaea;* ripe ♂, reduced.
Fig. 1118. *Tilapia guinasana;* adult ♂, reduced.
Fig. 1119. *Tilapia lepidura;* adult ♂, reduced.
Fig. 1120. *Tilapia heudeloti;* adult ♂, reduced. The relative size of the head is too small in this illustration.

The coloration is very changeable. So far a pale and a dark variety have been imported into Europe.

Pale form: overall pale bluish, the flanks cobalt-blue by reflected light. 2 dark longitudinal bands (the upper being considerably shorter) and numerous transverse bands are only occasionally distinct. The gill-cover and breast are often adorned with pearly spots. Fins transparent or checkered with dark and almost always bordered with black.

Dark form: coloration considerably more attractive. Underside velvet black right back to the caudal fin. Upper half of the body clay-yellow with a fine bronze lustre. Dorsal and caudal fins deep yellow with rust-red markings.

♀ dorsal and anal fins usually rounded. Body considerably more robust at spawning time.

Care and breeding, see under *T.heudeloti*, below. Quite a peaceful species which, as in its natural habitat, should be provided with suitable hiding-places between stones. Not a mouth-brooder; spawns in pits. Supplementary plant food absolutely essential. 1938/+.

Tilapia guineensis (*Bleeker* 1863)
Countries bordering the Gulf of Guinea, especially in brackish lagoons; to 20 cm. or more, but attaining this size only in large tanks.

D XV–XVI/11–13; A III/9; LL 30–31. Body rather deep, compressed; forehead-nape line steep, especially in larger fishes. Dorsal, anal and corners of caudal fin often prolonged. Colouring varies with environment and condition. In brackish lagoons often rich green with bronze reflections; chest and belly white, often with a smutty irregular spotting and a cherry-red flush. A round dark spot (the 'Tilapia-mark') at the junction of the spinous and soft parts of the dorsal fin. Caudal fin often with upper half yellowish and lower half spotted. Young barred.

Sexes coloured alike; although one of a pair may be more brilliantly coloured this is not always the ♂.

Care, as given under *T.heudeloti*, below. Not a mouth-brooder. Both parents share in guarding and fanning the eggs, which are laid on the cleaned surface of some hard object. The young are transferred, often several times, to prepared pits until they swim freely, when they are led in a shoal for a while by the parents. Warmth-loving; peaceable except at breeding time; they grub up plants, and need a vegetable element in their diet.

This species is often kept under the name of *T.zillii*, to which it is closely related. Because of this confusion the date of import cannot be given.

Tilapia heudeloti *Duméril* 1859 (Figs. 936, 938, 1120)   Senegal Cichlid/Mouth-
brooder

West Africa, in coastal districts from Senegal to the Congo, mainly in brackish
waters; to 30 cm., sexually mature at 10–12 cm.

D XV–XVII/9–14; A III/7–11; LL 27–31; TR 2–3/11–13. Body elongate,
rather deep, strongly compressed. Upper profile equally or more strongly convex
than lower; forehead-nape line steep in larger fishes. Very variable in form and
colour, as is to be expected from the wide range of distribution. Dr. E. Trewavas,
who is the leading authority on this genus, considers *Tilapia macrocephala* (Bleeker
1863) and *T. dolloi* Boulenger 1899 to be synonyms of this species. As an additional complication the colouring is also changeable in individuals.

Upperside darker, brown-olive to olive-green, usually with a brassy glint. Flanks
grey-blue to grey-silver or sea-green, with a pearly or brassy sheen. Scales on the
upper part of the body often dark-edged, creating a pattern of zig-zag lines. Underside yellowish, white-silver or pale reddish to violet. Gill-cover with a golden glint
in mature ♂♂, translucent and showing the red gills through in ♀♀, and with a black
blotch which is not always apparent. Throat, lower part of head, chest and belly
often blotched with black. Fins very variable, usually shades of yellowish to
brownish, spotted and marked with darker colours. During the breeding season the
dorsal fin becomes bordered with rust-red. Iris golden or dark. The young display
6 bold transverse bands, and a dark ocellus at the beginning of the soft dorsal.

Care: the *Tilapia* spp. of Africa are not quite so pugnacious as their relatives the *Cichlasoma* spp. of South America. Generalisations on behaviour are
rather difficult to make, since not only variations between fishes from different
districts and frequent misidentifications have to be taken into account, but also the
fact that the Tilapias, which are rather larger than the usual run of aquarium fishes,
are obviously likely to display less than agreeable behaviour when kept under less
than agreeable conditions of captivity. *T. guinasana, heudeloti, sparrmanii* and others
have, however, achieved a reputation for being quite peaceful among themselves and
towards other fishes; practically all the others are said to be pugnacious and snappish. (It would be as well to treat these assessments with caution since, in revising
Prof. Sterba's text for the English edition, it has been found that quite contrasted behaviour has been attributed to fishes which are synonyms of the same species. – Ed.)

A *Tilapia* aquarium should not only be the largest possible, but should contain
numerous hiding-places in crevices in stone walls, piles of stones, hollow tree-
stumps, tangles of roots, etc. Only in this way can each adult fish provide itself
with a satisfactory station from which it can control a well-defined territory and

so to some extent reduce its general aggressiveness towards its companions. Almost all *Tilapia* spp. like to eat plant materials, with a preference for algae and soft-leaved aquatic plants. On this account one should take good care at the outset to choose a suitable arrangement and selection of plants, even for such species as *T.heudeloti* which are less hungry in this respect. Marsh plants are especially recommended for domestic aquaria and can be planted in flowerpots stood in the aquarium; the upper parts of these plants must stand clear above the water. The bottom-soil, also, should consist only of not-too-fine, well-washed gravel since many species, at least during the breeding season, do a great deal of digging *(T.mossambica, tholloni, vorax, zillii)*. All *Tilapia* spp. are very voracious and greedily accept all kinds of animal food and dried food. Supplementary plant food is vital to their health, and may be given in the form of lettuce leaves, cooked spinach, filamentous algae, *Elodea*, softened oat-flakes, etc. Most species are very resistant to temporary falls in temperature and some *(T.mossambica, zillii)* can even be wintered at 15–17°C.

Breeding is usually not difficult. The large eggs are laid, with circling movements, in shallow pits and are usually taken up in the mouth of the ♀. In *T.galilaea* the care of the brood is shared by both sexes. *T. guinasana, sparrmanii, guineensis* and *zillii*, on the other hand, are not mouth-brooders but spawn in typical Cichlid fashion on stones previously well-cleaned. The newly-hatched young are repeatedly moved from place to place at first and later led. Whereas the number of eggs in the last-mentioned species may be as high as 1000, the mouth-brooders seldom lay more than 150, or a few hundred in the case of very large ♀♀. With abundant food (including algae!) the growth of the young is very rapid. Fundamentally it must be observed that fishes which undertake direct brood-care, that is to say, which shelter the eggs or young fishes in a throat-sac, must be interfered with as little as possible since when they take fright they often swallow the whole brood. It is also advisable to remove the non-brooding partner, in most cases the ♂, immediately after spawning. (See also family description.)

The young of most *Tilapia* spp. display a dark ocellus ('Tilapia-mark') on the dorsal fin, always on the anterior part of the soft dorsal.

T.heudeloti is reputed to be peaceful with other fishes and towards its own kind. The young hatch after 6–10 days and are carried in the throat-sac for a further 8–14 days. There is a conflict of evidence concerning its digging propensities. Temperature 22–24°C., resistant to temperatures not far below 20°C. In fishes from brackish-water localities the addition of a little sea-salt to the aquarium water is recommended. 1907/+.

Tilapia lepidura *Boulenger* 1899 (Figs. 939, 940, 1119)
Angola and Congo area, also in brackish water; to 20 cm.

D XVI/10–12; A III/8–9; LL 29–32; TR 3/12–13. Shape similar to that of the preceding species. Overall shimmering light gold; upperside considerably darker. Breast and belly yellowish to blood-red. 6–8 usually very distinct transverse bands on the flanks. Longitudinal rows of red spots, on the lower parts of the flanks especially (each scale with a red spot). Fins delicate yellowish to greenish with brownish bands. Eye golden-red.

♀ less brilliantly coloured and usually smaller. Dorsal and anal fins rounded posteriorly.

Care and breeding of this warmth-loving species, as given under *T. heudeloti*, above. A very peaceful species; unfortunately nothing is known about its reproduction. 1911/+.

Tilapia mossambica (*Peters* 1852) (Figs. 934, 1121)   Mozambique Cichlid/
                                                                   Mouth-brooder
East Africa, in fresh to brackish waters; to 36 cm., sexually mature at 12–14 cm.

D XV–XVI/10–12; A III(–IV)/9–10; P 14–15; LL 29–33. Dr. E. Trewavas states that the name *T. mossambica* was first given to ♂♂, while the ♀♀ became known as *T. natalensis* (Weber 1897). *T. vorax* (Pfeffer 1893) is also the ♂ of *T. mossambica* or of a closely-related species.

♀ and non-breeding ♂ watery-grey to yellowish, with 3 or 4 dark blotches sometimes apparent along the side.
♂ in the breeding season with a much-enlarged mouth and snout and thick lips. Body deep black; throat and lower part of head chalky or pale greyish-white. Upper lip blue. Dorsal fin black with a red border; caudal with a broad red margin; pectorals translucent red.

Populations resembling *T. mossambica* occur in the eastern rivers of Africa and in Zanzibar, and it is not clear whether some of them are specifically distinct or merely local variants. ♂♂ in some aquarium samples, instead of being deep black, are mottled black and iridescent blue and have iridescent spots on the vertical fins, but whether these represent different species or not is again uncertain.

For care, see family description and under *T. heudeloti*, above. Breeding is not difficult, but the ♂♂ require considerable territory which they guard, accosting each intruder with hostile behaviour, or inviting a suitably-responding ♀ to the 'nest'. When the eggs are laid the ♀ immediately takes them into her mouth and

743

the ♂ ejects sperm onto the spot where they were laid. This the ♀ also takes into her mouth, where the eggs are fertilised. The young hatch in 10–12 days and for a further week return for shelter to the mouth of the ♀, at least at night. During this time the ♀ should be protected from the ♂ and at the end of the brooding period the ♀ too should be removed, since the brooding instinct is liable to give place to cannibalism. *T. mossambica* will breed in fresh or salt water.

Unfortunately this hardy species, peaceable outside the breeding season, grows too large for domestic aquaria. It withstands temporary falls in temperature quite well. 1925/+.

Tilapia nilotica (*Linnaeus* 1766) (Figs. 932, 1122)   Nile Mouth-brooder
Widely distributed, from Syria through Egypt and the whole of East Africa, through the streams of the Congo to West Africa and in brackish waters; to 50 cm., remaining considerably smaller in captivity.

D (XV–)XVI–XVII(–XVIII)/11–15; A III/8–11; P 15; LL 31–35. Body elongate, rather deep, strongly compressed. Upper and lower profiles about equally convex. Coloration very variable, in relation to the wide distribution. Uniform dull grey-silver with a light violet sheen on the flanks; underside white-silver or delicate reddish. Several transverse bands, not very distinct in older fishes especially. A bold black blotch on the gill-cover. Vertical fins delicate brownish to red-brown and usually bordered with bright red; pale and dark blotches or curved bands are often absent or restricted to the soft dorsal. During the breeding season the throat, the pectoral fins and usually the ventrals as well become dark red. Eye grey with a fine gold rim to the pupil.

♀ smaller and less intensely coloured. During the breeding season the throat is at most delicate red.

Care and breeding, as given under *T. heudeloti*. The species unfortunately grows very large but is quite extraordinarily hardy; fishes from Syria and Palestine, especially, can be kept at room-temperature in winter. Fairly peaceable. Breeding is hardly possible in domestic aquaria since the fishes do not become sexually

Figs. 1121–1124
Fig. 1121. *Tilapia mossambica;* half-grown, natural size.
Fig. 1122. *Tilapia nilotica* (Nile Mouth-brooder); young, natural size.
Fig. 1123. *Tilapia tholloni;* half-grown, somewhat reduced.
Fig. 1124. *Tilapia mossambica;* half-grown ♂, natural size.

mature until they are about 30 cm. in total length. Supplementary plant food absolutely essential. The ♀♀ are mouth-brooders. 1902/ − .

Tilapia sparrmanii *A. Smith* 1840 (Fig. 1125)
Widely distributed through South Africa; to 19 cm.

D XIII–XV/9–11; A III/9–10; P 15; LL 27–29. Body rather deep, strongly compressed. Upper and lower profiles about equally convex. An attractive species with a predominantly green ground-colour. Back dark olive-brown. Flanks brilliant sea-green towards the back and caudal peduncle; more yellow-green towards the belly. Underside yellowish. Several wedge-shaped dark transverse bands and 2 parallel longitudinal bands, usually distinct only in the young. Scales with large orange or red spots, especially on the middle of the side. Throat and gill-cover a beautiful bronze-colour, the latter also with a dark blotch. An intense blue band from the lower jaw to the gill-cover. Vertical fins olive-green with broad rust-red margins and red spotting: fin-rays often pale blue. Ventral fins almost colourless, commonly with iridescent blue-green tips.

Sex-distinctions in coloration not known.

Care, as given under *T. heudeloti*. An undemanding and peaceful species, but a great digger. *T. sparrmanii* is not a mouth-brooder but spawns on stones after the fashion of Cichlids. 1926/ − .

Tilapia tholloni (*Sauvage* 1884) (Figs. 933, 1123)
Tropical West Africa, from the Cameroons to south of the Congo; to 18 cm.

D XV–XVI/8–10; A III/8–9; LL 29–30. Body elongate, strongly compressed. Overall greenish. Upperside rather dark. Flanks yellow-green with 2 longitudinal rows of long narrow blotches and several transverse bands; these are usually apparent only in the young. Underside brass-colour. Gill-cover with a brilliant blue-black blotch which often has a greenish lustre. Vertical fins greenish to yellow-green, to some extent with violet-blue spots or dark bands, and bordered with red or yellow-red. The dark ocellus on the dorsal fin is very characteristic, since in this species it becomes more prominent with age whereas in most *Tilapia* spp. this 'Tilapia-mark' is typically present only in the young. Ventral fins dark, usually with blue fin-membranes. According to Meinken the throat and belly become cherry-red when the fishes are excited and during the breeding season.

Sex-distinctions in coloration unknown.

Care, as given under *T. heudeloti*. A pugnacious species and an enthusiastic digger which, in the wild state, feeds almost exclusively on plants. Mouth-brooding is probably undertaken by the ♀♀. 1912/ + .

Tilapia zillii (*Gervais* 1848) (Figs. 888–890, 892–894)

Africa, north of the Equator, Jordan, Syria; to 30 cm., remaining considerably smaller in captivity.

D XIV–XVI/10–13; A III/7–10; P 14–15; LL 28–30. Body elongate, rather deep, strongly compressed. Numerous colour-varieties are known, related to the wide area of distribution. Silver-grey to dark olive-green, often with a greenish, yellow-ish or reddish sheen on the flanks. Several wedge-shaped bands become prominent when the fishes are excited. Sides of head and gill-cover with a green to brassy glint. A blotch, usually very distinct, in the upper corner of the gill-cover. Throat, chest and belly usually dark in colour. Fins brownish, rust-coloured or yellowish. Dorsal fin with yellow spots and, in ♂♂ especially, a distinct yellow-ringed ocellus on the soft-rayed part. Very attractively coloured during the breeding-season: transverse bands distinct; upperside shining olive-green; lower flanks a beautiful red; throat and belly brilliant blood-red; belly and head to some extent blue-black, the latter with blue-green markings.

♀ quite attractively coloured, but not so brilliant as the ♂ in the breeding season. Dorsal fin with two sharply-delimited milky blotches towards the base.

Care, as given under *T. heudeloti*, above. A fine species, but unfortunately pugnacious and a great digger. Feeds eagerly upon plants. Not a mouth-brooder; brood-care as in *Cichlasoma* spp. Specimens from North Africa, especially, are very resistant to low temperatures (14–16°C.) and can be wintered at room-temperature. 1903/+.

Family Eleotridae (Sleeper Gobies)

The Sleeper Gobies are closely related to the marine Gobies (*Gobiidae*) and are grouped together with these to form the sub-order *Gobioidea*. In contrast to the *Gobiidae*, in which the ventral fins are united to form a cup-shaped sucker, the *Eleotridae* always have their ventral fins completely separated. Body elongate to very long, usually cylindrical anteriorly, slightly to strongly compressed posteriorly. Two clearly separated dorsal fins; the first usually consists of shorter, flexible spines while the second is composed of soft rays which are often preceded by a single spine. Caudal fin rounded. Anal fin usually about as long as the second dorsal. Ctenoid scales. Lateral line usually absent.

747

The Sleeper Gobies are worldwide in their distribution, but especially numerous in the brackish-water zones of tropical seas. Some species live in pure freshwater. Their swimming in mid-water is very laboured; on the bottom, however, they can move with lightning speed and stop dead just as suddenly, a peculiarity which makes their course very difficult to follow. Some members of the genus *Eleotris* are relatively good swimmers. Many fishes of this family are predatory and feed on the spawn or young of other bottom-fishes. Some are very attractively coloured. The species so far imported have chiefly been fresh- and brackish-water forms.

The *Eleotridae* are thoroughly well-suited to the domestic aquarium and, apart from their extreme voracity, their care presents scarcely any difficulty. Their natural need to conceal themselves, and also to dig themselves into the sand Flounder-fashion, should be catered for by the provision of a soft bottom-soil and suitable hiding-places between stones or under roots.

Freshwater species like to hide themselves in thick plant-stands. With proper care most of the Sleeper Gobies become quite tame. The bottom-living species can usually be kept in company with other, not too small, free-swimming species. In all cases medium-hard water is more suitable than soft. It is fundamentally important to add some sea-salt to the aquarium water for these fishes: 1–2 teaspoons to 10 litres of water in the case of the fresh-water species; 50–100 gm. to the same for the marine. Temperature 18–25°C. Live food of all kinds, also kitchen scraps and dried food; meat as well for some species. Very voracious creatures which, in many cases, consume their own weight in food each day.

Some species are easily bred. Many Sleeper Gobies, mostly the brackish-water forms (e.g. *Dormitator*, *Mogurnda*), spawn Cichlid-fashion on stones; others on fine-leaved plants (e. g. *Eleotris*). The ♂♂ undertake brood-care to some extent, fanning the eggs with their pectoral fins and initially keeping the very small fry together. The young, as a rule, swim freely in mid-water during the early days and do not assume the bottom-living habit of the adults until later. Feed them on the finest nauplii and rotifers. Growth rapid.

Carassiops compressus (*Krefft* 1864) (Fig. 1126)   Australian Sleeper Goby
Coastal districts of eastern Australia, in brackish and fresh water; to 15 cm.

D_1 VI–VII, D_2 I/9–10; A I/10–11; LL 27–30; TR 8 between D_2 and A. Body elongate, relatively strongly compressed *(compressus)*. Head likewise compressed. Mouth rather small; lower jaw projecting somewhat. Brown-green to grey-green, the upperside with dark marbling. Middle of the side blue with rows of rust-red to dark red blotches. Red vermiform lines running back from the eye to the hinder edge of the gill-cover, to some extent confluent with a red blotch at the root of the pectoral fin. Fins greenish; vertical fins spotted with red-brown at the base and to some extent bordered with yellow. During the breeding season the usually quite matt colouring becomes very brilliant; the red and blue colours, especially, often develop a lacquer-like gloss.

♀ second dorsal and anal fins smaller. Colouring more grey-green to uniform brownish.

Care, as given in the family description. 1907/–.

A further species, *Carassiops gali* Ogilby 1898, from the inland waters near the coasts of north-eastern Australia, was imported in 1933. Its colouring is chiefly blue and orange.

Dormitator latifrons (*Richardson* 1844) (Fig. 1127)   Broad-headed Sleeper Goby
Brackish waters of the Pacific coasts of Mexico and Central America, also in pure seawater; to 25 cm., sexually mature at 10 cm.

D_1 VI–VIII, D_2 I/9–10; A I/10; P 14–16; V I/5; LL 34–36. Shape similar to that of the previous and better-known species. The forehead region of full-grown fishes is very broad. Body brownish to delicate red-brown with more or less of a greenish sheen. Flanks paler than the back, with longitudinal rows of bright red-brown spots (each scale with a red-brown spot). Underside yellowish to reddish. Gill-cover with red-brown vermiform lines; behind it there is a pale blue, slightly iridescent blotch. Dorsal and caudal fins with rows of red-brown spots on an almost colourless ground. Anal fin and lower edge of caudal reddish. The young are grey, with dark oblique bands running forwards and downwards.

♀ paler; rows of spots and vermiform lines indistinct.

Care and breeding, as given in the family description and for the next species. 1913/–.

Dormitator maculatus (*Bloch* 1785) (Fig.975)   Spotted or Striped Sleeper Goby
Atlantic coast of tropical America, in the sea and in brackish water, occasionally
entering river-mouths; to 25 cm., becoming sexually ripe at 10 cm.

D_1 VI–VIII, D_2 I/9–10; A I/10–11; P 13–14; V I/5; LL 34–36. The genus
Dormitator is chiefly characterised by the rather stocky and little-compressed body,
which is completely scaled, and by the toothless vomer. There are no spines on the
gill-cover. Grey-brown to dark brown, with a greenish lustre. Large, irregular
blotches or dark transverse bars on the flanks, less frequently a dark longitudinal
band and narrow, irregular and partly yellowish transverse lines. Head and gill-
cover with dark vermiform lines. Vertical fins transparent with close, dark rows of
spots. An iridescent blue blotch on the anal fin.

♀ paler. Fins not as thickly spotted.

The robust *Dormitator* spp. should be kept in heated brackish-water or marine
aquaria; it is not generally possible to keep them in pure freshwater. They need a
great deal of oxygen but are quite hardy and, once they have settled in, require
little special treatment. *D. maculatus* preys upon smaller fishes and on this account
can only be kept with species larger than itself. Live food of all kinds. The fishes
spawn on stones, which are previously cleaned by the ♂ and ♀. The bulky ♀♀ are
driven very hard by the ♂♂. The eggs are laid in rows and are small but exceedingly
numerous. As soon as the minute young hatch (after 20–26 hours at 25°C.) the
parents should be removed. The young should be reared on Infusoria, later on the
smallest nauplii and rotifers. Growth very rapid. 1901/ –.

Eleotris africana *Steindachner* 1880 (Fig.1128)
Tropical West Africa, Guinea to the mouth of the Congo, in brackish creeks, also
ascending river-mouths; to 16 cm.

D_1 VI, D_2 I/9; A I/8; LL 90–95; TR 32–35 between D and A. Body elongate,
anteriorly scarcely compressed, posteriorly strongly so. Chiefly characterised by the
very small cycloid scales. Very sober grey-brown, underside yellowish to white.
In the young cloudy blotches or transverse bars are more or less apparent. Adults

Figs.1125–1128

Fig.1125. *Tilapia sparrmanii;* adult ♂, reduced.
Fig.1126. *Carassiops compressus* (Australian Sleeper Goby); adult, reduced.
Fig.1127. *Dormitator latifrons* (Broad-headed Sleeper Goby); ripe adult, slightly reduced.
Fig.1128. *Eleotris africana;* adult, reduced.

750

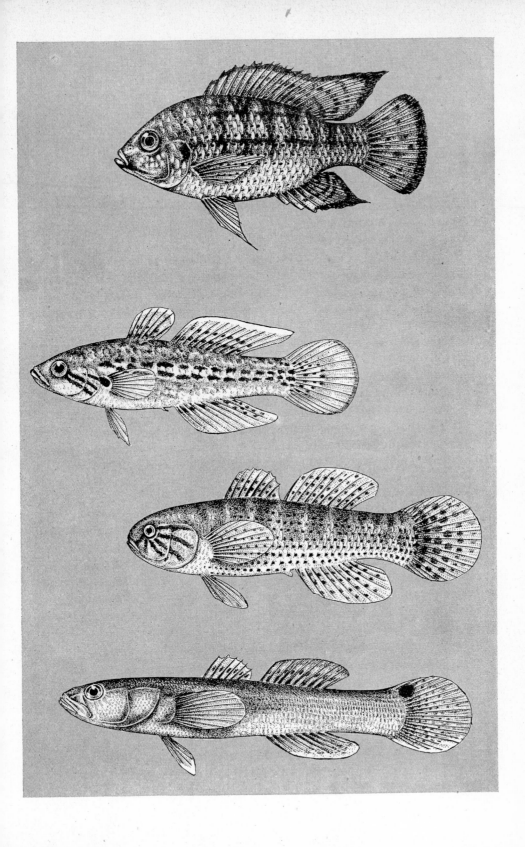

usually self-coloured. A bold round black blotch on the upper part of the caudal peduncle. Dorsal and caudal fins with rows of brown spots on a yellowish ground. Lower edge of caudal fin, edge of anal and tips of ventrals pale to bluish-white. ♀ spots on fins considerably smaller.

Care, as given in the family description. A rather predatory species. 1935/+.

Eleotris butis (*Hamilton-Buchanan* 1822) (Fig. 1134)
From East Africa, through the Malay Archipelago to Australia, in brackish water and in the sea; to 14·5 cm.

D_1 VI, D_2 I/8; A I/8; P 18–21; LL 30; TR 9–10; about 20 scales in front of D_1. Body elongate, distinctly compressed only posteriorly. Head large and flat. Mouth large; lower jaw projecting. Coloration variable, depending on locality of origin and condition. Yellow-brown to grey-brown with reddish or dark brown spots; very irregular transverse bars may be present or absent. Underside paler. Dark bands radiate from the eye to the snout and gill-cover. First dorsal fin grey to blackish, often with a red tip. The other fins are yellowish to violet, to some extent with reddish fin-rays. The anal fin has a broad yellow border and is often spotted with silver. Ventral fins with a dark blotch, outlined in brilliant red, at the base.
Sex-distinctions not yet described.

This generally quite undemanding brackish-water species can be kept in fresh water only with difficulty but does very well in pure seawater. Temperature 18–28 °C. Live food of all kinds; very voracious. See also family description. 1932/−.

Eleotris lebretonis *Steindachner* 1870 (Fig. 977)
West Africa, Senegambia to Angola, chiefly in fresh water; to 12 cm.

D_1 VII–VIII, D_2 I/8–9; A I/9–10; LL 28–32; TR 8–10 between D_2 and A. Body elongate, anteriorly cylindrical, posteriorly strongly compressed. Head scaled; upperside flattened. Mouth large; lower jaw projecting. Body yellowish to olive-brown, darker towards the back. Belly dirty yellow. A large brilliant bluish blotch behind the gill-cover. A dark brown-red spot on every scale. Considerably gayer during the breeding season: upperside brilliant dark olive-green, passing into red posteriorly. Flanks orange. Anterior part of belly cinnabar-red. Blotch behind the gill-cover sharp-edged and dark violet. Spots on the fins blue-violet.
♂ Second dorsal fin produced to a point; ventral fins pointed.
♀ Posterior rays of second dorsal not produced; ventrals rounded.

This attractive species is very commonly imported and so more often met with than other *Eleotris* spp. *E. lebretonis* may be considered as very hardy and extraordinarily easily satisfied. Live food of all kinds, also kitchen scraps. Temperature 18–28 °C. The fishes spawn readily on fine-leaved plants and are very prolific. Spawning behaviour as given in family description. The rearing of the very minute young is difficult; they should be fed with Infusoria, and later with nauplii, rotifers and perhaps some cooked spinach. 1905/+.

Eleotris melanosoma *Bleeker* 1852 (Fig. 1135)
From the Malay Archipelago to the coast of Central America, in brackish and salt water; to 13·5 cm.

D_1 VI, D_2 I/8; A I/8; P 15–19; LL 45–55; TR 14–15; about 40 scales in front of D_1. Body elongate, distinctly compressed only in the hinder part. Snout rather blunt. Coloration variable. Body uniformly dark, or spotted or netted with a pale colour on a dark ground. Back sharply delimited, clay-yellow or red-brown. Brilliant pale green bands radiating from the eye. Fins pale- to yellow-brown with irregular dark blotches or faint rows of spots. Dorsal and anal fins often with dark longitudinal bands.

Sex-distinctions unknown.

This very hardy species can be kept quite well in pure seawater. Breeding biology unknown. 1935/+.

Eleotris monteiri *O'Shaughnessy* 1875 (Fig. 1136)
West Africa, from Guinea to Angola, in brackish and fresh water; to 23 cm., sexually mature at about 12 cm.

D_1 VI, D_2 I/8; LL 60–70; TR 21–22 between D_2 and A. Body elongate, low. Head rather pointed. A distinct spine on the preoperculum. Coloration very variable. Brownish. Upperside dark brown. Flanks considerably paler with cloudy blotches which are especially apparent in the region of the caudal peduncle. Young with a dark lateral band. Gill-cover with a light brassy glint by reflected light. Vertical fins fine dark brown, marbled with yellowish. D_1 with a lacquer-black edge. Anal fin light reddish.

Sex-distinctions unknown.

Care, as given in the family description. A predatory, quarrelsome species. 1938/−.

Eleotris omosema *Ahl* 1935
Tropical West Africa (mouth of the Congo?); to 10 cm. (?).

D_1 VII, D_2 I/8; A I/10; LL 30; TR 9 between D_2 and A. Shape similar to that of *E. pleurops*, from which *E. omosema* is readily distinguished by the wider

753

separation of the dorsal fins and by the coloration. *E. omosema* is also rather slimmer while little less compressed. Coloration of spirit specimens, according to Ahl 1935: Pale brownish, with about 9–10 indistinct irregular transverse bands; a large black shoulder-blotch over the pectoral. Dorsal, anal and caudal with longitudinal rows of dark blotches. A dark stripe, anteriorly with a broad pale border, runs obliquely forwards from the lower edge of the eye to the corner of the mouth. Pectorals rather dark. Ventrals pale.

Care probably as for other African *Eleotris* spp.; see family description. 1935/—.

Eleotris pisonis (*Gmelin* 1788) (Fig. 1137)
Coast of Florida to Rio de Janeiro and through the West Indies, in the sea and in brackish water, also in pure freshwater in rivers; to 12 cm.

D_1 VI, D_2 9; A I/8; LL 57–66; TR 18–24. Body elongate, compressed only in the hinder part. Upperside of head flattened. Mouth large; lower jaw projecting. Insertion of ventral fins hardly behind that of the pectorals. Upperside pale clay-colour to fawn. Flanks and belly dark brown, to some extent with dark marbling. Head and gill-cover with blackish vermiform lines radiating from the eye. Fins delicate yellowish; dorsal and caudal with bright brown bands or rows of spots; ventral fins dark.

Care, as given in the family description. Quarrelsome and predatory and burrows rather a lot. Breeding not yet achieved in captivity. 1912/—.

Eleotris pleurops *Boulenger* 1909 (Fig. 1138)
Lower Niger, especially in mangrove swamps in the Niger Delta; to 10 cm.

D_1 VII, D_2 I/8; A I/10; LL 32; TR 10 between D_2 and A. Body elongate, relatively deep, strongly compressed. Preoperculum without spines. Coloration, according to Arnold (1936): fins brownish. Dorsal fin with white blotches. The flanks frequently exhibit dark areas and blotches, which may rapidly disappear even when they have been visible.

Sex-distinctions unknown.

Care, as given in the family description. Breeding biology unknown. 1909/—.

Eleotris vittata *Duméril* 1860 (Fig. 1129)
Tropical West Africa, from Senegambia to the mouth of the Congo, usually in streams and pools near the coast, less frequently in brackish water; to 22 cm.

D_1 VI, D_2 I/8; LL 40–50; TR 15–17 between D_2 and A. Body elongate, compressed only in the caudal region. Preoperculum with a distinct spine. Upperside fawn to red-brown, spotted with dark. Flanks paler, commonly with a dark longitudinal band in the young which is bordered by a pale stripe above. Older fishes usually have irregular cloudy spots. Gill-cover with shining brassy or blue-silvery areas. Underside of head often dark, with pale spots. Vertical fins transparent yellowish with close rows of brown to rust-red spots. D_1 with a brown longitudinal band and bordered with white.

♀ D_2 lower than in the ♂; markings and coloration weaker.

Care, as given in the family description. 1912/−.

Hypseleotris modestus (*Bleeker* 1853)
Singapore, Sumatra, Java, in rivers and in brackish water; to 7 cm.

D_1 VI, D_2 I/9; A I/9; LL 28; 15 scales in front of D_1. Body elongate, moderately compressed. Lower jaw slightly projecting. Strongly translucent throughout. Upperside delicate reddish-green; flanks and underside paler. Fins orange or yellowish, to some extent spotted with pale blue. The species is characterised by the absence of any striping or spotting on the body and fins; only exceptionally are there dark transverse bands at the bases of the pectoral fins.

Sex-distinctions unknown.

Care, as given in the family description. 1952.

Hypseleotris cyprinoides (*Cuvier* and *Valenciennes* 1837) (Fig. 967)
A species described from the Celebes which Weber and de Beaufort consider to be probably only a colour-variety of *Hypseleotris modestus*.

♂ Delicate translucent ochre-colour to clay-yellow, rather paler on the underside. A dark longitudinal band from the gill-cover to the root of the tail always remains below the middle of the side. Transverse dark stripes frequently present on the lower part of the caudal peduncle. Upperside rarely with cloudy blotches. Fins glass-clear. Vertical fins and ventrals with brilliant pale blue margins, often with an inner border of black against the transparent parts. Dorsal fin also with large pale blue round spots.

♀ Irregular brownish blotches on an ochre-coloured ground above the dark lateral band. Fins transparent, without pale blue borders. Fin-rays with dark markings.

An attractive species which swims quite well and prefers to remain in mid-water. Care easy; see family description. Already successfully bred in captivity, but no details are available. 1936/+.

According to Arnold, in 1935 a specimen of the Philippine species *Hypseleotris bipartita* Herre 1931 was also imported.

Mogurnda mogurnda (*Richardson* 1844) (Fig. 974)

Australian or Purple-striped Gudgeon; Sleepy Trout Rivers and coasts of Central, Northern and Eastern Australia, New Guinea; to 17 cm.

D_1VII–X, D_2 I/12–14; A I/11–15; P 16; LL 38–48; TR 15–16; 18–20 scales in front of D_1. Robust in appearance. Body elongate, anteriorly cylindrical, posteriorly rather compressed. Coloration very variable. Upperside usually olive-brown; flanks clay-brown; underside yellowish. Numerous dark spots along the middle of the side which may run together into a longitudinal row of blotches. Occasionally rust-red to blood-red spots, or very indistinct transverse bars, may be present above and below the mid-lateral row. Two bright green or dark stripes from the eye to the insertion of the ventral fins. A blue, pale-bordered blotch behind the gill-cover. Fins rather dark, to some extent with red spots and a pale border. All colours become intensified during the breeding season.

♀ usually larger; coloration more modest, markings simpler.

This very attractive and undemanding species should be kept in pure fresh water. Its welfare depends on the provision of suitable hiding-places and a somewhat mulmy bottom-soil. Temperature 20–28 °C. Omnivorous (see also family description). *Mogurnda* breeds very readily in captivity. It is best to keep a ♀ together with several ♂♂. The eggs (100–150) hang by threads and are laid either on previously cleaned stones or on the glass sides of the tank. They are there fanned by the ♂; different accounts mention the use of the pectoral, ventral and anal fins for this purpose. The ♀ and redundant ♂♂ should be removed after spawning; the brood-caring ♂ after the young hatch (after about a week). The young should be fed immediately with the finest nauplii and rotifers. 1932/+.

Figs. 1129–1133

Fig. 1129. *Eleotris vittata;* adult, reduced.
Fig. 1130. *Ophiocara apores;* reduced.
Fig. 1131. *Ophiocara porocephala;* young, natural size.
Fig. 1132. *Oxyeleotris marmorata* (Marbled Sleeper Goby); adult, greatly reduced.
Fig. 1133. *Gobiopterus chuno;* greatly reduced.

Ophiocara apores (*Bleeker* 1854) (Fig. 1130)
From Madagascar through south-east Asia, including the Malay Archipelago, to the Philippines, in the sea and in fresh water; to 30 cm.

D_1 V–VI, D_2 I/8–9; A I/9; P 14–15; LL 30; TR 10–11; about 15 scales in front of D_1. Shaped like the following species. Coloration very variable. Upperside dark brown to olive-green; underside orange to yellowish. Flanks very irregular, often with rows of blue-black to black spots. Fine fishes also have green blotches. Three bright red bands from the eye to the gill-cover. Fins dark; fin-rays yellowish. Dorsal, ventral and anal fins bordered with red; caudal spotted with yellow; pectorals with a black, red-bordered transverse band at the base. Some colour-varieties exhibit wedge-shaped transverse bars or a longitudinal band.

♀ altogether more brown, almost always without green spots on the flanks.

This undemanding species does very well in captivity. Breeding has already been achieved but further particulars are not available. 1935/+.

Ophiocara porocephala (*Cuvier* and *Valenciennes* 1837) (Fig. 1131)
South-east Asia, Malay Archipelago, China, Australia, Madagascar, in brackish and fresh water; to 32 cm.

D_1 VI, D_2 I/8–9; A I/6–7; P 15; LL 38–40; TR 11–13; about 25 scales in front of D_1. Body elongate, posterior part only compressed. Upperside of head flattened. Coloration variable. Upperside usually rather dark red-brown to olive-green; underside paler, often clear clay-yellow. Irregular dark blotches or longitudinal bands (which disappear with age) along the sides. Young fishes often with pale to silvery transverse bands. Fins brownish to violet; fin-rays often orange. D_2 and the caudal fin with rows of brown spots and whitish or more or less red borders. In especially fine fishes the head, body, second dorsal and anal fin are spotted with orange.

Sex-distinctions unknown.

Care, as given in the family description. Not yet bred in captivity. 1913/–.

Figs. 1134–1138
Fig. 1134. *Eleotris butis;* adult, somewhat reduced.
Fig. 1135. *Eleotris melanosoma;* somewhat reduced.
Fig. 1136. *Eleotris monteiri;* adult, natural size.
Fig. 1137. *Eleotris pisonis;* ripe adult, natural size.
Fig. 1138. *Eleotris pleurops;* adult, reduced.

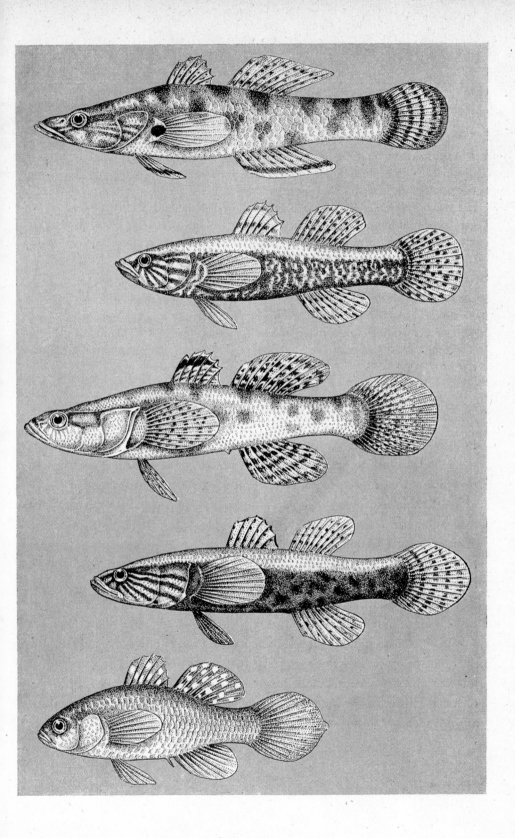

Oxyeleotris marmorata (*Bleeker* 1853) (Fig. 1132)　　　Marbled Sleeper Goby
Greater Sunda Islands, Malay Archipelago, Thailand, in fresh water; to 40 cm.

D_1 VI, D_2 I/9; A I/9–10; P 17–18; V I/5; LL 73–83. Body elongate, only compressed in the caudal region. Head large, upperside somewhat flattened. Mouth
deeply cleft, directed obliquely upwards. Coloration very variable and depending
in the first instance on the nature of the bottom and the lighting. Numerous
cloudy, occasionally transverse band-like, vaguely-delimited dark blotches on a
grey-brown or more rarely light yellow-green ground. Underside rather paler. Fins
brownish to grey-brown with dark spots which are usually scattered at random.
♀ similarly coloured, but with the dark blotches less apparent.

O. marmorata is a very predatory and voracious Sleeper Goby which can
consume its own weight in food daily. It is a crepuscular fish and likes to dig itself in;
the aquarium should therefore be dark, have a soft bottom-soil, and be provided
with suitable hiding-places under stones. Temperature 22–28 °C. Omnivorous, with
a preference for worms and red midge-larvae. Breeding not yet achieved in captivity. 1905/–.

Family Gobiidae (Gobies)

Bottom-fishes, with a world-wide distribution, whose chief characteristic is
the usually complete, less often partial, union of the ventral fins. Through
this fusion a basin-shaped sucker is produced which enables the Gobies to
attach themselves to any firm support; in the aquarium, for example, they
may adhere in a vertical position to the glass sides of the tank or to the
aeration tube. This adaptation enables the fishes to avoid the battering which
they would otherwise receive in the rough waters of their littoral habitats. As
regards their form the Gobies resemble their near relatives the *Eleotridae*,
in which, however, the ventral fins are never united. Two distinct dorsal fins.
Caudal fin rounded. The anal fin usually lies opposite the second dorsal.

Most *Gobiidae* inhabit the shallow coastal waters of warmer seas; a few
seek out the brackish-water regions at the mouths of rivers and only a very
few are able to penetrate into absolutely fresh water. In conclusion, the
members of the subfamily *Periophthalminae* have made a further evolutionary advance which has adapted them to spending periods out of the water

in moisture-saturated air. The natural food of the whole group consists chiefly of small bottom-living animals.

In captivity many species do very well; others, however, refuse to accept any food and slowly perish. With the exception of the *Periophthalmus* spp., which require special treatment (see p. 768), Gobies should be kept in a shallow aquarium with a soft, sandy bottom and provided with suitable hiding-places among stones or under halved flowerpots. Depending on the origin of the fishes the water should be more or less treated with sea-salt; even freshwater species are hardier for the addition of 1–2 tablespoons of sea-salt to each 10 litres of water, while brackish-water species need 100 to 150 gm. of sea-salt to the same. Temperature 18–26°C. The fishes should never be kept in soft water. Live food, such as worms or red midge-larvae, also scraps; some species require supplementary algal food. After a delightful courtship almost all the species spawn on stones, with a special preference for the shelter of miniature caves. The eggs adhere very strongly, like those of the Sleeper Gobies, and are often stalked. The young hatch after 3–8 days and are to some extent guarded by the parents. Almost all the species are peaceful and can very well be kept with mid-water fishes. Unfortunately very little is really known about this group; here, then, is a very profitable field of research for any interested aquarist.

Bathygobius fuscus (*Rüppel* 1828)
From the Red Sea and east coast of Africa over the whole of South-East Asia to the Pacific coast of America, in brackish water and in the sea; to 12 cm.

D_1 VI, D_2 I/9–10; A I/8–9; P 19–20; LL 38–40; TR 11–13; 18–24 scales in front of D_1. Body elongate, lightly compressed posteriorly. Profile of head strongly rounded, so that the head appears rather plump. Coloration very variable, in relation to the wide distribution, and also depending very much on condition. Upperside olive-green; flanks more brownish; underside yellow to grey. Head and body more or less extensively covered with dark blotches which are occasionally arranged in a chessboard pattern. Some shining green spots are usually confined to the head and gill-cover. Fins translucent or grey, to some extent with brown spotting on the fin-rays. D_1 often with a blue border.

Sex-distinctions unknown.

In my opinion isolated specimens of this species are often imported but find little favour on account of their unattractive appearance. The more attractive colouring only appears after a long period of acclimatisation, otherwise the species is quite undemanding.

Care, as given in the family description. Brackish water absolutely essential. Breeding biology unknown. 1937/+.

Fig. 1139

Basic colour-patterns of the Golden-banded Gobies. Left to right: *Brachygobius xanthozona – Brachygobius nunus – Brachygobius aggregatus*

Brachygobius xanthozona (*Bleeker* 1849)
Brachygobius nunus (*Hamilton-Buchanan* 1822)
Brachygobius aggregatus (*Herre* 1940) } Golden-banded Gobies, Bumblebee-fishes

The extremely variable coloration and markings of the very similarly shaped species of the genus *Brachygobius* make identification of the living fishes very difficult. M. Weber and L. F. de Beaufort (1953) give the following key to the species:

1. Over 50 scales in a longitudinal series; D_2 and A I/8–9 .... *B. xanthozona;*
to 4·5 cm.

2. 25–27 scales in a longitudinal series; D_2 and A I/7 .... *B. nunus;*
to 4·2 cm.
(= *B. doriae*
(Günther 1868))

3. 22–26 scales in a longitudinal series; D_2 and A I/6 .... *B. aggregatus;*
to 4·4 cm.

B. xanthozona appears to be confined to Sumatra, Borneo and Java, where it chiefly inhabits rivers and their mouths. *B. nanus*, the commonest species, is widely distributed and occurs in Thailand, the Malay Peninsula and the Greater Sunda

Islands, where it may be found in brackish and fresh water. Finally *B. aggregatus* is only known from North Borneo and the Philippines, where it occurs in brackish water and in the sea.

The *Brachygobius* spp. are all rather stocky in appearance. Body cylindrical anteriorly, posteriorly slightly compressed. Profile of head rounded. All the species, when healthy, display a butter-yellow to honey-yellow ground-colour and, in the typical case, an extraordinarily variable pattern of broad, dark brown to deep black bands. Throughout the characteristic band-markings of any one species may be so variable as to embrace the typical pattern of any other. Occasionally the bands may be completely broken up into irregular blotches and spots; finally there are individuals which are almost entirely black. According to Weber and de Beaufort the typical patterns are as follows:

B. xanthozona has 4 dark brown transverse bands which are about as broad as the intervals between them. Dorsal fins (D_1 and D_2) and anal fin black; the remaining fins are yellow. The pectoral and ventral fins have black bases. The transverse bands are commonly broken up into wedges or narrow bands (Figs. 942, 1139).

B. nunus has 4 dark brown transverse bands which are broader than the intervals between them. Dorsal fins (D_1 and D_2) and anal fin dark with a yellow border or entirely yellow; the remaining fins are yellow. The pectoral and ventral fins have black bases. In this species, too, the transverse bands are commonly broken up into wedges. Head usually grey (Fig. 1139).

B. aggregatus has 4 dark brown transverse bands, whose arrangement is best indicated by reference to Fig. 1139. The snout and the interocular space are quite dark in this species and the sides of the head and the throat are spotted with dark brown.

♀ Usually rather less intensely coloured; considerably more robust than the ♂ during the breeding season.

Care. Bottom-fishes which should be kept in slightly brackish water (1–2 table-spoons of sea-salt or common salt to 10 litres of water); not difficult. The Gold-banded Gobies are often very delicate if kept in pure freshwater. Only suitable for the community aquarium with qualifications; on the other hand, kept in an aquarium by themselves and provided with plenty of hiding-places they are among the most comical of fishes. Temperature 24–30 °C. Small live food of all kinds. When abundantly fed on a varied diet and given changes of fresh water the fishes will spawn, preferably under stones or inside flowerpots. The eggs are large and number about 100–150 at a spawning. The young hatch after about 4–5 days, often even earlier, and are guarded by the ♂. The band-markings make their appearance very early. In the early days the young swim freely in mid-water like most other fishes; only later do they become typical bottom-fishes. Gold-banded Gobies of various species were first imported in 1905.

Evorthodus breviceps *Gill* 1859 (Fig. 1050)
Trinidad and Surinam, in fresh water; to 8 cm.

D_1 VI, D_2 I/10; A I/11; LL 30–35. Body elongate, low, cylindrical anteriorly. Head blunt, forehead steep. D_1 in the ♂ strongly produced. D_2 and anal opposite, long-based. Grey-brown to milky-grey with irregular dark blotches or transverse bands which may occasionally combine into a longitudinal band. Two blotches, one above the other, on the caudal peduncle are especially prominent. Underside yellowish. 3–5 short, dark vermiform lines radiate forwards and downwards from the eye. Fins delicate milky-grey. D_1 with two lacquer-black, comma-shaped stripes on the hinder part; D_2 with dark longitudinal lines. Caudal fin in the ♂ with two rather oblique pale longitudinal bands and dark to golden transverse lines.

Care, as given in the family description. 1911/+.

Gobiopterus chuno (*Hamilton-Buchanan* 1822) (Fig. 1133)   Glass Goby
Singapore, Thailand, Burma, in fresh water; to 2·5 cm.

D_1 V, D_2 I/7–8; A I/10–11; P 13–14; LL 27; TR 7. Body elongate, anteriorly cylindrical, posteriorly somewhat compressed. Cleft of mouth directed obliquely upwards, almost vertical; lower jaw projecting. Glass-clear with a slight yellowish sheen and a few minute pigment spots on the back and on the anal fin only.
Sex-distinctions unknown.

Unfortunately this highly interesting species is as delicate as it is transparent. The few specimens imported up till now perished after a short time despite adequate feeding (small Enchytraeids, *Cyclops*). 1954.

Gobius guineensis *Peters* 1876 (Fig. 1140)
Tropical West Africa, from Sierra Leone to Angola, mainly in inland waters near the coast; to 15 cm.

D_1 VI, D_2 I/10; A I/10; LL 61–70; TR 14–16 between D_2 and A. Body elongate, cylindrical. Head scaleless. Mouth directed slightly downwards. D_2 and anal fin rather long-based. Clay-colour to grey-yellow, with irregular dark or often light reddish blotches which may either form a longitudinal row or else a series of irregular transverse bands. Belly light reddish. Several pale red vermiform lines radiate from the eye. Fins colourless; dorsal and caudal usually spotted with red-brown.

♀ without spots on the fins.

Care, as given in the family description. 1909/+.

Gobius lyricus *Girard* 1858 (Fig. 1141)
Central America and the West Indies, Cuba, usually in brackish water, more rarely in either seawater or pure fresh water; to 10 cm.

D_1 VI, D_2 11; A I/10; LL 27–29. Body elongate, cylindrical, posteriorly a little compressed. Head short; forehead very steep. Eye small, situated high up on the head. D_1 high, with 2–3 produced fin-rays.

♂ Upperside dark olive, with 4–5 broad, very irregular transverse bars. Flanks rather paler with dark brown to brown-red spots or transverse blotches. Underside yellowish to delicate reddish. Head pale, with bands radiating from the eye. Lips black. Dorsal fin usually colourless, but fawn, at least at the base, when the fish is excited. Caudal fin dark blue with two red longitudinal bands; 1–3 ocelli in the upper part. Anal fin translucent brownish. All the colours become considerably brighter during the breeding season.

♀ Finnage smaller. D_1 without produced fin-rays and plainly coloured.

Care of this attractive species, as given in the family description. 1905/−.

Stigmatogobius hoeveni (*Bleeker* 1851) (Fig. 941)
Malay Peninsula and Archipelago, New Guinea, Philippines, in sea, brackish, and fresh water; to 6 cm.

D_1 VI, D_2 I/7–8; A I/7–8; P 16; LL 28–32; TR 8–10; 11–13 scales before D_1. Body rather elongate, low, anteriorly cylindrical, posteriorly compressed. Upperside grey- to green-yellow; flanks often light red-brown; underside pale. Two bold dark blotches, one above the other, on the caudal peduncle. D_1 with a broad blue to deep-black inner part, externally bordered with white and with a blue edge; D_2 likewise with a milky inner border and a black edge.

♀ More soberly coloured, usually considerably more robust.

♂ Middle rays of D_1 often produced, flag-like.

Care: this very interesting species is not difficult to keep in slightly brackish water. The fishes like to hang by their united ventral fins in a vertical position on the side of the tank. Temperature 22–26°C. Small live food of all kinds. 1912/+.

Stigmatogobius sadanundio (*Hamilton-Buchanan* 1822) (Fig. 943)

Southern Asia, Greater Sunda Islands, Philippines, mainly in fresh water; to 8·5 cm.

D_1 VI, D_2 I/7; A I/8; P 18–19; LL 27–30; TR 8–9; 8–9 scales in front of D_1. Body rather short, anteriorly cylindrical, posteriorly slightly compressed. Head large. Overall blue-grey or smoke-grey to silver-grey with isolated round, sharp-edged, dark spots on the flanks and fins. D_2 and anal fin with additional rows of white blotches. The ground-colour of some specimens is more yellowish.

♀ Fins generally smaller; coloration usually light yellowish.

This species is best kept in very slightly brackish water (1–2 tablespoons of sea-salt to 10 litres of water). See also family description. 1905/+.

The Mudskippers

Periophthalmus chrysospilos *Bleeker* 1853 (Figs. 1145, 1146)

India (Vizagapatam), Malay Peninsula, Sumatra, Java, Banka, in brackish water; to 12 cm.

D_1 IX–X, D_2 I/11–13; A I/10–12; P 14–15; LL 70–75; TR 17 at the level of D_1; 25 scales in front of D_1. Body very elongate, anteriorly only slightly compressed, posteriorly strongly so. Profile of back almost straight. Head large, bulldog-like, with protruding and closely adjacent eyes. The pectoral fins, which, in the *Periophthalminae*, are used for locomotion on land, are very powerful and have muscular pediculate bases. Dorsal fins separated. Ventral fins completely united; basal membranes conspicuous.

Head and trunk blue-grey to brown-yellow with round orange spots. Underside smoke-grey. D_1 blue-green at the base, yellow to yellow-green in the centre, outer part with large black spots lying between the red fin-rays and with an edge which is white anteriorly, reddish posteriorly. D_2 with a broad, deep black longitudinal band. Caudal fin blue-green above, brownish below. Ventral and anal fins whitish.

Figs. 1140–1144

Fig. 1140. *Gobius guineensis;* half-grown, natural size.
Fig. 1141. *Gobius lyricus;* ripe ♂, natural size.
Fig. 1142. *Boleophthalmus boddaerti;* natural size.
Fig. 1143. *Boleophthalmus pectinirostris;* somewhat reduced.
Fig. 1144. *Scartelaos viridis;* ripe young, natural size.

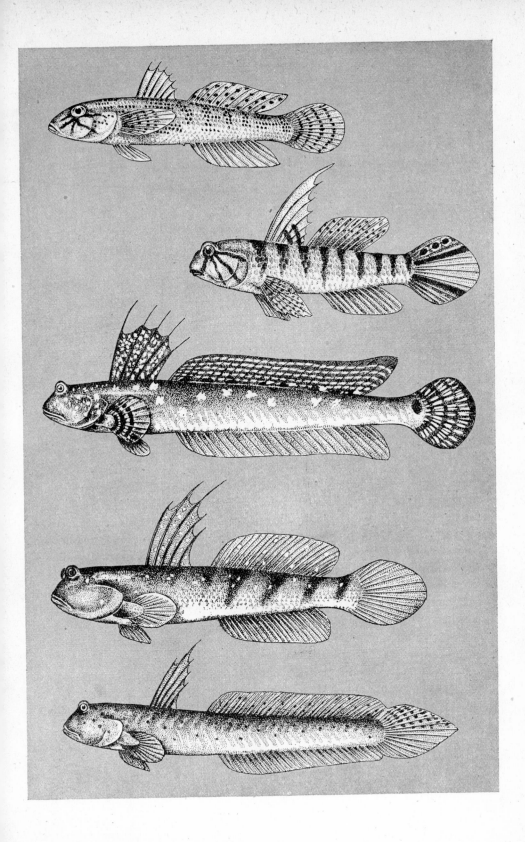

♀ Fin-rays of D₁ not produced.
♂ D₁ with the anterior rays produced, flag-like.

The Mudskippers are extremely interesting fishes but not easy to keep in aquaria where the ecological conditions of their natural habitat, the tropical brackish-

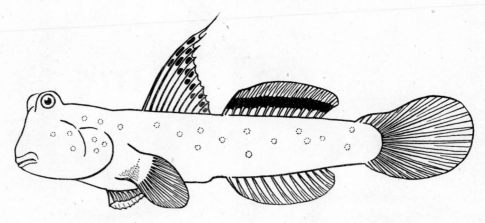

Fig. 1145
Periophthalmus chrysospilos (Mudskipper); maximum size.

water regions and especially the mangrove swamps, can only be very imperfectly simulated. Their highly peculiar way of life is adapted to such conditions; they can not only travel overland using their pectoral fins but also leap for distances of several metres. Moisture-laden air is an essential condition for this sojourn on land. *Periophthalmus* is generally found in shallow pools, ditches and mudholes which rapidly become isolated and dry out at low tide. Here the fishes heave themselves out of the water and, with their dorsally-protruded eyes, survey their surroundings. In the effort to see as far as possible they will also creep up onto obliquely growing roots or fallen trees.

Spawning takes place in deep, funnel-shaped mudholes (nests); the ♀♀ take care of the brood.

Large-surfaced aquaria are most suitable for the care of Mudskippers. Here a sort of bank can be made with very soft sand strengthened by tangles of roots or flat stones. Brackish water. Temperature 26–30°C.; the air over the water should be similarly warm and moist. The tank must be well covered.

The fishes are very shy at first but soon become accustomed to their owner and may become very tame. They are not choosy over food and accept any kind of worm-food, but not insect-larvae, cockroaches, flies, etc. Unfortunately they have not yet been bred in captivity. 1932/—.

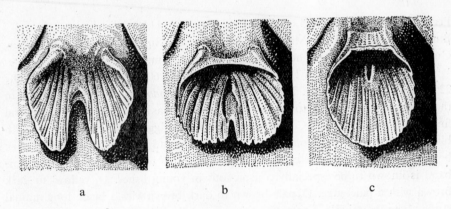

a b c

Fig. 1146

Different degrees of fusion between the ventral fins of *Periophthalmus* spp.:
(a) *P. barbarus;* (b) *P. schlosseri;* (c) *P. chrysospilos.*

Periophthalmus barbarus (*Linnaeus* 1766) (Figs. 977, 978, 1146)   Mudskipper
From the Red Sea and East Africa through Madagascar, southern Asia, the Greater and Lesser Sunda Islands, Australia and the South Seas, chiefly in brackish water at the mouths of rivers; to 15 cm.

D_1 X–XVII, D_2 I/11; A I/10–11; P 13; LL 70–90; TR 17 at the level of D_1; about 35 scales in front of D_1. Shape similar to that of the previous species, except that the ventral fins are not completely united but only at the most connected by a small fold of skin at their bases. Dorsal fins separate. The first ray of D_1 is almost always rather shorter than the succeeding ones; the fin itself is usually quadrangular. There are numerous colour-varieties, as is to be expected from the wide distribution. Upperside generally dark blue-grey or brown; flanks rather paler; underside pale brown to yellowish. Cloudy blackish blotches or irregular transverse bars on the flanks. Pale, often shining, spots, chiefly strewn over the gill-cover and trunk. D_1 brown to dark blue with a broad, very dark edge and occasionally a pale inner border or pale spots towards the base. D_2 dark brown to blue with pale spots over the base, with a broad black longitudinal band and a pale edge. Caudal and anal fins pale olive to pale yellow.

Sex-distinctions unknown.

Care, as given for the previous species. 1896/+.

Periophthalmodon schlosseri (*Pallas* 1770) (Figs. 701, 1146)
Burma, Assam, Thailand, Malay Peninsula, Greater Sunda Islands, Celebes, New Guinea; in brackish water-holes and ditches; to 27 cm.

D_1 III–X; D_2 I/12–13; A I/11–12; P 16–20; LL 50–60; TR 14 at the level of D_1; 22–23 scales in front of D_1. The genus *Periophthalmodon* has two rows of teeth in the upper jaw, in contrast to *Periophthalmus* which has only one row. The ventral fins are completely united. Coloration, according to Eggert: body dark brown with blue spots, or with numerous iridescent blotches, and a paler underside. A dark brown band runs from the eye above the lateral line to the shoulder-region; this band is known to be especially conspicuous in young fishes. D_1 yellow- to dark brown with a pale edge. D_2 pale brown to dark brown with a black longitudinal stripe along the middle. Ventral and anal fins yellowish; the dorsal surface of the former dusted with dark.

Several (4) races of this species are known.

Sex-distinctions unknown.

Care, as given for *Periophthalmus chrysospilos*. The species chiefly inhabits inshore mangrove swamps and lives in a 'nest' up to 1 m. in diameter. 1932/−.

Boleophthalmus boddaerti (*Pallas* 1770) (Fig. 1142)
The small genus *Boleophthalmus* is distinguished from the nearly-related genus *Periophthalmus* mainly by peculiarities of dentition. The *Boleophthalmus* spp., as a rule, do not venture out on land. Coasts of eastern and southern Asia, Malay Archipelago, chiefly in brackish water, more rarely in fresh water or in the sea; to 13 cm.

D_1 V, D_2 I/24–27; A I/26; P 18–19; LL 75–100; TR 19 at the level of D_1. Body elongate, only slightly compressed, anteriorly almost cylindrical. D_1 short-based, with greatly-produced fin-rays. D_2 not united with the caudal. Pectoral fins with a muscular peduncle. Ventral fins united to form an attachment-organ. Eyes projecting. Brown to clay-yellow; upperside darker; belly whitish. Several dark, vaguely-delimited transverse bands are chiefly apparent on the hinder part of the body. Isolated round, pale brown to silvery spots are loosely scattered over the

770

body and dorsal fins. Ventral fins with an orange border or orange overall; remaining fins grey.

♂ Fin-rays of D_1 longer than in the ♀.

Care, as given for *Periophthalmus chrysospilos*. According to Holly this species can be kept for a long while in pure freshwater. Live food of all kinds, especially larger insects and worms. Not yet bred in captivity. 1911/−.

Boleophthalmus pectinirostris (*Linnaeus* 1758) (Fig. 1143)
Coasts of eastern and southern Asia, Sumatra; to 20 cm.

D_1 V, D_2 I/23–26; A I/23–26; P 17–20; TR 20 at the level of D_1. Shape similar to that of the previous species, but still more strongly elongate. Coloration very beautiful in healthy individuals. Grey to pale grey-brown, occasionally flesh-coloured; upperside darker; belly pale, usually whitish. Several large blotches, composed of numerous iridescent pale blue spots, on the head and body. Fins brownish, with similar pale blue spots forming rows or stripes. A large black blotch on the upper part of the caudal peduncle.
Sex-distinctions unknown.
Care and breeding, as given for *Periophthalmus chrysospilos*. 1909/−.

Scartelaos viridis (*Hamilton-Buchanan* 1822) (Fig. 1144)
Coasts of eastern and southern Asia, Malay Archipelago, in brackish water; to 15 cm.

D_1 V, D_2 I/25–26; A I/23–26; P 21. Body very elongate, anteriorly cylindrical, posteriorly rather compressed. D_2 and anal fins very long-based and about opposite. D_2 united with the caudal fin by a membrane. Pectoral fins with muscular peduncles. Ventral fins united to form an attachment-organ. Scales very small, reduced. Grey-green, underside paler. Head pale blue. Gill-cover and body loosely strewn with black spots. Fins brownish to rust-red, similarly spotted with black. In healthy fishes the whole head, including the gill-cover, is iridescent blue-white and the body delicate velvet-green.
Sex-distinctions unknown.
Care, as given for *Periophthalmus chrysospilos*. The present species likes to dig in at the water's edge until half its body is buried in the mud, but otherwise seldom ventures out on land or not at all. Very voracious and not choosy over its food. 1909/+.

771

Family Ophicephalidae* (Snake-heads)

The Snake-heads are very elongated fishes which are native to Africa and southern and south-eastern Asia. The body is almost cylindrical anteriorly but somewhat compressed posteriorly. Head large; mouth very deeply cleft and widely distensible, with a complete dentition. Anterior nasal opening

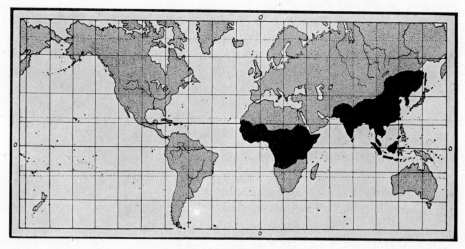

Fig. 1147
Distribution of the *Ophicephalidae*

produced into a tubular process. Dorsal and anal fins very long-based, without spines. Ventral fins relatively small (absent in *Channa asiatica*), six-rayed, inserted well forward but still behind the pectorals and not attached to the pectoral girdle. Cycloid or ctenoid scales. Scales on the upper surface of the head large and plate-like. Lateral line present. The Snake-heads possess an accessory respiratory organ in the form of a simple diverticulum

* The variant spellings *Ophiocephalus*, *Ophiocephalidae*, are incorrect.

Strictly speaking the family should be called *Channidae*, since *Channa* is the typical genus. We have retained the name *Ophicephalidae*, however, because the monotypic *Channa* can hardly be regarded as 'typical' in the everyday sense. Ed.

from the gill-chamber which allows them to carry on supplementary air-breathing and thus to exist in very dirty water or even to wriggle overland during droughts. The smallest species *(O. guacha)* grows to barely 15 cm. in length; other species attain a length of more than 1 m. when full-grown. Many species are highly regarded as food-fishes.

All the species are, as the deeply-cleft mouth indicates, typical predators which are even able to prey upon fishes as long as themselves; only small, young fishes feed upon earthworms or tadpoles. As Grobe (1956) has very nicely shown, only small prey are seized at random; in the case of larger fishes the predators approach stealthily from in front, bend themselves into an S-shape and seize their prey with a sudden jerk.

Care of Snake-heads in aquaria is not difficult since all the species are extraordinarily hardy. Young fishes like to conceal themselves in plant-thickets; the adults, once they have sated themselves, usually lie idly on the bottom. These cunning fishes settle down very well and soon learn to recognise their keeper. The only difficulty that arises is in the matter of food-supply; the quick-growing Snake-heads require live fishes and their appetites are almost insatiable. Occasionally, however, it is possible to accustom them to meat. Only fishes of the same size are suitable as companions.

Several species have already been successfully bred in captivity. Pairing is quite a quiet affair. By reason of their contained oil-droplets the large eggs rise to the surface, where they develop very quickly. The young hatch after only 2–3 days at 26–28°C. and, broader at first, move belly-up against the surface. Only after a further 6–8 days, that is to say, after complete absorption of the yolk-sac, are the fishes able to leave the surface and to swim normally. In some species brood-care is undertaken by the ♂♂, but there is no building of bubble-nests. All the species are very good leapers, so the aquarium must be well-covered.

Channa asiatica *(Linnaeus* 1758) (Fig. 1019)
Southern Asia, chiefly in south China; to 30 cm.

D 43–46; A 28–30; LL 52–55. Shape as given in the family description. The absence of ventral fins is characteristic of this species. Rather uniformly grey-olive

69 Sterba

773

to brown; underside paler. Upon this self-coloured ground appear silvery to gleaming pearly spots, variously arranged in groups and zig-zag lines. A sharply-delimited dark blotch, often ringed with spots, at the root of the tail. Fins grey, the dorsal and anal likewise with silvery spots. The young also exhibit dark, wedge-shaped transverse bars.

Sex-distinctions unknown.

Care, as given in the family description. Breeding already achieved in captivity. 1929/+.

Ophicephalus africanus (*Steindachner* 1879) (Fig. 1148)   African Snake-head
West Africa, Lagos to the Cameroons; to 32 cm.

D 42–49; A 30–34; LL 74–82; TR 6/12–15 at the level of the first dorsal fin-ray. Shape as given in the family description. Coloration rather unpretentious. Sexually mature fishes: ground-colour clay-colour to yellow-grey. Flanks with numerous chevron-shaped dark bands, of which, occasionally, only the central parts are distinct. The eye is linked by an almost black band to a very bold blotch on the gill-cover. Underside pale. Fins opaque grey-green or brownish, to some extent spotted with dark brown. Young fishes are yellowish and display a very bold dark longitudinal band.

Sex-distinctions in coloration not known.

Care, as given in the family description. 1908/+.

Ophicephalus marulius (*Hamilton-Buchanan* 1822) (Fig. 1149)   Murrul
Widely distributed, from India to south China; to 120 cm.

D 49–55; A 28–36; LL 60–70; TR 4–5/12–13 at the level of the first dorsal fin-ray. Shape as given in the family description. This species resembles the African *O. obscurus* in coloration and markings but differs in having the large blotches arranged in three longitudinal rows. Fins rather pale; vertical fins with dark spots. The young display, instead of blotches, a brown longitudinal band with a yellow zone above it.

Figs. 1148–1152

Fig. 1148. *Ophicephalus africanus* (African Snake-head); adult, greatly reduced.
Fig. 1149. *Ophicephalus marulius* (Murrul); very greatly reduced.
Fig. 1150. *Ophicephalus pleurophthalmus;* greatly reduced.
Fig. 1151. *Ophicephalus striatus;* half-grown, greatly reduced.
Fig. 1152. *Ctenops nobilis;* adult, reduced.

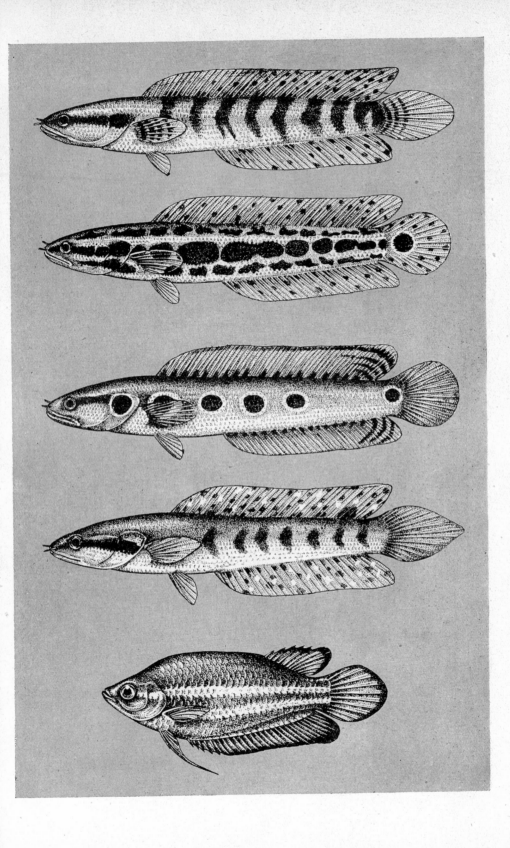

Sex-distinctions in coloration unknown.

Care, as given in the family description. In many districts this species is greatly esteemed as a food-fish. On the other hand Hamilton and Day report that in many other areas *O. marulius*, especially, is an object of strong superstition. In the wild the ♂ clears a space in the reeds at the edge of a pond where the eggs are laid and float at the surface, guarded by the ♂, until they hatch. 1906/−.

Ophicephalus obscurus (*Günther* 1861) (Fig. 990)
Widely distributed in Africa, from the White Nile to West Africa; to 35 cm.

D 40–45; A 26–31; LL 62–76; TR 6–7/12–15 at the level of the first dorsal fin-ray. Shape as given in the family description. Ochre-colour, fawn or pale grey-brown. From the snout to the root of the tail there extends a very broad band, posteriorly broken up into large elongate blotches whose grey-brown sharply contrasts with the pale ground-colour. Underside pale yellow, blotched with brown. Fins handsomely mottled with yellow-brown. Eye with a rust-red horizontal band. The markings and colouring give an altogether snake-like appearance to the fish. They alter considerably with age.

Sex-distinctions unknown.

Care, as given in the family description. 1908/+.

Ophicephalus pleurophthalmus (*Bleeker* 1850) (Fig. 1150)
Sumatra and Borneo, in rivers; to 40 cm.

D 40–43; A 28–31; LL 57–58; TR $5\frac{1}{2}$/11 at the level of the first dorsal fin-ray. Shape as given in the family description. Upperside usually brown; underside considerably paler, usually yellowish. Flanks fawn, grey-brown in older fishes, with 4–5 large, round, deep-black blotches which are usually rimmed with yellow (ocelli) and are arranged in a row (see Fig. 1150). Vertical fins blotched with brown, often with brown transverse bars.

Sex-distinctions in coloration and markings unknown.

Care, as given in the family description. 1908/+.

Ophicephalus striatus (*Bloch* 1797) (Fig. 1151)
Very widely distributed, from India through Thailand to south China, also in the Philippines, Malay Peninsula, Singapore and the Sunda Islands; to 90 cm.

D 38–43; A 23–27; LL 52–57; TR 4–5/8–10 at the level of the first dorsal fin-ray. Shape as given in the family description. Adults grey-green to black-green on the upperside; from the middle of the side upwards very pale, yellow to silvery;

belly usually pure white. In young fishes the upperside is paler and there are dark blotches on the flanks which may form angular bands. A dark band runs obliquely upwards from the snout to the edge of the gill-cover. Dorsal and anal fins sprinkled with light and dark; caudal fin dark brown. The dorsal fin in the young has a black blotch at the hinder end.

Sex-distinctions unknown.

Care, as given in the family description. This species is valued as a food-fish in many districts.

Individual specimens of the following species have also been imported:

Ophicephalus lucius (Cuvier and Valenciennes 1831) from Sumatra.

Ophicephalus guacha (Hamilton-Buchanan 1822) from the neighbourhood of Bangkok.

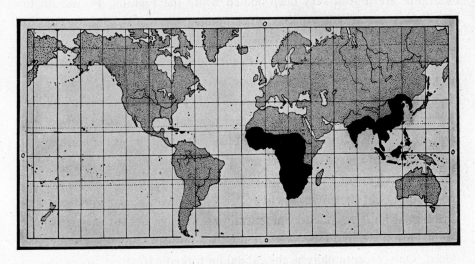

Fig. 1153
Distribution of the *Anabantidae*

Family Anabantidae (Labyrinth Fishes)

The wide distribution of the *Anabantidae* – appropriately known to the aquarium world as Labyrinth Fishes – extends about from Korea over the whole of China, southern and south-eastern Asia, including the Philippines and the

Malay Archipelago, to Africa. Several Asiatic forms are very well known to aquarists; the African species, on the other hand, have so far received considerably less attention. Since, moreover, the Asiatic and African genera are quite strikingly different in many respects, they will accordingly be separately dealt with here.

Care and Breeding of the Asiatic Labyrinth Fishes

The Asiatic *Anabantidae* are all of elongate, more or less deep and strongly compressed form; some species, such as the Gouramies and the Kissing Gourami, are indeed very deep-bodied while the Fighting Fishes, on the other hand, are very low-bodied. The finnage of most species is especially noteworthy. All of them have a very long-based anal fin, often further produced and pointed, which is composed anteriorly of hard rays and posteriorly of soft rays. In some genera *(Anabas, Macropodus, Colisa, Sphaerichthys, Belontia, Osphronemus, Parosphronemus,* etc.) the dorsal fin is similarly formed and constituted. Again, in other genera *(Trichogaster, Betta, Trichopsis)* the dorsal is short-based and sail-like. The ventral fins may be long and pointed, like lateen sails, or more or less completely modified as long feelers serving as organs of touch, taste and smell which provide independent information about the environment *(Colisa, Trichogaster, Osphronemus,* etc.). The caudal fin is rounded in practically all the species, but the centre part may be produced and lobe-like; often only a few of the middle rays are produced. Only exceptionally is the caudal fin forked *(Macropodus opercularis, Trichogaster* spp.). As well as very large species, such as *Osphronemus gorami* (to 60 cm.), the family also includes fish-dwarfs which are full-grown at 3·5 cm. *(Trichopsis pumilus, Parosphronemus dreissneri)*.

A special feature of the whole family is an accessory respiratory organ which enables the fishes to obtain atmospheric oxygen. This structure, the Labyrinth, is composed of lamellae, covered over with a highly vascular layer of skin and many times folded and convoluted, and lies on both sides of the gill-chamber in a large upwardly-directed diverticulum (see Fig. 1154). Atmospheric air taken in through the mouth is forced into the labyrinth where gaseous exchange then takes place. The labyrinth is not present in the young and only develops some weeks after hatching. Like the various air-breathing organs which have evolved independently in several other groups of fishes, the labyrinth permits the *Anabantidae* to live in waters which are oxygen-poor owing to the presence of rotting vegetation or pollution through

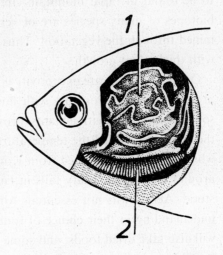

Fig. 1154
Dissection of the gill-chamber of a Labyrinth Fish. (1) The so-called Labyrinth Organ, an accessory respiratory organ which makes possible the breathing of atmospheric air; (2) A gill-arch.

other causes. On the other hand, in the *Anabantidae* the more normal gill-respiration has become so reduced that it can no longer satisfy the oxygen-requirement of these fishes; if air-breathing is impeded the fish drowns, or, more correctly, suffocates.

In all *Anabantidae*, too, the posterior part of the body-cavity is considerably extended and often penetrates deep into the tail.

The German name *Kletterfische* (= Climbing Fishes) refers to a peculiar faculty of only one species, although this is indeed the typical species of the family. This – *Anabas testudineus* – is able, provided the air is sufficiently humid, as during a downpour of rain or early in the morning, to wander for wide distances overland and in doing so to climb over any stones or fallen

779

tree-trunks which may lie in its path. (See p. 782.) The same species buries itself deep in the mud during the dry season and awaits the next rains in a dormant condition and with greatly reduced respiration; during the dry season Climbing Fishes can thus be 'fished' with a spade!

The natural habitats of the *Anabantidae* include very weedy rivers, streams and ponds, irrigation ditches, flooded ricefields and also very dirty accumulations of water such as drains; some species (e. g. *Betta pictum*) are said to be found in rapid mountain streams. It can be said that in general the biotopes of many species are of very little consequence, or are only determined through the vegetation. Thus Dwarf Gouramies only occur in waters with thick plant growth.

On this account care in captivity is generally not difficult. Aquaria standing in a rather sunny position, with flourishing plants, a dark bottom-soil and some cushions of floating plants, provide satisfactory living-conditions for all the species, provided the temperature is kept suitably high (23–26 °C.); fishes which have been imported from Korea or northern China should be kept at around 20°C. Temporary falls in temperature are almost always well withstood. Aeration is not essential. Almost all the Labyrinth Fishes are quite undemanding in their choice of food; as well as live food of all kinds they will also take dried foods, and some even acquire a preference for the latter. Supplementary vegetable food is required in some cases (e. g. *Osphronemus gorami*). Many species live to a ripe old age. Compatibility with other fishes and with other members of their own kind varies a great deal. Although only a few are typically predatory and snappish (e.g. *Macropodus opercularis*, *Belontia signata*, *Anabas testudineus*), sexually mature fishes are commonly very quarrelsome among themselves; the ♂♂, especially, fight bitterly and will also worry to death any ♀♀ which are too young or otherwise unready to breed. Care must therefore be exercised in mating pairs.

Breeding is often very easy and, by raising the temperature, can even be induced in a community aquarium. In the typical case the ♂ builds a foam-nest from air-bubbles surrounded by a hardened secretion of the mouth, and usually prefers to site this among floating plants. Occasionally algae are also woven into the nest. The ♀ is thereupon enticed to the bubble-nest, or dragged there with more or less violence, embraced from the side and rotated onto her back. After several false pairings a few or several eggs are laid which usually float up into the nest through the buoyancy of their own contained oil-droplets. Any eggs which fall to the bottom are picked up by the ♂ and spat into the nest. A spawning involves a great many such sex-acts. The eggs are small in almost all the species, but may be very numerous, often 1500 to 2000 in *Trichogaster* spp. When the spawning is complete the ♂ drives the ♀ away from the nest, sometimes by biting her, and undertakes the care of the brood alone. This duty involves the continual repair of the bubble-nest and the replacement of any eggs or young which fall out of it. At this stage the ♀ should be cautiously removed. The young generally hatch after only 24–30 hours and are able to swim freely after a further 2–3 days. It is best to remove the ♂ a short time before this, since not infrequently the brood-care instinct rapidly abates and the whole brood are then eaten up. The young are very minute at first and during the earliest days must be provided with only the very finest grades of food. With good feeding growth is very rapid in almost all species. At the time of labyrinth-organ formation (2–3 weeks after hatching) the young are usually rather sensitive to low temperatures.

In contrast to this typical pattern of reproduction some species do not build a nest but lay floating eggs indiscriminately in the water, e.g. *Anabas testudineus, Helostoma temmincki*. Some *Betta* spp. are mouth-brooders (see p. 783).

Anabas testudineus (*Bloch* 1795) (Fig. 991)   Climbing Fish, Climbing Perch
Widely distributed: India, Ceylon, Malay Archipelago, Philippines, south China; to 25 cm., remaining considerably smaller in captivity.

D XVI–XIX/7–10; A IX–XI/8–11; LL 26–31. Perch-like in shape. Body elongate, moderately deep; head and anterior part of body rather broad, hinder part compressed. Older fishes, especially, are quite self-coloured, grey-green to grey-silver, occasionally very dark. The underside is always paler, usually grey-yellow to silver. Fins translucent or brown, less frequently yellowish. Young fishes in addition may display various markings, such as transverse or longitudinal bands, which are usually especially distinct on the caudal peduncle. There is always a dark blotch on the gill-cover and another at the root of the tail; especially prominent, however, almost always, is a bold band from the eye to the mouth.

♀ soft dorsal and anal shorter; the latter not produced.

Care of this biologically very interesting species is unfortunately not exactly easy. The generic name (*Anabas* = climber), like the common name, refers to a mode of locomotion unusual among fishes. While movement overland with the aid of the pectoral fins and gill-covers is not exactly true climbing, one does, however, find this species on fallen tree-trunks lying in a conveniently oblique position. The tail remains the main organ of propulsion on land as in the water, the pectoral fins and gill-covers merely serving in the first instance as props. Gathered in troops the fishes wander in this way, usually early in the morning or during a downpour of rain, over distances of several hundred metres from one water or another. At the beginning of the dry season *Anabas* burrows into the mud and passes into a resting state similar to that observed in the African Lung-fishes. In India the species is often found in large quantities and is used as a food-fish which, according to Brehm, is often eaten raw.

In captivity *Anabas* remains, even under optimum conditions (large tank, rich planting), very shy and pugnacious. Omnivorous; also lettuce leaves and algae. The species is resistant to temperature changes and low temperatures around 15°C.; temperature for breeding 25–29°C. Not a bubble-nester; the eggs are stated to be laid at random and to rise to the surface. There is no brood-care, but according to Meinken the young (which hatch after 24–36 hours) are not molested by the parents. The fishes leap well and with a sure aim. 1891/+.

Belontia signata (*Günther* 1861) (Fig. 992)   Comb-tail Paradise-fish
Ceylon; to 13 cm.

D XVI–XVIII/7–10; A XIV–XVII/9–12; LL 29–32. Body elongate, egg-shaped. Dorsal and anal fins very long-based and produced to points posteriorly. Caudal fin roundish. The anterior rays of the ventral fins are produced into two moderately long thread-like processes. Back grey-green to olive-green; flanks paler; belly whitish. In older fishes the whole body has quite a fine reddish sheen. Irregular greenish or violet to reddish shading is visible on the flanks by reflected light. Dorsal, anal and caudal fins reddish, turning to red towards the edges. A round, dark blotch, often indistinct, at the end of the dorsal. The paired fins are colourless or greenish.

782

♀ coloration duller; dorsal and anal fins only moderately produced.

Care and breeding, as given in the family description. Warmth-loving, 24–28 °C. Less suitable for the community aquarium. Predatory and shy. 1933/+.

Betta bellica *Sauvage* 1884 (Fig. 993)   Slim Fighting Fish
Malaya Peninsula, Perak State; to 11 cm.

D I/10; A II/30–32; LL 35; TR 9½. Body elongate, slim, slightly compressed. Posterior rays of anal fin greatly produced. Insertion of dorsal nearer to the root of the tail than to the head. Dark blue-grey, brown or violet-brown. Upper surface of head boldly marbled. Some dark transverse bars, only occasionally distinct. The anterior parts of the scales on the flanks are brilliant green; the overall impression is thereby produced that the scales have been inserted in the reverse direction. Fins colourless or dark, their membranes having to some extent a greenish sheen. According to Meinken, in larger ♂♂ the lower half of the caudal and the produced part of the anal are bright red. Ventral fins red, often with greenish tips.

♀ coloration not so intense; fins smaller or strongly produced.

Care and breeding, in general as given for *Betta splendens*, below. This species, however, is rather sluggish and mainly keeps to the neighbourhood of the bottom. 1905/+.

Betta brederi *Myers* 1935 (Fig. 995)   Javan Mouth-brooding Fighting Fish
Java, Sumatra; to 8 cm.

D II/8–9; A II/23–24; P 12; LL 29. Body very robust; caudal peduncle almost as deep as the body. Dorsal fin short-based, inserted nearer to the caudal than to the head. Anal fin long-based and produced to a point. Middle caudal rays produced. Quite uniformly brown to yellow-brown with several quite irregular pale transverse bands which begin underneath the dark back. Upper surface of head and nape with pale and dark marbling. A broad, dark band, pale-edged above, from the mouth across the head to the gill-cover. Scales on the flanks with a light bluish sheen, especially in the ♂. Fins yellowish or grey, occasionally with light stripes parallel to the fin-rays.

Care and breeding, as given under *Betta splendens*, below. This very robust species is a mouth-brooder, like *B. pugnax*. According to Innes the large eggs are snatched up by the anal fin of the ♂, gathered into the mouth by the ♀ and finally spat across to the ♂ who collects them in his mouth. The young hatch after about 40 hours and are retained in the mouth until they are able to swim. 1935/+.

Betta fasciata *Regan* 1909 (Fig. 994) Striped Fighting Fish
Sumatra, in ponds and ditches; to 10 cm.

D I/9–11; A II/28–30; P 13; LL 34–36; TR 10½. Body elongate, very slim, only slightly compressed, altogether similar to *B. bellica*. Insertion of dorsal fin nearer to the root of the tail than to the head. Blue-black to dark blue-green or reddish, with some usually indistinct transverse bands. Scales on the flanks each with a large, iridescent white-green spot. Fins pale or dark, to some extent spotted with black; caudal and anal fins with iridescent green spots as well. Dorsal fin often colourless.

♀ finnage, especially the anal fin, meagre and little produced.

Care, as given under *B. splendens*, below. This species, however, is rather more delicate and also often choosy over its food. Very warmth-loving, 26–28 °C. 1906/ +.

Betta pictum (*Cuvier* and *Valenciennes* 1846) Javan Mouth-brooding Fighting Fish
Singapore, Sumatra, Java; to 5 cm.

D I/6–8; A II/18–22; P 12; LL 28–30; TR 9½–10½. Body elongate, only slightly compressed. Upper profile slightly convex. Head pointed. Insertion of the dorsal fin nearer to the head than to the root of the tail. Coloration very variable. Clay-colour to dark brown, occasionally red-brown, with three prominent narrow longitudinal bands, of which the centre one extends from the eye to the root of the tail and is united across the jaw with its fellow of the opposite side. The underside of the head is often almost black in specimens from Sumatra. Fins colourless to yellowish with dark blotches and rows of spots. Anal and caudal fins often black-edged.

♀ fins usually shorter and often devoid of markings.

Care, as given under *B. splendens*, below. *B. pictum* is a mouth-brooding Fighting Fish, whose natural habitat is in high mountain streams and which, on this account is resistant to low temperatures close to 20 °C. Breeding temperature 26–29 °C. 1935/ –.

Betta pugnax (*Cantor* 1849) (Figs. 1001, 1156) Penang Mouth-brooding Fighting Fish
Penang Island, west of the Malay Peninsula; to 9 cm.

D I/8–9; A II/26; LL 30–32. Rather large and very elongate. Insertion of dorsal about midway between the head and the root of the tail. Coloration very variable.

Sober grey-blue to fine red-brown, with several dark transverse bands and a longitudinal band, edged above and below with yellow-brown, which extends from the snout to the anterior part of the body or even to the root of the tail. Upper surface of head and nape pale brown. Fins yellowish with rows of brown spots. According to Meinken this species is occasionally very attractively coloured and may display a strikingly contrasted red-brown colour over the underside of the head and the belly. All scales with shining blue-green spots. Fins bright red.

♀ coloration duller; anal fin not so much produced.

Care and breeding, as given under *B.splendens*. A mouth-brooder. Probably not yet bred in a domestic aquarium. 1905/+.

Betta splendens *Regan* 1909 (Fig. 1033)   Siamese Fighting Fish
Malay Peninsula and Thailand; to 6 cm.

D I/8–9; A II–IV/21–24; LL 30–32. Body elongate. Anal fin long-based and deep. Dorsal fin inserted well back, sail-like. Caudal fin rounded. Ventral fins long and narrow. Very variable in colouring, in relation to the wide distribution. Fine specimens are red-brown with a strong blue-green glint and numerous shining metallic spots, usually arranged in rows and green in colour but occasionally also blue or red. Dorsal fin red-brown, with a brilliant green stripe and a chessboard pattern on the hinder part. Caudal fin red-brown, with a fan-like pattern of green stripes and usually with an orange edge. Anal fin blue-green with brown and reddish stripes. Ventral fins fiery red with white tips. Young ♂♂ similar to ♀♀.

♀ yellowish-brown with faintly-indicated transverse bands and often with the longitudinal bands closely approaching to a golden colour. Ventral fins short. All fins yellowish-green with a narrow red border.

The Fighting Fishes of south-east Asia and the Malay Archipelago owe their popular name to the extraordinary pugnacity of rival males, a peculiarity which, in Thailand especially, is exploited in public contests and has led, like horse-racing, to wholesale breeding for this purpose. In the wild, *Betta* spp. are found in clear, usually very weedy waters, also in irrigation ditches and dirty ponds; some species, however, *(B.pugnax* and *B.picta)* are said to be found only in mountain streams. The care of some *Betta* spp. is quite easy; *B.splendens* itself is indeed one of the most undemanding of all tropical fishes. This characteristic must not, however, be abused by inadequate attention. The demands of almost every species may be met by shallow aquaria, standing in a sunny position, with not too high a water-level, a soft bottom-soil, some loose clumps of plants and a thin screen of floating plants. *Betta bellica, B.fasciata* and *B.pugnax* also require soft, slightly acid water if they are to remain healthy. According to E.Schmidt filtration through a peat-containing soil and compressed air are also to be recommended in these cases. All *Betta* spp. are very warmth-loving, 25–28°C., at least at spawning time. *B.picta* and *B.pugnax* can withstand temporary falls of temperature to close below 20°C. All Fighting Fishes are very rapid-growing and on this account require a particularly copious and varied diet; as well as all kinds of live food they often also like to take dried food.

Breeding-behaviour broadly resembles that of other *Anabantidae*. The ♂♂ build a large, loose bubble-nest, preferably among floating plants, and eventually drive the ♀ underneath it, embrace her side and turn her on her back. After several false pairings the ♀ lays eggs in this position which, if they do not go immediately into the nest, are followed up, chiefly by the ♂, and spat into it. After numerous pairings which often produce, in all, several hundred eggs, the ♂ takes over the duties of brood-care, returning fallen eggs, and later young, to the nest. The ♀ should be removed after spawning; the ♂ after about 2–3 days. The young hatch after only 24–30 hours and are very small at first; they should be fed on the finest grades of food and their growth is then rapid. *Betta brederi* and *B. pugnax* are mouth-brooders and spawn in shallow depressions in the sand (see under *B.brederi*). The eggs in these species are usually large and not very numerous and are taken up in the mouth of the ♂ and stowed in a throat-sac until the young fishes are able to swim freely.

The ♂♂ of almost all Fighting Fishes can be very vicious towards ♀♀ which are not ready to spawn or are too young, and may even bite them to death; care must therefore be exercised when putting together pairs which are not known to be compatible. *Betta splendens* was first bred in France in 1893 and from thence introduced into Germany in 1896.

Numerous long-finned varieties of *B.splendens* have been developed under domestication, using the techniques of selective breeding and isolation to produce forms in which enhanced beauty of colouring are allied to extremely long finnage. These are now available in a great variety of colours: white with iridescent blue flanks, emerald green, cornflower-blue, wine-red, brick-red, black, etc.

Care and breeding are similar to those for the ordinary Fighting Fish. In order to produce especially fine ♂♂ – the ♀♀ are less attractive – the ♂♂ should be transferred to individual glass vessels as soon as their sex is apparent. Small all-glass tanks or jampots are most suitable for this purpose and should be arranged in a row next to one another. Bottom-soil is not necessary. The ♂♂ can then see one another through the glass and are thereby continually provoked to rivalry. The consequent continual fin-spreading leads to enlargement of the fins and the development of especially bright colouring. Of course there are at the same time some fishes which revert to the wild type. The peak splendour is attained after only 4–5 months and unfortunately does not last long; long-finned Fighting Fishes are short-lived and usually die after only one year. If several fishes are put together, or the ♂♂ are mated, all this splendour is often destroyed in a few hours and the fishes are reduced to a condition like that of plucked fighting-cocks. No Fighting Fish should be kept in a community aquarium; under such conditions they do not exhibit the beauty which they do when kept in isolation. According to Lederer the races are not very susceptible to inbreeding, provided the choice of parents takes into account not only fine colouring but also robustness of body, high vitality and strongly-developed finnage as well.

Betta taeniata *Regan* 1909 (Fig. 1157)
Sumatra, Borneo; to 8·5 cm.

D I/7–9; A II/20–25; P 12–14; LL 28–30; TR 9½–10½. As regards body-form very similar to the better-known *Betta* s*plendens*. Insertion of dorsal fin nearer to the head than to the root of the tail. Usually brown to yellow-brown, less frequently light fawn. Especially characteristic of this species are two longitudinal bands, of which the upper extends from the snout across the eye to the root of the tail; the lower band originates close by the gill-cover and runs underneath the pectoral base to the lower caudal root. The two bands are united posteriorly by a large dark blotch at the root of the tail. Fins brownish or colourless, with red-brown spots.

Sex-distinctions in coloration unknown.

Care, as given under *B.splendens*; probably a mouth-brooder. 1937/+.

Colisa fasciata (*Bloch* and *Schneider* 1801) (Fig. 1008)   Giant Gourami,
Striped or Banded Gourami

Bengal, Burma, Thailand, Malay Peninsula; to 12 cm.

D XV–XVII/9–14; A XV–XVIII/14–19; P 9–10; LL 29–31. Body egg-shaped, strongly compressed. Dorsal and anal fins long-based. Ventral fins thread-like. Upper lip thick, especially in old ♂♂. Very variable in colouring, in relation to the wide distribution. Greenish-brown, with a sky-blue sheen by reflected light. Back more brownish; chest and belly blue-green, often with a violet sheen. Eye rust-red to carmine-red. A brilliant green blotch on the gill-cover, often surrounded by

787

several small dots. Several narrow, rather backwardly-directed, orange-red to red transverse bands on the shining sky-blue to green-blue flanks. Fins pale blue to blue. Dorsal with red spots. Anal sea-green with a red border. Ventrals with yellow-white bases and brilliant red tips.

♀ coloration duller; dorsal and anal fins rounded.

Care and breeding, as given in the family description. This species only displays its full brilliance of colouring at around 25–26°C., but is resistant to a fall in temperature to below 20°C. Well-matched pairs are usually very prolific; one spawning can produce 600–1000 eggs. The fishes kept in Central Germany (see below) almost all develop a clouding of the lens of the eye which is often evident even in young fishes; cause unknown. (Possibly related to excessive inbreeding: Beebe has reported a similar condition in an isolated population of seals. – Ed.) As Arnold (1950) has very impressively shown, all the so-called *Colisa labiosa* kept in Germany are very similar to *C. fasciata* and probably represent an inadequately investigated variety of the latter. 1897/+.

Colisa labiosa (*Day* 1878)   Thick-lipped Gourami
Southern Burma; to 8 cm.
According to Arnold (1950) all the former so-called *C. labiosa* kept in Germany were very probably a variety of *Colisa fasciata*. The true *C. labiosa* has been repeatedly imported in recent years.

D XV–XVIII/8–10; A XVI–XVIII/17–20; LL 29–31. Shape similar to that of the previous species, but the lips of the ♂♂ are especially thick. Coloration, according to Innes: the light markings on the sides are blue-green, while the irregular dark bars are orange-brown. The projecting rays of the dorsal and anal fins are tipped blood-red. In the anal fin these fiery tips are supported by a narrow line of intense, deep blue. Tail fin, light warm brown. Thread fins in male red; in female colourless. The rear end of the anal fin in the female is red, while in the male it is blue.

Figs. 1155–1159

Fig. 1155. *Parosphronemus dreissneri;* adult ♂, enlarged.
Fig. 1156. *Betta pugnax* (Penang Mouth-brooding Fighting Fish); adult ♂, somewhat reduced.
Fig. 1157. *Betta taeniata;* maximum size.
Fig. 1158. *Ctenopoma argentoventer* (Silver-bellied Climbing Perch); young, natural size.
Fig. 1159. *Ctenopoma multispinis* (Many-spined Climbing Perch); adult, reduced.

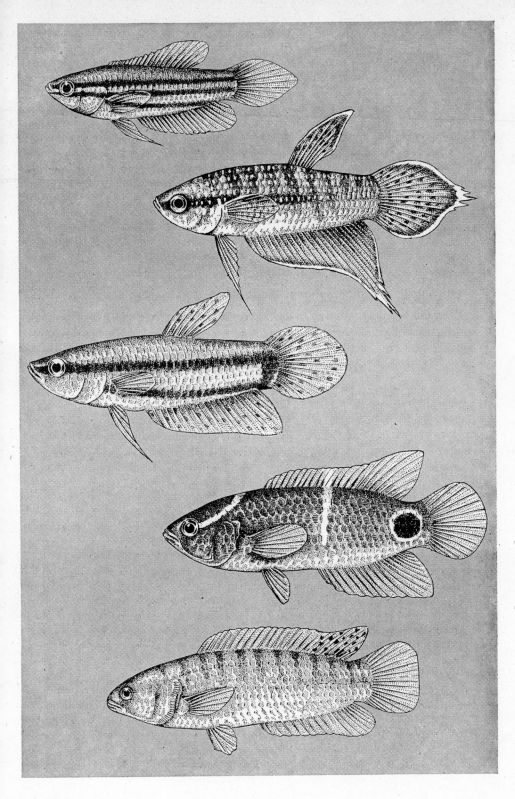

Care and breeding, as given in the family description. The eggs are lighter than water. 1904/+.

Colisa lalia (*Hamilton-Buchanan* 1822) (Fig. 1043)   Dwarf Gourami
India, especially Bengal and Assam; to 5 cm.

D XV–XVII/7–10; A XVII–XVIII/13–17; P 10; V 1; LL 27–28. Body longish, egg-shaped, strongly compressed. On the flanks oblique double rows of brilliant pale blue to emerald-green spots stand out from the bright cinnabar-red to wine-red ground-colour. These double rows also extend onto the vertical fins. The whole head is brilliant blue-green, and usually the part of the body lying immediately behind the gill-cover as well. Caudal fin and posterior part of the anal brilliant red; the thread-like ventrals are orange-red.

♀ substantially duller in colouring; dorsal and anal fins rounded posteriorly.

Care and breeding, as given in the family description. Prefers to spawn in tanks with plenty of algae and bright sunshine. Bubble-nest not very large but correspondingly deeper. One of the loveliest aquarium favourites, but unfortunately rather susceptible to disease (the Colisa-parasite: *Oodinium limneticum*). 1903/+.

Ctenops nobilis *McClelland* 1844 (Fig. 1152)
India, north-eastern Bengal and Assam; to 10 cm.

D V–VI/7–8; A IV–V/23–28; LL 28–32. Body elongate, relatively deep, strongly compressed. Dorsal fin short-based, inserted well back. Caudal fin rounded. Coloration, according to Rachow: the brownish ground-colour, rather lighter below the middle of the side, is interrupted by two whitish longitudinal bands which are often punctuated with dark spots; the upper of these bands extends from the middle of the head to the caudal fin while the lower runs from the insertion of the pectoral to the root of the caudal. Often, too, the anal fin is fully delimited from the body by a pale longitudinal stripe. Fins pale, colourless. Presumed ♂♂ have a brownish tinge to the hinder parts of the dorsal and anal fins and a dark brown edging as on the free edge of the caudal.

Care, as given in the family description. Said to be very frail; not yet bred in captivity. 1912/–.

Macropodus chinensis (*Bloch* 1790) (Fig. 1009)   Round-tailed Paradisefish
Korea to southern China; to 7 cm.

D XIV–XVIII/5–7; A XVIII–XX/9–12; LL 28–30. Body elongate. Head pointed. Dorsal and anal fins long-based, produced to points. Caudal rounded. Back greenish-brown; flanks dirty yellow-brown; belly yellowish. Numerous indistinct transverse bands on the flanks. Dorsal and anal fins bluish-black with brilliant greenish membranes, with reddish spots in the hinder portions; both of these fins have pale borders. Caudal fin bluish-black with an orange-yellow border.

♂ the posterior points of the dorsal and anal fins extend over the caudal.
♀ the posterior points of the dorsal and anal fins do not extend over the caudal.

Care and breeding, as given in the family description; 24°C. at the most. Very peaceful, but not very prolific. 1914/+.

Macropodus cupanus cupanus (*Cuvier* and *Valenciennes* 1831)   Spike-tailed
Paradisefish

India, Ceylon, in coastal districts; to 7·5 cm.

D XIII–XIV/5–7; A XVI–XXI/9–11; P 11–12; V I/5; LL 29–32. Body elongate, compressed. Dorsal and anal fins a little produced. Caudal fin produced to a point. Coloration very variable. Pale, reddish or dark brown, with a strong green lustre, especially apparent on the head and gill-cover. Throat and chest regions usually very dark, rarely black. On the flanks there are often 2, sometimes several, shining green bands with pale interspaces. A dark caudal blotch is only occasionally present. Eye bright red. Fins pale grey or slate-grey. Dorsal, and anal caudal fins with rows of reddish spots and bluish borders. Ventrals orange to reddish.

♂ posterior ends of dorsal and anal fins produced to points.
♀ posterior ends of dorsal and anal fins rounded.

Care, as given in the family description. These fishes are very peaceful, even in the community aquarium, and are satisfied with a temperature of 15–20°C. They are active swimmers and accept any food. The ♀♀ often take on a velvet-black colouring during the breeding season. 1903/+.

Macropodus cupanus dayi (*Köhler* 1909) (Fig. 1006)   Brown Spike-tailed
Paradisefish

Malabar Coast, Burma and South Vietnam; to 7·5 cm.

D XIII–XVII/5–7; A XVI–XXI/10–12; LL 27–30. Shape similar to that of the typical subspecies, but rather more graceful. Pale brown to chestnut-brown; back darker. Head delicately spotted with brownish. Throat, chest and belly red-brown to blood-red. Two parallel dark brown bands along the flanks, one beginning at the upper corner of the gill-cover and the other at the corner of the mouth. Fins reddish, with brilliant green borders. Dorsal finely spotted with brownish. Caudal fin red-brown at the base, bright red in the centre; middle produced rays blue-black. Produced pectoral fin-rays whitish.

♂ dorsal and anal fins long and produced to points; middle rays of caudal greatly produced.

♀ dorsal and anal fins rounded posteriorly; caudal fin without produced rays.

Care and breeding, as given in the family description. Very easily contented, but warmth-loving. The ♂♂ undertake brood-care. The bubble-nest is occasionally made in a cavity. 1908/+.

Macropodus opercularis (*Linnaeus* 1758) (Fig. 1035)   Paradisefish
Korea, China, South Vietnam, Formosa; to 9 cm., sexually mature at 5–6 cm.

D XIII–XVII/6–8; A XVII–XX/11–15; P 11; V I/5; LL 28–31. Body elongate, compressed. Vertical fins strongly produced. One of the most beautiful, undemanding and hardy aquarium fishes. Ground-colour brownish or greenish-grey to grey. Upper surface of head and nape marbled with brown to black and olive-green. On the gill-cover there is a large, elongate, dark-brown to blackish blotch, bordered with orange to brick-red; this blotch has a greenish lustre by reflected light. The flanks have blue-green and brilliant carmine-red transverse bands which are irregularly distributed and often run together. Fins red-brown to bright red, with rows of dark or pale spots, and the dorsal and anal especially bordered with white. Caudal fin predominantly red. Ventrals bright red with whitish tips.

♂ coloration as described above; fins greatly produced.
♀ coloration paler, with only red transverse bands; fins moderately long.

Care and breeding, as given in the family description. Very undemanding. Temperature 15–20°C.; for breeding, 20–24°C. Not suitable for the community aquarium; very pugnacious towards other species and among its own kind. Breeding very easily induced by raising the temperature. *Macropodus opercularis* is an excellent Planarian-destroyer and will clear an infested tank in a very short time. 1876/+.

In the scientific periodicals there is frequent argument as to whether *Macropodus opercularis* is a wild form or whether it is one of the masterpieces produced by Chinese breeders. Originally the latter opinion was advocated, nowadays the former, and no final clarification has yet been provided. We can, however, agree with Dr. Ladiges when he says that the newly-arrived Paradisefish (*M. opercularis concolor* Ahl 1935) is most nearly related to *M. opercularis* and has possibly been produced from this stem-form.

Osphronemus goramy *Lacépède* 1802 (Figs. 1018, 1020) Gourami
Greater Sunda Islands, thence widely distributed as a food-fish; to 60 cm., only
suitable for the domestic aquarium when young.

D XII–XIII/11–13; A IX–XI/19–21; P 15–16; LL 30–33; TR 5–6/13–14. Body
oval, strongly compressed. Head always relatively small. Lower jaw with a tuberous
projection. Ventral fins produced, thread-like. Young rather slimmer, with a
pointed head. Sexually mature fishes are brownish to dull reddish with a slight pale
sheen on the flanks. Upperside darker; underside light yellowish. The body, and
especially the head, is strewn with large and small black spots. Fins grey to reddish-
grey. Old fishes, according to Rachow, are said to be completely black. Young
fishes of this species are delicate red-brown and exhibit several irregular dark
transverse bands as well as a pale-bordered round blotch on the hinder part of the
anal fin. Fins bluish; ventrals bright orange.

♀ dorsal and anal fins rounded, in contrast to those of the ♂.

Care, as given in the family description. Growth is very rapid with good feeding,
which should also include vegetable materials such as oat-flakes, etc. Said to be
very resistant to low temperatures. Fishes of two years and more (20–30 cm.) are
attractive exhibits in large aquaria. The very peculiar facial expression of older
fishes is noteworthy (see Fig. 1020). A bubble-nest builder. The ♂♂ undertake
brood-care. The flesh of these fishes, which inhabit clear waters, is said to be first-
rate eating. 1895/+.

Parosphronemus dreissneri (*Bleeker* 1859) (Fig. 1155)
Banka Island, Sumatra; to 3·5 cm.

D XIII/7; A XIII/8; P 2; V I/5; LL 30. Body elongate, slim, low and strongly
compressed. Anal and dorsal fins very long-based; the latter is inserted at the
level of the ventrals. The central portion of the caudal fin is produced to a cone.
Clay-yellow; upperside more brown-yellow. Two very bold longitudinal stripes
from the snout to the root of the tail and one from the pectoral insertion to the
lower edge of the caudal peduncle are especially characteristic. Indistinct transverse
bands appear but seldom. Fins yellowish; base of caudal reddish.

♂ more brilliantly coloured. Fine fishes display some shining green spots on
the gill-cover and others on the edges of the somewhat produced dorsal and
anal fins.

Care, as given in the family description. This species is distinguished from the
often very similarly coloured *Trichopsis pumilus* by, among other characters, the
much longer-based dorsal fin. Probably not yet bred in captivity. 1937/+.

Helostoma temmincki (*Cuvier* and *Valenciennes* 1831) (Fig. 1017) Kissing Gourami
Malay Peninsula, Thailand, Greater Sunda Islands; to 30 cm., remaining smaller
in captivity.

D XVI–XVIII/13–16; A XIII–XV/17–19; LL 43–48; Body egg-shaped, strongly
compressed. Head pointed, with thin, broad lips. Rather uniformly green-silver to
yellowish-silver; upperside dark olive-green; belly almost white. Numerous dark
longitudinal stripes are often present on the flanks. Gill-cover with two short, dark
vertical bands. Fins greenish to grey-yellow. Healthy fishes exhibit a rather curious
dark band which commences as a brown edge to the anterior part of the dorsal fin,
bends upwards in an arch on the hinder part of the fin, skips across to the root of
the tail and again arches across the posterior rays of the anal fin and continues to
the leading-edge of the same. Eye brown-yellow. There is an unpigmented variety
of the Kissing Gourami which is a uniform dull pink with a pearly sheen on the
flanks, the only pigment being in the black eyes.

The sexes are difficult to distinguish.

Care of this usually rather timid but relatively peaceful species is not difficult.
Rapid growth certainly calls for a large aquarium at the outset. Omnivorous;
supplementary vegetable food necessary. Warmth-loving, not to be kept below
24°C. (See also family description.) The popular name 'Kissing Gourami' refers
to the habit these fishes have of reciprocally touching or grasping one another
with their widely-extended broad-lipped mouths, a behaviour-pattern which is
probably a form of threat-display. Successful breeding has probably not yet been
achieved in Germany; American reports, which require confirmation, speak of a
Betta-like courtship and large numbers of floating eggs without either a bubble-
nest or any brood-care. This species is valued as a food-fish in its native countries.
1924/+.

Sphaerichthys osphronemoides *Canestrini* 1860 (Figs. 1003, 1036)   Chocolate
Sumatra, Malay Peninsula; to 6 cm.   Gourami

D VIII–XI/8–9; A VII–IX/19–22; P 8–10; V I/5; LL 26–30. Body deep, relatively short. Head pointed. One ventral ray very greatly produced. Fine chocolate
brown to faint red-brown, to some extent with a faint greenish sheen. Several
pale yellow to white transverse bands on the flanks, very irregularly arranged and
extremely variable in their extent. The young fishes, only, exhibit a distinct longitudinal band. Fins brown, to some extent with dark spots. Anal fin in fine fishes
red-brown with a dark border and a narrow yellow edge.

The sexes are not easy to distinguish. In the ♀♀ the vertical fins may be narrower
and the dorsal less pointed. The ♀♀ are often quite stout at spawning time.

This very beautiful species is unfortunately rather delicate and susceptible to various skin-parasites. Its health depends not only upon the provision of a well-matured tank but to a high degree upon water-conditions. Soft, slightly acid, peaty water is strongly recommended. The aquarium should not stand in too light a position; shaded top-lighting if possible. Very warmth-loving; 26–30 °C. Live food, especially midge-larvae. A mouth-brooder. Number of young small; growth slow. 1933/+.

Trichogaster leeri (*Bleeker* 1852) (Fig. 1042)   Pearl or Mosaic Gourami
Malay Peninsula, Thailand, Sumatra, Borneo; to 11 cm.

D V–VII/8–10; A XII–XIV/25–30; P 9; V I/3–4; LL 44–50. Body elongate, deep, strongly compressed. Dorsal fin, in contrast to that of the often very similar *Colisa* spp., relatively short-based. Ventral fins produced, thread-like. Caudal fin with two distinct but not strongly produced lobes. Coloration variable. Back yellowish-brown, with a strong pearly sheen by reflected light. Flanks and fins brownish, set with numerous round, whitish to yellowish or sometimes pearly, spots; only the head and pectoral fins are free from these. Throat, breast, pectoral fins and anterior part of the anal fin orange, red or violet; the remaining fins are yellowish, especially at the edges. The long, thread-like ventrals are reddish. A dark, ragged longitudinal band along the side.

♀ more brownish; throat and breast silver; dorsal fin rounded.

Care and breeding, as given in the family description. Very peaceful. Warmth-loving. Builds a large bubble-nest and conducts a delightful courtship. Not sexually ripe until almost full-grown. One of the most beautiful of the *Anabantidae*. 1933/+.

Trichogaster microlepis (*Günther* 1861) (Fig. 1011)   Moonlight Gourami
Thailand; to 15 cm.

D III–IV/7–9; A X–XI/36–40; LL about 58–65. Shape similar to that of *T. leeri*, but still slimmer and more graceful. Scales very small. Uniform dull silky bluish-silver. Young often with faint longitudinal rows of dark spots. Eye large, to some extent bright red. The ♂♂ are easily recognised by the orange-red colour of the thread-like ventral fins.

Care and breeding, as given in the family description. The behaviour of this very peaceful species is similar in every respect to that of *T. leeri*; according to Ladiges this species, too, is relatively late in attaining maturity. Bubble-nest very large and shallow. Valued as a food-fish in Thailand. 1952.

Trichogaster pectoralis (*Regan* 1910) (Fig. 1012)   Snake-skinned Gourami
South Vietnam, Thailand, Malay Peninsula; to 25 cm., becoming sexually mature at 8–10 cm.

D VII/10–11; A IX–XI/36–38; P 11; V I/2; LL 55–63. Body rather lower than in the better-known *T. trichopterus*. Body-depth about three times in length without caudal. Quite unpretentiously coloured, in contrast to most other Labyrinth Fishes. Pale grey-green to olive-green with numerous rather oblique, irregular, yellowish to golden transverse bars. A dark longitudinal band from the snout to the root of the tail is often confined to the head-region and usually reduced to a row of spots. Fins translucent. Anal fin light amber-coloured with some golden spots and a blackish edge.

♀ dorsal fin shorter; anal fin usually only quite faintly yellowish.

Care and breeding, as given in the family description. Very peaceful with its own kind and towards other fishes; it does not eat even the smallest young fishes. In contrast to many other Labyrinth Fishes the ♂♂ remain peaceful towards the ♀♀ even during the breeding season. Very undemanding and hardy. Bubble-nest large. Very prolific. 1952.

Trichogaster trichopterus trichopterus (*Pallas* 1777) (Fig. 1013)   Three-spot
Gourami
Malay Peninsula, Thailand, South Vietnam, Greater Sunda Islands; to 15 cm.

D VI–VIII/8–10; A X–XII/33–38; P 9–10; V I/3–4; LL 40–42. Shape similar to that of *T. leeri*, but considerably more robust and rather thick-set. Body-depth 2–2·5 times in length without caudal. Very variable in form, finnage and colouring. Silvery-olive; back bluish-olive; belly rather silvery. Two more or less distinct round, dark spots on the body, one underneath the dorsal fin, the other at the root of the tail. (The eye makes the third "spot" referred to in the popular name!) Rarely up to 20 dark transverse bands may be faintly indicated. A longitudinal band running back from the mouth is likewise not always distinct. Fins greenish to grey with numerous white to yellowish or orange spots, especially at the ends of the dorsal, caudal and anal fins. The fish has a bluish sheen by reflected light.

♀ dorsal fin short, rounded.

Care and breeding, as given in the family description. Usually peaceful and contented. Ardent ♂♂ become rather violent. Sexually mature at as little as 7–8 cm. Very prolific. 1896/+.

Trichogaster trichopterus sumatranus *Ladiges* 1933 (Fig. 1016)   Blue Gourami
Sumatra; to 13 cm.

This subspecies is said to have arisen as a cultivated variety in Sumatra (?). Form rather more elongate; colouring more blue-green. The transverse bands are usually more apparent than in the typical subspecies. By reflected light the fish is shining blue, while the pale spots on the fins have a pearly sheen.

Care and breeding, as given for the typical subspecies.

Trichopsis pumilus (*Arnold* 1936) (Figs. 1002, 1004)   Dwarf Gourami
South Vietnam; according to Herm (1953) also in Thailand and Sumatra; to 3·5 cm.

D III/7–8; A V/20–25; P 10–11; LL 27–28. Body elongate, strongly compressed. Dorsal fin short-based, pointed, sail-like. Caudal fin rounded or produced to a blunt point. Back dark olive; flanks pale olive; belly and caudal peduncle greenish-white. A row of blue-black blotches, frequently interrupted, and flanked above and below by rows of pale blue to sea-green dots, extends from the mouth to the root of the tail. Dorsal fin greenish to yellowish, with rows of brown-red spots, a yellow border and a dark red edge. Caudal and anal fins similarly coloured. Ventral fins yellowish-white. Pectorals colourless. The fish has a pearly iridescence by reflected light and is a very beautiful species. According to Herm specimens from Thailand have two parallel longitudinal rows of blotches.

♀ coloration duller; anal fin rounded posteriorly.

Care and breeding, as given in the family description. A thick layer of mulm is especially welcome to this species. Like *T. vittatus*, *T. pumilus* produces quite audible sounds during courtship. Sensitive to changes in temperature; 27–28 °C. The water-level should be low for breeding. The small and often spherical bubble-nest is often constructed quite some distance below the surface of the water, among fine-leaved plants or under large leaves; occasionally this species spawns directly on the bottom. Eggs few. The young hatch after 36 hours. 1913/+.

Trichopsis vittatus (*Cuvier* and *Valenciennes* 1831) (Fig. 1005) Talking or Croaking
Gourami
Thailand, South Vietnam, Malay Peninsula, Greater Sunda Islands; to 6·5 cm.

D II–IV/6–8; A VI–VII/24–28; P 11; V I/5; LL 28–29. Body elongate, compressed. Vertical fins large, greatly produced, usually ending in a few elongated rays. Yellowish to brownish; back darker; belly yellowish-white. Flanks with a blue-

797

white glint by reflected light. 3–4 more or less distinct dark brown to black longitudinal bands along the flanks; the 2nd commences at the eye. Fins reddish, with a
violet and blue sheen and with red and greenish dots. Eye very beautiful, externally
deep red, inwardly brilliant blue-green.

♂ coloration as given above. Anal fin long and produced to a point, with dark
    pigment-spots at the base and a red-brown border.
♀ soberly coloured. Anal fin not especially long drawn-out.

Care and breeding, as given in the family description. Unfortunately this
species can often only with difficulty be induced to breed. It is best to start breeding
in spring; a sunny position, thick planting and temperatures of 28–30°C. are the
essential requirements. Both sexes have the capacity to produce croaking noises,
probably to some extent with the assistance of the labyrinth organ. 1903/+.

Care and Breeding of the African Labyrinth Fishes

In Africa the *Anabantidae* are represented almost exclusively by the genus
Ctenopoma, the African Climbing Perches, for which Ladiges has invented
the popular German name 'Buschfische' (= Bush-fishes). By contrast with
the majority of their relatives in south-east Asia, which are often quite
peaceful, the larger African forms, at least, are typical predators which, just
like *Anabas testudineus*, superficially look more like Cichlids than Labyrinth
Fishes. These elongate, more or less deep-bodied fishes are usually strongly
compressed and, with their large, protrusible mouths and powerful dorsal
and anal fins, present a very massive appearance. The ventral fins are not
produced and thread-like. Scales ctenoid.

In their natural habitats the African Climbing Perches frequent weedy
forest streams, quiet backwaters of large rivers and also ponds, swamps and
irrigation ditches. While the small species, such as *Ctenopoma nanum*,
C. ansorgei and *C. congicum*, feed chiefly on small animals, the larger ones
prey chiefly upon fishes and large insect-larvae. Like other predators they
glide quietly through the plant-thickets, almost without moving their fins,
and seize their prey with a lightning rush. Some species to the same end let
themselves drift like dead leaves through the water. The adaptations of form

and markings in this latter group are especially interesting; thus the outer parts of the soft dorsal and anal fins, as well as the caudal, are completely transparent and so complete the mimetic resemblance to an unbroken leaf-shape, a peculiarity which is shared with other groups of predatory fishes *(Monocirrhus, Polycentrus)*. Some African Climbing Perches probably eat vegetable food as well. Air-breathing does not play such an important role here as it does in the Asiatic forms.

These fishes prove themselves to be tough and hardy in captivity. Most of them are very warmth-loving and should not be kept below 24° C. Larger live food of all kinds, especially small earthworms, midge-larvae, mealworms, ant-pupae and, above all, small fishes; possibly supplementary plant food as well. Very voracious feeders. A mixed community with other large fishes is only possible in very spacious aquaria. Some species are already known to have been bred, e.g., *Ctenopoma oxyrhynchus, C. argentoventer, congicum, ansorgei* and *nanum*. According to Ladiges, *C. oxyrhynchus* does not build a bubble-nest, like most Asiatic forms, but lays very small eggs, without any preliminaries, which rise to the surface through the buoyancy of their contained oil-droplets. The young hatch after 3 to 4 days. Smaller species, like *C. congicum*, do build bubble-nests. Some are probably mouth-brooders *(C. multispinis)*. Better supplies of this genus are greatly to be desired.

Ctenopoma acutirostre *Pellegrin* 1899 (Fig. 1031)　　　　Spotted Climbing Perch
Middle and Upper Congo Basin; to 15 cm.

D XIV–XVIII/9–12; A IX–X/10–12; LL 26–28. The deepest-bodied species of *Ctenopoma*; the body-depth is about half the standard length (without caudal). The dorsal, caudal and anal fins are completely separate but present a uniformly broad surface when erected. Head large, pointed. Throat-chest profile convex; forehead-nape profile concave. Mouth very large. Brown-yellow, olive-brown or yellow-brown, with numerous dark blotches which also extend onto the fins and often appear almost black. A black blotch, rimmed with yellowish to orange, on the caudal peduncle. Fins olive-green to green-yellow; edges of soft dorsal and anal, and of caudal, glass-clear. Pectoral fins with orange leading-edges.

Sex-distinctions unknown, although the spots on the fins appear to be less numerous in the ♀♀.

Care of this attractive and interesting species, as given on p. 799. It may only be kept in company with large fishes. Usually timid in a small aquarium; natural and tame in a large one. 1952.

Ctenopoma ansorgei (*Boulenger* 1912) (Fig. 1027)
Tropical West Africa, Chiloango; to 7 cm.

D XVII–XVIII/7; A X–XI/7; LL 28–30. Body elongate, compressed. A very beautifully coloured species. Brownish to yellow-brown, with a strong bluish or violet sheen on the flanks. Underside often yellowish. Especially characteristic of this species are 6–7 very sharply-defined dark transverse bands, which are narrower than the interspaces between them and which extend onto the dorsal and anal fins to some extent. Fins in some degree fine yellowish and violet. Tips of the dorsal and anal fin-rays white.

♂ more robust and often more beautifully coloured.

This species is quite peaceful and may be kept in company with other fishes. Breeding already achieved in captivity; the ♂ is said to build a strong bubble-nest. Care, as given on p. 799. 1955.

Ctenopoma argentoventer (*Schreitmüller* and *Ahl* 1922) (Fig. 1158)   Silver-bellied Climbing Perch
Niger Basin; to 15 cm.

D XVI/10; A IX/10; LL 26. Body very low. Coloration extremely changeable. Apart from the silvery underside the whole body, including the fins, may be yellow-grey to dark brown-black. Characteristic of this species is a large and usually distinct pale blotch, occasionally gold-rimmed, at the root of the tail.

The sexes, according to Rachow, can only be distinguished when young, at which stage the ♂♂ show two pale yellow stripes; one of these is transverse and proceeds from the dorsal fin, while the other extends from the nape to the gold-rimmed eye.

Care and breeding, as given on p. 799. According to Schreitmüller this species can be successfully crossed with *Anabas testudineus* (?). 1912/+.

Figs. 1160–1164

Fig. 1160. *Ctenopoma fasciolatum* (Banded Climbing Perch); half-grown, natural size.
Fig. 1161. *Ctenopoma nigropannosum* (Two-spotted Climbing Perch); reduced.
Fig. 1162. *Alepidomus evermanni* (Cuban Glassfish); maximum size.
Fig. 1163. *Pseudomugil signatus;* slightly reduced.
Fig. 1164. *Austromenidia bonariensis* (Kingfish); adult, greatly reduced.

Ctenopoma congicum *Boulenger* 1887 (Fig. 1028)   Congo Climbing Perch
Lower Congo Basin, Chiloango, Ubangi; to 8·5 cm.

D XVI–XVII/8–9; A IX–XI/9–11; LL 26–28. Body moderately deep; body-depth contained almost three times in standard length (without caudal). Body brownish to yellowish; lower part of caudal peduncle rather dark. Dark bands radiate from the eye to the nape and obliquely downwards in the direction of the pectoral fin. Especially characteristic of this species are isolated pale and dark scales; the pale scales, especially between the dorsal and anal fins, may form chain-like rows. Dorsal and anal fins yellowish to green, with numerous brown spots on their membranes towards the bases.

♀ stockier; ventral fins shorter.

Care, as given on p. 799. Very peaceful and strongly recommended to aquarists. This species in recent years has often been wrongly described in the literature as *C. fasciolatum*. Breeding not difficult. The ♂ builds a bubble-nest in a dark position, preferably under large leaves near the surface. In pairing the ♀ is embraced vertically under the nest, as occurs in *Betta*. Spawning lasts for several weeks. The young hatch after 24–30 hours and swim freely after 2–3 days. Rearing is not difficult. 1953.

Ctenopoma fasciolatum (*Boulenger* 1899) (Fig. 1160)   Banded Climbing Perch
Congo Basin; to 8 cm.

D XVI/8–9; A X/9–11; LL 27–28. One of the deeper-bodied species, whose body-depth is contained less than three times in the standard length (without caudal). Upperside olive-brown. Flanks more yellow-brown, with 6–7 irregular, broad, dark transverse bars which do not extend onto the fins. Underside dirty yellow. Head with dark bands. Gill-cover often brass-coloured. Fins grey-green, pale brown or yellowish. Vertical fins with numerous dark brown (dark blue, according to Meinken) spots and streaks.

♀ coloration less brilliant.

♂ (according to Meinken) with strongly produced dorsal, anal and ventral fins, as in the Gouramies.

Care, as given for the previous species and on p. 799. 1912/+.

Ctenopoma kingsleyae *Günther* 1896 (Fig. 1029)   Tail-spot Climbing Perch
Widely distributed, from Senegambia to the Congo Basin; to 20 cm.

D XVI–XVIII/8–10; A IX(–X)/9–11; LL 25–29. A large, deep-bodied species. Overall grey-brown to black-brown with a more or less obvious greenish sheen.

A large, dark blotch in front of the caudal root; in the young this blotch is rimmed with pale yellow. Soft dorsal and anal fins, also the caudal, with glass-clear borders.

Sex-distinctions unknown.

Care, as given on p. 799. A very predatory and snappish species. 1933/+.

Ctenopoma multispinis *Peters* 1844 (Fig. 1159)   Many-spined Climbing Perch
East Africa, Zambesi Basin; to 15 cm.

D XVII–XVIII/8–9; A VIII–X/8–9; LL 31–35. An elongate, low-bodied species (see also *C. fasciolatum*); body-depth contained four times in standard length (without caudal). Grey-green to brown, paling considerably towards the underside. The whole body is often set with small spots. Numerous narrow, dark transverse bands, usually indistinct. Fins grey-green; soft dorsal spotted with black.

Sex-distinctions unknown.

Care, as given on p. 799. Very snappish and predatory. Possibly a mouth-brooder, since Boulenger observed eggs deep inside the gill-chamber in a specimen in the collections of the British Museum (Natural History). 1935/−.

Ctenopoma nanum *Günther* 1896   Dwarf Climbing Perch
Southern Cameroons, Congo; to 7·5 cm.

D XV–XVII/7–10; A VII–IX/9–11; LL 25–30. Body moderately deep; depth contained about three times in standard length (without caudal). Olive-brown or delicate red-brown, with 6–9, not always distinct, transverse bands which are deepest in the ♂♂ and extend somewhat onto the dorsal and anal fins. Several dark bands may radiate from the eye. Fins delicate grey-green or yellowish. Young with a round black spot at the root of the tail.

♂ (according to Arnold) with pointed dorsal and anal fins.

Care, as given on p. 799. Very peaceful and hardy. 1933/+.

Ctenopoma nigropannosum (*Reichenow* 1875) (Fig. 1161)   Two-spotted Climbing Perch
Niger Delta and Congo; to 17 cm.

D XIX–XX/9–10; A IX–X/9–10; LL 30–33. A long, low-bodied species; body-depth contained 3–3·5 times in standard length (without caudal). Coloration, according to Arnold: ground-colour brownish-yellow to yellow-grey, with a number of dark irregular transverse bands on the flanks, sometimes distinct, sometimes faint or completely absent. Hinder half of body strewn with round dark spots. Lower side of head with dark bands. A deep black blotch on the gill-cover and another at the root of the tail. Fins grey-green to yellowish.

Sex-distinctions unknown.

Care, as given on p. 799. According to Arnold this lively species also eats plants *(Elodea)*. 1933/−.

Ctenopoma ocellatum *Pellegrin* 1899 (Fig. 1030)   Eye-spot Climbing Perch
Body-form similar to *C. kingsleyae*. Characterised by a large, pale-rimmed blotch at the root of the tail.

Care, as given on p. 799. A recent import from the Congo.

Ctenopoma oxyrhynchus *(Boulenger* 1902) (Fig. 1026)   Sharp-nosed or Marbled Climbing Perch
Tributaries of the Lower Congo; to 10 cm.

D XV/10; A VIII/10; LL 27–29. Body deep, strongly compressed. Body-depth about 2·5 times in standard length (without caudal). Head pointed. Fine brown to red-brown, with cloudy dark marbling. Underside grey-silver. A broad, irregular, pale transverse bar on the middle of the side, or alternatively a large pale-bordered spot. A very bold narrow band extends from the snout across the eye to the dorsal fin. Fins brown; edges often blackish. Caudal fin with a cloudy dark base, a milky to glass-clear centre and a dark border. Eye reddish.

♀ dorsal and anal fins rounded, or at least less pointed.

Care and breeding, as given on p. 799. Ladiges points out that this species especially is very like the South American Leaf-fish *(Monocirrhus polyacanthus)* in its behaviour and leaf-mimicking markings. Like many species this, too, has a typical juvenile pattern which only later changes to the characteristic adult markings. Thus, in quite small fishes, the hinder half of the body is black. 1952.

Family Luciocephalidae (Pike-heads)

This family contains only the following species:

Luciocephalus pulcher *(Gray* 1830/34) (Figs. 1010, 1034)   Pike-head
Malay Archipelago, Banka, Billiton, Sumatra, Borneo, in streams; to 18 cm.

D 9–12; A 18–19; P 15–16; V I/5; LL 40–42; TR 12–13. Body very elongate, Pike-like, a little compressed. Head large, pointed. Mouth deeply cleft, with a system of folds which enable it to be distended to a funnel-shape (Fig. 1010).

804

Dorsal fin small, inserted well back. Caudal fin rounded. Anal fin almost divided into two by a deep notch. Ventral fins with a produced, thread-like ray. This species possesses an accessory air-breathing organ (labyrinth), but has no swim-bladder.

Yellow-brown to red-brown with a broad, dark longitudinal band with a pale edge above and below, from the snout to the root of the tail. Above this band,

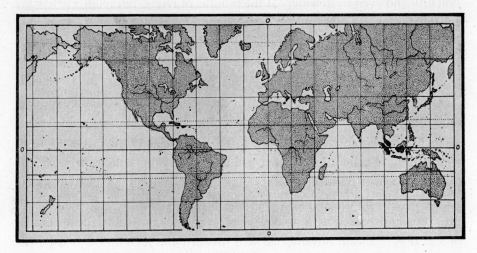

Fig. 1165
Distribution of the *Luciocephalidae;* note the Greater Sunda Islands.

especially, there may be prominent rows of spots. Underside pale, often rather reddish. Fins clay-yellow or faint greenish, to some extent with brown spots which, on the caudal fin especially, may be arranged in bands.

Attempts to keep this very interesting species for any length of time in captivity have unfortunately so far met with little real success. Despite the application of modern knowledge and techniques the fishes die after a short while without any apparent reason. The causes of this failure are twofold and have to do with the special ecological conditions of the natural habitat and with unsuitable feeding. The Pike-head inhabits running water and prefers places where food collects through a suitable disposition of currents. The fish also likes to drift motionless with the stream close under the surface where it can snap up prey (insects). Warmth-loving; temperature 22–24°C. Insect food, flies, etc. Very little is known about breeding; probably a mouth-brooder. 1905/+.

71 Sterba

Family Atherinidae (Silversides, Sand Smelts, Whitebait)

The characteristic habitats of the Sand Smelts are the shallow inshore waters of temperate, and especially tropical, seas. Some species penetrate into brackish and even fresh waters at the mouths of rivers, but relatively few are entirely freshwater in habit, and these usually in regions like Madagascar and Australia where other freshwater fishes are relatively scarce. Lakes in Mexico have about a score of species of *Chirostoma* which are important as food-fishes.

Body elongate or stocky, more or less compressed, rarely cylindrical anteriorly, and often *Barbus*-like.

The *Atherinidae* are closely related to the *Mugilidae* (Grey Mullets), from which they are primarily distinguished by their greater number of vertebrae (31–60 as compared with 24–29). In the great majority there are two widely separated dorsal fins, the first consisting of flexible spines, the second of soft rays usually preceded by a single spine. Anal fin of one spine and a number of soft rays. Pectoral fins inserted well forward and high on the body. (The Australian genus *Nannatherina* is exceptional in having the dorsal fins united at their bases; three spines in the second dorsal and anal; pectoral fins inserted low on the body.) Cycloid or ctenoid scales. Lateral line present or absent. The eggs of most species have filamentous outgrowths. Many marine *Atherinidae* occur in large shoals and are economically important. Some freshwater species make attractive aquarium fishes.

Alepidomus evermanni (*Eigenmann* 1902) (Fig. 1162)   Cuban Glassfish
Cuba and Pine Island (Florida); to 5 cm.

D_1 V, D_2 I/9–11; A I/12–15; P I/5; LL 32–33. Body elongate, strongly compressed. Eye large. Glass-clear, with a grass-green sheen by reflected light. Gillcover bronze-green with a silver iridescence. Fins likewise glass-clear (according to Grenberg).

This species has not yet been imported into Germany but is said to have been successfully bred in England. Live and dried food. Temperature 23–25 °C.

806

Austromenidia bonariensis (*Cuvier* and *Valenciennes* 1835) Kingfish
Mouth of the La Plata, chiefly in fresh water; to 48 cm.

D_1 V, D_2 I/9–11; A I/16–18; LL 50–60. Body elongate, Pike-like, slightly compressed. Snout pointed. Mouth deeply cleft; upper jaw protrusible. Caudal fin deeply forked. Scales small. Translucent, pale clay-colour to delicate fawn, with a greenish tinge to the upperside and dark pigment spots on the head region. A faint silvery band along the middle of the side. Fins colourless.

Sex-distinctions unknown.

Care only possible in a large aquarium. According to Rachow this species does very well in captivity as long as it is given plenty of room to move around. Said to take only animal food. An interesting subject for public aquaria. 1913/−.

Melanotaenia maccullochi *Ogilby* 1915 (Fig. 969) Dwarf Rainbowfish
  Black-lined Rainbowfish
Northern Australia, Cairns neighbourhood; to 7 cm.

D_1 IV–VII, D_2 I/8–10; A I/14–15; P 12–13; V I/5; LL 33–34. Body elongate, rather deep, strongly compressed. Second dorsal and anal fins very long-based. Grey-silver with a bluish sheen. Back brown. Belly delicate yellow-green. 7 more or less distinct red-brown to dark brown longitudinal bands extend along the sides, parallel to the rows of scales; the individual scales in the interspaces between these bands shine like rows of pearls. Gill-cover blue-green with a brilliant red blotch rimmed with gold-green. In healthy fishes and during the breeding season the whole body, especially the chest-region, has a reddish to red sheen. Dorsal and anal fins greenish at the base with a brick-red centre and yellow edge. Caudal fin brown-red to brick-red.

♀ coloration duller; throat and chest delicate orange-red at the most.

These easily contented and very peaceful shoaling-fishes should be kept in spacious and moderately-planted tanks; they are also at ease in a community aquarium. Temperature 23–25 °C. Live and dried food. There should be no lack of morning sunshine. The fishes often spawn on several consecutive mornings, preferably among fine-leaved plants; breeding easy. The eggs adhere by short filamentous processes to the plants and the young hatch after 7–10 days at 25 °C. They are dark in colour and at first hang from plants and from the sides of the tank; a few days later they begin to swim freely at the surface. The adults may be left in the breeding tank until the young hatch, since they are not spawn-robbers. The eggs are laid so that they are sheltered from the light and the total may amount to 150–200. Rearing easy. 1934/+.

Melanotaenia nigrans (*Richardson* 1843) (Fig. 1049) Rainbowfish
Australian Red-tailed Rainbowfish
Australia, as far south as Sydney; to 10 cm.

D_1 IV–VII, D_2 I/10–12; A I/17–21; P 14–16; V I/5; LL 34–35. Shape similar to that of the previous species. Scales large.

Adult fishes: Nape and back yellow to yellow-grey, occasionally pale olive-green. Flanks grass-green to blue-green, depending on the lighting. Caudal peduncle always grass-green. Belly whitish. Scales with dark edges on the anterior part of the body, with dark red ones on the caudal peduncle; on this account the body appears to be covered with a network. There are usually several dark longitudinal bands, sometimes zig-zag in shape, and the interspaces between these have a rainbow iridescence. Gill-cover with a blood-red triangular blotch which is edged above with metallic gold-green, below with white. Dorsal and anal fins dirty yellow, with red stripes and spots and black edges. Ventral fins yellow, the first fin-ray black.

Young fishes are rather unpretentiously coloured.

♀ coloration plainer; dorsal and anal fins smaller, without the black edges.

Care and breeding, as given for the previous species. Withstands room-temperatures, 18–22°C.; for breeding 24–26°C. The addition of a little sea-salt to the water is beneficial. 1927/+.

Menidia thomasi *Meinken* 1931 (Fig. 1167)
South America, neighbourhood of Montevideo; to 8 cm.

D_1 IV, D_2 I/8; A I/9; LL 52. Body very slim, compressed. Eyes large. Premaxillaries protractile. Cycloid scales. Both the dorsal fins are small and inserted well back. Coloration, according to Meinken: back blackish olive-green, with darker edges to the scales. Flanks and caudal peduncle paler, more yellowish, with lovely blue and violet tints. A striking shining silver stripe, from above the pectoral insertion to the base of the ventrals. The gill-cover also has a strong silver gleam.

Figs. 1166–1170

Fig. 1166. *Agonostomus monticola;* half-grown, reduced.
Fig. 1167. *Menidia thomasi;* natural size.
Fig. 1168. *Chelon falcipinnis;* reduced.
Fig. 1169. *Chelon oligolepis;* half-grown, natural size.
Fig. 1170. *Chelon macrolepis;* greatly reduced.

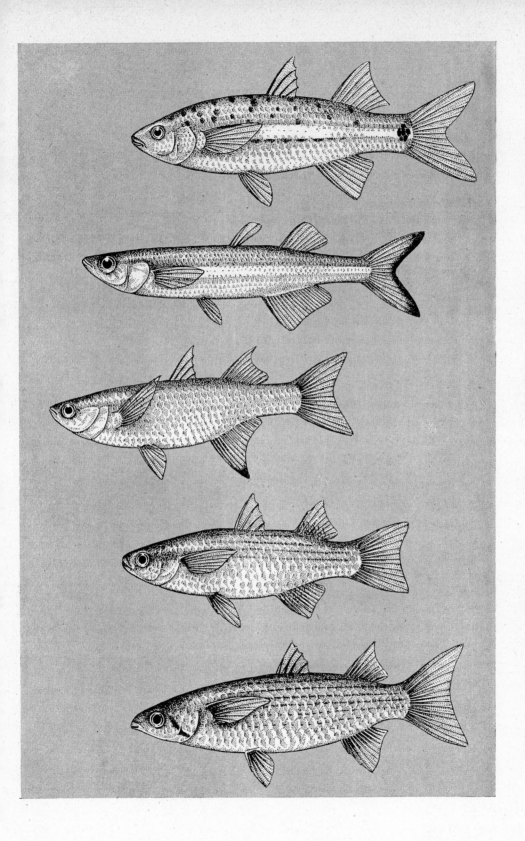

Both dorsal fins have a slight blackish tinge. Caudal fin with a broad blackish edge. Belly yellowish-white. Iris silvery.

Sex-distinctions unknown.

Care, as given for *Telmatherina ladigesi*, below. A very lively species. Up till now only a very few specimens have been imported. 1931/−.

Pseudomugil signatus (*Günther* 1867) (Fig. 1163)
Northern and eastern Queensland (Australia); to 4·5 cm.

D_1 IV, D_2 V/7–13; A I/11–12. Shape similar to that of the ♀♀ of the better-known Celebes Sailfish (below). First dorsal fin produced in the ♂. Mouth upwardly directed. Overall very translucent yellow-green, with a light bluish sheen by reflected light, especially on the lower half of the body. Belly white-silver. Eye grey to iridescent bluish. First dorsal fin glass-clear to light frosty whitish, the first ray black in the ♂. Second dorsal fin, caudal and anal delicate yellowish, often bright yellow in adult ♂♂, to some extent with black fin-rays.

Care and breeding, as given for *Telmatherina ladigesi*, below. A very lively shoaling-fish. 1936/−.

Telmatherina ladigesi *Ahl* 1936 (Fig. 970) Celebes Sailfish, Celebes Rainbowfish
Celebes, hinterland of Macassar; to 7 cm.

D_1 V, D_2 I/7–8; A I/11–12; LL 28–29. Body elongate, compressed. Dorsal and ventral profiles equally convex. The fin-rays are not produced in the first dorsal, but the second dorsal is considerably larger and, in the adult ♂♂, has strongly produced fin-rays and rather tattered-looking fin-membranes. The anal fin is similarly constructed. Back and belly, also upper and lower edges of caudal peduncle, lemon-yellow. Flanks olive-yellow. A brilliant blue-green band along the middle of the side from the middle of the body to the root of the tail. The whole fish has an iridescent dull bluish to greenish gleam by reflected light. Iris yellow-green. First dorsal fin black, with white to yellow rays; second dorsal with an orange-yellow base, a lemon-yellow centre and the first (♀) or first two (♂) rays black. Caudal fin yellowish, with a broad dark stripe near the edges of the upper and lower lobes. Anal fin similar in colour to the second dorsal, the first ray black in the ♂. Ventral fins yellowish; pectorals colourless.

♀ coloration duller; dorsal and anal fin-rays never produced.

This attractive species should be kept in large, moderately planted aquaria. Temperature 23–28 °C. Live food. Regular additions of fresh water, in addition to filtration, desirable. Hard, neutral water. The aquarium should receive as much morning sunshine as possible. The fishes spawn on fine-leaved plants, or on the roots of floating plants, after vigorous driving and a peculiar courtship. Spawning lasts for several months. Eggs yellow. The fishes are rather given to spawn-robbing, especially if there is not plenty of food available. The young hatch after 8–11 days and at first remain near the surface, where they should be fed with fine-grade food. They reach sexual maturity themselves after only 7 months. Nowadays this species is not nearly so delicate as it used to be originally. Very suitable as a companion for *Micropanchax macrophthalmus.* 1935/+.

Family Mugilidae (Grey Mullets)

The Grey Mullets are very closely related to the *Atherinidae*, from which they are mainly distinguished by their lower number of vertebrae (24–29 as compared with 31–60). The first dorsal has only 4 fin-rays. The intestine is very long and often spiral. Like the Silversides the Grey Mullets are shoaling-fishes whose headquarters is in the sea. A few species penetrate brackish water and only a very few live in fresh water. Hardly any members of this family are known to be suitable for domestic aquaria but, on the other hand, a large shoal of these lively, nimble fishes makes a fine spectacle in a public aquarium.

Agonostomus monticola (*Bancroft* 1834) (Fig. 1166)
Mexico, Central America, West Indies, chiefly in streams and near the coast; to 25 cm.

D_1 IV, D_2 I/8; A II/10; LL 38–44; TR 12 between D_2 and A. Body slim, strongly compressed. Coloration, according to Rachow: in life this species, at least to a length of 10–12 cm. – the size generally imported – may be described as generally lemon-yellow or brass-coloured. The region of the back, which in not-too-large specimens is sprinkled with blackish dots and small blotches, has a dark greenish or bluish-green metallic glint. The underside of the head and the chest and belly regions are whitish but with a pearly sheen. A silver-white band with a rather yellowish sheen, accompanied below very often by a series of horizontally-elongate dark blotches, runs from above the pectoral insertion to the root of the tail. The caudal blotch, although often quite black, is not always present. The yellow of the fins – in quite small specimens generally with a touch of red – is chiefly noticeable at the bases. The leading-edges of the anal and ventral fins are often whitish.

811

Sex-distinctions unknown.

Care, as given under *Chelon macrolepis*, below. 1909/−.

Chelon falcipinnis (*Cuvier* and *Valenciennes* 1836) (Fig. 1168)

Coasts of tropical West Africa, also in the lower reaches of rivers; to 25 cm.

D_1 IV, D_2 I/9; A III/11; LL 29–42; TR 13–15 between D_2 and A. Body elongate, moderately compressed. Mouth quite small, rather ventral. Uniform silver with a rather olive-green back. Fins translucent grey.

Sex-distinctions unknown.

Care, as given under the following, better-known species. According to Arnold and Ahl this species requires rather more strongly brackish water (6–7 teaspoons of sea-salt to 10 litres of water). 1910/−.

Chelon macrolepis (*A. Smith* 1849) (Fig. 1170)

Widely distributed, from East and South-east Africa through Madagascar to the South Pacific, in the sea but also penetrating into freshwater; to 35 cm.

D_1 IV, D_2 I/(7–)8; A III/9; LL 30–35; TR 11–12. Body elongate, moderately compressed. Two small, separate dorsal fins. Scales large. No lateral line. Uniform silver, with a light brassy sheen by reflected light. Upperside rather darker. In young fishes, at least, there are some dark longitudinal lines on the upper parts of the flanks. Fins dark, opaque.

Sex-distinctions unknown.

A shoaling-fish which is very well-suited to display in large public aquaria. Like other Grey Mullets it can be kept in almost pure freshwater, to which a little common salt, or better, sea-salt, has been added (1–3 teaspoons to each 10 litres). The fishes are very lively when they are in good condition and like to gather in small schools. Greedy omnivores, which will even hunt out kitchen scraps and also like to eat vegetable food. Temperature 18–25°C. All Grey Mullets are excellent jumpers and are susceptible to injuries. 1925/+.

Chelon oligolepis (*Bleeker* 1858/59) (Fig. 1169)

Very widely distributed, from southern and south-eastern Asia to the coasts of the Philippines, the Sunda Islands and other southern Pacific groups; in fresh water and in the sea; to 15 cm.

D_1 IV, D_2 I/8–9; A III/9; LL 24–28; TR 10–11. Shape similar to that of the previous species. Coloration, according to Rachow: back dark grey-green; belly silver. Narrow dark bands, not sharply delimited, along the rows of scales. All fins blackish.

Sex-distinctions unknown.

Care, as given for the previous species. 1923/—.

Family Cottidae (Bull-heads and Sea-scorpions)

The *Cottidae* are marine fishes, belonging to the order *Scleroparei*, the Mail-cheeked Fishes. As the name of this order implies, the second suborbital bone, one of the series forming a bony ring under the eye, is produced across the cheek to support the preopercular bone of the gill-cover. The preopercular itself is usually armed with spines. Well-known representatives of the order are the Redfish or Norway Haddock *(Sebastes)*, the Gurnards *(Trigla)* and the Indo-Pacific Dragon-fish or Scorpionfish *(Pterois)*.

The *Cottidae* are fishes of the northern seas and contain very few species which penetrate into fresh water. The head is often beset with spines and is considerably broader than the tapering, conical body. Most species are naked; some are covered with spinous bony plates. Lateral line present. No swim-bladder. The two dorsal fins are separate, rarely more or less united, and the first is composed of weak, flexible spines. Caudal fin rounded. Anal fin about as large as the second dorsal. Pectoral fins broad. Ventral fins reduced, thoracic. The ♂♂ are commonly more brightly coloured and further distinguished by a protruding genital papilla. Some species occur in British seas, such as the Father Lasher (*Cottus scorpius* Linnaeus); a great many more are found in Arctic Boreal seas, especially in the North Pacific. The few fresh-water representatives include a peculiar group in Lake Baikal.

Cottus gobio *Linnaeus* 1758 (Figs. 1047, 1048) Miller's Thumb, Bull-head
Widely distributed, almost throughout Europe, Siberia, Asia Minor, in clear mountain and lowland streams, also not infrequent in brackish water in the Baltic; to about 17 cm.

813

D₁ VI–IX, D₂ XV–XVIII; A XII–XIII. Body elongate, low, anteriorly almost cylindrical, posteriorly compressed. Head very large, depressed. Mouth rather large, surrounded by broad lips. Gill-cover with a stout, upcurved spine. Scales absent, except for a specially-modified row of tiny ones along the lateral line. No swim-bladder. Ventral fins thoracic. First and second dorsal fins united by a low membrane. Coloration very changeable and largely dependent on the nature of the bottom and the intensity of the light. Clay-colour to brown with utterly irregular cloudy blotches. Underside pale. Throat often light violet.

♂ often more robust and exhibiting a very distinct protruding genital papilla. Coloration more strongly contrasted.

The Miller's Thumb inhabits gravelly brooks and clear lakes, where it prefers the shallower reaches and, being a typical crepuscular animal, remains hidden under stones during the daytime. It may also be found in mountainous regions up to a height of 1500–2000 metres. The fish feeds chiefly on insect-larvae, watershrimps and other small creatures and does not spare fish-spawn and young fry; on this account it is persecuted as a pest in some districts. Breeding season from February to the beginning of May; as late as July in the mountains. The ♂♂ first of all prepare a shallow spawning-place between or under overhanging stones and then, with characteristic dancing movements, court a ♀ which eventually lays a relatively small number (100–200) of large, orange-coloured eggs in clusters. The ♂ defends these eggs very valiantly and fans fresh water over them with his fins. The young hatch after 4–6 weeks.

Catching Millers' Thumbs is a common game of skill among children; indeed, the quest for these fishes, in which stone after stone has to be cautiously turned over, is a pleasant occupation in itself! The fishes remain motionless for a while after the stone has been turned and so, when one has eventually been uncovered, the youngster has a chance to obtain proof of his dexterity. The beginner has sufficient difficulty at first just to keep his eye on the fleeing fishes. In North America species of *Boleosoma* and *Etheostoma* are caught in the same way.

In captivity the Miller's Thumb proves to be a very interesting subject for the coldwater aquarium. With quiet management of the tank the initial shyness is soon dispelled and these cunning little fishes even become quite tame and learn to recognise their keeper. It is, of course, necessary to imitate their natural environment as far as possible by the provision of suitable hiding-places. Since the ♂♂ are often very quarrelsome among themselves, only fishes of approximately equal size should be kept together. The Miller's Thumb eats almost any food, with a special preference for red midge-larvae (bloodworms = *Chironomus*) and watershrimps. The breeding of freshly-caught fishes in aquaria has already been achieved, but no details are available.

In the mountainous regions of Europe another species occurs, *Cottus poecilopterus* (Heckel), which may be described as a smaller version of the Miller's Thumb.

Family Gasterosteidae (Sticklebacks)

The Sticklebacks form one of the very few families belonging to the order *Thoracostei*, fishes in which the second suborbital bone is produced across the cheek as in the *Scleroparei* (see previous family), but in which the preopercular bone of the gill-cover is, in contrast to that order, not armed with spines. The ventral fins (each including a stout erectile spine which can be locked into position) are inserted well forwards, and the broad pelvic bones are connected to the pectoral girdle.

The *Gasterosteidae* are inhabitants of the North Temperate Zone, where they live both in fresh water and in the sea; the majority of the species are found in North America. Body torpedo-shaped, slightly compressed. Head, in some species, very pointed. Caudal peduncle very slim. Jaws toothed; lower jaw usually projecting. Premaxillaries protractile. Palatines and vomer toothless. Skin naked, or with transverse bony plates; the number and form of the latter are subject to considerable modification through environmental conditions of temperature and salinity. Three or more erectile spines in front of the dorsal fin. Anal fin similar to the soft dorsal. Ventral fins small, of one spine (see above) and at most four soft rays.

Active swimmers, which feed mostly on small prey and, in many cases, build nests during the breeding season.

Apeltes quadracus (*Mitchill* 1815)   American or Four-spined Stickleback
From Labrador to Virginia, chiefly in brackish water and in the sea; to 6 cm.

D_1 III, D_2 I/11–12; A I/8–9; P 10–11; V I/1. Similar in shape to the familiar European Stickleback, but with the characteristic three spines inserted well in front of the soft dorsal fin. Coloration very variable, in relation to the wide distribution.

Upperside mostly brown to greenish; underside pale, silvery. A few cloudy blotches on the flanks. During the breeding season the ♂♂ are almost velvet-black on the underside, dark olive-green on the upperside. Ventral fins red.

As regards biology, and especially reproduction, *Apeltes quadracus* is almost completely similar to the Three-spined Stickleback (see below). It can only be kept successfully in brackish water (80–100 gm. sea-salt to each 10 litres of water). 1933/−.

Gasterosteus aculeatus *Linnaeus* 1758 (Fig. 774)   Three-spined Stickleback
Very widely distributed in Europe, with the exception of the Danube Basin; Algeria, Northern Asia, North America, also common in brackish water; to 10 cm.

D_1 III(–IV), D_2 10–12; A I/8; P 9–10; V I/1–2. Three erectile spines, of which the second is the largest, in front of the dorsal fin. Each spine supports a short, sail-like fin-membrane. Body with or without bony plates. It is of especial biological interest that the number of bony plates depends on the salinity of the water, the Sticklebacks from brackish water being the most strongly armoured while those from fresh water are occasionally almost naked. Old fishes are often very deep-bodied. Upperside greenish to brownish, often marbled, rarely blue-black. The colour of the back passes through a transitional, more or less yellowish, zone into the silver of the underside. During the breeding season the underside of the ♂ is orange-red, the upperside shining sea-green. The iris is brilliant blue-green.

♀ belly silver or greenish-grey during the breeding season. Eye silvery with a fine green sheen, sometimes rather red.

The Stickleback is highly recommended as a subject for the coldwater aquarium, especially to the aquarist with serious biological leanings. It is best to select fishes from standing water for this purpose. Provide them with a large aquarium, standing in a sunny position and well-planted with native water-plants; under such conditions aeration can be dispensed with. The temperature should not rise above 22°C. even in summer, while in winter it must be kept really cold at about 5–8°C. Live food, such as small crustacea, worms, midge-larvae, etc. In the wild fish-spawn and young fry are also eaten.

The breeding season, after a cold wintering, lasts from April to June. It is best to keep several ♀♀ with one ♂. The ♂ soon commences to build a nest, collecting algae and pieces of plant detritus on the bottom among the stems of waterplants and cementing this material together, with a substance discharged from the kidney, to form a barrel-shaped structure. Any water-insect or fish that approaches is driven off, while insect-larvae are usually seized with the mouth and carried away to the opposite corner of the tank. Once the nest has been completed the ♂ endeavours to entice a ♀ along and eventually one is sufficiently persuaded and slips through the built-in entrance to the nest to lay a few eggs. Immediately afterwards the ♂ glides alongside her, rubs his flank against hers and fertilises the eggs. The ♀ now breaks through the rear wall of the nest and escapes to the open water, leaving behind her a nest which is now provided with both an entrance and an exit. This performance is several times repeated; occasionally, too, another ♀ is urged into the nest until a sufficient quota of eggs is present. At this stage the ♀♀ are best removed, since the ♂ signals the commencement of a prolonged and zealous period of brood-care by biting them hard. The ♂ stations himself, quivering, in front of the nest, fanning the water over the eggs with his pectoral and caudal fins, repairing the nest from time to time, and driving off any larger animal that ventures into the vicinity. Throughout this time he takes no food. The young hatch after 10–14 days and continue to be tended by the father until they have grown so large that they themselves are regarded as a danger and are themselves removed. From now on their father becomes a part of this danger.

Pygosteus pungitius (*Linnaeus* 1758) (Fig. 1051)   Ten-spined Stickleback
Coasts of Northern Europe, Baltic, also common in inland waters; to 6 cm.

D_1 IX–XIII, D_2 10–11; A I/9–11; V II/1. Body slimmer than in the Three-spined Stickleback, naked, or with a few bony scutes on the caudal peduncle. Nine to ten spines in front of the dorsal fin, exceptionally up to thirteen. Upperside grey-green to brown. Flanks paler, yellowish, often with vague dark blotches or transverse bars. Underside silvery. During the breeding season the throat and chest of the ♂♂ assume a velvet-black colour; more rarely the whole fish becomes quite black.

Care and breeding, as given for the previous species, except that *P. pungitius* is much more difficult to breed in captivity. Brackish-water specimens require a long period of acclimatisation to fresh water. The ♂♂ do not build their barrel-shaped nests on the bottom but in clumps of plants.

Order Heterosomata (Flat-fishes)

Fishes with an asymmetrical head and body. The body is very strongly compressed and the fish lives with one side, right or left depending on the family, habitually against the bottom. In association with this habit both eyes are situated on the same side of the head and the mouth is more or less twisted, with stronger jaws and teeth on the blind side. There is no swim-bladder. Fins usually without spines. The dorsal and anal fins are very long-based and often extend from the nape (and correspondingly far forward on the belly) to the small, rounded caudal fin. The upperside (left or right) of adult fishes is usually rough (ctenoid scales with spinous processes) and dark-coloured; the underside usually soft and pale.

The transparent young stages (larvae) are symmetrical and swim in a normal upright position near the surface of the water. In the course of their subsequent development, however, the cartilage over one eye is resorbed and that eye migrates over the top of the head to lie next to its partner on the opposite side. The young fish now sinks to the bottom and settles down on its blind side. Young flat-fishes are very nimble. The full-grown flat-fishes are bottom-dwellers which mainly live in shallower seas and swim rather poorly by means of undulating movements of their unpaired fins. Although most species are protectively coloured, and further have a marked capacity for colour-change, they still tend to dig themselves into the sand. Prey is not actively pursued but dragged out of its hiding-place by the rapidly protrusible mouth, frequently with a quick arching of the body.

The order contains many species in almost all seas. A great many are important as food-fishes (Plaice, Sole, Flounder, Dab, Halibut, Turbot, etc.). Some species penetrate into brackish water when young but very few are finally able to conquer fresh water. The following species, belonging to the family *Soleidae*, is the one most frequently imported into Europe.

Achirus fasciatus (*Lacépède* 1803) (Fig. 1052)   Dwarf Flounder
East Coast of U.S.A., Florida, Texas, in salt, brackish and fresh water; to 15 cm.

D 50–56; A 36–42; LL 66–75. Body typically flounder-shaped. The coloration of the upperside is very variable, depending on the nature of the bottom and the emotional condition of the fish; generally a sandy ground-colour irregularly marbled with grey-brown to dark brown. Underside uniformly white. Older fishes with narrow dark transverse bands.

Sex-distinctions unknown.

Care. A large aquarium with a bottom of fine sand. Slightly brackish water (2–3 teaspoons of sea-salt to 10 litres of water). Temperature 20–24°C. Live food, mainly worms and red midge-larvae, also scraps and even decayed plant-material. Quite an interesting subject, but unfortunately one which spends the day buried in the sand with only the small eyes protruding, a habit which is hardly ever abandoned except at night or when food is offered. When the Flounder is frightened it makes a lightning dash across the bottom and quickly digs in in another place. Breeding unknown. The fishes occasionally rest against the glass side of the tank. 1949.

Family Tetraodontidae*
(Globe-fishes, Puffer-fishes or Swell-fishes)

The *Tetraodontidae* belong to the order *Plectognathi* (= 'fused-jawed ones'), an order distinguished from the *Percomorphi* mainly by certain rather technical differences in the skull, and by the facts that the premaxillary and maxillary bones of the upper jaw are generally firmly united and that the teeth are few and strong. The *Plectognathi* include mainly brightly-coloured tropical marine fishes, often very bizarre in shape, such as the *Balistidae* (Trigger-fishes), *Ostraciontidae* (Coffer-fishes), *Diodontidae* (Porcupine-fishes), *Molidae* (Ocean Sun-fishes) and, of course, the present family.

The *Tetraodontidae* include the only Plectognath fishes which venture into brackish and fresh water. They are chiefly tropical and sub-tropical in their distribution and are among the most remarkable and most interesting of fishes. The body is usually more or less club-shaped and consequently

* Original German text written in collaboration with P. Chlupaty, Munich.

819

presents a rather clumsy appearance. Head generally large, occasionally very large *(T. miurus)*. Eyes widely separated. The teeth, which have a general tendency to fuse in the *Plectognathi*, are fully united in this family to form sharp ridges which, in their entirety, are shaped not unlike a parrot's beak. The upper and lower mandibles of the beak each consist of right and left

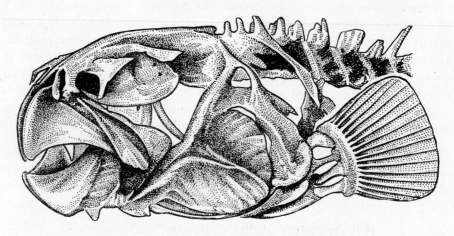

Fig. 1171
Skull of a Globe-fish, showing the dentition

tooth-plates (4 in all, hence *Tetraodontidae* = '4-toothed ones'), which are united in the mid-line. The mandibles may be more or less broadly covered by swollen lips. A similar beak is found in the Porcupine-fishes *(Diodontidae)* and, as an interesting example of convergent evolution, in the quite unrelated Parrot-fishes *(Scaridae*, order *Percomorphi)*.

The fins also display anatomical and functional peculiarities. Whereas in the typical fish the tail and caudal fin together form the main organ of propulsion while the paired fins act as steering-organs, in the Globe-fishes the situation is quite the contrary. Here the body is driven along by screw-like movements of the powerful pectoral fins, assisted to some extent by the dorsal and anal fins, while the tail and the usually small anal fin do the steering. The pectoral fins, moreover, can work independently and so determine the direction of movement without the help of the vertical fins. As a final refinement the specialised musculature of the pectoral fins also makes it possible for the fish to swim backwards. These varied types of movement give these fishes a very much greater manœuvrability than a first impression of their clumsy appearance and performance would suggest. There are no ventral fins in this family, and all the fins are composed only of soft rays.

The muscular skin is sometimes naked, more often beset with trifid spines which are laid back when the fish is undisturbed. Very rarely plate-like dermal bones are present, such as are characteristic of some other Plectognath families. The gill-openings are very narrow and slot-like, and situated immediately in front of the pectoral fins.

The popular names 'Globe-fishes', 'Puffer-fishes' or 'Swell-fishes' indicate the most striking peculiarity of this family. Almost all Globe-fishes, like the Porcupine-fishes, have a large sac-like diverticulum of the gullet, extending broadly under the skin of the chest and belly, and capable of being distended with water or air. With the aid of this structure the fish can inflate itself into a sphere, an adaptation which probably serves mainly as a means of defence. With its greatly increased size the fish probably impresses an aggressor as being no longer swallowable, and as a further deterrent the spines of the body become erected in the course of the swelling. Eventually the aggressor may be further intimidated by the backward expulsion of the water which has been taken in. Many species, furthermore, are highly toxic and, like other groups of animals, advertise this fact by bright warning-coloration. The toxin (Tetragonin) is produced in the gonads of the fish and is subsequently stored in various other organs of the body.

Most Globe-fishes are not difficult to keep. Wild stock, derived from the coastal districts of Asia, Africa and America, should be put into brackish water at the outset and gradually acclimatised to fresh. Normally freshwater species, such as *Tetraodon schoutedeni, T. lineatus, T. miurus, T. mbu*, etc., can naturally be put straightway into freshwater. Those who wish to provide a natural biotope for brackish-water species should cover the bottom of the aquarium with fine sand and shell-gravel and build suitable hiding-places with stones, tangles of roots or pieces of coral. With the possible exception of the African species these fishes make no special demands but, in so far as they are accustomed to freshwater, they prefer a well-matured aquarium. Many of the less snappish species do quite well in company with other not-too-small fishes. Water-hardness and pH generally play a relatively small role. Almost all the species are sensitive to low pH values, however, and undoubtedly prefer slightly alkaline water. African species, on the other hand, should be kept in not-too-hard, rather peaty water.

The peculiar dentition already described represents an extensive adaptation to crushing hard-shelled prey, chiefly molluscs. Almost all the snappish freshwater species so far imported prefer small snails and mussels (not *Lymnaea*!) first and accept earthworms, midge-larvae, mealworms and water-fleas as second-best; a few like *Tubifex*. Some species, such as *Tetraodon miurus*, feed chiefly on small fishes.

It is usually possible to induce a Globe-fish to give a demonstration of its capacity for self-inflation by lifting it out of the water and gently stroking its belly (Fig.1060). On being returned to the water it floats belly-up like a ball, then, with a hissing expulsion of air, rapidly submerges and tries to hide itself. Squeaky noises may often be heard also during the process of inflation.

Little is known about the reproduction of the Globe-fishes. *Tetraodon cutcutia* has been several times bred in captivity, however, and Paul Schäme has produced several broods, in freshwater throughout and even in concrete tanks. The breeding-behaviour is described as follows:

After a peculiar courtship in which the ♂ and ♀ circle on the bottom, the ♀ lays her 200–300 glass-clear eggs on stones, etc., where they are fertilised by the ♂ and then guarded and defended by him. The ♂ actually sits on the spawn, as though brooding it with his body, in order to conceal it from

Figs.1172–1174

Fig.1172. *Plecostomus commersoni;* adult, greatly reduced.
Fig.1173. *Plecostomus punctatus;* adult, greatly reduced.
Fig.1174. *Plecostomus rachowi;* adult, natural size.

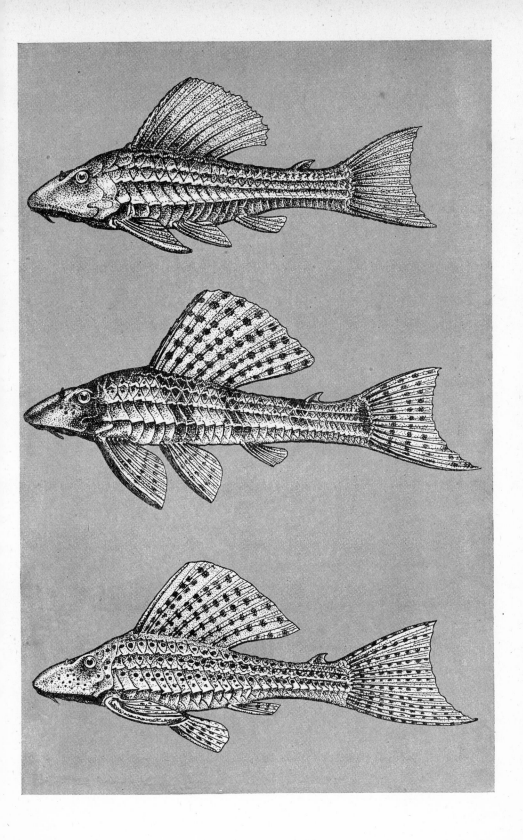

enemies. The eggs take 6–8 days to develop, depending on water-temperature, and when the round, tadpole-like young hatch they remain resting on the bottom for a few days. After a while the ♂ accommodates them in a kind of trench in the sand and guards them for a further period. The ♀ takes no part in this brood-care, but on the contrary feeds to a remarkable extent during this period and does not conceal herself. In the early days the young live off their yolk-sacs and later take to feeding upon Infusoria and nauplii.

Similar breeding behaviour is exhibited by *Tetraodon fluviatilis* and *T. leiurus brevirostris*. *T. schoutedeni* has certainly been bred in captivity, first of all by the importers Andreas Werner of Munich in November 1954. Careful observations made by Feigs in 1955 show that in this species two ♂♂ attach themselves firmly by their teeth to the underside of a ♀, the eggs being spawned near the surface of the water. *T. schoutedeni* does not undertake any definite brood-care; indeed, it has been observed that the ♀ takes the spawn into her mouth and, further, plays with it. The rather small young hatch after 3 days at 28 °C. and are already similar to their parents in shape. The young fishes apparently did not find any suitable food among the Infusoria richly provided, and they also refused small Enchytraeids and nauplii of *Cyclops* and *Artemia salina* and perished after a short time. It has also been reported of *T. cutcutia* that it has apparently not found any initial food to its liking and that it can only with difficulty be induced to accept small crustacea.

Globe-fishes are very intelligent and often lose every trace of shyness as far as their owner is concerned.

Carinotetraodon somphongsi (*Klausewitz* 1957) (Figs. 976, 1177)
Thailand, in fresh water; maximum length unknown, average length 6 cm.

D 13; A 11; P 17; C 12. Body club-shaped, somewhat compressed, with skin-folds on the anterior part of the belly. In the inflated condition, however, it is lens-shaped with a comb-like ridge along the back and a sharp ventral keel. Dorsal and anal fins short. Nasal tubes short. Dermal spines weakly developed. Coloration very variable. Ground-colour yellow to dark grey; back darker; belly paler to dirty white. A pale area between the eyes. Two very irregular dark transverse stripes across the back. A very variable and striking dark band between the eye and the dorsal fin. Underside with rust-coloured longitudinal stripes. Dorsal and anal fins opposite, dirty red. Caudal fin brilliant blue, with a white hinder edge. Iris red, pupil iridescent bluish. (Data after Benl.)

This species is especially interesting for its capacity to produce a dorsal comb-ridge and a ventral keel, and is said to be very peaceful. Keep it in pure freshwater; see also the family description. 1956.

Carinotetraodon chlupatyi Benl 1957 is a synonym which has been given to the ♂ of this species.

Colomesus psittacus (*Schneider* 1801) (Fig. 1076)   Parrot Puffer-fish
West Indies, Venezuela, Guiana, Amazon River and a few of its tributaries; usually in fresh water, rarely in brackish; to 15 cm.

D 10–13; A 10. Head rather square. Eyes large. Jaws powerful, projecting somewhat. The dark brown or olive-black of the upperside extends in various completely irregular patterns of transverse bars down to the underside, the inter-vening spaces on the upper half of the body, as well as the numerous spots on the upperside, being pure white. Eye very mobile, with an intense blue-green iridescence, especially in the region of the pupil.

Sex-distinctions not certainly known.

Care, as given in the family description. Very peaceful towards other species, despite its size; a little pugnacious with its own kind, but usually quite harmless. Often suddenly inflates itself with water without provocation until it is about three times its original girth. Unfortunately very timid. As well as rather large snails it likes to eat midge-larvae, earthworms, mealworms and Enchytraeids. 23–28 °C. Quite healthy in seawater in captivity. Not yet bred. 1952.

Tetraodon cutcutia *Hamilton-Buchanan* 1822 (Fig. 1056)   Common Puffer-fish
India and Further India, Malay Archipelago (Philippines?), in fresh and brackish water; to 15 cm.

D 10–12; A 10; P 21. Shape as given in the family description. Skin leathery, without dermal spines. Nasal tubes undivided, very short or absent. The bones of the upper and lower jaws form prominent enamel-covered ridges. Back dark-green to olive-green; flanks yellowish to pale grey; belly dirty white. A pale stripe uniting the eyes. A round, dark blotch, broadly bordered with shining gold, in front of the dorsal fin and on the flanks. Whole body netted with dark brown. Fins yellow-grey to olive-green. Caudal fin bordered with greenish, with a narrow brown to carmine-red band below the upper edge; rarely completely bordered with carmine-red. Coloration very variable. Eye iridescent greenish.

♀ rather smaller; more yellowish in colour.

Care and breeding, as given in the family description. This species inflates itself relatively often while submerged, is easy to keep and has repeatedly been bred. Unfortunately almost always snappish and very quarrelsome. 1903/+.

Tetraodon erythrotaenia *Bleeker* 1853 (Fig. 1175)   Red-lined Puffer-fish
Celebes, Amboina, New Guinea, Australia, in fresh and brackish water; to 9 cm.

D 9–10; A 9–11. Shape similar to that of *T. fluviatilis*. Nasal tentacles forked. Skin with prominent dermal spines. The uniformly grey-brown to black-brown upperside is sharply delimited at about the level of the pectoral fin by a bright rust-red to carmine-red longitudinal line which separates it from the white or light yellowish underside.

Sex-distinctions unknown.

Care, as given in the family description. This species prefers a well-planted aquarium with a bottom of fine sand. 23–28°C. Quarrelsome. Not yet bred. 1935/−.

Tetraodon lineatus *Linnaeus* 1758 (Fig. 1176)   Arab or Nile Puffer-fish
Nile, streams of Lake Chad, Niger, Senegambia, only in coastal regions; to 40 cm.

D 12–14; A 10–11. Head and body set with small dermal spines; none on the tail. Two short, forked nasal tentacles. Upperside dark, grey to blackish. Flanks grey-yellow, with numerous dark longitudinal bands which are inclined slightly upwards towards the back and, especially on the head and the anterior part of the body, may be more or less united into a marbled pattern. In young fishes, especially, this pattern of markings is present only in the form of rows of blotches. Underside yellowish. Dorsal, anal and pectoral fins yellow. Caudal fin dark grey-olive, bordered with orange. Very young fishes have rows of spots on the flanks.

Sex-distinctions not certainly known.

Care, as given in the family description. Very snappish. 22–26°C. Not yet bred. 1902/+.

Recently several subspecies have been recognised:

T. lineatus lineatus (Nile).

T. lineatus strigosus (Niger).

T. lineatus rudolfianus (Lake Rudolf; remains very small, 6 cm.).

T. fahaka Hasselquist 1762 is a junior synonym of this species.

Tetraodon fluviatilis *Hamilton-Buchanan* 1822 (Figs. 1059–1061, 1075)

Green Puffer-fish

India, Ceylon, Burma, Thailand, Malay Peninsula, Sunda Islands and Philippines, in fresh and slightly brackish waters; to 17 cm.

D 14–16; A 12–15; P 22. Head and body more or less thickly set with dermal spines; rarely quite naked. Two short, forked nasal tentacles. Coloration and markings very variable, depending on locality of origin. Upperside and flanks with large, round, brown to black blotches which often have pale borders and which, especially on the back, may unite into broad chevron-like markings. The interspaces are a brilliant emerald-green to yellow-green. Brilliant but vaguely-delimited lines may be present between the eyes and on the nape. A uniformly pale green iridescent blotch may also be present. Underside white, grey in older fishes, occasionally with dark spots.

Sex-distinctions unknown.

Care of this lovely species, as given in the family description. *T. fluviatilis* often cannot tolerate pure seawater, but does very well in freshwater. Add a little sea-salt when breeding (1 tablespoon to 10 litres of water). Breeding behaviour as in *T. cutcutia* (see family description). Peaceful when young, snappish later. This species often nibbles plants. 1905/+.

Tetraodon leiurus brevirostris *Benl* 1957 (Fig. 1057)

Probably Thailand; to about 12 cm.

D 14; A 11. Body similar in shape to that of *T. fluviatilis*, but with a very short snout, a character which also distinguishes this from the typical subspecies. Skin set with dermal spines. Nasal tentacles simple, divided into two lobes at the ends (according to Benl). Body with close-set dark polygonal blotches on a grey-brown to grey-yellow ground. On the lower part of the flanks and on the belly the blotches are more cocoa-coloured. On the middle of the side, somewhat in front of the dorsal fin, there is a very striking field which may be considerably darker or lighter and is surrounded by a corona of small blotches. Similar markings may also be present on the anterior half of the body. The cornea of the eye projects as a hemisphere and is brownish. A pale transverse bar between the eyes.

♀ bloated during the breeding season.

Geiser of the Zurich Zoo has successfully bred this species on several occasions. *T. leiurus brevirostris* is very snappish and quarrelsome. 1956.

Tetraodon mbu *Boulenger* 1899 (Fig. 1077)
Middle and Lower Congo, always in fresh water; to 75 cm., usually smaller.

D 11–12; A 10–11. Body rather elongate, with two forked nasal tentacles on each side. Head and body, with the exception of the snout and the lower caudal region, set with tiny dermal spines. Attractively coloured. Upperside, and flanks down as far as the level of the pectoral fins, yellow to orange, with numerous dark brown to black vermiform lines. Underside pure yellow. Fins orange to yellow. Caudal fin occasionally with black longitudinal bands. The young fishes exhibit large black spots instead of the vermiform lines, with 1–2 longitudinal bands on the caudal peduncle.

Sex-distinctions unknown.

Care, as given in the family description. Unfortunately very snappish and quarrelsome. This species eats snails for preference. 23–28 °C. 1952.

Tetraodon miurus *Boulenger* 1902 (Fig. 1044)
Middle and Lower Congo, only in fresh water; to 10 cm.

D 9–10; A 8–9. Head very large (about $1/3$ of the total length) and broad. Snout somewhat tuberous. Eyes small, upwardly directed. Underside of head flat. The species has a remarkable capacity for cryptic colour-change; in relation to different factors it can become almost black or reddish or quite pale grey, with a correspondingly variable pattern of markings. Although it is often well enough concealed in this way, the fish still likes to dig itself into the sand, like a Flounder, until only the eyes are visible.

Sex-distinctions unknown.

Care, as given in the family description. The fishes must be provided with a soft bottom-soil to cater for their peculiar habits. *T. miurus* has little appetite for snails and small mussels but prefers slow-swimming fishes which it often bites in two across the middle of the body and devours at leisure. It will also eat earthworms and midge-larvae, but with rather less enthusiasm. Very snappish. 23–28 °C. Not yet bred. 1953.

Figs. 1175–1179

Fig. 1175. *Tetraodon erythrotaenia* (Red-lined Puffer-fish); natural size.
Fig. 1176. *Tetraodon lineatus* (Arab or Nile Puffer-fish); half-grown, reduced.
Fig. 1177. *Carinotetraodon somphongsi;* somewhat enlarged.
Fig. 1178. *Amphipnous cuchia* (Cuchia); greatly reduced.
Fig. 1179. *Monopterus alba;* greatly reduced.

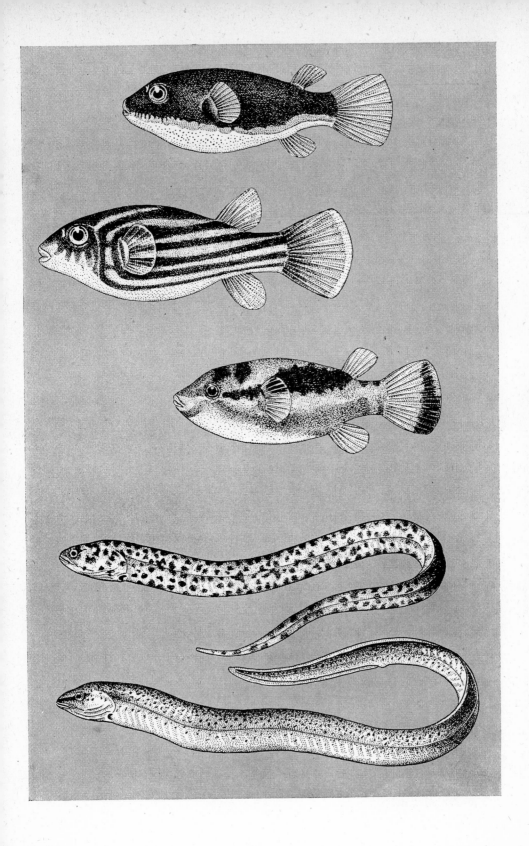

Tetraodon palembangensis *Bleeker* 1852 (Fig. 1045)
Thailand, Sumatra, Borneo, in fresh water; to 20 cm.

D 10–14; A 11–12. Shape similar to that of *T. fluviatilis*. One nasal tentacle on each side. Skin with prominent dermal spines. Coloration, according to Benl: upperside lemon-yellow to deep green; underside white or yellow. Superimposed on these ground-colours there is an irregular, ornamental and very variable network of lines, which includes black blotches on the flanks. Fishes from Sumatra are mainly distinguished by the possession of a black, pale-bordered ocellus under the dorsal fin, another on the caudal peduncle and a black blotch on the shoulder.

Sex-distinctions unknown.

Care, as given in the family description. The statement that *T. palembangensis* has been bred in the Zurich Zoo is based, I am sure, on a confusion with another species (see under *T. leiurus brevirostris*). *T. palembangensis* is quarrelsome both with its own kind and with other fishes. 1953.

Tetraodon schoutedeni *Pellegrin* 1926 (Fig. 1058)
Lower Congo, Stanley Pool, only in fresh water; to 8 cm., the ♂♂ remaining smaller.

D 9–10; A 8–9. Shape similar to that of *T. fluviatilis*. Two long, forked nasal tentacles on either side. On a pastel to ochre-coloured ground, darker on the upperside, appear numerous sepia to black blotches of diverse sizes which are most extensive on the upper half of the body. Eye iridescent reddish. The considerably smaller ♂♂ are easily recognised.

Care and breeding, as given in the family description. *T. schoutedeni* is one of the most peaceable Puffer-fishes and can easily be kept in company with other peaceful species. Their phlegmatic temperament is upset from time to time by prolonged though harmless feuds with one another which are probably to be regarded as being due to sexual rivalry or courtship behaviour. As soon as two fishes observe one another they commence a reciprocal nudging, with an excitement which is evident from the outspread fins and slight inflation of the body. This species is only able to crack small, thin-shelled snails and mussels, and prefers Enchytraeids and *Tubifex*. Unfortunately it likes to nibble the widest variety of plants without, however, actually eating them. Breeding, as described under the family description. 1953.

Family Mastacembelidae* (Spiny Eels)

The family *Mastacembelidae*, together with the very small family *Chaudhuri-idae*, form the order *Opisthomi*, the Spiny Eels. It must be emphasised at the outset that, despite their popular name, they have nothing in common with the true Eels apart from a certain similarity of form. A far more striking

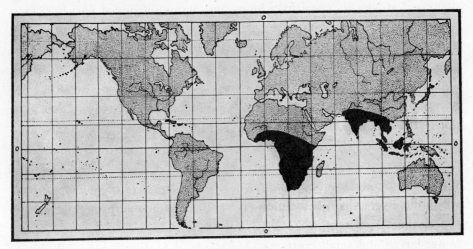

Fig. 1180
Distribution of the *Mastacembelidae*

resemblance can be seen between *Mastacembelus* and the deep-sea genus *Polyacanthonotus* (family *Notacanthidae*, order *Heteromi*), although here again there is merely a convergent similarity and no phyletic relationship.

The Spiny Eels are natives of the fresh and brackish waters of tropical Africa, the Euphrates region, and south and south-east Asia north to Peking. They are eel-like to band-shaped in form, varying from very low-bodied species in which the body-depth is contained 15 to 20 times in the total length (*Mastacembelus loennbergi*) to those in which it is contained only 6–7 times in the total length (*M. pancalus*). Older fishes are, as a rule, relatively deeper

* The spelling variants *Mastocembelus, Mastocembelidae* are incorrect.

831

than young ones. The head is elongate, with the snout produced into a fleshy, mobile, proboscis-like process (Fig. 1082). The anterior nasal openings are carried forward to open through small tubes on either side of the base of the proboscis, while the posterior ones remain well back and are situated just in front of the small eyes. The mouth and gill-openings are small, the latter displaced towards the throat. The body is covered with small scales. The dorsal fin consists of a row of isolated spines, which can be erected or depressed at will, followed by a long, continuous soft-rayed fin which may or may not be united with the caudal and through this with the long-based anal fin. In the genus *Macrognathus* these three fins are separate and distinct. Ventral fins absent.

In their natural habitats the Spiny Eels mainly frequent very weedy waters over a muddy or sandy bottom. Like typical crepuscular creatures they hide during the daytime among plants, or even buried in the bottom, and towards nightfall set forth in search of small prey, chiefly worms, insect-larvae and small crustacea. Most species do well in captivity when provided with sufficient hiding-places under stones, halved flowerpots or hollow roots, from which these very shy fishes can observe and smell their surroundings during the daytime. Temperature 22–28 °C. Live food of all kinds, such as worms, midge-larvae and small crustacea. The mode of feeding is especially interesting. First of all the movable rostral appendage is orientated to feel the prey, then the food is sipped in with a jerking motion. The same structure is also used to forage for worms in the soil.

Water-quality is of relatively little consequence to these fishes, although one should, in any case, add 2–3 teaspoons of sea-salt to every 10 litres of water and top up with fresh water from time to time.

Figs. 1181–1185

Fig. 1181. *Mastacembelus argus;* adult, reduced.
Fig. 1182. *Mastacembelus armatus armatus;* half-grown, reduced.
Fig. 1183. *Mastacembelus loennbergi;* adult, reduced.
Fig. 1184. *Mastacembelus maculatus;* greatly reduced.
Fig. 1185. *Synbranchus afer;* greatly reduced.

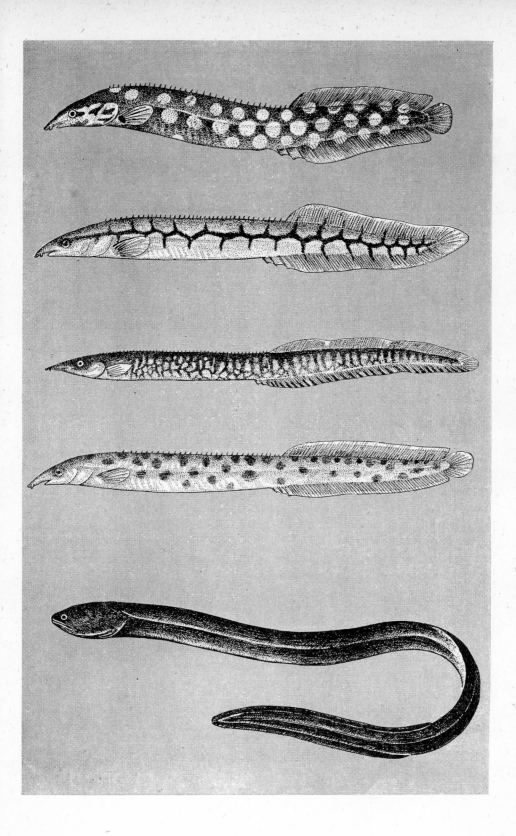

The main organs of propulsion are the anal and caudal fins, although locomotion is also assisted by serpentine movements of the body. Many species like to dig themselves so deep into the bottom that only the eyes and the rostral appendage remain visible. This hiding is generally vacated in the early evening.

Mastacembelus pancalus has several times been bred in captivity. Pairing seems to be relatively easy. During the breeding season the very robust ♀♀ are constantly pursued by the ♂♂ with, as Schönbeck has observed, the rostral appendage nudging the region of the vent. The eggs are probably strewn at random over the bottom; the duration of their development is unknown. The young fishes hide themselves in the mulm on the bottom or in thick clumps of plants.

Many Spiny Eels are attractively coloured. Almost all become tame and learn to recognise their keeper when they are kept in tanks reserved for single species.

Macrognathus aculeatus (*Bloch* 1787) (Figs. 1081, 1082)
Widely distributed, from India over the whole of southern Asia, also in some islands of the Malay Archipelago and the Moluccas, in brackish and fresh water; to 35 cm.

D XIV–XV/50–55; A II/49–53. The genus *Macrognathus* is characterised, among other features, by the corrugation of the underside of the rostral appendage. Body elongate, relatively deep in older fishes. Chocolate-brown to fawn, often with conspicuous marbling on the upperside; underside pale. The very striking ocelli (varying in number between 3 and 10) on the delicate brownish dorsal fin are especially characteristic of this species. Caudal fin usually with transverse bands. Anal fin pale brownish to delicate olive.

♀ considerably more robust, and very stout during the breeding season.

Care, as given in the family description. Sexually ripe at 12–15 cm. 1922/+.

Mastacembelus argus *Günther* 1861 (Fig. 1181)
Thailand, very rare; to 25 cm.

D XXXII–XXXIV/60–75; A III/56–75. The genus *Mastacembelus* comprises most of the species in the entire order *Opisthomi*. *M. argus* occupies an intermediate position between the very low-bodied and the deeper-bodied forms. Preopercular bone of the gill-cover with 2–3 spines. Body yellow-brown to dark brown with longitudinal rows of pale green to white blotches on the flanks and pale lines on the back. Underside white. Fins opaque brown, to some extent with yellowish borders.

Sex-distinctions and care, as given in the family description. 1906/−.

Mastacembelus armatus armatus *Günther* 1861 (Fig. 1182)
Widely distributed from India and Ceylon through Thailand to southern China, also in Sumatra; to 75 cm., usually smaller.

D XXXIV–XXXIX/79–90; A III/79–90. *M. armatus armatus* belongs to the relatively low-bodied species. Body-depth contained 13 to 11 times in total length, depending on age. The species is easily recognised by the characteristic markings. Upperside bright brown; underside yellowish. From the eye to the root of the tail extends an irregular dark zig-zag band which gives off branches alternately towards the dorsal and anal fins. Young fishes often display cloudy blotches.

Sex-distinction and care, as given in the family description. 1922/+.

Mastacembelus loennbergi *Boulenger* 1898 (Fig. 1183)
Tropical West Africa, Cameroons, Sierra Leone, tributary streams of Lake Chad; to 19 cm.

D XXVIII–XXXII/100–130; A II/100–130. Body very slim, depth contained 17 to 13 times in the total length. Body rather dark olive-brown to almost blackish, with numerous pale yellow to brownish spots and streaks. Lower half of flanks paler, with a reticulated pattern. Margin of dorsal fin with dark spots. Border of anal fin with alternating pale and dark transverse stripes. Eye reddish.

Sex-distinctions and care, as given in the family description. 1913/+.

Mastacembelus maculatus (*Cuvier* and *Valenciennes* 1831) (Fig. 1184)
Thailand, Greater Sunda Islands, in fresh water; to 45 cm.

D XXVI–XXX/60–70; A III/59–69. Snout scaly, in contrast to the other species dealt with here. This species also has very characteristic markings and colouring. Body brown, with dark blotches. Vertical fins with a yellow edge; a row of black spots along the base of the dorsal. (Description according to Smith, 1945.)

Sex-distinctions and care, as given in the family description. 1939/−.

Mastacembelus pancalus (*Hamilton-Buchanan* 1822) (Fig. 1078)
Further India, in large rivers and coastal regions; to 20 cm.

D XXIV–XXVI/30–44; A III/31–46; P 19. *M. pancalus* is relatively deep-bodied (body-depth contained 7 to 6·5 times in the total length) and strongly compressed. Upperside olive-green; flanks brownish to grey; underside pale to bright yellow. Numerous pale yellow spots are very striking against this ground-colour. A pale stripe along the lateral line, often with dark transverse stripes, especially on the hinder half of the body. Fins yellowish, with dark spots.

♀ considerably more robust and rather deeper; underside pale grey to pure white.

Care and breeding, as given in the family description. *M. pancalus* has been successfully bred on several occasions. 1904/+.

The African species *Mastacembelus laticauda* Ahl 1938 has also been imported recently from Sierra Leone.

Order Synbranchia* (Synbranchoid Eels)

Fishes of superficially eel-like shape, although not related to the true Eels and, indeed, of very uncertain systematic position. They are widely distributed in fresh and brackish waters of the tropical regions of America, Africa and Asia and their outlying islands, and Australia.

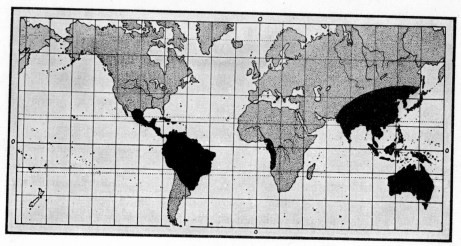

Fig. 1186
Distribution of the order *Synbranchia*

* The variant spellings *Symbranchus, Symbranchidae, Symbranchia* are incorrect.

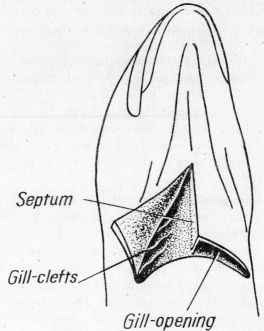

Fig. 1187
Ventral view of the head of *Monopterus alba*, showing the single transverse gill-opening. The gill-chamber has been opened on the right side to display the three rudimentary gills and the median septum.

Septum

Gill-clefts

Gill-opening

The dorsal and anal fins contain no fin-rays, are greatly reduced and fused with the caudal to form a continuous fringing fin. The caudal fin, if present, consists of 8–10 rays. There are no paired fins. Scales very small or rudimentary. Lateral line present. There is a single slit-like gill-opening across the middle of the throat, formed by the coalescence of the right and left gill-openings. This gill-opening may be internally divided by a median septum (Fig. 1187). Dentition complete. Eyes small, covered over with skin, or absent. The gill-elements are often reduced; in association with this feature air-breathing organs are often developed, either a pair of highly vascular lung-like sacs opening from the gill-chamber or a specialised portion of the hind-gut. Species so adapted regularly rise to the surface of the water to expel exhausted air and take in fresh; air exhausted in intestinal respiration is expelled through the vent. Accessory air-breathing enables these fishes to inhabit waters which are poor in oxygen and liable to dry out. During the dry season they burrow in the mud and pass into a kind of summer sleep, in which respiration is carried on by the accessory organs and greatly diminished.

The order *Synbranchia* is further classified as follows: –

Family *Alabetidae*, containing only the genus *Alabes* (Shore-eels) from the coasts of Australia, which retain fin-rays in the dorsal and anal fins and have two-rayed ventrals as well.

Family *Synbranchidae*, comprising the genera *Macrotrema*, *Monopterus*, *Synbranchus* and the blind *Typhlosynbranchus*.

Family *Amphipnoïdae*, containing only the genus *Amphipnous*.

Amphipnous cuchia (*Hamilton-Buchanan* 1822) (Fig. 1178)   Cuchia
India, in the States of Bengal, Orissa, the Punjab and in Assam and Burma; to 70 cm.

The genus *Amphipnous* is distinguished from all others of the order by the possession of an accessory respiratory organ, formed by right and left lung-like sacs opening off from the gill-chamber and extending under the skin of the nape and rather further posteriorly. These sacs not only show through the skin of the nape but also distend this and cause it to bulge. Very small scales present. Gills greatly reduced. Coloration, according to Arnold: upperside of body dark green; underside dirty pale red. The whole body is covered with small round spots and dots and short yellowish streaks.

The Indian Cuchia, like its relatives (see *Monopterus* and *Synbranchus marmoratus*), can live in water poor in oxygen and, when the air is sufficiently humid, spends much of its life out of the water wriggling about on the banks. During the dry season it burrows into the mud and aestivates. It is very light-shy in captivity and often burrows into the bottom-soil. A very voracious predator, capable of consuming about its own weight in food daily. Natural food–worms and molluscs. A case for solitary confinement. 1922/–.

Monopterus alba (*Zuiew* 1793) (Figs. 1179, 1187)
Very widely distributed, from northern China and Japan to Thailand and Burma, also common in the Malay Archipelago; to 90 cm.

Body eel-like, anteriorly cylindrical, posteriorly compressed. Caudal peduncle short, produced to a point. Vertical fins greatly reduced, the dorsal and anal being merely skin-folds without rays and united with the very small caudal. No pectoral or ventral fins. Head short, broad. Mouth deeply cleft and bordered by thick lips.

838

Gill-opening internally divided by a septum; gills greatly reduced (Fig. 1187), with only three arches on either side. Skin naked. Lateral line present.

Old fishes: upperside uniform olive-brown, or lightly marbled with olive- and yellow-brown; underside very pale, almost white.

Young fishes: upperside pale brown, finely spotted with dark brown; underside yellowish. A dark band from the snout to the eye.

Sex-distinctions unknown.

Monopterus alba is found in rivers and ponds, also in ditches, mudholes and ricefields. It is a crepuscular creature, with habits rather like the Common Eel, which hunts at night and feeds upon a variety of larger aquatic animals, chiefly smaller fishes. The hind-gut is used as an accessory respiratory-organ. The ♂♂ build large, free-floating bubble-nests into which the eggs are spat when they are laid. The ♂ undertakes brood-care and apparently also guards the young. In many localities *Monopterus* is valued as a food-fish.

Young specimens do very well in aquaria. Soft, slightly muddy bottom-soil and large quantities of food are their main requirements. Being very predatory fishes they are best kept separately. Specimens from south-east Asia are very warmth-loving; temperature 25–28 °C. Unfortunately this interesting species is but rarely imported. 1905/+.

Fluta Bloch and Schneider 1801 is a synonym of *Monopterus* Lacépède 1800.

Synbranchus afer *Boulenger* 1909 (Fig. 1185)
Lower Niger and Guinea; to 32 cm.

Body-form and biological peculiarities as given for the following species.

Old fishes: coloration very dark, often uniformly black.

Young fishes (10–12 cm.): Ground-colour dark brown, with small rust-red to blood-red spots on the anterior part of the body. Specimens also occur which are marbled with black and red. 1935/−.

Synbranchus marmoratus *Bloch* 1795 (Fig. 88)
Southern Mexico to southern Brazil; to 150 cm.

Body eel-like, anteriorly cylindrical, posteriorly compressed. Generally similar to *Monopterus alba*. The genus *Synbranchus* is distinguished from *Monopterus* by the absence of an internal septum dividing the gill-chamber, and in this case the transverse, slit-like gill-opening therefore opens into a common gill-cavity. Also in *Synbranchus* the teeth on the jaws and palatine bones are arranged in a single series, except anteriorly where there are several rows; in *Monopterus* the teeth are arranged in bands. Four pairs of gill-arches. Upperside quite dark, often marbled with light; underside yellowish, rarely orange. The whole body is strewn with dark, often quite black, spots. Young fishes are commonly uniform grey-brown.

Biology and care, as given for *Monopterus alba*, above. The whole of the distensible, balloon-like gill-chamber serves as an accessory respiratory-organ, and the fishes are able to wriggle for considerable distances overland. Many interesting observations have still to be made on this species; so far practically nothing is known about its breeding-behaviour and brood-care, the form of the young or the normal span of life. Very snappish and greedy predators. 1909/+.

Order Dipnoi or Dipneusti (Lung-fishes)

The Lung-fishes still surviving today are 'living fossils', relicts of a formerly abundant group which had their heyday between the world's infancy and its middle-age (Devonian to Triassic). Their great antiquity accounts not only for their very striking anatomical peculiarities but also for their discontinuous geographical distribution in Australia, Africa and South America. We have noted similar ranges already in other groups of freshwater fishes, such as the family *Nandidae*. It is not necessary, however, to postulate archaic land-bridges between the continents to explain the distribution of the *Dipnoi*, for the fossil record shows that they were once an almost world-wide group; just as the existing Lung-fishes are relicts of an archaic group, so their existing habitats may be regarded as relicts of a once widespread environment of warm, poorly-oxygenated swamps.

The six extant species are classified into two families: the *Lepidosirenidae*, containing the South American *Lepidosiren* and the African *Protopterus*, and the *Ceratodontidae*, containing only the Australian *Neoceratodus*. Related to the Lung-fishes are the order *Crossopterygii*, those interesting fishes from which, in the Devonian (about 350 million years ago), the ancestors of the *Amphibia* and hence of all land vertebrates evolved. Just as the *Dipnoi* were first known only from fossils so also the *Crossopterygii* were assumed to be extinct until, in 1938, the living *Latimeria chalumnae* J. L. B. Smith was discovered north of Madagascar and subsequently around the Comoro Islands.

The shape of the body in Lung-fishes has something in common with that of the tailed *Amphibia* (order *Urodela*). This is especially so in the *Lepidosirenidae*, in which the superficially newt-like appearance is enhanced by the apparently naked skin, the scales being concealed deep under a richly

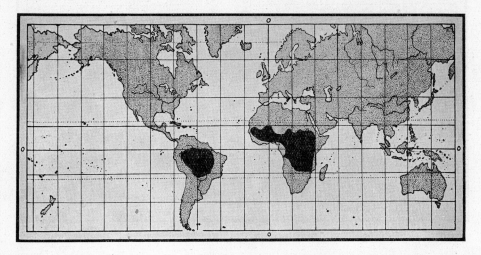

Fig. 1188
Distribution of the *Lepidosirenidae*

glandular epidermis. *Neoceratodus* is less newt-like, its plump, somewhat compressed body being covered with large cycloid scales which emphasise rather its kinship with fishes.

The anatomical peculiarities of Lung-fishes are many and to some extent also quite primitive. One of the most striking is implicit in the popular name; in this group, in contrast to all other living fishes, air-breathing organs are developed which, primitive as they are, really do correspond to the lungs of higher vertebrates. These structures must be sharply distinguished from all the other manifold forms of accessory air-breathing organs found in other groups of freshwater fishes; from the labyrinth organs of the *Anabantidae*,

841

the arborescent structures in the *Clariidae*, the partly-respiratory swim-bladders in *Erythrinus, Gymnarchus,* etc., and the respiratory hind-gut in such families as the *Cobitidae*. The lungs of the *Dipnoi* arise as an outgrowth from the floor of the oesophagus, with which they remain connected by a common pneumatic duct. The *Lepidosirenidae* have a pair of lungs which lie ventral

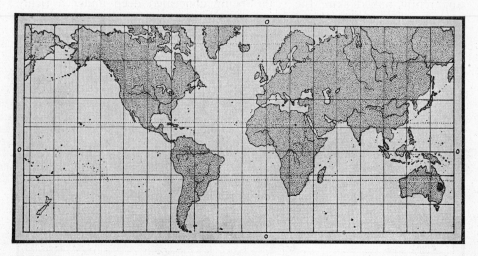

Fig. 1189
Distribution of the *Ceratodontidae;* note Australia.

to the gut, while the *Ceratodontidae* have only one lung which is dorsal. While the Lung-fish lung is homologous with the Teleostean swim-bladder it has a very different blood-vascular system and the heart shows correlated advances. As a rule the lungs are filled with air every 30 to 60 minutes.

The lungs assume their greatest importance during the dry season, when *Lepidosiren* and *Protopterus* bury themselves in the mud as soon as the water dries up, roll up their bodies and secrete mucus which congeals to form a cocoon which keeps the body moist. This capsule is perforated over the mouth so as to allow breathing. The summer sleep ends with the beginning of the rains and the fishes then leave their burrows and, after a time, commence to feed again. *Neoceratodus* is unable to protect itself against the dry season in this way, but its lung-breathing enables it to hold out in the smallest stagnant puddles where there are also frequently excellent feeding-conditions among the enforced concentration of other, less fortunate fishes. It must, of course, be emphasised that all Lung-fishes are also still able to breathe with their more or less strongly reduced gills.

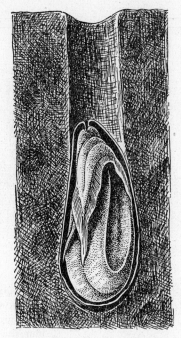

Fig. 1190

An African Lung-fish in its burrow during the dry season. The viscous cocoon enveloping the fish is attached to the edges of the mouth so as to leave a narrow slit through which to breathe. (Re-drawn, after Parker)

Further important peculiarities are shown by the paired fins, which are more or less modified as props and have gone some way towards becoming leg-like (Fig. 1193). Whereas in the Teleostean paired fin the supporting skeleton is concentrated towards the base and the fin-membrane is supported by a fan-like arrangement of dermal rays, in the *Dipnoi* the fin has a long, segmented, supporting axis and the rays, when present, are arranged to form a fringe along either edge. In *Protopterus* these fins are slender, whip-like and very mobile and are put down like legs in ordinary quiet locomotion, giving the impression that the fish is walking. Closer observation soon reveals that the body is resting on the bottom and is not properly lifted as it is in walking; on the contrary, the resting fish can raise its front end a little by means of its pectoral fins. A narrow fin-membrane is often present along one edge, supported by small horny rays. *Lepidosiren* – the American Lung-fish – has similarly-constructed pectoral and ventral fins which are very short indeed

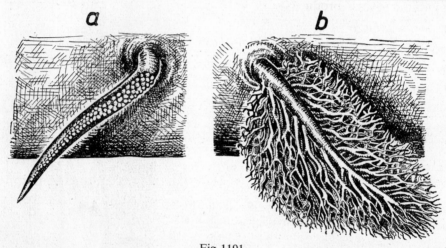

Fig. 1191

Ventral fins of *Lepidosiren paradoxa*, showing vascular structures. (a) Out of the breeding season; fin turned forward to show the numerous small, warty projections. (b) During the breeding season; the warts have grown into long, repeatedly-bifurcated, vascular filaments. (Composite drawings from various sources)

and barely reach the ground. The paired fins of *Neoceratodus* consist of a powerful, externally scaled shaft with an anterior and posterior fin-margin supported by cartilaginous and horny rays. In the water *Neoceratodus* is able to support itself upon these fins and even to proceed on them; on land, however, even these relatively powerful fins are unable to drag the plump, heavy body. In all Lung-fishes the dorsal, caudal and anal fins are united into a common median fin and the caudal is produced to a point and symmetrical about its axis.

Various peculiar structural features of the mainly cartilaginous skeleton are of interest, especially in the skull and dentition. The nostrils are ventral, and one of each side is inside the mouth (but, contrary to many textbooks, only just within the upper lip and in front of the jaw). The teeth are fused into a number of sharp-ridged bony plates. The intestine has a long spiral valve, as in the *Selachii* (Sharks and Rays) and in the Bichirs and Gar-pikes. The condition of the reproductive organs, especially of the ♀♀, also resembles that in the *Selachii*.

Almost all Lung-fishes are very inactive and inhabit stagnant or sluggish waters. Their preferred habitats are the quiet backwaters and weedy lagoons of large rivers, which become isolated and later dry out during the dry season. Exceptions are *Protopterus aethiopicus*, which chiefly occurs in large lakes, and *Neoceratodus*, which always seeks waters which do not entirely dry out. They are predatory creatures all, pursuing feeble-swimming bottom-fishes, snails, mussels, etc. *Neoceratodus* crops aquatic vegetation for the sake of the small animals contained therein and passes a considerable amount of plant-material undigested through its gut. Young fishes eat worms, insect-larvae and small crustacea.

Breeding takes place as a rule at the beginning of the rainy season. *Lepidosiren* spawns in a burrow at the bottom of a swamp; *Protopterus* in a mudhole in a space which it clears among marginal swamp vegetation; *Neoceratodus* among submerged aquatic plants. The eggs are large, very yolky and to some extent surrounded by swollen gelatinous membranes like Amphibian eggs; the development also approaches nearer to that of the Amphibian than of the fish-egg. The ♂♂ undertake brood-care, guarding the spawn and also the newly-hatched young.

A still unresolved problem is associated with the brood-care of *Lepidosiren*, in which the ventral fins of the ♂ develop a great many branched vascular filaments at this time. Some have regarded these as accessory respiratory-organs; others have suggested that, since these fins are inserted among the eggs during brooding, oxygen may actually diffuse out of them from the blood-stream to the developing eggs. There is also a conflict of evidence as to whether the ♂ does or does not leave the nest during brooding in order to breathe atmospheric air, an obviously highly relevant point. It is, of course, physiologically possible for either or both interpretations of the function of the filaments to be correct, since the direction of gas-diffusion will depend on the relative oxygen-tensions in the blood and in the outside water. An oxygen-starved ♂ would thus absorb oxygen through the pelvic filaments when swimming, while on the other hand oxygen might well pass from the filaments into the stagnant, de-oxygenated water bathing the eggs in the nest.

The young of *Lepidosiren* and *Protopterus* have four pairs of feathery external gills and resemble newt-larvae (Fig. 1085). Like these, too, they have an adhesive ventral cement-organ by which they at first hang vertically from plants or adhere to the mud. After a larval period of 2–3 months' duration the larval characters become modified in the course of a metamorphosis and the fishes assume the adult form; in some *Protopterus* spp., however (see *P. amphibius*), quite long finger-shaped processes are retained. The young *Neoceratodus* have no external gills and develop directly.

All Lung-fishes are sought after as food-fishes and, owing to their sluggishness, are not difficult to find. *Protopterus* is dug out during the dry season when its store of reserve fat makes it especially attractive as food. *Neoceratodus* is now rare and under Australian Government protection.

Only small Lung-fishes can be kept in domestic aquaria, but adults are important exhibits in zoological gardens. As long as they are kept warm they will put up with almost any surroundings and are markedly tenacious of life. Feeding is usually the difficult problem. Quite apart from fishes which have been upset in transit and refuse to take food, the choice of food is not easy. Try slow-swimming live fishes, such as Guppies, small snails and mussels, or strips of meat which should, of course, be suspended for the early presentations. All the species are very voracious but do have periods of abstinence from food. Large specimens must be handled with care; they can inflict a nasty bite. Only fishes of similar size can be kept together. Bitten fins and tail-tips are usually rapidly regenerated.

Large specimens are sometimes transported complete with their clay capsules. It is best simply to lay these in water; the fishes very soon emerge and, though somewhat unsteady at first, go in search of food after a few days. It is also possible to induce a demonstration of cocoon-formation in captivity by providing a soft clay bottom and reducing the water-level.

Figs. 1192–1193

Fig. 1192. *Lepidosiren paradoxa* (South American Lung-fish); young, reduced.
Fig. 1193. *Neoceratodus forsteri* (Australian Lung-fish); reduced.

Lepidosiren paradoxa *Fitzinger* 1836 (Figs. 1191, 1192)   South American Lung-fish Central South America, especially in the northern Gran Chaco; to 125 cm.

   L. paradoxa is the most eel-like of the Lung-fishes. Body very elongate, anterior to the ventral fins almost cylindrical. Paired fins relatively short. Scales very small. Uniformly pale to dark grey-brown, paler on the underside, and occasionally with large black spots. Young fishes are often quite black.

   For anatomical and biological details and care, see family description. 1928/+.

Neoceratodus forsteri (*Krefft* 1870) (Fig. 1193) Australian Lung-fish, Barramunda, Burnett Salmon
Queensland, in the Burnett and Mary Rivers; to 175 cm.

   Body elongate, plump, a little compressed. Paired fins paddle-shaped, with a stout axis and a fin along either margin. Scales very large and conspicuous. Lateral line complete. Coloration uniform brown to blue-grey, rather paler on the flanks, usually white-silver to light yellowish on the underside.

847

For anatomical and biological details and care, see family description. Probably not yet imported into Germany; there is, however, a fine specimen in the London Zoo Aquarium.

Epiceratodus blanchardi Castelnau 1876 is a junior synonym.

Protopterus aethiopicus *Heckel* 1851 (Figs. 1085, 1086)
From the eastern Sudan to Lake Tanganyika; to 140 cm.

This species is mainly distinguished from *P. annectens* and *P. amphibius* by its relatively shorter head (head-length contained $3^2/_5$–5 times in the distance from the tip of the snout to the vent); by the higher scale-count between the gill-opening and the ventral fin-insertion (55–70); and by the greater number of ribs (35–41). Upperside blue-grey, underside pale, usually sprinkled or marbled all over with pale and light grey.

Peculiarities and care, as given in the family description. 1954.

Protopterus amphibius (*Peters* 1844)
Africa, Zambesi Delta and rivers south-east of Lake Rudolf; to about 30 (?) cm.

According to Trewavas (1954) this well-characterised species is distinguished from *P. annectens* by the lower number of ribs (27–29); by the relatively longer head (head-length contained about 3 times in the distance from the tip of the snout to the vent); by the rather more anterior insertion of the dorsal fin; by the broader membranes to the paired fins, and by the three pairs of external gills which persist even in very large specimens. Blue-grey to dark-grey, either without blotches or with isolated small black blotches on the flanks. The colour of the underside of the head (dark spotted with white) is characteristic. Belly pale grey to very dark, with white spots, occasionally pure white.

Protopterus annectens (*Owen* 1839)   African Lung-fish
Africa, Senegal, Niger, Lake Chad, Katanga, Zambesi, chiefly in rather marshy marginal regions; to about 70 cm.

Body elongate, anterior part cylindrical, part posterior to the ventral fins compressed. 34–35 ribs. Head-length contained about 4 times in the distance from the tip of the snout to the vent. The dorsal fin is inserted rather behind the middle of this distance. 41–55 scales between the gill-opening and the ventral fin-insertion. Two, rarely three, pairs of short, finger-shaped external gills. Young fishes are very dark, often almost black. Older fishes, at about 16–20 cm. length, become paler. Back grey-brown to dark brown; flanks paler, with very irregular rows of dark brown spots. Underside pale, usually dirty yellow and as a rule without spots as far as the throat. Lateral line canal darkly delineated.

Peculiarities and care, as given in the family description. The summer aestivation period often lasts for 5–6 months in this species. 1910/+.

Protopterus dolloi *Boulenger* 1900 (Figs. 1083, 1084)
Congo Basin; to 85 cm.

P. dolloi is the most elongate of the African Lung-fishes, the head-length being contained 5–6 times in the distance from the tip of the snout to the vent. 86–91 scales between the gill-opening and the ventral fin-insertion. 54 pairs of ribs. Upperside very dark brown, flanks rather paler. Belly yellowish, throat often light red. Lateral line canals pale. At the most quite isolated dark spots.

Peculiarities and care, as given in the family description. 1954.

With few exceptions all the species which have been kept in Central Europe are taken into consideration. Date-line: 30.6.1958.

Select Bibliography

(1) Aquarium Periodicals

In English:

The Aquarist and Pondkeeper. Buckley Press Ltd., The Butts, Half Acre, Brentford, Middlesex, England.

The Aquarium. Innes Publishing Co., Philadelphia, Pa., U.S.A.

Tropical Fish Hobbyist. T.F.H. Publications, Inc., 245 Cornelison Av., Jersey City 2, N.J., U.S.A.

Tropical Fish Hobbyist. T.F.H. Publications (London) Ltd., 34 Nutley Lane, Reigate, Surrey, England.

Water Life and Aquaria World. Dorset House, Stamford Street, London, S.E.1., England.

In French:

Traité d'Aquariologie. Société Métropolitaine d'Editions Artistiques, Paris, France.

In German:

Aquarien und Terrarien. Deutscher Kulturbund: Urania Verlag, Leipzig, E. Germany.

Die Aquarien- und Terrarien-Zeitschrift. W. Sachs: Alfred Kernen Verlag, Stuttgart, W. Germany.

In Dutch:

Het Aquarium. Nederlandse Bond "Aqua-terra", Alkmar, Netherlands.

In Swedish:

Akvariet. Sveriges Akvarieföreningars Riksförbund, Stockholm, Sweden.

(2) Books on Aquarium Fishes and Aquarium Technique

This section of the bibliography is deliberately brief. For one thing, there is inevitably a great deal of duplication in this class of literature; for another, most of the books listed below include lengthy bibliographies of similar material.

Since it may be assumed that most readers will not, for preference, choose foreign-language works, these have been restricted to a handful of the indispensable German classics; further titles are to be found in other bibliographies, such as those given by Axelrod & Schultz (1955); Hervey & Hems (1952); Sterba (1954–56).

Besides the substantial books listed, there are also a great many cheap introductory pamphlets on aquarium-keeping and on the special treatment of various genera and families; numerous advertisements of these are to be found in the periodicals 'Tropical Fish Hobbyist' and 'Water Life'. D.W.T.

ARNOLD, P.J., & AHL, E. (1936). Fremdländische Süßwasserfische. Brunswick, W. Germany: Gustav Wenzel.

AXELROD, H.R., & SCHULTZ, L.P. (1955). Handbook of Tropical Aquarium Fishes. New York & London: McGraw Hill.

AXELROD, H.R., and others (1961). Exotic Tropical Fishes. Jersey City, N.J.: T.F.H. Books.

AXELROD, H.R., & VORDERWINKLER, W. (1961). Encyclopaedia of Tropical Fishes. Jersey City, N.J.: Sterling & T.F.H. Books.

FREY, H., trans. by SCHULTZ, A.V.W. (1961). Illustrated Dictionary of Tropical Fishes. Jersey City, N.J.: T.F.H. Books

HERVEY, G.F. & HEMS, J. (1952). Freshwater Tropical Aquarium Fishes. London: Batchworth Press.

HOLLY, M., MEINKEN, H., & RACHOW, A. (1932–). Die Aquarienfische in Wort und Bild. Stuttgart, W. Germany: Alfred Kernen Verlag.

INNES, W.T. (1959). Exotic Aquarium Fishes. Philadelphia: Innes Publications.

MELLEN, I.M. & LANIER, R.J. (1936). 1001 Questions Answered about Your Aquarium. London: Harrap.

STERBA, G. (1959–60). Aquarienkunde. (2 vols.), 2nd Ed., Leipzig, E. Germany: Urania-Verlag.

(3) Principles of Taxonomy and Nomenclature

It cannot be too firmly stressed that the description of a supposed 'new' species is a serious responsibility, requiring a considerable degree of knowledge and skill and strict compliance with a complicated and internationally-agreed 'Code' of rules. In most branches of science it is possible to ignore bad work; the trouble with taxonomy, however, is that even the worst work has to be taken into account, with the result that good taxonomists are forced to waste a disproportionate amount of time and effort in dealing, not merely with the real problems imposed by Nature, but with the utterly artificial and redundant problems created by bad taxonomists.

Amateurs should therefore steer clear of taxonomic publication, at least until they have acquired a respectable understanding and competence, and should especially refrain from publishing 'new' species in obscure aquarium journals where they are liable to be overlooked for years and subsequently rediscovered to upset names established in the interim period. They should also take care to deposit properly-authenticated 'type' specimens with one of the great museums whose continuity of curatorial policy and tradi-

851

tion of active taxonomy will ensure that they are safeguarded for posterity. In Britain the British Museum (Natural History) is the only such institution; in the United States the U.S. National Museum at Washington, the Museum of Comparative Zoology at Harvard, and the Natural History Museums at Stanford and at Chicago may be recommended.

Those wishing to obtain an understanding of the general principles of taxonomy should consult the following works. Calman (1949) provides the simplest and cheapest introduction and should be followed by Cain (1954).   D.W.T.

CAIN, A.J. (1954). Animal Species and their Evolution. London & New York: Hutchinson.

CALMAN, W.T. (1949). The Classification of Animals: an introduction to Zoological Taxonomy. London: Methuen.

MAYR, E. (1949). Systematics and the Origin of Species, from the viewpoint of a Zoologist. New York: Columbia University Press.

MAYR, E., LINSLEY, E.G. & USINGER, R.L. (1953). Methods and Principles of Systematic Zoology. New York & London: McGraw-Hill.

STOLL, N.R. (Ed.) (1961). International Code of Zoological Nomenclature adopted by the XV International Congress of Zoology. London: International Trust for Zoological Nomenclature.

(4) Higher-level Classification of Fishes

The scientific classification of the classes, orders and families of fishes requires a considerable understanding of osteology and anatomy. Those wishing to enter the subject at the shallow end will find the following references useful. Older references, and those introducing undue divergence from the Regan classification adopted in the present book, are intentionally omitted.   D.W.T.

HERALD, E.S. (1961). Living Fishes of the World. Garden City, N.Y.: Doubleday & Co. (London: Hamish Hamilton).

It must be confessed that this book contains a sprinkling of errors, but it may be recommended as a lavishly-illustrated and readable text which may serve to put some palatable flesh on the dry bones of Regan (1929).

REGAN, C.T. (1929). Articles on 'Cyclostomata', 'Selachians' and 'Fishes' in *The Encyclopaedia Britannica* (14th edn.), vols. **6**, **20** and **9**, respectively. New York & London.

These articles give the only concise and reasoned presentation of Regan's classification. Plans are in hand for their re-publication, together with some of Regan's more important scientific papers, by the Stanford University Press, Cal., U.S.A. Subsequent editions of *The Encyclopaedia Britannica* replaced Regan's articles by others written by American authors.

REGAN, C.T. (Ed.) (1936). Natural History. London: Ward Lock.

The chapter on fishes (pp. 192–296), written by Regan in this still available book edited by him, contains a rather less forbidding, more discursive and better illustrated version of his classification of 1929.

TREWAVAS, E. (1962). Articles on 'Fish', 'Cyclostomes', 'Selachii' and 'Osteichthyes' in *Chambers's Encyclopaedia*, vols. **5**, **4**, **12** and **10**, respectively. London: George Newnes.

Trewavas has revised her articles in the latest edition, but any other post-war printing of the encyclopaedia will serve. The one on 'Osteichthyes' gives a useful comparison of the several modern classifications of bony fishes, and all of them provide copious references to further literature.

(5) General Biology of Fishes

BAERENDS, G.P. & BAERENDS-VAN-ROON, J.M. (1950). An Introduction to the Study of the Ethology of Cichlid Fishes. Leiden: E.J.Brill.
Recommended as an introduction to the modern approach to fish-behaviour.

BRIDGE, T.W., & BOULENGER, G.A. (1910). Fishes (in *The Cambridge Natural History* Vol. **7**: 141–727). London & New York: Macmillan. (Facsimile reprint (1958) London: Wheldon & Wesley.)

BROWN, M.E. (Ed.) (1957). The Physiology of Fishes. 2 vols. New York: Academic Press.

COTT, H.B. (1957). Adaptive Coloration in Animals. London: Methuen.

CURTIS, B. (1949). The Life Story of the Fish. New York: Harcourt Brace.

GOODRICH, E.S. (1930). Studies on the Structure and Development of Vertebrates. London: Macmillan. (Paper-back facsimile reprint, 2 vols. (1958) New York: Dover. (London: Constable)).

GRAY, J. (1959). How Animals Move. Harmondsworth & New York: Penguin Books.

HESSE, R., ALLEE, W.C. & SCHMIDT, K.P. (1951). Ecological Animal Geography. New York: John Wiley.

LANHAM, U. (1962). The Fishes. New York: Columbia University Press.

LISSMANN, H.W. (1958). On the function and evolution of electric organs in fish. *Journal of Experimental Biology*, Vol. **35**: 156–191.

NORMAN, J.R., & GREENWOOD, P.H. (1962). A History of Fishes. London: Benn.

SCHÄPERCLAUS, W. (1954). Fischkrankheiten. (Diseases of Fishes: in German.) Berlin: Akademic-Verlag.

SCHULTZ, L.P., & STERN, E.M. (1948). The Ways of Fishes. New York: Van Nostrand.

YOUNG, J.Z. (1950). The Life of Vertebrates. Oxford: University Press.

(6) Geographical Distribution and Regional Fish-Faunas

General Zoogeography of Freshwater Fishes

DE BEAUFORT, L.F. (1951). Zoogeography of the Land and Inland Waters. London: Sidgwick & Jackson. (New York: Macmillan.)

DARLINGTON, P.J. (1957). Zoogeography: The Geographical Distribution of Animals. New York: John Wiley.

This, one of the most brilliant zoological textbooks of the 20th century, gives an excellent description and explanation of the distribution of freshwater fishes, with a substantial bibliography.

British Isles

Compared with the voluminous literature on Our Feathered Friends, the representation of British fishes is exceedingly meagre. The earlier works by Yarrell, Couch, Buckland, Houghton, Maxwell, etc., are obviously sadly out-of-date, while some of the more modern efforts are execrably bad. The following are recommended: –

DAY, F. (1880–1884). The Fishes of Great Britain and Ireland. 2 vols. London & Edinburgh: Williams & Norgate.

JENKINS, J.T. (1936). The Fishes of the British Isles. London: Warne.

MACMAHON, A.F.M. (1946). Fishlore: British Freshwater Fishes. Harmondsworth & New York: Penguin Books.

REGAN, C.T. (1911). The Freshwater Fishes of the British Isles. London: Methuen.

SCHINDLER, O., & ORKIN, P.A. (1957). Freshwater Fishes. London & New York: Thames & Hudson.

Continental Europe and Iceland

ANDERSSON, K.A. (1942). Fiskar och Fiske i Norden. 2 vols. Stockholm: Bokvorlaget Natur & Kultur.

BERG, L.S. (1948–49). Рыбы пресных вод СССР (Freshwater Fishes of the U.S.S.R.). 3 vols. Leningrad & Moscow: Academy of Sciences of the U.S.S.R.

The text of this book is in Russian, but all the species are illustrated and the legends to the figures give the scientific names in Roman type. There are also distribution-tables in which the names of fishes and the names of rivers are given in Roman type.

FRIES, B., EKSTRÖM, C.U. & SUNDEVALL, C., Ed. SMITT, F.A. (1893–95). Scandinavian Fishes. 2 vols. Stockholm: Norstedt & Söner. (London: Sampson Low, Marston.)

GROTE, W., VOGT, C. & HOFER, B. (1909). Die Süßwasserfische von Mitteleuropa. Frankfurt a. M. & Leipzig: Engelmann.

LOZANO Y REY, L. (1947). Peces Ganoideos y Fisostomos. (*Ictiologia Iberica* Tomo **2**.) Madrid: Real Acad. Ciencias.

NYBELIN, O. (1943). Fiskar i sött och bräckt vatten. (*Vara fiskar* Del. **1**) Stockholm: Albert Bonniers Förlag.

OTTERSTRØM, C.V. (1912–1917). Fiske. (*Danmark's Fauna*). 3 vols. Copenhagen: G. E. C. Gads Forlag.

SAEMUNDSSON, B. (1927). Synopsis of the Fishes of Iceland. *Rit. Visind. Island. Réykjavík*, Vol. **2**.

SCHINDLER, O. (1953). Unsere Süßwasserfische. Stuttgart, W. Germany: Kosmos, Franckische Verlagshandlung.

SEELEY, H.G. (1886). The Fresh-water Fishes of Europe. London: Cassell.

SPILLMANN, C.J. (1961). Poissons d'eau douce. (*Faune de France*, Vol. **65**) Paris: Lechevalier.

Asia, including Ceylon and Japan.

BERG, L.S. (1948–49). See reference under '*Continental Europe*', above.

DAY, F. (1875–1878). The Fishes of India, Burma and Ceylon. 2 vols. London: Quaritch. (Facsimile reprint (1958) London: Wm. Dawson.)

DAY, F. (1889). Fishes. (*The Fauna of British India, including Ceylon and Burma*) 2 vols. London: Taylor & Francis.

KHALAF, K.T. (1961). The marine and fresh water fishes of Iraq. Baghdad: Ar-Rabitta Press.

MAHDI, N. (1956). Fishes of Iraq. Baghdad: Ministry of Education.

MUNRO, I.S.R. (1955). The Marine and Freshwater Fishes of Ceylon. Canberra, Australia: Department of External Affairs.

NICHOLS, J.T. (1943). The Freshwater Fishes of China (*Natural History of Central Asia*, Vol. **9**). New York: American Museum of Natural History.

OKADA, Y. (1955). Fishes of Japan. Tokyo: Maruzen Co.

SMITH, H.M. (1945). The Freshwater Fishes of Siam, or Thailand. *Bull. U. S. Nat. Mus. Washington*, Vol. **188**.

STEINITZ, H. (1953). The freshwater fishes of Palestine: an annotated list. *Bull. Res. Council Israel*, Vol. **3**: 207–227.

STEINITZ, H. (1954). The distribution and evolution of the fishes of Palestine. *Publ. hydrobiol. Inst. Faculty of Sci. Univ. Istanbul (B)*, Vol. **1**: 225–275.

TREWAVAS, E. (1941). Freshwater Fishes (of Arabia). *Brit. Mus. (Nat. Hist.) Exp. South-west Arabia* 1937–1938. Vol. **1**: 7–15.

Indo-Malay Archipelago, Philippine Islands

BLEEKER, P. (1862–1877). Atlas Ichthyologique des Indes Orientales Néderlandaises. 9 vols. Amsterdam: F. Müller.

HERRE, A.W.C.T. (1928). True freshwater fishes of the Philippines. (In DICKERSON, R.E., *et al., Distribution of life in the Philippines*). Manila: Bureau of Sci. Monograph No. **21**.

HERRE, A.W.C.T. (1953). Check List of Philippine Fishes. *U.S. Fish & Wildlife Service Res. Rept.* **20**.

WEBER, M. & DE BEAUFORT, L.F. (1911–). The Fishes of the Indo-Australian Archipelago. 10 vols. to date. Leiden: E.J.Brill. (Vol. 8 is by DE BEAUFORT only; Vol. 9 by DE BEAUFORT & W.M.CHAPMAN; Vol. 10 by F.P.KOUMANS.)

WHITLEY, G.P. (1943). The Fishes of New Guinea. *Austral. Mus. Mag. Sydney*, Vol. **8**: 141–144.

Australia and New Zealand

STOKELL, G. (1955). Fresh Water Fishes of New Zealand. Christchurch, N.Z.: Simpson & Williams.

WHITLEY, G.P. (1959). The Freshwater Fishes of Australia. (In *Biogeography and Ecology in Australia.*) *Monogr. Biol.* Vol. **8**. The Hague: W. Junk.

Africa, including Madagascar

BARNARD, K.H. (1943). Revision of the Indigenous Fishes of the S.W. Cape Region *Annals of the S. Afr. Museum Cape Town*, Vol. **36**.

BARNARD, K.H. (1947). A pictorial guide to South African Fishes. Cape Town: Maskew Miller Ltd.

BOULENGER, G.A. (1907). The Fishes of the Nile. (In ANDERSON: *Zoology of Egypt.*) 2 vols. London: Hugh Rees.

BOULENGER, G.A. (1909–1916). Catalogue of the Freshwater Fishes of Africa. 4 vols. London: British Museum (Natural History).

CRASS, R.S. (1960). Notes on the Freshwater Fishes of Natal, with Descriptions of Four New Species. *Annals of the Natal Museum Pietermaritzburg*, Vol. **14**, part. 3.

DAGET, J. (1954). Les poissons du Niger supérieure. *Mém. Inst. fr. Afr. Noire Dakar*, No. **31**.

GREENWOOD, P.H. (1955–1957). The Fishes of Uganda. Parts 1–4. Kampala: Uganda Society.

HOLLY, M. (1930). Synopsis der Süßwasserfische Kameruns. *Sitzber. K. Akad. Wiss. Wien Math.-Nat. Kl.* Abt. 1, **1930**.

JACKSON, P.B.N. (1961). The Fishes of Northern Rhodesia. Lusaka: Govt. Printer.

JUBB, R.A. (1961). An illustrated guide to the Freshwater Fishes of the Zambesi River, Lake Kariba, Pungwe, Sabi, Lundi and Limpopo Rivers. Bulawayo: Stuart Manning.

PELLEGRIN, J. (1921). Les Poissons d'eau douce d'Afrique du Nord Francaise: Maroc, Algérie, Tunisie, Sahara. *Mém. Soc. Sci. Nat. Maroc.* Vol. **1**, No. 2.

PELLEGRIN, J. (1923). Les Poissons des eaux douces de l'Afrique Occidentale (du Sénégal au Niger). Paris: Emile Larose.

PELLEGRIN, J. (1933). Les Poissons des eaux douces de Madagascar. *Mém. Acad. Malgache Tananarive*, Vol. **14**.

POLL, M. (1946). Révision de la faune ichthyologique du Lac Tanganika. *Ann. Mus. Congo Belge Zool.* (1) **4**: 145–364.

POLL, M. (1953). Les poissons d'Aquarium du Congo Belge. *Bull. Soc. Roy. Zool. d'Anvers, Antwerp*, No. **2**.

POLL, M. (1953). Poissons non Cichlidae. *Rés. sci. Exploration hydrobiologique du Lac Tanganika*, Vol. **3**, fasc. 5A: 1–251.

POLL, M. (1956). Poissons Cichlidae. *tom. cit.* fasc. 5B: 1–619.

POLL, M. (1957). Les genres des poissons d'eau douce de l'Afrique. *Ann. Mus. Congo Belge* (8) Vol. **84**: 1–191.

North and Central America, including the West Indies

CARL, G.C. & CLEMENS, W.A. (1948). The freshwater fishes of British Columbia. *Brit. Columb. Provincial Museum Handbk.* No. **5**.

HILDEBRAND, S.F. (1938). A new catalogue of the freshwater fishes of Panama. *Pub. Field Mus. Nat. Hist. Chicago, Zool. Ser.*, Vol. **22**, No. 4: 215–359.

HUBBS, C.L. (1936). Fishes of the Yucatan Peninsula. (In *The Cenotes of Yucatan.*) *Pub. Carnegie Inst. Washington*, **457**: 157–282.

HUBBS, C.L. & LAGLER, K.F. (1947). Fishes of the Great Lakes Region. *Bull. Cranbrook Inst. Sci.* **26**.

JORDAN, D.S., & EVERMANN, B.W. (1896–1900). The Fishes of North and Middle America. 4 vols. Washington: Govt. Print. Office.

LEGENDRE, V. (1954). Key to the game and commercial fishes of the Province of Quebec. Montreal: Quebec Biol. Bureau.

LIVINGSTONE, D.A. (1953). The freshwater fishes of Nova Scotia. *Proc. Nova. Scot. Inst. Sci.*, Vol. **23**: 1–90.

MYERS, G.S. (1938). Freshwater Fishes and West Indian Zoogeography. *Rep. Smithsonian Inst. Washington* **1937**: 339–364.

SCHRENKEISEN, R. (1938). Field Book of the Freshwater Fishes of North America. New York: Putnam.

SLASTENENKO, E.P. (1958). The freshwater fishes of Canada. Toronto: Kiev Printers.

WYNNE-EDWARDS, V.C. (1952). Freshwater vertebrates of the arctic and subarctic. *Bull. Fisheries Res. Board Canada*, No. **94**.

South America

EIGENMANN, C.H. (1909). The freshwater fishes of Patagonia. *Rep. Princeton Univ. Exp. Patagonia* 1896–1899, Vol. **3**, part 3; 225–374.

EIGENMANN, C.H. (1910). Catalogue of the freshwater fishes of tropical and south temperate America. *tom. cit.*, part 4: 375–511.

EIGENMANN, C.H. (1912). The freshwater fishes of British Guiana. *Mem. Carnegie Mus.*, Vol. **5**.

EIGENMANN, C.H. (1922). The fishes of western South America. *Mem. Carnegie Mus.*, Vol. **9**.

EIGENMANN, C.H. (1927). The freshwater fishes of Chile. *Mem. Nat. Acad. Sci. Washington*, Vol. **22**, no. 2.

EIGENMANN, C.H. & ALLEN, W.R. (1942). Fishes of western South America. Lexington Kentucky: University of Kentucky.

MIRANDO RIBEIRO, A. DE (1911). Fauna Brasiliense: Peixes (Catfishes only). *Arch. Mus. Naç. Rio de Janeiro*, Vol. **16**, 1–511.

SCHULTZ, L.P. (1944). The Catfishes of Venezuela, etc. *Proc. U.S. Nat. Mus.* Vol. **94**: 173–338.

SCHULTZ, L.P. (1944). The fishes of the family Characinidae from Venezuela, etc. *Proc. U.S. Nat. Mus.* Vol. **95**: 235–367.

SCHULTZ, L.P. (1949). A further contribution to the ichthyology of Venezuela. *Proc. U.S. Nat. Mus.* Vol. **99**: 1–211.

857

(7) Early Classics of Ichthyology

The following works, unfortunately nearly all now rare and valuable, are listed for convenience since they contain a high proportion of the first descriptions of species in the present work.

BLOCH, M.E. (1782-84). Naturgeschichte der Fische Deutschlands. 3 vols. Berlin: Privately published.

BLOCH, M.E. (1785–95). Naturgeschichte der ausländischen Fische. 9 vols. Berlin: Privately published (1–3) & Morinoschen Kunsthandlung (4–9).

CUVIER, G.L.C. (1817). Le Règne Animale. 1st edn. 2 vols. (Fishes in Vol. 2.) Paris: Deterville.

CUVIER, G.L.C. (1829). Ditto. 2nd edn. 5 vols. (Fishes in Vol. 2.) Paris: Deterville.

CUVIER, G.L.C., & VALENCIENNES, A. (1828–49). Histoire naturelle des Poissons. 24 vols. Paris: Levrault.

GÜNTHER, A.C.L. (1859–1870). Catalogue of the Fishes in the British Museum. 8 vols. London: British Museum (Natural History). (Facsimile reprint (1937) Do.: Do.)

LACÉPÈDE, B.G.E. (1798–1803). Histoire naturelle des Poissons. 5 vols. Paris: Plassan.

LINNAEUS, C. (1758). Systema Naturae. 10th edn. Vol.1. Regnum Animale. Stockholm: Salvius. (Facsimile reprint (1956). London: British Museum (Natural History).)

SCHNEIDER, J.G. (1801). M.E. Blochii Systema Ichthyologiae iconibus CX illustratum. Berlin: Privately published.

SPIX, J.B. DE, & AGASSIZ, L. (1829–1831). Selecta genere et species piscium...Brasiliam. 2 parts. Monaco: Wolf.

(8) Key-References to Families

This is the obituary to a section that was stillborn. Professor Sterba's original unclassified bibliography in the German edition of this book contained three references to monographs of families. An attempt to expand this to a list giving one good key-reference to each family proved to be impracticable. In most cases a good family-revision stimulates interest, with the result that further short papers are published which very soon put it out of date. Thus, for example, some thirty new species of *Callichthyidae* have been described since the revision by Gosline (1940). On the other hand, it frequently happens that the only paper with an adequate bibliography is one which is itself too specialised to have any other immediate application. Few aquarists are likely ever to concern themselves with *Dinotopterus*, for instance, yet the most useful list of references to the *Clariidae* is contained in the revision of that genus by Greenwood (1961).

Once again, therefore, the hard way is the only practical one. We can only advise the reader to consult the last half-dozen issues of 'The Zoological Record' to find what recent literature has been published in his field. If the title specifies a genus of no immediate interest, no matter; the appended list of references may still provide a useful short cut.

The same procedure can be taken further in order to offset the delay inherent in the compilation of 'The Zoological Record'. Note the names of the authors who are actively working on the interesting group, and the titles of the journals in which they habitually publish. Most large natural history libraries display current issues of periodicals on a separate table or rack, and it thus becomes a simple matter to keep track of recent developments in any field.

D. W. T.

Index

INDEX

867

873

Metric-British Conversion Tables

LENGTH		TEMPERATURE	
cm.	in.	°C.	°F.
0·5	0·1968	0	32
1	0·3937	1	33·8
2	0·787	2	35·6
3	1·181	3	37·4
4	1·575	4	39·2
5	1·969	5	41
6	2·362	6	42·8
7	2·756	7	44·6
8	3·150	8	46·4
9	3·543	9	48·2
10	3·937	10	50
11	4·331	11	51·8
12	4·724	12	53·6
13	5·118	13	55·4
14	5·512	14	57·2
15	5·906	15	59
16	6·299	16	60·8
17	6·693	17	62·6
18	7·087	18	64·4
19	7·480	19	66·2
20	7·874	20	68
25	9·843	21	69·8
35	13·780	22	71·6
45	17·717	23	73·4
55	21·654	24	75·2
65	25·591	25	77
75	29·528	26	78·8
85	33·465	27	80·6
95	37·402	28	82·4
		29	84·2
100	39·37	30	86
(1 m.)	(3 ft. 3⅜ in.)		

VOLUME

1 cubic foot = 28·315 litres. (28,315 cc.)
1 Imperial gallon = 4·544 litres.
1 U.S. gallon = 3·785 litres.